Date Due		
JAN 2 May27'47		
OCT 22 Feb 22'51		
DEC 17 May 11'51		
JAN 29 Feb23'55		
MAR 26 Jun 21'56		
MAY 28 Dec 17'58		
FEB 13		
JAN 15		
Apr 30'35		
May 15		
May 24'35		
Jan 5		
Mar 29'45		
Apr 21'45		
Apr 21'45		

MY STUDY WINDOWS

BY

JAMES RUSSELL LOWELL

BOSTON AND NEW YORK

HOUGHTON MIFFLIN COMPANY

The Riverside Press Cambridge

PREFATORY NOTE.

——◆——

MY former volume of Essays has been so kindly received that I am emboldened to make another and more miscellaneous collection. The papers here gathered have been written at intervals during the last fifteen years, and I knew no way so effectual to rid my mind of them and make ready for a new departure, as this of shutting them between two covers where they can haunt me, at least, no more. I should have preferred a simpler title, but publishers nowadays are inexorable on this point, and I was too much occupied for happiness of choice. That which I have desperately snatched is meant to imply both the books within and the world without, and perhaps may pass muster in the case of one who has always found his most fruitful study in the open air.

TO

PROFESSOR F. J. CHILD.

MY DEAR CHILD, —

You were good enough to like my Essay on Chaucer (about whom you know so much more than I), and I shall accordingly so far presume upon our long friendsnip as to inscribe the volume containing it with your name.

Always heartily yours,

J. R. LOWELL.

CAMBRIDGE, Christmas, 1870.

CONTENTS.

———

	Page
My Garden Acquaintance	1
A Good Word for Winter	24
On a Certain Condescension in Foreigners	54
A Great Public Character	83
Carlyle	115
Abraham Lincoln	150
The Life and Letters of James Gates Percival	178
Thoreau	193
Swinburne's Tragedies	210
Chaucer	227
Library of Old Authors	290
Emerson, the Lecturer	375
Pope	385

MY GARDEN ACQUAINTANCE.

ONE of the most delightful books in my father's library was White's Natural History of Selborne. For me it has rather gained in charm with years. I used to read it without knowing the secret of the pleasure I found in it, but as I grow older I begin to detect some of the simple expedients of this natural magic. Open the book where you will, it takes you out of doors. In our broiling July weather one can walk out with this genially garrulous Fellow of Oriel and find refreshment instead of fatigue. You have no trouble in keeping abreast of him as he ambles along on his hobby-horse, now pointing to a pretty view, now stopping to watch the motions of a bird or an insect, or to bag a specimen for the Honourable Daines Barrington or Mr. Pennant. In simplicity of taste and natural refinement he reminds one of Walton; in tenderness toward what he would have called the brute creation, of Cowper. I do not know whether his descriptions of scenery are good or not, but they have made me familiar with his neighborhood. Since I first read him, I have walked over some of his favorite haunts, but I still see them through his eyes rather than by any recollection of actual and personal vision. The book has also the delightfulness of absolute leisure. Mr. White seems never to have had any harder work to do than to study the habits of his feathered fellow-townsfolk, or to watch the ripening of his peaches on the wall. His volumes are the journal of Adam in Paradise,

1   A

> " Annihilating all that's made
> To a green thought in a green shade."

It is positive rest only to look into that garden of his.
It is vastly better than to

> " See great Diocletian walk
> In the Salonian garden's noble shade,"

for thither ambassadors intrude to bring with them the
noises of Rome, while here the world has no entrance.
No rumor of the revolt of the American Colonies seems
to have reached him. " The natural term of an hog's
life " has more interest for him than that of an empire.
Burgoyne may surrender and welcome ; of what consequence is *that* compared with the fact that we can explain
the odd tumbling of rooks in the air by their turning over
" to scratch themselves with one claw " ?   All the couriers
in Europe spurring rowel-deep make no stir in Mr.
White's little Chartreuse ; but the arrival of the house-
martin a day earlier or later than last year is a piece of
news worth sending express to all his correspondents.

Another secret charm of this book is its inadvertent
humor, so much the more delicious because unsuspected
by the author. How pleasant is his innocent vanity in
adding to the list of the British, and still more of the
Selbornian, *fauna!* I believe he would gladly have consented to be eaten by a tiger or a crocodile, if by that
means the occasional presence within the parish limits of
either of these anthropophagous brutes could have been
established.   He brags of no fine society, but is plainly a
little elated by " having considerable acquaintance with
a tame brown owl." Most of us have known our share
of owls, but few can boast of intimacy with a feathered
one.   The great events of Mr. White's life, too, have that
disproportionate importance which is always humorous.
To think of his hands having actually been thought
worthy (as neither Willoughby's nor Ray's were) to hold

a stilted plover, the *Charadrius himantopus*, with no back toe, and therefore "liable, in speculation, to perpetual vacillations"! I wonder, by the way, if metaphysicians have no hind toes. In 1770 he makes the acquaintance in Sussex of "an old family tortoise," which had then been domesticated for thirty years. It is clear that he fell in love with it at first sight. We have no means of tracing the growth of his passion; but in 1780 we find him eloping with its object in a post-chaise. "The rattle and hurry of the journey so perfectly roused it that, when I turned it out in a border, it walked twice down to the bottom of my garden." It reads like a Court Journal: "Yesterday morning H. R. H. the Princess Alice took an airing of half an hour on the terrace of Windsor Castle." This tortoise might have been a member of the Royal Society, if he could have condescended to so ignoble an ambition. It had but just been discovered that a surface inclined at a certain angle with the plane of the horizon took more of the sun's rays. The tortoise had always known this (though he unostentatiously made no parade of it), and used accordingly to tilt himself up against the garden-wall in the autumn. He seems to have been more of a philosopher than even Mr. White himself, caring for nothing but to get under a cabbage-leaf when it rained, or the sun was too hot, and to bury himself alive before frost, — a four-footed Diogenes, who carried his tub on his back.

There are moods in which this kind of history is infinitely refreshing. These creatures whom we affect to look down upon as the drudges of instinct are members of a commonwealth whose constitution rests on immovable bases. Never any need of reconstruction there! *They* never dream of settling it by vote that eight hours are equal to ten, or that one creature is as clever as another and no more. *They* do not use their poor wits in

regulating God's clocks, nor think they cannot go astray
so long as they carry their guide-board about with them,
— a delusion we often practise upon ourselves with our
high and mighty reason, that admirable finger-post which
points every way and always right.   It is good for us now
and then to converse with a world like Mr. White's, where
Man is the least important of animals.   But one who,
like me, has always lived in the country and always on
the same spot, is drawn to his book by other occult sympathies.   Do we not share his indignation at that stupid
Martin who had graduated his thermometer no lower
than 4° above zero of Fahrenheit, so that in the coldest
weather ever known the mercury basely absconded into
the bulb, and left us to see the victory slip through our
fingers just as they were closing upon it ?   No man, I
suspect, ever lived long in the country without being
bitten by these meteorological ambitions.   He likes to
be hotter and colder, to have been more deeply snowed
up, to have more trees and larger blown down than his
neighbors.   With us descendants of the Puritans especially, these weather-competitions supply the abnegated
excitement of the race-course.   Men learn to value ther-
mometers of the true imaginative temperament, capable
of prodigious elations and corresponding dejections.   The
other day (5th July) I marked 98° in the shade, my high-
water mark, higher by one degree than I had ever seen
it before.   I happened to meet a neighbor ; as we mopped
our brows at each other, he told me that he had just
cleared 100°, and I went home a beaten man.   I had not
felt the heat before, save as a beautiful exaggeration of
sunshine ; but now it oppressed me with the prosaic vulgarity of an oven.   What had been poetic intensity became all at once rhetorical hyperbole.   I might suspect
his thermometer (as indeed I did, for we Harvard men
are apt to think ill of any graduation but our own) ; but

it was a poor consolation. The fact remained that his herald Mercury, standing a-tiptoe, could look down on mine. I seem to glimpse something of this familiar weakness in Mr. White. He, too, has shared in these mercurial triumphs and defeats. Nor do I doubt that he had a true country-gentleman's interest in the weather-cock; that his first question on coming down of a morning was, like Barabas's,

"Into what quarter peers my halcyon's bill?"

It is an innocent and healthful employment of the mind, distracting one from too continual study of himself, and leading him to dwell rather upon the indigestions of the elements than his own. "Did the wind back round, or go about with the sun?" is a rational question that bears not remotely on the making of hay and the prosperity of crops. I have little doubt that the regulated observation of the vane in many different places, and the interchange of results by telegraph, would put the weather, as it were, in our power, by betraying its ambushes before it is ready to give the assault. At first sight, nothing seems more drolly trivial than the lives of those whose single achievement is to record the wind and the temperature three times a day. Yet such men are doubtless sent into the world for this special end, and perhaps there is no kind of accurate observation, whatever its object, that has not its final use and value for some one or other. It is even to be hoped that the speculations of our newspaper editors and their myriad correspondents upon the signs of the political atmosphere may also fill their appointed place in a well-regulated universe, if it be only that of supplying so many more jack-o'-lanterns to the future historian. Nay, the observations on finance of an M. C. whose sole knowledge of the subject has been derived from a lifelong success in getting a living out of the public without paying any

equivalent therefor, will perhaps be of interest hereafter
to some explorer of our *cloaca maxima*, whenever it is
cleansed.

For many years I have been in the habit of noting
down some of the leading events of my embowered solitude, such as the coming of certain birds and the like, —
a kind of *mémoires pour servir*, after the fashion of White,
rather than properly digested natural history. I thought
it not impossible that a few simple stories of my winged
acquaintances might be found entertaining by persons
of kindred taste.

There is a common notion that animals are better
meteorologists than men, and I have little doubt that in
immediate weather-wisdom they have the advantage of
our sophisticated senses (though I suspect a sailor or
shepherd would be their match), but I have seen nothing
that leads me to believe their minds capable of erecting
the horoscope of a whole season, and letting us know beforehand whether the winter will be severe or the summer rainless. I more than suspect that the clerk of the
weather himself does not always know very long in advance whether he is to draw an order for hot or cold,
dry or moist, and the musquash is scarce likely to be
wiser. I have noted but two days' difference in the
coming of the song-sparrow between a very early and a
very backward spring. This very year I saw the linnets
at work thatching, just before a snow-storm which
covered the ground several inches deep for a number of
days. They struck work and left us for a while, no
doubt in search of food. Birds frequently perish from
sudden changes in our whimsical spring weather of
which they had no foreboding. More than thirty years
ago, a cherry-tree, then in full bloom, near my window,
was covered with humming-birds benumbed by a fall of
mingled rain and snow, which probably killed many of

them. It should seem that their coming was dated by the height of the sun, which betrays them into unthrifty matrimony ;

" So nature pricketh hem in their corages ";

but their going is another matter. The chimney-swallows leave us early, for example, apparently so soon as their latest fledglings are firm enough of wing to attempt the long rowing-match that is before them. On the other hand, the wild-geese probably do not leave the North till they are frozen out, for I have heard their bugles sounding southward so late as the middle of December. What may be called local migrations are doubtless dictated by the chances of food. I have once been visited by large flights of cross-bills ; and whenever the snow lies long and deep on the ground, a flock of cedar-birds comes in midwinter to eat the berries on my hawthorns. I have never been quite able to fathom the local, or rather geographical partialities of birds. Never before this summer (1870) have the king-birds, handsomest of flycatchers, built in my orchard ; though I always know where to find them within half a mile. The rose-breasted grosbeak has been a familiar bird in Brookline (three miles away), yet I never saw one here till last July, when I found a female busy among my raspberries and surprisingly bold. I hope she was *prospecting* with a view to settlement in our garden. She seemed, on the whole, to think well of my fruit, and I would gladly plant another bed if it would help to win over so delightful a neighbor.

The return of the robin is commonly announced by the newspapers, like that of eminent or notorious people to a watering-place, as the first authentic notification of spring. And such his appearance in the orchard and garden undoubtedly is. But, in spite of his name of migratory thrush, he stays with us all winter, and I have seen him when the thermometer marked 15 degrees below zero of Fahrenheit, armed impregnably within, like Emerson's Titmouse, and as cheerful as he. The robin has a bad reputation among people who do not value themselves less for being fond of cherries. There is, I admit, a spice of vulgarity in him, and his song is rather of the Bloomfield sort, too largely ballasted with prose. His ethics are of the Poor Richard school, and the main chance which calls forth all his energy is altogether of the belly. He never has those fine intervals of lunacy into which his cousins, the catbird and the mavis, are apt to fall. But for a' that and twice as muckle 's a' that, I would not exchange him for all the cherries that ever came out of Asia Minor. With whatever faults, he has not wholly forfeited that superiority which belongs to the children of nature. He has a finer taste in fruit than could be distilled from many successive committees of the Horticultural Society, and he eats with a relishing gulp not inferior to Dr. Johnson's. He feels and freely exercises his right of eminent domain. His is the earliest mess of green peas; his all the mulberries I had fancied mine. But if he get also the lion's share of the raspberries, he is a great planter, and sows those wild ones in the woods, that solace the pedestrian and give a momentary calm even to the jaded victims of the White Hills. He keeps a strict eye over one's fruit, and knows to a shade of purple when your grapes have cooked long enough in the sun. During the severe drought a few years ago, the robins wholly vanished from my garden. I neither saw nor heard one for three weeks. Meanwhile a small foreign grape-vine, rather shy of bearing, seemed to find the dusty air congenial, and, dreaming perhaps of its sweet Argos across the sea, decked itself with a score or so of fair bunches. I watched them from day to day till they should have secreted sugar enough from the sunbeams, and at last made up my mind that I would celebrate my vintage the next morning. But the robins too had somehow kept note of them. They must have sent out spies, as did the Jews into the promised land, before I was stirring. When I went with my basket, at least a dozen of these winged vintagers bustled out from among the leaves, and alighting on the nearest trees interchanged some shrill remarks about me of a derogatory nature. They had fairly sacked the vine. Not Wellington's veterans made cleaner work of a Spanish town; not Federals or Confederates were ever more impartial in the confiscation of neutral chickens. I was keeping my grapes a secret to surprise the fair Fidele with, but the robins made them a profounder secret to her than I had meant. The tattered remnant of a single bunch was all my harvest-home. How paltry it looked at the bottom of my basket, — as if a humming-bird had laid her egg in an eagle's nest! I could not help laughing; and the robins seemed to join heartily in the merriment. There was a native grape-vine close by, blue with its less refined abundance, but my cunning thieves preferred the foreign flavor. Could I tax them with want of taste?

The robins are not good solo singers, but their chorus, aʊ, like primitive fire-worshippers, they hail the return of light and warmth to the world, is unrivalled. There are a hundred singing like one. They are noisy enough then, and sing, as poets should, with no afterthought. But when they come after cherries to the tree near my window, they muffle their voices, and their faint *pip, pip, pop!* sounds far away at the bottom of the garden, where they know I shall not suspect them of robbing the great black-walnut of its bitter-rinded store.*

* The screech-owl, whose cry, despite his ill name, is one of the sweetest sounds in nature, softens his voice in the same way with the most beguiling mockery of distance.

They are feathered Pecksniffs, to be sure, but then how brightly their breasts, that look rather shabby in the sunlight, shine in a rainy day against the dark green of the fringe-tree ! After they have pinched and shaken all the life out of an earthworm, as Italian cooks pound all the spirit out of a steak, and then gulped him, they stand up in honest self-confidence, expand their red waistcoats with the virtuous air of a lobby member, and outface you with an eye that calmly challenges inquiry. " Do *I* look like a bird that knows the flavor of raw vermin ? I throw myself upon a jury of my peers. Ask any robin if he ever ate anything less ascetic than the frugal berry of the juniper, and he will answer that his vow forbids him." Can such an open bosom cover such depravity ? Alas, yes ! I have no doubt his breast was redder at that very moment with the blood of my raspberries. On the whole, he is a doubtful friend in the garden. He makes his dessert of all kinds of berries, and is not averse from early pears. But when we remember how omnivorous he is, eating his own weight in an incredibly short time, and that Nature seems exhaustless in her invention of new insects hostile to vegetation, perhaps we may reckon that he does more good than harm. For my own part, I would rather have his cheerfulness and kind neighborhood than many berries.

For his cousin, the catbird, I have a still warmer regard. Always a good singer, he sometimes nearly equals the brown thrush, and has the merit of keeping up his music later in the evening than any bird of my familiar acquaintance. Ever since I can remember, a pair of them have built in a gigantic syringa, near our front door, and I have known the male to sing almost uninterruptedly during the evenings of early summer till twilight duskened into dark. They differ greatly in vocal talent, but all have a delightful way of crooning

over, and, as it were, rehearsing their song in an undertone, which makes their nearness always unobtrusive.
Though there is the most trustworthy witness to the
imitative propensity of this bird, I have only once,
during an intimacy of more than forty years, heard him
indulge it. In that case, the imitation was by no means
so close as to deceive, but a free reproduction of the
notes of some other birds, especially of the oriole, as a
kind of variation in his own song. The catbird is as
shy as the robin is vulgarly familiar. Only when his
nest or his fledglings are approached does he become
noisy and almost aggressive. I have known him to
station his young in a thick cornel-bush on the edge of
the raspberry-bed, after the fruit began to ripen, and
feed them there for a week or more. In such cases he
shows none of that conscious guilt which makes the
robin contemptible. On the contrary, he will maintain
his post in the thicket, and sharply scold the intruder
who ventures to steal *his* berries. After all, his claim is
only for tithes, while the robin will bag your entire crop
if he get a chance.

Dr. Watts's statement that " birds in their little nests
agree," like too many others intended to form the infant
mind, is very far from being true. On the contrary, the
most peaceful relation of the different species to each
other is that of armed neutrality. They are very jealous
of neighbors. A few years ago, I was much interested
in the housebuilding of a pair of summer yellow-birds.
They had chosen a very pretty site near the top of a tall
white lilac, within easy eye-shot of a chamber window.
A very pleasant thing it was to see their little home
growing with mutual help, to watch their industrious
skill interrupted only by little flirts and snatches of
endearment, frugally cut short by the common-sense
of the tiny housewife. They had brought their work

nearly to an end, and had already begun to line it with
fern-down, the gathering of which demanded more distant journeys and longer absences. But, alas! the
syringa, immemorial manor of the catbirds, was not
more than twenty feet away, and these "giddy neighbors" had, as it appeared, been all along jealously watch-
ful, though silent, witnesses of what they deemed an
intrusion of squatters. No sooner were the pretty
mates fairly gone for a new load of lining, than

> "To their unguarded nest these weasel Scots
> Came stealing."

Silently they flew back and forth, each giving a vengeful
dab at the nest in passing. They did not fall-to and
deliberately destroy it, for they might have been caught
at their mischief. As it was, whenever the yellow-
birds came back, their enemies were hidden in their own
sight-proof bush. Several times their unconscious victims repaired damages, but at length, after counsel taken
together, they gave it up. Perhaps, like other unlet-
tered folk, they came to the conclusion that the Devil
was in it, and yielded to the invisible persecutions of
witchcraft.

The robins, by constant attacks and annoyances, have
succeeded in driving off the blue-jays who used to build
in our pines, their gay colors and quaint noisy ways
making them welcome and amusing neighbors. I once
had the chance of doing a kindness to a household of
them, which they received with very friendly condescension. I had had my eye for some time upon a nest, and
was puzzled by a constant fluttering of what seemed
full-grown wings in it whenever I drew nigh. At last I
climbed the tree, in spite of angry protests from the
old birds against my intrusion. The mystery had a
very simple solution. In building the nest, a long piece
of packthread had been somewhat loosely woven in.

Three of the young had contrived to entangle themselves in it, and had become full-grown without being able to launch themselves upon the air. One was unharmed ; another had so tightly twisted the cord about its shank that one foot was curled up and seemed paralyzed ; the third, in its struggles to escape, had sawn through the flesh of the thigh and so much harmed itself that I thought it humane to put an end to its misery. When I took out my knife to cut their hempen bonds, the heads of the family seemed to divine my friendly intent. Suddenly ceasing their cries and threats, they perched quietly within reach of my hand, and watched me in my work of manumission. This, owing to the fluttering terror of the prisoners, was an affair of some delicacy ; but erelong I was rewarded by seeing one of them fly away to a neighboring tree, while the cripple, making a parachute of his wings, came lightly to the ground, and hopped off as well as he could with one leg, obsequiously waited on by his elders. A week later I had the satisfaction of meeting him in the pine-walk, in good spirits, and already so far recovered as to be able to balance himself with the lame foot. I have no doubt that in his old age he accounted for his lameness by some handsome story of a wound received at the famous Battle of the Pines, when our tribe, overcome by numbers, was driven from its ancient camping-ground. Of late years the jays have visited us only at intervals ; and in winter their bright plumage, set off by the snow, and their cheerful cry, are especially welcome. They would have furnished Æsop with a fable, for the feathered crest in which they seem to take so much satisfaction is often their fatal snare. Country boys make a hole with their finger in the snow-crust just large enough to admit the jay's head, and, hollowing it out somewhat beneath, bait it with a few kernels of corn. The crest slips easily into the trap, but refuses to be pulled out again, and he who came to feast remains a prey.

Twice have the crow-blackbirds attempted a settlement in my pines, and twice have the robins, who claim a right of pre-emption, so successfully played the part of border-ruffians as to drive them away, — to my great regret, for they are the best substitute we have for rooks. At Shady Hill (now, alas! empty of its so long-loved household) they build by hundreds, and nothing can be more cheery than their creaking clatter (like a convention of old-fashioned tavern-signs) as they gather at evening to debate in mass meeting their windy politics, or to gossip at their tent-doors over the events of the day. Their port is grave, and their stalk across the turf as martial as that of a second-rate ghost in Hamlet. They never meddled with my corn, so far as I could discover.

For a few years I had crows, but their nests are an irresistible bait for boys, and their settlement was broken up. They grew so wonted as to throw off a great part of their shyness, and to tolerate my near approach. One very hot day I stood for some time within twenty feet of a mother and three children, who sat on an elm bough over my head, gasping in the sultry air, and holding their wings half-spread for coolness. All birds during the pairing season become more or less sentimental, and murmur soft nothings in a tone very unlike the grinding-organ repetition and loudness of their habitual song. The crow is very comical as a lover, and to hear him trying to soften his croak to the proper Saint Preux standard, has something the effect of a Mississippi boatman quoting Tennyson. Yet there are few things to my ear more melodious than his caw of a clear winter morning as it drops to you filtered through five hundred fathoms of crisp blue air. The hostility of all smaller birds makes the moral character of the crow, for all his deaconlike demeanor and garb, somewhat questionable. He could never sally forth without insult. The golden robins, especially, would chase him as far as I could follow with my eye, making him duck clumsily to avoid their importunate bills. I do not believe, however, that he robbed any nests hereabouts, for the refuse of the gas-works, which, in our free-and-easy community, is allowed to poison the river, supplied him with dead alewives in abundance. I used to watch him making his periodical visits to the salt-marshes and coming back with a fish in his beak to his young savages, who, no doubt, like it in that condition which makes it savory to the Kanakas and other corvine races of men.

Orioles are in great plenty with me. I have seen seven males flashing about the garden at once. A merry crew of them swing their hammocks from the pendulous boughs. During one of these latter years, when the canker-worms stripped our elms as bare as winter, these birds went to the trouble of rebuilding their unroofed nests, and chose for the purpose trees which are safe from those swarming vandals, such as the ash and the button-wood. One year a pair (disturbed, I suppose, elsewhere) built a second nest in an elm, within a few yards of the house. My friend, Edward E. Hale, told me once that the oriole rejected from his web all strands of brilliant color, and I thought it a striking example of that instinct of concealment noticeable in many birds, though it should seem in this instance that the nest was amply protected by its position from all marauders but owls and squirrels. Last year, however, I had the fullest proof that Mr. Hale was mistaken. A pair of orioles built on the lowest trailer of a weeping elm, which hung within ten feet of our drawing-room window, and so low that I could reach it from the ground. The nest was wholly woven and felted with ravellings of woollen carpet in which scarlet predominated. Would the same thing have happened in the woods? Or did the nearness of a human dwelling perhaps give the birds a greater feeling of security? They are very bold, by the way, in quest of cordage, and I have often watched them stripping the fibrous bark from a honeysuckle growing over the very door. But, indeed, all my birds look upon me as if I were a mere tenant at will, and they were landlords. With shame I confess it, I have been bullied even by a humming-bird. This spring, as I was cleansing a pear-tree of its lichens, one of these little zigzagging blurs came purring toward me, couching his long bill like a lance, his throat sparkling with angry fire, to warn me off from a Missouri-currant whose honey he was sipping. And many a time he has driven me out of a flower-bed. This summer, by the way, a pair of these winged emeralds fastened their mossy acorn-cup upon a bough of the same elm which the orioles had enlivened the year before. We watched all their proceedings from the window through an opera-glass, and saw their two nestlings grow from black needles with a tuft of down at the lower end, till they whirled away on their first short experimental flights. They became strong of wing in a surprisingly short time, and I never saw them or the male bird after, though the female was regular as usual in her visits to our petunias and verbenas. I do not think it ground enough for a generalization, but in the many times when I watched the old birds feeding their young, the mother always alighted, while the father as uniformly remained upon the wing.

The bobolinks are generally chance visitors, tinkling through the garden in blossoming-time, but this year, owing to the long rains early in the season, their favorite meadows were flooded, and they were driven to the upland. So I had a pair of them domiciled in my grass-field. The male used to perch in an apple-tree, then in full bloom, and, while I stood perfectly still close by, he would circle away, quivering round the entire field of five acres, with no break in his song, and settle down again among the blossoms, to be hurried away almost immediately by a new rapture of music. He had the volubility of an Italian charlatan at a fair, and, like him, appeared to be proclaiming the merits of some quack remedy. *Opodeldoc-opodeldoc-try-Doctor-Lincoln's-opodeldoc !* he seemed to repeat over and over again, with a rapidity that would have distanced the deftest-tongued Figaro that ever rattled. I remember Count Gurowski saying once, with that easy superiority of knowledge about this country which is the monopoly of foreigners, that we had no singing-birds ! Well, well, Mr. Hepworth Dixon has found the typical America in Oneida and Salt Lake City. Of course, an intelligent European is the best judge of these matters. The truth is there are more singing-birds in Europe because there are fewer forests. These songsters love the neighborhood of man because hawks and owls are rarer, while their own food is more abundant. Most people seem to think, the more trees, the more birds. Even Châteaubriand, who first tried the primitive-forest-cure, and whose description of the wilderness in its imaginative effects is unmatched, fancies the "people of the air singing their hymns to him." So far as my own observation goes, the farther one penetrates the sombre solitudes of the woods, the more seldom does he hear the voice of any singing-bird. In spite of Châteaubriand's minuteness of detail, in spite of that marvellous reverberation of the decrepit tree falling of its own weight, which he was the first to

B

notice, I cannot help doubting whether he made his way very deep into the wilderness. At any rate, in a letter to Fontanes, written in 1804, he speaks of *mes chevaux paissant à quelque distance.* To be sure Châteaubriand was apt to mount the high horse, and this may have been but an afterthought of the *grand seigneur,* but certainly one would not make much headway on horseback toward the druid fastnesses of the primæval pine.

The bobolinks build in considerable numbers in a meadow within a quarter of a mile of us. A houseless lane passes through the midst of their camp, and in clear westerly weather, at the right season, one may hear a score of them singing at once. When they are breeding, if I chance to pass, one of the male birds always accompanies me like a constable, flitting from post to post of the rail-fence, with a short note of reproof continually repeated, till I am fairly out of the neighborhood. Then he will swing away into the air and run down the wind, gurgling music without stint over the unheeding tussocks of meadow-grass and dark clumps of bulrushes that mark his domain.

We have no bird whose song will match the nightingale's in compass, none whose note is so rich as that of the European blackbird ; but for mere rapture I have never heard the bobolink's rival. But his operaseason is a short one. The ground and tree sparrows are our most constant performers. It is now late in August, and one of the latter sings every day and all day long in the garden. Till within a fortnight, a pair of indigo-birds would keep up their lively *duo* for an hour together. While I write, I hear an oriole gay as in June, and the plaintive *may-be* of the goldfinch tells me he is stealing my lettuce-seeds. I know not what the experience of others may have been, but the only bird I have ever heard sing in the night has been the chip-bird. I should say he sang about as often during the darkness as cocks crow. One can hardly help fancying that he sings in his dreams.

> " Father of light, what sunnie seed,
>   What glance of day hast thou confined
>   Into this bird? To all the breed
>   This busie ray thou hast assigned;
>   Their magnetism works all night,
>   And dreams of Paradise and light."

On second thought, I remember to have heard the cuckoo strike the hours nearly all night with the regularity of a Swiss clock.

The dead limbs of our elms, which I spare to that end, bring us the flicker every summer, and almost daily I hear his wild scream and laugh close at hand, himself invisible. He is a shy bird, but a few days ago I had the satisfaction of studying him through the blinds as he sat on a tree within a few feet of me. Seen so near and at rest, he makes good his claim to the title of pigeon-woodpecker. Lumberers have a notion that he is harmful to timber, digging little holes through the bark to encourage the settlement of insects. The regular rings of such perforations which one may see in almost any apple-orchard seem to give some probability to this theory. Almost every season a solitary quail visits us, and, unseen among the currant-bushes, calls *Bob White, Bob White*, as if he were playing at hide-and-seek with that imaginary being. A rarer visitant is the turtle-dove, whose pleasant coo (something like the muffled crow of a cock from a coop covered with snow) I have sometimes heard, and whom I once had the good luck to see close by me in the mulberry-tree. The wild-pigeon, once numerous, I have not seen for many years.[*] Of savage birds, a hen-hawk now and then quarters himself upon us for a few days, sitting sluggish in a tree

[*] They made their appearance again this summer (1870).

after a surfeit of poultry.   One of them once offered me
a near shot from my study-window one drizzly day for
several hours.   But it was Sunday, and I gave him the
benefit of its gracious truce of God.

Certain birds have disappeared from our neighborhood
within my memory.   I remember when the whippoorwill
could be heard in Sweet Auburn.   The night-hawk, once
common, is now rare.   The brown thrush has moved farther up country.   For years I have not seen or heard
any of the larger owls, whose hooting was one of my boyish terrors.   The cliff-swallow, strange emigrant, that
eastward takes his way, has come and gone again in my
time.   The bank-swallows, wellnigh innumerable during
my boyhood, no longer frequent the crumbly cliff of the
gravel-pit by the river.   The barn-swallows, which once
swarmed in our barn, flashing through the dusty sun-
streaks of the mow, have been gone these many years.
My father would lead me out to see them gather on the
roof, and take counsel before their yearly migration, as
Mr. White used to see them at Selborne.   *Eheu, fugaces!*
Thank fortune, the swift still glues his nest, and rolls his
distant thunders night and day in the wide-throated chimneys, still sprinkles the evening air with his merry twit-
tering.   The populous heronry in Fresh Pond meadows
has been wellnigh broken up, but still a pair or two
haunt the old home, as the gypsies of Ellangowan their
ruined huts, and every evening fly over us riverwards,
clearing their throats with a hoarse hawk as they go, and,
in cloudy weather, scarce higher than the tops of the
chimneys.   Sometimes I have known one to alight in
one of our trees, though for what purpose I never could
divine.   Kingfishers have sometimes puzzled me in the
same way, perched at high noon in a pine, springing their
watchman's rattle when they flitted away from my curiosity, and seeming to shove their top-heavy heads along
as a man does a wheelbarrow.

Some birds have left us, I suppose, because the country is growing less wild.   I once found a summer duck's nest within quarter of a mile of our house, but such a *trouvaille* would be impossible now as Kidd's treasure.   And yet the mere taming of the neighborhood does not quite satisfy me as an explanation.   Twenty years ago, on my way to bathe in the river, I saw every day a brace of woodcock, on the miry edge of a spring within a few rods of a house, and constantly visited by thirsty cows.   There was no growth of any kind to conceal them, and yet these ordinarily shy birds were almost as indifferent to my passing as common poultry would have been.   Since bird-nesting has become scientific, and dignified itself as oölogy, that, no doubt, is partly to blame for some of our losses.   But some old friends are constant.   Wilson's thrush comes every year to remind me of that most poetic of ornithologists.   He flits before me through the pine-walk like the very genius of solitude.   A pair of pewees have built immemorially on a jutting brick in the arched entrance to the ice-house.   Always on the same brick, and never more than a single pair, though two broods of five each are raised there every summer.   How do they settle their claim to the homestead?   By what right of primogeniture?   Once the children of a man employed about the place *oölogized* the nest, and the pewees left us for a year or two.   I felt towards those boys as the messmates of the Ancient Mariner did towards him after he had shot the albatross.   But the pewees came back at last, and one of them is now on his wonted perch, so near my window that I can hear the click of his bill as he snaps a fly on the wing with the unerring precision a stately Trasteverina shows in the capture of her smaller deer.   The pewee is the first bird to pipe up in the morning; and, during the early summer he preludes his matutinal ejaculation of *pewee* with a slender whistle, unheard at any other time.   He saddens with the season, and, as summer declines, he changes his note to *eheu, pewee!* as if in lamentation.   Had he been an Italian bird, Ovid would have had a plaintive tale to tell about him. He is so familiar as often to pursue a fly through the open window into my library.

There is something inexpressibly dear to me in these old friendships of a lifetime.   There is scarce a tree of mine but has had, at some time or other, a happy homestead among its boughs, to which I cannot say,

> " Many light hearts and wings,
> Which now be dead, lodged in thy living bowers."

My walk under the pines would lose half its summer charm were I to miss that shy anchorite, the Wilson's thrush, nor hear in haying-time the metallic ring of his song, that justifies his rustic name of *scythe-whet*. I protect my game as jealously as an English squire. If anybody had oölogized a certain cuckoo's nest I know of (I have a pair in my garden every year), it would have left me a sore place in my mind for weeks.   I love to bring these aborigines back to the mansuetude they showed to the early voyagers, and before (forgive the involuntary pun) they had grown accustomed to man and knew his savage ways.   And they repay your kindness with a sweet familiarity too delicate ever to breed contempt.   I have made a Penn-treaty with them, preferring that to the Puritan way with the natives, which converted them to a little Hebraism and a great deal of Medford rum.   If they will not come near enough to me (as most of them will), I bring them close with an opera-glass, — a much better weapon than a gun.   I would not, if I could, convert them from their pretty pagan ways.   The only one I sometimes have savage doubts about is the red squirrel.   I *think* he oölogizes. I *know* he eats cherries (we counted five of them at one

time in a single tree, the stones pattering down like the
sparse hail that preludes a storm), and that he gnaws off
the small end of pears to get at the seeds. He steals
the corn from under the noses of my poultry. But what
would you have ? He will come down upon the limb of
the tree I am lying under till he is within a yard of me.
He and his mate will scurry up and down the great black-
walnut for my diversion, chattering like monkeys. Can
I sign his death-warrant who has tolerated me about his
grounds so long ? Not I. Let them steal, and welcome.
I am sure I should, had I had the same bringing up and
the same temptation. As for the birds, I do not believe
there is one of them but does more good than harm ; and
of how many featherless bipeds can this be said ?

A GOOD WORD FOR WINTER.

"MEN scarcely know how beautiful fire is," says
Shelley; and I am apt to think there are a
good many other things concerning which their knowledge might be largely increased without becoming burden-
some. Nor are they altogether reluctant to be taught,
— not so reluctant, perhaps, as unable, — and education
is sure to find one fulcrum ready to her hand by which
to get a purchase on them. For most of us, I have noticed, are not without an amiable willingness to assist at
any spectacle or entertainment (loosely so called) for
which no fee is charged at the door. If special tickets
are sent us, another element of pleasure is added in a
sense of privilege and pre-eminence (pitiably scarce in
a democracy) so deeply rooted in human nature that I
have seen people take a strange satisfaction in being
near of kin to the mute chief personage in a funeral. It
gave them a moment's advantage over the rest of us
whose grief was rated at a lower place in the procession.
But the words "admission free" at the bottom of a hand-
bill, though holding out no bait of inequality, have yet
a singular charm for many minds, especially in the country. There is something touching in the constancy with
which men attend free lectures, and in the honest
patience with which they listen to them. He who pays
may yawn or shift testily in his seat, or even go out with
an awful reverberation of criticism, for he has bought the
right to do any or all of these and paid for it. But gra-

tuitous hearers are anæsthetized to suffering by a sense
ot virtue. They are performing perhaps the noblest, as
it is one of the most difficult, of human functions in getting Something (no matter how small) for Nothing.
They are not pestered by the awful duty of securing
their money's worth. They are wasting time, to do
which elegantly and without lassitude is the highest
achievement of civilization. If they are cheated, it is, at
worst, only of a superfluous hour which was rotting on
their hands. Not only is mere amusement made more
piquant, but instruction more palatable, by this universally relished sauce of gratuity. And if the philosophic
observer finds an object of agreeable contemplation in
the audience, as they listen to a discourse on the probability of making missionaries go down better with the
Feejee-Islanders by balancing the hymn-book in one
pocket with a bottle of Worcestershire in the other, or
to a plea for arming the female gorilla with the ballot,
he also takes a friendly interest in the lecturer, and admires the wise economy of Nature who thus contrives
an ample field of honest labor for her bores. Even
when the insidious hat is passed round after one of these
eleemosynary feasts, the relish is but heightened by a
conscientious refusal to disturb the satisfaction's completeness with the rattle of a single contributory penny.
So firmly persuaded am I of this *gratis*-instinct in our
common humanity, that I believe I could fill a house by
advertising a free lecture on Tupper considered as a
philosophic poet, or on my personal recollections of the
late James K. Polk. This being so, I have sometimes
wondered that the peep-shows which Nature provides
with such endless variety for her children, and to which
we are admitted on the bare condition of having eyes,
should be so generally neglected. To be sure, eyes
are not so common as people think, or poets would be

2

plentier, and perhaps also these exhibitions of hers are cheapened in estimation by the fact that in enjoying them we are not getting the better of anybody else. Your true lovers of nature, however, contrive to get even *this* solace ; and Wordsworth looking upon mountains as his own peculiar sweethearts, was jealous of anybody else who ventured upon even the most innocent flirtation with them. As if *such* fellows, indeed, could pretend to that nicer sense of what-d'ye-call-it which was so remarkable in him ! Marry come up ! Mountains, no doubt, may inspire a profounder and more exclusive passion, but on the whole I am not sorry to have been born and bred among more domestic scenes, where I can be hospitable without a pang. I am going to ask you presently to take potluck with me at a board where Winter shall supply whatever there is of cheer.

I think the old fellow has hitherto had scant justice done him in the main. We make him the symbol of old age or death, and think we have settled the matter. As if old age were never kindly as well as frosty ; as if it had no reverend graces of its own as good in their way as the noisy impertinence of childhood, the elbowing self-conceit of youth, or the pompous mediocrity of middle life ! As if there were anything discreditable in death, or nobody had ever longed for it ! Suppose we grant that Winter is the sleep of the year, what then ? I take it upon me to say that his dreams are finer than the best reality of his waking rivals.

" Sleep, Silence' child, the father of soft Rest,"

is a very agreeable acquaintance, and most of us are better employed in his company than anywhere else. For my own part, I think Winter a pretty wide-awake old boy, and his bluff sincerity and hearty ways are more congenial to my mood, and more wholesome for me,

than any charms of which his rivals are capable.
Spring is a fickle mistress, who either does not know her
own mind, or is so long in making it up, whether you
shall have her or not have her, that one gets tired at
last of her pretty miffs and reconciliations. You go to
her to be cheered up a bit, and ten to one catch her in
the sulks, expecting you to find enough good-humor for
both. After she has become Mrs. Summer she grows a
little more staid in her demeanor ; and her abundant
table, where you are sure to get the earliest fruits and
vegetables of the season, is a good foundation for steady
friendship; but she has lost that delicious aroma of
maidenhood, and what was delicately rounded grace in
the girl gives more than hints of something like redun-
dance in the matron. Autumn is the poet of the family.
He gets you up a splendor that you would say was
made out of real sunset ; but it is nothing more than a
few hectic leaves, when all is done. He is but a sentimentalist, after all ; a kind of Lamartine whining along
the ancestral avenues he has made bare timber of, and
begging a contribution of good-spirits from your own
savings to keep him in countenance. But Winter has
his delicate sensibilities too, only he does not make them
as good as indelicate by thrusting them forever in your
face. He is a better poet than Autumn, when he has a
mind, but, like a truly great one as he is, he brings you
down to your bare manhood, and bids you understand
him out of that, with no adventitious helps of association, or he will none of you. He does not touch those
melancholy chords on which Autumn is as great a
master as Heine. Well, is there no such thing as
thrumming on them and maundering over them till
they get out of tune, and you wish some manly hand
would crash through them and leave them dangling
brokenly forever ? Take Winter as you find him, and he

turns out to be a thoroughly honest fellow, with no nonsense in him, and tolerating none in you, which is a
great comfort in the long run.   He is not what they
call a genial critic; but bring a real man along with you,
and you will find there is a crabbed generosity about
the old cynic that you would not exchange for all the
creamy concessions of Autumn.   "Season of mists and
mellow fruitfulness," quotha ?   That 's just it; Winter
soon blows your head clear of fog and makes you see
things as they are ; I thank him for it !   The truth is,
between ourselves, I have a very good opinion of the
whole family, who always welcome me without making
me feel as if I were too much of a poor relation.   There
ought to be some kind of distance, never so little, you
know, to give the true relish.   They are as good company, the worst of them, as any I know, and I am not a
little flattered by a condescension from any one of them;
but I happen to hold Winter's retainer, this time, and,
like an honest advocate, am bound to make as good a
showing as I can for him, even if it cost a few slurs upon
the rest of the household.   Moreover, Winter is coming,
and one would like to get on the blind side of him.

The love of Nature in and for herself, or as a mirror
for the moods of the mind, is a modern thing.   The fleeing to her as an escape from man was brought into
fashion by Rousseau ; for his prototype Petrarch, though
he had a taste for pretty scenery, had a true antique
horror for the grander aspects of nature.   He got once
to the top of Mont Ventoux, but it is very plain that he
did not enjoy it.   Indeed, it is only within a century or so
that the search after the picturesque has been a safe employment.   It is not so even now in Greece or Southern
Italy.   Where the Anglo-Saxon carves his cold fowl, and
leaves the relics of his picnic, the ancient or mediæval
man might be pretty confident that some ruffian would

try the edge of his knife on a chicken of the Platonic sort, and leave more precious bones as an offering to the genius of the place. The ancients were certainly more social than we, though that, perhaps, was natural enough, when a good part of the world was still covered with forest. They huddled together in cities as well for safety as to keep their minds warm. The Romans had a fondness for country life, but they had fine roads, and Rome was always within easy reach. The author of the Book of Job is the earliest I know of who showed any profound sense of the moral meaning of the outward world ; and I think none has approached him since, though Wordsworth comes nearest with the first two books of the " Prelude." But their feeling is not precisely of the kind I speak of as modern, and which gave rise to what is called descriptive poetry. Chaucer opens his Clerk's Tale with a bit of landscape admirable for its large style, and as well composed as any Claude.

> " There is right at the west end of Itaille,
> Down at the root of Vesulus the cold,
> A lusty plain abundant of vitaille,
> Where many a tower and town thou mayst behold,
> That founded were in time of fathers old,
> And many an other délectable sight ;
> And Salucës this noble country hight."

What an airy precision of touch there is here, and what a sure eye for the points of character in landscape ! But the picture is altogether subsidiary. No doubt the works of Salvator Rosa and Gaspar Poussin show that there must have been some amateur taste for the grand and terrible in scenery ; but the British poet Thomson (" sweet-souled " is Wordsworth's apt word) was the first to do with words what they had done partially with colors. He was turgid, no good metrist, and his English is like a translation from one of those poets who wrote in Latin after it was dead ; but he was a man of sincere genius, and not only English, but European literature is largely in his debt. He was the inventor of cheap amusement for the million, to be had of All-out-doors for the asking. It was his impulse which unconsciously gave direction to Rousseau, and it is to the school of Jean Jacques that we owe St. Pierre, Cowper, Châteaubriand, Wordsworth, Byron, Lamartine, George Sand, Ruskin,— the great painters of ideal landscape.

So long as men had slender means, whether of keeping out cold or checkmating it with artificial heat, Winter was an unwelcome guest, especially in the country. There he was the bearer of a *lettre de cachet*, which shut its victims in solitary confinement with few resources but to boose round the fire and repeat ghost-stories, which had lost all their freshness and none of their terror. To go to bed was to lie awake of cold, with an added shudder of fright whenever a loose casement or a waving curtain chose to give you the goose-flesh. Bussy Rabutin, in one of his letters, gives us a notion how uncomfortable it was in the country, with green wood, smoky chimneys, and doors and windows that thought it was their duty to make the wind whistle, not to keep it out. With fuel so dear, it could not have been much better in the city, to judge by Ménage's warning against the danger of our dressing-gowns taking fire, while we cuddle too closely over the sparing blaze. The poet of Winter himself is said to have written in bed, with his hand through a hole in the blanket ; and we may suspect that it was the warmth quite as much as the company that first drew men together at the coffee-house. Coleridge, in January, 1800, writes to Wedgewood : "I am sitting by a fire in a rug great-coat. . . . . It is most barbarously cold, and you, I fear, can shield yourself from it only by perpetual imprisonment." This thermometrical view of winter is, I grant, a depressing one ; for I think there is nothing so demoralizing as cold. I know of a boy who, when his father, a bitter economist, was brought home dead, said only, " Now we can burn as much wood as we like." I would not off-hand prophesy the gallows for that boy. I remember with a shudder a pinch I got from the cold once in a railroad-car. A born fanatic of fresh air, I found myself glad to see the windows hermetically sealed by the freezing vapor of our breath, and plotted the assassination of the conductor every time he opened the door. I felt myself sensibly barbarizing, and would have shared Colonel Jack's bed in the ash-hole of the glass-furnace with a grateful heart. Since then I have had more charity for the prevailing ill-opinion of winter. It was natural enough that Ovid should measure the years of his exile in Pontus by the number of winters.

> Ut sumus in Ponto, ter frigore constitit Ister,
> Facta est Euxini dura ter unda maris:
>
> Thrice hath the cold bound Ister fast, since I
> In Pontus was, thrice Euxine's wave made hard.

Jubinal has printed an Anglo-Norman piece of doggerel in which Winter and Summer dispute which is the better man. It is not without a kind of rough and inchoate humor, and I like it because old Whitebeard gets tolerably fair play. The jolly old fellow boasts of his rate of living, with that contempt of poverty which is the weak spot in the burly English nature.

> Jà Dieu ne place que me avyenge
> Que ne face plus honour
> Et plus despenz en un soul jour
> Que vus en tote vostre vie:
>
> Now God forbid it hap to me
> That I make not more great display,
> And spend more in a single day
> Than you can do in all your life.

The best touch, perhaps, is Winter's claim for credit as a mender of the highways, which was not without point when every road in Europe was a quagmire during a good part of the year unless it was bottomed on some remains of Roman engineering.

> Je su, fet-il, seignur et mestre
> Et à bon droit le dey estre,
> Quant de la bowe face caucé
> Par un petit de geelé:

> Master and lord I am, says he,
> And of good right so ought to be,
> Since I make causeys, safely crost,
> Of mud, with just a pinch of frost.

But there is no recognition of Winter as the best of out-door company.

Even Emerson, an open-air man, and a bringer of it, if ever any, confesses,

> " The frost-king ties my fumbling feet,
> Sings in my ear, my hands are stones,
> Curdles the blood to the marble bones,
> Tugs at the heartstrings, numbs the sense,
> And hems in life with narrowing fence."

Winter was literally " the inverted year," as Thomson called him; for such entertainments as could be had must be got within doors. What cheerfulness there was in brumal verse was that of Horace's *dissolve frigus ligna super foco large reponens,* so pleasantly associated with the cleverest scene in Roderick Random. This is the tone of that poem of Walton's friend Cotton, which won the praise of Wordsworth : —

> " Let us home,
> Our mortal enemy is come;
> Winter and all his blustering train
> Have made a voyage o'er the main.

> . . . . .

> " Fly, fly, the foe advances fast;
> Into our fortress let us haste.
> Where all the roarers of the north
> Can neither storm nor starve us forth.

> " There underground a magazine
> Of sovereign juice is cellared in,
> Liquor that will the siege maintain
> Should Phœbus ne'er return again.

> . . . . .

> "Whilst we together jovial sit
> Careless, and crowned with mirth and wit,
> Where, though bleak winds confine us home
> Our fancies round the world shall roam."

Thomson's view of Winter is also, on the whole, a hostile one, though he does justice to his grandeur.

> " Thus Winter falls,
> A heavy gloom oppressive o'er the world,
> Through Nature shedding influence malign."

He finds his consolations, like Cotton, in the house, though more refined : —

> " While without
> The ceaseless winds blow ice, be my retreat
> Between the groaning forest and the shore
> Beat by the boundless multitude of waves,
> A rural, sheltered, solitary scene,
> Where ruddy fire and beaming tapers join
> To cheer the gloom.   There studious let me sit
> And hold high converse with the mighty dead."

Doctor Akenside, a man to be spoken of with respect, follows Thomson. With him, too, " Winter desolates the year," and

> " How pleasing wears the wintry night
> Spent with the old illustrious dead !
> While by the taper's trembling light
> I seem those awful scenes to tread
> Where chiefs or legislators lie," &c.

Akenside had evidently been reading Thomson. He had the conceptions of a great poet with less faculty than many a little one, and is one of those versifiers of whom it is enough to say that we are always willing to break him off in the middle with an &c., well knowing that what follows is but the coming-round again of what went before, marching in a circle with the cheap numerosity of a stage-army. In truth, it is no wonder that the short days of that cloudy northern climate should have added to winter a gloom borrowed of the mind. We hardly know, till we have experienced the contrast, how sensibly our winter is alleviated by the longer daylight and the

2 *   c

pellucid atmosphere. I once spent a winter in Dresden, a southern climate compared with England, and really almost lost my respect for the sun when I saw him groping among the chimney-pots opposite my windows as he described his impoverished arc in the sky. The enforced seclusion of the season makes it the time for serious study and occupations that demand fixed incomes of unbroken time. This is why Milton said "that his vein never happily flowed but from the autumnal equinox to the vernal," though in his twentieth year he had written, on the return of spring, —

> Fallor ? an et nobis redeunt in carmina vires
> Ingeniumque mihi munere veris adest ?
>
> Err I ? or do the powers of song return
> To me, and genius too, the gifts of Spring ?

Goethe, so far as I remember, was the first to notice the cheerfulness of snow in sunshine. His *Harz-reise im Winter* gives no hint of it, for that is a diluted reminiscence of Greek tragic choruses and the Book of Job in nearly equal parts. In one of the singularly interesting and characteristic letters to Frau von Stein, however, written during the journey, he says : " It is beautiful indeed ; the mist heaps itself together in light snow-clouds, the sun looks through, and the snow over everything gives back a feeling of gayety." But I find in Cowper the first recognition of a general amiability in Winter. The gentleness of his temper, and the wide charity of his sympathies, made it natural for him to find good in everything except the human heart. A dreadful creed distilled from the darkest moments of dyspeptic solitaries compelled him against his will to see in *that* the one evil thing made by a God whose goodness is over all his works. Cowper's two walks in the morning and noon of a winter's day are delightful, so long as he contrives to let himself be happy in the graciousness of the landscape

Your muscles grow springy, and your lungs dilate with the crisp air as you walk along with him. You laugh with him at the grotesque shadow of your legs lengthened across the snow by the just-risen sun. I know nothing that gives a purer feeling of out-door exhilaration than the easy verses of this escaped hypochondriac. But Cowper also preferred his sheltered garden-walk to those robuster joys, and bitterly acknowledged the depressing influence of the darkened year. In December, 1780, he writes : " At this season of the year, and in this gloomy uncomfortable climate, it is no easy matter for the owner of a mind like mine to divert it from sad subjects, and to fix it upon such as may administer to its amusement." Or was it because he was writing to the dreadful Newton ? Perhaps his poetry bears truer witness to his habitual feeling, for it is only there that poets disenthral themselves of their reserve and become fully possessed of their greatest charm, — the power of being franker than other men. In the Third Book of the Task he boldly affirms his preference of the country to the city even in winter : —

> " But are not wholesome airs, though unperfumed
> By roses, and clear suns, though scarcely felt,
> And groves, if inharmonious, yet secure
> From clamor, and whose very silence charms,
> To be preferred to smoke ? . . . .
> They would be, were not madness in the head
> And folly in the heart ; were England now
> What England was, plain, hospitable kind,
> And undebauched."

The conclusion shows, however, that he was thinking mainly of fireside delights, not of the blusterous companionship of nature. This appears even more clearly in the Fourth Book : —

> " O Winter, ruler of the inverted year " ;

but I cannot help interrupting him to say how pleasant it always is to track poets through the gardens of their predecessors and find out their likings by a flower snapped off here and there to garnish their own nosegays. Cowper had been reading Thomson, and "the inverted year" pleased his fancy with its suggestion of that starry wheel of the zodiac moving round through its spaces infinite. He could not help loving a handy Latinism (especially with elision beauty added), any more than Gray, any more than Wordsworth, — on the sly. But the member for Olney has the floor : —

> " O Winter, ruler of the inverted year,
> Thy scattered hair with sleet like ashes filled,
> Thy breath congealed upon thy lips, thy cheeks
> Fringed with a beard made white with other snows
> Than those of age, thy forehead wrapt in clouds,
> A leafless branch thy sceptre, and thy throne
> A sliding car, indebted to no wheels,
> But urged by storms along its slippery way,
> I love thee all unlovely as thou seem'st,
> And dreaded as thou art ! Thou hold'st the sun
> A prisoner in the yet undawning east,
> Shortening his journey between morn and noon,
> And hurrying him, impatient of his stay,
> Down to the rosy west, but kindly still
> Compensating his loss with added hours
> Of social converse and instructive ease,
> And gathering at short notice, in one group,
> The family dispersed, and fixing thought,
> Not less dispersed by daylight and its cares.
> I crown thee king of intimate delights,
> Fireside enjoyments, homeborn happiness,
> And all the comforts that the lowly roof
> Of undisturbed Retirement, and the hours
> Of long uninterrupted evening know."

I call this a good *human* bit of writing, imaginative, too, — not so flushed, not so . . . . highfaluting (let me dare the odious word !) as the modern style since poets have got hold of a theory that imagination is common-sense turned inside out, and not common-sense sublimed, — but wholesome, masculine, and strong in the simplicity of a mind wholly occupied with its theme. To me Cowper is still the best of our descriptive poets for every-day wear. And what unobtrusive skill he has! How he heightens, for example, your sense of winter-evening seclusion, by the twanging horn of the postman on the bridge! That horn has rung in my ears ever since I first heard it, during the consulate of the second Adams. Wordsworth strikes a deeper note; but does it not sometimes come over one (just the least in the world) that one would give anything for a bit of nature pure and simple, without quite so strong a flavor of W. W.? W. W. is, of course, sublime and all that — but! For my part, I will make a clean breast of it, and confess that I can't look at a mountain without fancying the late laureate's gigantic Roman nose thrust between me and it, and thinking of Dean Swift's profane version of *Romanos rerum dominos* into *Roman nose! a rare un! dom your nose!* But do I judge verses, then, by the impression made on me by the man who wrote them? Not so fast, my good friend, but, for good or evil, the character and its intellectual product are inextricably interfused.

If I remember aright, Wordsworth himself (except in his magnificent skating-scene in the "Prelude") has not much to say for winter out of doors. I cannot recall any picture by him of a snow-storm. The reason may possibly be that in the Lake Country even the winter storms bring rain rather than snow. He was thankful for the Christmas visits of Crabb Robinson, because they "helped him through the winter." His only hearty praise of winter is when, as Général Février, he defeats the French : —

> " Humanity, delighting to behold
> A fond reflection of her own decay,
> Hath painted Winter like a traveller old,
> Propped on a staff, and, through the sullen day,
> In hooded mantle, limping o'er the plain
> As though his weakness were disturbed by pain:

> Or, if a juster fancy should allow
> An undisputed symbol of command,
> The chosen sceptre is a withered bough
> Infirmly grasped within a withered hand.
> These emblems suit the helpless and forlorn;
> But mighty Winter the device shall scorn."

The Scottish poet Grahame, in his "Sabbath," says
manfully : —

> " Now is the time
> To visit Nature in her grand attire";

and he has one little picture which no other poet has
surpassed : —

> "High-ridged the whirlëd drift has almost reached
> The powdered keystone of the churchyard porch:
> Mute hangs the hooded bell; the tombs lie buried."

Even in our own climate, where the sun shows his winter face as long and as brightly as in central Italy, the
seduction of the chimney-corner is apt to predominate in
the mind over the severer satisfactions of muffled fields
and penitential woods.   The very title of Whittier's delightful " Snow-Bound " shows what *he* was thinking of,
though he does vapor a little about digging out paths.
The verses of Emerson, perfect as a Greek fragment
(despite the archaism of a dissyllabic fire), which he has
chosen for his epigraph, tell us, too, how the

> " Housemates sit
> Around the radiant fireplace, enclosed
> In a tumultuous privacy of storm."

They are all in a tale.   It is always the *tristis Hiems*
of Virgil.   Catch one of them having a kind word for old
Barbe Fleurie, unless he whines through some cranny,
like a beggar, to heighten their enjoyment while they
toast their slippered toes.   I grant there is a keen relish
of contrast about the bickering flame as it gives an
emphasis beyond Gherardo della Notte to loved faces, or
kindles the gloomy gold of volumes scarce less friendly,
especially when a tempest is blundering round the

house.   Wordsworth has a fine touch that brings home
to us the comfortable contrast of without and within,
during a storm at night, and the passage is highly
characteristic of a poet whose inspiration always has an
undertone of *bourgeois* : —

> " How touching, when, at midnight, sweep
> Snow-muffled winds, and all is dark,
> To hear, — and sink again to sleep ! "

J. H., one of those choice poets who will not tarnish
their bright fancies by publication, always insists on a
snow-storm as essential to the true atmosphere of whist.
Mrs. Battles, in her famous rule for the game, implies
winter, and would doubtless have added tempest, if it
could be had for the asking.   For a good solid read also,
into the small hours, there is nothing like that sense of
safety against having your evening laid waste, which
Euroclydon brings, as he bellows down the chimney,
making your fire gasp, or rustles snow-flakes against the
pane with a sound more soothing than silence.   Emerson, as he is apt to do, not only hit the nail on the
head, but drove it home, in that last phrase of the
" tumultuous privacy."

But I would exchange this, and give something to
boot, for the privilege of walking out into the vast blur
of a north-northeast snow-storm, and getting a strong
draught on the furnace within, by drawing the first furrows through its sandy drifts.   I love those

> " Noontide twilights which snow makes
> With tempest of the blinding flakes."

If the wind veer too much toward the east, you get the
heavy snow that gives a true Alpine slope to the boughs
of your evergreens, and traces a skeleton of your elms in
white ; but you must have plenty of north in your gale
if you want those driving nettles of frost that sting the
cheeks to a crimson manlier than that of fire.   During

the great storm of two winters ago, the most robustious
periwig-pated fellow of late years, I waded and floun-
dered a couple of miles through the whispering night,
and brought home that feeling of expansion we have
after being in good company. " Great things doeth He
which we cannot comprehend ; for he saith to the snow,
' Be thou on the earth.' "

There is admirable snow scenery in Judd's " Margaret," but some one has confiscated my copy of that admirable book, and, perhaps, Homer's picture of a snow-
storm is the best yet in its large simplicity :—

" And as in winter-time, when Jove his cold sharp javelins throws
  Amongst us mortals, and is moved to white the earth with snows,
  The winds asleep, he freely pours till highest prominents,
  Hill-tops, low meadows, and the fields that crown with most contents
  The toils of men, seaports and shores, are hid, and every place,
  But floods, that fair snow's tender flakes, as their own brood, em-
      brace."

Chapman, after all, though he makes very free with
him, comes nearer Homer than anybody else. There is
nothing in the original of that fair snow's tender flakes,
but neither Pope nor Cowper could get out of their
heads the Psalmist's tender phrase, " He giveth his snow
like wool," for which also Homer affords no hint. Pope
talks of " dissolving fleeces," and Cowper of a "fleecy
mantle." But David is nobly simple, while Pope is
simply nonsensical, and Cowper pretty. If they must
have prettiness, Martial would have supplied them with
it in his

Densum tacitarum vellus aquarum,

which is too pretty, though I fear it would have pleased
Dr. Donne. Eustathius of Thessalonica calls snow ὕδωρ
ἐρίωδες, woolly water, which a poor old French poet,
Godeau, has amplified into this :—

Lorsque la froidure inhumaine
De leur verd ornement depouille les forêts
Sous une neige épaisse il couvre les guérets,
Et la neige a pour eux la chaleur de la laine.

In this, as in Pope's version of the passage in Homer,
there is, at least, a sort of suggestion of snow-storm in
the blinding drift of words. But, on the whole, if one
would know what snow is, I should advise him not to
hunt up what the poets have said about it, but to look
at the sweet miracle itself.

The preludings of Winter are as beautiful as those of
Spring. In a gray December day, when, as the farmers
say, it is too cold to snow, his numbed fingers will let
fall doubtfully a few star-shaped flakes, the snow-drops
and anemones that harbinger his more assured reign.
Now, and now only, may be seen, heaped on the horizon's eastern edge, those "blue clouds" from forth
which Shakespeare says that Mars "doth pluck the
masoned turrets." Sometimes also, when the sun is
low, you will see a single cloud trailing a flurry of snow
along the southern hills in a wavering fringe of purple.
And when at last the real snow-storm comes, it leaves
the earth with a virginal look on it that no other of the
seasons can rival, — compared with which, indeed, they
seem soiled and vulgar.

And what is there in nature so beautiful as the next
morning after such confusion of the elements? Night
has no silence like this of busy day. All the batteries
of noise are spiked. We see the movement of life as a
deaf man sees it, a mere wraith of the clamorous existence that inflicts itself on our ears when the ground is
bare. The earth is clothed in innocence as a garment.
Every wound of the landscape is healed; whatever was
stiff has been sweetly rounded as the breasts of Aphro-
dite; what was unsightly has been covered gently with
a soft splendor, as if, Cowley would have said, Nature
had cleverly let fall her handkerchief to hide it. If the
Virgin (*Nôtre Dame de la neige*) were to come back, here
is an earth that would not bruise her foot nor stain it.

It is

"The fanned snow
That 's bolted by the northern blasts twice o'er," —
Soffiata e stretta dai venti Schiavi,
Winnowed and packed by the Sclavonian winds, —

packed so hard sometimes on hill-slopes that it will bear
your weight. What grace is in all the curves, as if
every one of them had been swept by that inspired
thumb of Phidias's journeyman !

Poets have fancied the footprints of the wind in those
light ripples that sometimes scurry across smooth water
with a sudden blur. But on this gleaming hush the
aerial deluge has left plain marks of its course ; and
in gullies through which it rushed torrent-like, the eye
finds its bed irregularly scooped like that of a brook in
hard beach-sand, or, in more sheltered spots, traced with
outlines like those left by the sliding edges of the surf
upon the shore. The air, after all, is only an infinitely
thinner kind of water, such as I suppose we shall have
to drink when the state does her whole duty as a moral
reformer. Nor is the wind the only thing whose trail
you will notice on this sensitive surface. You will find
that you have more neighbors and night visitors than
you dreamed of. Here is the dainty footprint of a cat ;
here a dog has looked in on you like an amateur watchman to see if all is right, slumping clumsily about in the
mealy treachery. And look ! before you were up in the
morning, though you were a punctual courtier at the
sun's levee, here has been a squirrel zigzagging to and
fro like a hound gathering the scent, and some tiny bird
searching for unimaginable food, — perhaps for the tinier
creature, whatever it is, that drew this slender continuous trail like those made on the wet beach by light
borderers of the sea. The earliest autographs were as
frail as these. Poseidon traced his lines, or giant birds
made their mark, on preadamite sea-margins ; and the

thunder-gust left the tear-stains of its sudden passion
there ; nay, we have the signatures of delicatest fern-
leaves on the soft ooze of æons that dozed away their
dreamless leisure before consciousness came upon the
earth with man.   Some whim of nature locked them fast
in stone for us after-thoughts of creation.   Which of us
shall leave a footprint as imperishable as that of the
ornithorhyncus, or much more so than that of these
Bedouins of the snow-desert ?   Perhaps it was only because the ripple and the rain-drop and the bird were not
thinking of themselves, that they had such luck.   The
chances of immortality depend very much on that.   How
often have we not seen poor mortals, dupes of a season's
notoriety, carving their names on seeming-solid rock of
merest beach-sand, whose feeble hold on memory shall
be washed away by the next wave of fickle opinion !
Well, well, honest Jacques, there are better things to be
found in the snow than sermons.

The snow that falls damp comes commonly in larger
flakes from windless skies, and is the prettiest of all to
watch from under cover.   This is the kind Homer had
in mind ; and Dante, who had never read him, compares
the *dilatate falde*, the flaring flakes, of his fiery rain, to
those of snow among the mountains without wind.   This
sort of snowfall has no fight in it, and does not challenge
you to a wrestle like that which drives well from the
northward, with all moisture thoroughly winnowed out
of it by the frosty wind.   Burns, who was more out of
doors than most poets, and whose barefoot Muse got the
color in her cheeks by vigorous exercise in all weathers,
was thinking of this drier deluge, when he speaks of the
" whirling drift," and tells how

> " Chanticleer
> Shook off the powthery snaw."

But the damper and more deliberate falls have a choice

knack at draping the trees ; and about eaves or stone-
walls, wherever, indeed, the evaporation is rapid, and it
finds a chance to cling, it will build itself out in curves
of wonderful beauty. I have seen one of these dumb
waves, thus caught in the act of breaking, curl four feet
beyond the edge of my roof and hang there for days, as
if Nature were too well pleased with her work to let it
crumble from its exquisite pause. After such a storm,
if you are lucky enough to have even a sluggish ditch
for a neighbor, be sure to pay it a visit. You will find
its banks corniced with what seems precipitated light,
and the dark current down below gleams as if with an
inward lustre. Dull of motion as it is, you never saw
water that seemed alive before. It has a brightness,
like that of the eyes of some smaller animals, which
gives assurance of life, but of a life foreign and unintelligible.

A damp snow-storm often turns to rain, and, in our
freakish climate, the wind will whisk sometimes into the
northwest so suddenly as to plate all the trees with crys-
tal before it has swept the sky clear of its last cobweb
of cloud. Ambrose Philips, in a poetical epistle from
Copenhagen to the Earl of Dorset, describes this strange
confectionery of Nature, — for such, I am half ashamed
to say, it always seems to me, recalling the "glorified
sugar-candy" of Lamb's first night at the theatre. It
has an artificial air, altogether beneath the grand artist
of the atmosphere, and besides does too much mischief
to the trees for a philodendrist to take unmixed pleasure
in it. Perhaps it deserves a poet like Philips, who
really loved Nature and yet liked her to be mighty fine,
as Pepys would say, with a heightening of powder and
rouge : —

> " And yet but lately have I seen e'en here
> The winter in a lovely dress appear.

> Ere yet the clouds let fall the treasured snow,
> Or winds begun through hazy skies to blow,
> At evening a keen eastern breeze arose,
> And the descending rain unsullied froze.
> Soon as the silent shades of night withdrew,
> The ruddy noon disclosed at once to view
> The face of Nature in a rich disguise,
> And brightened every object to my eyes;
> For every shrub, and every blade of grass,
> And every pointed thorn, seemed wrought in glass;
> In pearls and rubies rich the hawthorns show,
> And through the ice the crimson berries glow;
> The thick-sprung reeds, which watery marshes yield,
> Seem polished lances in a hostile field;
> The stag in limpid currents with surprise
> Sees crystal branches on his forehead rise;
> The spreading oak, the beech, the towering pine,
> Glazed over in the freezing ether shine;
> The frighted birds the rattling branches shun,
> Which wave and glitter in the distant sun,
> When, if a sudden gust of wind arise,
> The brittle forest into atoms flies,
> The crackling wood beneath the tempest bends
> And in a spangled shower the prospect ends."

It is not uninstructive to see how tolerable Ambrose is, so long as he sticks manfully to what he really saw. The moment he undertakes to improve on Nature he sinks into the mere court poet, and we surrender him to the jealousy of Pope without a sigh. His "rattling branches" and "crackling forest" are good, as truth always is after a fashion; but what shall we say of that dreadful stag which, there is little doubt, he valued above all the rest, because it was purely his own?

The damper snow tempts the amateur architect and sculptor. His Pentelicus has been brought to his very door, and if there are boys to be had (whose company beats all other recipes for prolonging life) a middle-aged Master of the Works will knock the years off his account and make the family Bible seem a dealer in foolish fables, by a few hours given heartily to this business. First comes the Sisyphean toil of rolling the clammy balls till they refuse to budge farther. Then, if you would play the statuary, they are piled one upon the other to the proper height; or if your aim be masonry, whether of house or fort, they must be squared and beaten solid with the shovel. The material is capable of very pretty effects, and your young companions meanwhile are unconsciously learning lessons in æsthetics. From the feeling of satisfaction with which one squats on the damp floor of his extemporized dwelling, I have been led to think that the backwoodsman must get a sweeter savor of self-reliance from the house his own hands have built than Bramante or Sansovino could ever give. Perhaps the fort is the best thing, for it calls out more masculine qualities and adds the cheer of battle with that dumb artillery which gives pain enough to test pluck without risk of serious hurt. Already, as I write, it is twenty-odd years ago. The balls fly thick and fast. The uncle defends the waist-high ramparts against a storm of nephews, his breast plastered with decorations like another Radetsky's. How well I recall the indomitable good-humor under fire of him who fell in the front at Ball's Bluff, the silent pertinacity of the gentle scholar who got his last hurt at Fair Oaks, the ardor in the charge of the gallant gentleman who, with the death-wound in his side, headed his brigade at Cedar Creek! How it all comes back, and they never come! I cannot again be the Vauban of fortresses in the innocent snow, but I shall never see children moulding their clumsy giants in it without longing to help. It was a pretty fancy of the young Vermont sculptor to make his first essay in this evanescent material. Was it a figure of Youth, I wonder? Would it not be well if all artists could begin in stuff as perishable, to melt away when the sun of prosperity began to shine, and leave nothing behind but the gain of practised hands? It is pleasant

to fancy that Shakespeare served his apprenticeship at
this trade, and owed to it that most pathetic of despair-
ing wishes, —

> "O, that I were a mockery-king of snow,
> Standing before the sun of Bolingbroke,
> To melt myself away in water-drops!"

I have spoken of the exquisite curves of snow sur-
faces. Not less rare are the tints of which they are
capable, — the faint blue of the hollows, for the shadows
in snow are always blue, and the tender rose of higher
points, as you stand with your back to the setting sun
and look upward across the soft rondure of a hillside.
I have seen within a mile of home effects of color as
lovely as any iridescence of the Silberhorn after sundown. Charles II., who never said a foolish thing, gave
the English climate the highest praise when he said that
it allowed you more hours out of doors than any other,
and I think our winter may fairly make the same boast
as compared with the rest of the year. Its still morn-
ings, with the thermometer near zero, put a premium on
walking. There is more sentiment in turf, perhaps, and
it is more elastic to the foot ; its silence, too, is wellnigh
as congenial with meditation as that of fallen pine-tassel;
but for exhilaration there is nothing like a stiff snow-
crust that creaks like a cricket at every step, and communicates its own sparkle to the senses. The air you
drink is *frappé*, all its grosser particles precipitated, and
the dregs of your blood with them. A purer current
mounts to the brain, courses sparkling through it, and
rinses it thoroughly of all dejected stuff. There is
nothing left to breed an exhalation of ill-humor or
despondency. They say that this rarefied atmosphere
has lessened the capacity of our lungs. Be it so. Quart-
pots are for muddier liquor than nectar. To me, the
city in winter is infinitely dreary, — the sharp street-

corners have such a chill in them, and the snow so soon loses its maidenhood to become a mere drab, — " doing shameful things," as Steele says of politicians, " without being ashamed." I pine for the Quaker purity of my country landscape. I am speaking, of course, of those winters that are not niggardly of snow, as ours too often are, giving us a gravelly dust instead. Nothing can be unsightlier than those piebald fields where the coarse brown hide of Earth shows through the holes of her ragged ermine. But even when there is abundance of snow, I find as I grow older that there are not so many good crusts as there used to be. When I first observed this, I rashly set it to the account of that general degeneracy in nature (keeping pace with the same melancholy phenomenon in man) which forces itself upon the attention and into the philosophy of middle life. But happening once to be weighed, it occurred to me that an arch which would bear fifty pounds could hardly be blamed for giving way under more than three times the weight. I have sometimes thought that if theologians would remember this in their arguments, and consider that the man may slump through, with no fault of his own, where the boy would have skimmed the surface in safety, it would be better for all parties. However, when you *do* get a crust that will bear, and know any brooklet that runs down a hillside, be sure to go and take a look at him, especially if your crust is due, as it commonly is, to a cold snap following eagerly on a thaw. You will never find him so cheerful. As he shrank away after the last thaw, he built for himself the most exquisite caverns of ice to run through, if not "measure- less to man " like those of Alph, the sacred river, yet perhaps more pleasing for their narrowness than those for their grandeur. What a cunning silversmith is Frost ! The rarest workmanship of Delhi or Genoa copies him but clumsily, as if the fingers of all other artists were thumbs. Fernwork and lacework and fila-gree in endless variety, and under it all the water tinkles like a distant guitar, or drums like a tambourine, or gurgles like the Tokay of an anchorite's dream. Be-yond doubt there is a fairy procession marching along those frail arcades and translucent corridors.

> " Their oaten pipes blow wondrous shrill,
> The hemlock small blow clear."

And hark ! is that the ringing of Titania's bridle, or the bells of the wee, wee hawk that sits on Oberon's wrist ? This wonder of Frost's handiwork may be had every winter, but he can do better than this, though I have seen it but once in my life. There had been a thaw without wind or rain, making the air fat with gray vapor. Towards sundown came that chill, the avant-courier of a northwesterly gale. Then, though there was no per-ceptible current in the atmosphere, the fog began to attach itself in frosty roots and filaments to the southern side of every twig and grass-stem. The very posts had poems traced upon them by this dumb minstrel. Wherever the moist seeds found lodgement grew an inch-deep moss fine as cobweb, a slender coral-reef, argentine, delicate, as of some silent sea in the moon, such as Agassiz dredges when he dreams. The frost, too, can wield a delicate graver, and in fancy leaves Piranesi far behind. He covers your window-pane with Alpine etchings, as if in memory of that sanctuary where he finds shelter even in midsummer.

Now look down from your hillside across the valley. The trees are leafless, but this is the season to study their anatomy, and did you ever notice before how much color there is in the twigs of many of them ? And the smoke from those chimneys is so blue it seems like a feeder of the sky into which it flows. Winter refines it

and gives it agreeable associations.   In summer it suggests cookery or the drudgery of steam-engines, but now
your fancy (if it can forget for a moment the dreary
usurpation of stoves) traces it down to the fireside and
the brightened faces of children.   Thoreau is the only
poet who has fitly sung it.   The wood-cutter rises before
day and

> " First in the dusky dawn he sends abroad
>   His early scout, his emissary, smoke,
>   The earliest, latest pilgrim from his roof,
>   To feel the frosty air ; . . . .
>   And, while he crouches still beside the hearth,
>   Nor musters courage to unbar the door,
>   It has gone down the glen with the light wind
>   And o'er the plain unfurled its venturous wreath.
>   Draped the tree-tops, loitered upon the hill,
>   And warmed the pinions of the early bird ;
>   And now, perchance, high in the crispy air,
>   Has caught sight of the day o'er the earth's edge,
>   And greets its master's eye at his low door
>   As some refulgent cloud in the upper sky."

Here is very bad verse and very good imagination.   He
had been reading Wordsworth, or he would not have
made *tree-tops* an iambus.   In the *Moretum* of Virgil (or,
if not his, better than most of his) is a pretty picture
of a peasant kindling his winter-morning fire.   He rises
before dawn,

> Sollicitaque manu tenebras explorat inertes
> Vestigatque focum læsus quem denique sensit.
> Parvulus exusto remanebat stipite fumus,
> Et cinis obductæ celabat lumina prunæ.
> Admovet his pronam submissa fronte lucernam,
> Et producit acu stupas humore carentes,
> Excitat et crebris languentem flatibus ignem ;
> Tandem concepto tenebræ fulgore recedunt,
> Oppositaque manu lumen defendit ab aura.

> With cautious hand he gropes the sluggish dark,
> Tracking the hearth which, scorched, he feels erelong.
> In burnt-out logs a slender smoke remained,
> And raked-up ashes hid the cinders' eyes;
> Stooping, to these the lamp outstretched he nears,

> And, with a needle loosening the dry wick,
> With frequent breath excites the languid flame.
> Before the gathering glow the shades recede,
> And his bent hand the new-caught light defends.

Ovid heightens the picture by a single touch : —

> Ipse genu poito flammas exsuscitat aura.
> Kneeling, his breath calls back to life the flames.

If you walk down now into the woods, you may find a robin or a blue-bird among the red-cedars, or a nuthatch scaling deviously the trunk of some hardwood tree with an eye as keen as that of a French soldier foraging for the *pot-au-feu* of his mess. Perhaps a blue-jay shrills *cah cah* in his corvine trebles, or a chickadee

> " Shows feats of his gymnastic play,
> Head downward, clinging to the spray."

But both him and the snow-bird I love better to see, tiny fluffs of feathered life, as they scurry about in a driving mist of snow, than in this serene air.

Coleridge has put into verse one of the most beautiful phenomena of a winter walk : —

> " The woodman winding westward up the glen
> At wintry dawn, where o'er the sheep-track's maze
> The viewless snow-mist weaves a glistening haze,
> Sees full before him, gliding without tread,
> An image with a halo round its head."

But this aureole is not peculiar to winter. I have noticed it often in a summer morning, when the grass was heavy with dew, and even later in the day, when the dewless grass was still fresh enough to have a gleam of its own.

For my own part I prefer a winter walk that takes in the nightfall and the intense silence that erelong follows it. The evening lamps looks yellower by contrast with the snow, and give the windows that hearty look of which our secretive fires have almost robbed them. The stars seem

> To hang, like twinkling winter lamps,
> Among the branches of the leafless trees,"

or, if you are on a hill-top (whence it is sweet to watch the home-lights gleam out one by one), they look nearer than in summer, and appear to take a conscious part in the cold. Especially in one of those stand-stills of the air that forebode a change of weather, the sky is dusted with motes of fire of which the summer-watcher never dreamed. Winter, too, is, on the whole, the triumphant season of the moon, a moon devoid of sentiment, if you choose, but with the refreshment of a purer intellectual light, — the cooler orb of middle life. Who ever saw anything to match that gleam, rather divined than seen, which runs before her over the snow, a breath of light, as she rises on the infinite silence of winter night ? High in the heavens, also she seems to bring out some intenser property of cold with her chilly polish. The poets have instinctively noted this. When Goody Blake imprecates a curse of perpetual chill upon Harry Gill, she has

> " The cold, cold moon above her head ";

and Coleridge speaks of

> " The silent icicles,
> Quietly gleaming to the quiet moon."

As you walk homeward, — for it is time that we should end our ramble, — you may perchance hear the most impressive sound in nature, unless it be the fall of a tree in the forest during the hush of summer noon. It is the stifled shriek of the lake yonder as the frost throttles it. Wordsworth has described it (too much, I fear, in the style of Dr. Armstrong) : —

> " And, interrupting oft that eager game,
> From under Esthwaite's splitting fields of ice,
> The pent-up air, struggling to free itself,
> Gave out to meadow-grounds and hills a loud
> Protracted yelling, like the noise of wolves
> Howling in troops along the Bothnic main."

Thoreau (unless the English lakes have a different dialect from ours) calls it admirably well a " whoop." But it is a noise like none other, as if Demogorgon were moaning inarticulately from under the earth. Let us get within doors, lest we hear it again, for there is something bodeful and uncanny in it.

ON A CERTAIN CONDESCENSION IN FOREIGNERS.

WALKING one day toward the Village, as we used to call it in the good old days when almost every dweller in the town had been born in it, I was enjoying that delicious sense of disenthralment from the actual which the deepening twilight brings with it, giving as it does a sort of obscure novelty to things familiar. The coolness, the hush, broken only by the distant bleat of some belated goat, querulous to be disburthened of her milky load, the few faint stars, more guessed as yet than seen, the sense that the coming dark would so soon fold me in the secure privacy of its disguise, — all things combined in a result as near absolute peace as can be hoped for by a man who knows that there is a writ out against him in the hands of the printer's devil. For the moment, I was enjoying the blessed privilege of thinking without being called on to stand and deliver what I thought to the small public who are good enough to take any interest therein. I love old ways, and the path I was walking felt kindly to the feet it had known for almost fifty years. How many fleeting impressions it had shared with me ! How many times I had lingered to study the shadows of the leaves mezzotinted upon the turf that edged it by the moon, of the bare boughs etched with a touch beyond Rembrandt by the same unconscious artist on the smooth page of snow ! If I turned round, through dusky tree-gaps came the first twinkle of evening lamps in the dear old homestead. On Corey's hill I could see these tiny pharoses of love and home and sweet domestic thoughts flash out one by one across the blackening salt-meadow between. How much has not kerosene added to the cheerfulness of our evening landscape ! A pair of night-herons flapped heavily over me toward the hidden river. The war was ended. I might walk townward without that aching dread of bulletins that had darkened the July sunshine and twice made the scarlet leaves of October seem stained with blood. I remembered with a pang, half-proud, half-painful, how, so many years ago, I had walked over the same path and felt round my finger the soft pressure of a little hand that was one day to harden with faithful grip of sabre. On how many paths, leading to how many homes where proud Memory does all she can to fill up the fireside gaps with shining shapes, must not men be walking in just such pensive mood as I ? Ah, young heroes, safe in immortal youth as those of Homer, you at least carried your ideal hence untarnished ! It is locked for you beyond moth or rust in the treasure-chamber of Death.

Is not a country, I thought, that has had such as they in it, that could give such as they a brave joy in dying for it, worth something, then ? And as I felt more and more the soothing magic of evening's cool palm upon my temples, as my fancy came home from its revery, and my senses, with reawakened curiosity, ran to the front windows again from the viewless closet of abstraction, and felt a strange charm in finding the old tree and shabby fence still there under the travesty of falling night, nay, were conscious of an unsuspected newness in familiar stars and the fading outlines of hills my earliest horizon, I was conscious of an immortal soul, and could not but rejoice in the unwaning goodliness of the world into which I had been born without any merit of my own. I thought of dear Henry Vaughan's rainbow, "Still young and fine!" I remembered people who had to go over to the Alps to learn what the divine silence of snow was, who must run to Italy before they were conscious of the miracle wrought every day under their very noses by the sunset, who must call upon the Berkshire hills to teach them what a painter autumn was, while close at hand the Fresh Pond meadows made all oriels cheap with hues that showed as if a sunset-cloud had been wrecked among their maples. One might be worse off than even in America, I thought. There are some things so elastic that even the heavy roller of democracy cannot flatten them altogether down. The mind can weave itself warmly in the cocoon of its own thoughts and dwell a hermit anywhere. A country without traditions, without ennobling associations, a scramble of *parvenus*, with a horrible consciousness of shoddy running through politics, manners, art, literature, nay, religion itself? I confess, it did not seem so to me there in that illimitable quiet, that serene self-possession of nature, where Collins might have brooded his "Ode to Evening," or where those verses on Solitude in Dodsley's Collection, that Hawthorne liked so much, might have been composed. Traditions? Granting that we had none, all that is worth having in them is the common property of the soul, — an estate in gavelkind for all the sons of Adam, — and, moreover, if a man cannot stand on his two feet (the prime quality of whoever has left any tradition behind him), were it not better for him to be honest about it at once, and go down on all fours? And for associations, if one have not the wit to make them for himself out of his native earth, no ready-made ones of other men will avail him much. Lexington is none the worse to me for not being in Greece, nor Gettysburg that its name is not Marathon. "Blessed old fields," I was just exclaiming to myself, like one of Mrs. Radcliffe's heroes, " dear acres, innocently secure from history, which these eyes first beheld, may you be also those to which they shall at last slowly darken ! " when I was interrupted by a voice which asked me in German whether I was the Herr Professor, Doctor, So-and-so ? The " Doctor " was by brevet or vaticination, to make the grade easier to my pocket.

One feels so intimately assured that he is made up, in part, of shreds and leavings of the past, in part of the interpolations of other people, that an honest man would be slow in saying *yes* to such a question. But " my name is So-and-so " is a safe answer, and I gave it. While I had been romancing with myself, the street-lamps had been lighted, and it was under one of these detectives that have robbed the Old Road of its privilege of sanctuary after nightfall that I was ambushed by my foe. The inexorable villain had taken my description, it appears, that I might have the less chance to escape him. Dr. Holmes tells us that we change our substance, not every seven years, as was once believed, but with every breath we draw. Why had I not the wit to avail myself of the subterfuge, and, like Peter, to renounce my identity, especially, as in certain moods of mind, I have often more than doubted of it myself ? When a man is, as it were, his own front-door, and is thus knocked at, why may he not assume the right of that sacred wood to make every house a castle, by denying himself to all visitations ? I was truly not at home when the question was put to me, but had to recall myself from all out-of-doors, and to piece my self-consciousness hastily together as well as I could before I answered it.

I knew perfectly well what was coming. It is seldom that debtors or good Samaritans waylay people under gas-lamps in order to force money upon them, so far as I

3 *

have seen or heard. I was also aware, from considerable experience, that every foreigner is persuaded that, by doing this country the favor of coming to it, he has laid every native thereof under an obligation, pecuniary or other, as the case may be, whose discharge he is entitled-to on demand duly made in person or by letter. Too much learning (of this kind) had made me mad in the provincial sense of the word. I had begun life with the theory of giving something to every beggar that came along, though sure of never finding a native-born countryman among them. In a small way, I was resolved to emulate Hatem Tai's tent, with its three hundred and sixty-five entrances, one for every day in the year, — I know not whether he was astronomer enough to add another for leap-years. The beggars were a kind of German-silver aristocracy ; not real plate, to be sure, but better than nothing. Where everybody was over-worked, they supplied the comfortable equipoise of absolute leisure, so æsthetically needful. Besides, I was but too conscious of a vagrant fibre in myself, which too often thrilled me in my solitary walks with the temptation to wander on into infinite space, and by a single spasm of resolution to emancipate myself from the drudgery of prosaic serfdom to respectability and the regular course of things. This prompting has been at times my familiar demon, and I could not but feel a kind of respectful sympathy for men who had dared what I had only sketched out to myself as a splendid possibility. For seven years I helped maintain one heroic man on an imaginary journey to Portland, — as fine an example as I have ever known of hopeless loyalty to an ideal. I assisted another so long in a fruitless attempt to reach Mecklenburg-Schwerin, that at last we grinned in each other's faces when we met, like a couple of augurs. He was possessed by this harmless mania

as some are by the North Pole, and I shall never forget
his look of regretful compassion (as for one who was
sacrificing his higher life to the fleshpots of Egypt) when
I at last advised him somewhat strenuously to go to the
D——, whither the road was so much travelled that he
could not miss it. General Banks, in his noble zeal for
the honor of his country, would confer on the Secretary
of State the power of imprisoning, in case of war, all
these seekers of the unattainable, thus by a stroke of
the pen annihilating the single poetic element in our
humdrum life. Alas! not everybody has the genius to
be a Bobbin-Boy, or doubtless all these also would have
chosen that more prosperous line of life! But moralists,
sociologists, political economists, and taxes have slowly
convinced me that my beggarly sympathies were a sin
against society. Especially was the Buckle doctrine of
averages (so flattering to our free-will) persuasive with
me ; for as there must be in every year a certain number who would bestow an alms on these abridged editions of the Wandering Jew, the withdrawal of my quota
could make no possible difference, since some destined
proxy must always step forward to fill my gap. Just
so many misdirected letters every year and no more!
Would it were as easy to reckon up the number of men
on whose backs fate has written the wrong address, so
that they arrive by mistake in Congress and other places
where they do not belong! May not these wanderers
of whom I speak have been sent into the world without
any proper address at all? Where is our Dead-Letter
Office for such? And if wiser social arrangements
should furnish us with something of the sort, fancy
(horrible thought!) how many a workingman's friend
(a kind of industry in which the labor is light and the
wages heavy) would be sent thither because not called
for in the office where he at present lies!

But I am leaving my new acquaintance too long under the lamp-post. The same Gano which had betrayed me to him revealed to me a well-set young man of about half my own age, as well dressed, so far as I could see, as I was, and with every natural qualification for getting his own livelihood as good, if not better, than my own. He had been reduced to the painful necessity of calling upon me by a series of crosses beginning with the Baden Revolution (for which, I own, he seemed rather young, — but perhaps he referred to a kind of revolution practised every season at Baden-Baden), continued by repeated failures in business, for amounts which must convince me of his entire respectability, and ending with our Civil War. During the latter, he had served with distinction as a soldier, taking a main part in every important battle, with a rapid list of which he favored me and no doubt would have admitted that, impartial as Jonathan Wild's great ancestor, he had been on both sides, had I baited him with a few hints of conservative opinions on a subject so distressing to a gentleman wishing to profit by one's sympathy and unhappily doubtful as to which way it might lean. For all these reasons, and, as he seemed to imply, for his merit in consenting to be born in Germany, he considered himself my natural creditor to the extent of five dollars, which he would handsomely consent to accept in greenbacks, though he preferred specie. The offer was certainly a generous one, and the claim presented with an assurance that carried conviction. But, unhappily, I had been led to remark a curious natural phenomenon. If I was ever weak enough to give anything to a petitioner of whatever nationality, it always rained decayed compatriots of his for a month after. *Post hoc ergo propter hoc* may not be always safe logic, but here I seemed to perceive a natural connection of cause and effect. Now, a few days before I had been so tickled with a paper (professedly written by a benevolent American clergyman) certifying that the bearer, a hard-working German, had long "sofered with rheumatic paints in his limps," that, after copying the passage into my note-book, I thought it but fair to pay a trifling *honorarium* to the author. I had pulled the string of the shower-bath ! It had been running shipwrecked sailors for some time, but forthwith it began to pour Teutons, redolent of *lager-bier*. I could not help associating the apparition of my new friend with this series of otherwise unaccountable phenomena. I accordingly made up my mind to deny the debt, and modestly did so, pleading a native bias towards impecuniosity to the full as strong as his own. He took a high tone with me at once, such as an honest man would naturally take with a confessed repudiator. He even brought down his proud stomach so far as to join himself to me for the rest of my townward walk, that he might give me his views of the American people, and thus inclusively of myself.

I know not whether it is because I am pigeon-livered and lack gall, or whether it is from an overmastering sense of drollery, but I am apt to submit to such bastings with a patience which afterwards surprises me, being not without my share of warmth in the blood. Perhaps it is because I so often meet with young persons who know vastly more than I do, and especially with so many foreigners whose knowledge of this country is superior to my own. However it may be, I listened for some time with tolerable composure as my self-appointed lecturer gave me in detail his opinions of my country and its people. America, he informed me, was without arts, science, literature, culture, or any native hope of supplying them. We were a people wholly given to money-getting, and who, having got it, knew no other

use for it than to hold it fast. I am fain to confess that
I felt a sensible itching of the biceps, and that my fingers
closed with such a grip as he had just informed me was
one of the effects of our unhappy climate. But happening just then to be where I could avoid temptation by
dodging down a by-street, I hastily left him to finish his
diatribe to the lamp-post, which could stand it better
than I. That young man will never know how near
he came to being assaulted by a respectable gentleman
of middle age, at the corner of Church Street. I have
never felt quite satisfied that I did all my duty by him
in not knocking him down. But perhaps he might have
knocked *me* down, and then ?

The capacity of indignation makes an essential part
of the outfit of every honest man, but I am inclined to
doubt whether he is a wise one who allows himself to act
upon its first hints. It should be rather, I suspect, a
latent heat in the blood, which makes itself felt in
character, a steady reserve for the brain, warming the
ovum of thought to life, rather than cooking it by a too
hasty enthusiasm in reaching the boiling-point. As my
pulse gradually fell back to its normal beat, I reflected
that I had been uncomfortably near making a fool of
myself, — a handy salve of euphuism for our vanity,
though it does not always make a just allowance to
Nature for her share in the business. What possible
claim had my Teutonic friend to rob me of my composure ? I am not, I think, specially thin-skinned as to
other people's opinions of myself, having, as I conceive,
later and fuller intelligence on that point than anybody
else can give me. Life is continually weighing us in
very sensitive scales, and telling every one of us precisely what his real weight is to the last grain of dust.
Whoever at fifty does not rate himself quite as low as
most of his acquaintance would be likely to put him,

must be either a fool or a great man, and I humbly disclaim being either. But if I was not smarting in person from any scattering shot of my late companion's commination, why should I grow hot at any implication of my country therein? Surely *her* shoulders are broad enough, if yours or mine are not, to bear up under a considerable avalanche of this kind. It is the bit of truth in every slander, the hint of likeness in every caricature, that makes us smart. "Art thou *there*, old Truepenny?" How did your blade know its way so well to that one loose rivet in our armor? I wondered whether Americans were over-sensitive in this respect, whether they were more touchy than other folks. On the whole, I thought we were not. Plutarch, who at least had studied philosophy, if he had not mastered it, could not stomach something Herodotus had said of Bœotia, and devoted an essay to showing up the delightful old traveller's malice and ill-breeding. French editors leave out of Montaigne's "Travels" some remarks of his about France, for reasons best known to themselves. Pachydermatous Deutschland, covered with trophies from every field of letters, still winces under that question which Père Bouhours put two centuries ago, *Si un Allemand peut être bel-esprit?* John Bull grew apoplectic with angry amazement at the audacious persiflage of Pückler-Muskau. To be sure, he was a prince, — but that was not all of it, for a chance phrase of gentle Hawthorne sent a spasm through all the journals of England. Then this tenderness is not peculiar to *us?* Console yourself, dear man and brother, whatever you may be sure of, be sure at least of this, that you are dreadfully like other people. Human nature has a much greater genius for sameness than for originality, or the world would be at a sad pass shortly. The surprising thing is that men have such a taste for this somewhat musty flavor, that an Englishman, for example, should feel himself defrauded, nay, even outraged, when he comes over here and finds a people speaking what he admits to be something like English, and yet so very different from (or, as he would say, to) those he left at home. Nothing, I am sure, equals *my* thankfulness when I meet an Englishman who is *not* like every other, or, I may add, an American of the same odd turn.

Certainly it is no shame to a man that he should be as nice about his country as about his sweetheart, and who ever heard even the friendliest appreciation of that unexpressive she that did not seem to fall infinitely short? Yet it would hardly be wise to hold every one an enemy who could not see her with our own enchanted eyes. It seems to be the common opinion of foreigners that Americans are *too* tender upon this point. Perhaps we are; and if so, there must be a reason for it. Have we had fair play? Could the eyes of what is called Good Society (though it is so seldom true either to the adjective or noun) look upon a nation of democrats with any chance of receiving an undistorted image? Were not those, moreover, who found in the old order of things an earthly paradise, paying them quarterly dividends for the wisdom of their ancestors, with the punctuality of the seasons, unconsciously bribed to misunderstand if not to misrepresent us? Whether at war or at peace, there we were, a standing menace to all earthly paradises of that kind, fatal underminers of the very credit on which the dividends were based, all the more hateful and terrible that our destructive agency was so insidious, working invisible in the elements, as it seemed, active while they slept, and coming upon them in the darkness like an armed man. *Could* Laius have the proper feelings of a father towards Œdipus, announced as his destined destroyer by infallible oracles, and felt to be such by every conscious fibre of his soul? For more than a century the Dutch were the laughing-stock of polite Europe. They were butter-firkins, swillers of beer and schnaps, and their *vrouws* from whom Holbein painted the all-but loveliest of Madonnas, Rembrandt the graceful girl who sits immortal on his knee in Dresden, and Rubens his abounding goddesses, were the synonymes of clumsy vulgarity. Even so late as Irving the ships of the greatest navigators in the world were represented as sailing equally well stern-foremost. That the aristocratic Venetians should have

"Riveted with gigantic piles
Thorough the centre their new-catchèd miles,"

was heroic. But the far more marvellous achievement of the Dutch in the same kind was ludicrous even to republican Marvell. Meanwhile, during that very century of scorn, they were the best artists, sailors, merchants, bankers, printers, scholars, jurisconsults, and statesmen in Europe, and the genius of Motley has revealed them to us, earning a right to themselves by the most heroic struggle in human annals. But, alas! they were not merely simple burghers who had fairly made themselves High Mightinesses, and could treat on equal terms with anointed kings, but their commonwealth carried in its bosom the germs of democracy. They even unmuzzled, at least after dark, that dreadful mastiff, the Press, whose scent is, or ought to be, so keen for wolves in sheep's clothing and for certain other animals in lions' skins. They made fun of Sacred Majesty, and, what was worse, managed uncommonly well without it. In an age when periwigs made so large a part of the natural dignity of man, people with such a turn of mind were dangerous. How could they seem other than vulgar and hateful?

E

In the natural course of things we succeeded to this unenviable position of general butt. The Dutch had thriven under it pretty well, and there was hope that we could at least contrive to worry along. And we certainly did in a very redoubtable fashion. Perhaps we deserved some of the sarcasm more than our Dutch predecessors in office. We had nothing to boast of in arts or letters, and were given to bragging overmuch of our merely material prosperity, due quite as much to the virtue of our continent as to our own. There was some truth in Carlyle's sneer, after all. Till we had succeeded in some higher way than this, we had only the success of physical growth. Our greatness, like that of enormous Russia, was greatness on the map, — barbarian mass only ; but had we gone down, like that other Atlantis, in some vast cataclysm, we should have covered but a pin's point on the chart of memory, compared with those ideal spaces occupied by tiny Attica and cramped England. At the same time, our critics somewhat too easily forgot that material must make ready the foundation for ideal triumphs, that the arts have no chance in poor countries. But it must be allowed that democracy stood for a great deal in our shortcoming. The Edinburgh Review never would have thought of asking, " Who reads a Russian book ? " and England was satisfied with iron from Sweden without being impertinently inquisitive after her painters and statuaries. Was it that they expected too much from the mere miracle of Freedom ? Is it not the highest art of a Republic to make men of flesh and blood, and not the marble ideals of such ? It may be fairly doubted whether we have produced this higher type of man yet. Perhaps it is the collective, not the individual, humanity that is to have a chance of nobler development among us. We shall see. We have a vast amount of imported ignorance, and, still worse, of native ready-made knowledge, to digest before even the preliminaries of such a consummation can be arranged. We have got to learn that statesmanship is the most complicated of all arts, and to come back to the apprenticeship-system too hastily abandoned. At present, we trust a man with making constitutions on less proof of competence than we should demand before we gave him our shoe to patch. We have nearly reached the limit of the reaction from the old notion, which paid too much regard to birth and station as qualifications for office, and have touched the extreme point in the opposite direction, putting the highest of human functions up at auction to be bid for by any creature capable of going upright on two legs. In some places, we have arrived at a point at which civil society is no longer possible, and already another reaction has begun, not backwards to the old system, but towards fit- ness either from natural aptitude or special training. But will it always be safe to let evils work their own cure by becoming unendurable? Every one of them leaves its taint in the constitution of the body-politic, each in itself, perhaps, trifling, yet all together powerful for evil.

But whatever we might do or leave undone, we were not genteel, and it was uncomfortable to be continually reminded that, though we should boast that we were the Great West till we were black in the face, it did not bring us an inch nearer to the world's West-End. That sacred enclosure of respectability was tabooed to us. The Holy Alliance did not inscribe us on its visiting-list. The Old World of wigs and orders and liveries would shop with us, but we must ring at the area-bell, and not venture to awaken the more august clamors of the knocker. Our manners, it must be granted, had none of those graces that stamp the caste of Vere de Vere, in whatever mu- seum of British antiquities they may be hidden. In short, we were vulgar.

This was one of those horribly vague accusations, the victim of which has no defence. An umbrella is of no avail against a Scotch mist. It envelops you, it penetrates at every pore, it wets you through without seeming to wet you at all. Vulgarity is an eighth deadly sin, added to the list in these latter days, and worse than all the others put together, since it perils your salvation in *this* world, — far the more important of the two in the minds of most men. It profits nothing to draw nice distinctions between essential and conventional, for the convention in this case *is* the essence, and you may break every command of the decalogue with perfect good-breeding, nay, if you are adroit, without losing caste. We, indeed, had it not to lose, for we had never gained it. " *How* am I vulgar ? " asks the culprit, shudderingly. " Because thou art not like unto Us," answers Lucifer, Son of the Morning, and there is no more to be said. The god of this world may be a fallen angel, but he has us *there !* We were as clean, — so far as my observation goes, I think we were cleaner, morally and physically, than the English, and therefore, of course, than everybody else. But we did not pronounce the diphthong *ou* as they did, and we said *eether* and not *eyther*, following therein the fashion of our ancestors, who unhappily could bring over no English better than Shakespeare's ; and we did not stammer as they had learned to do from the courtiers, who in this way flattered the Hanoverian king, a foreigner among the people he had come to reign over. Worse than all, we might have the noblest ideas and the finest sentiments in the world, but we vented them through that organ by which men are led rather than leaders, though some physiologists would persuade us that Nature furnishes her captains with a fine handle to their faces that Opportunity may get a good purchase on them for dragging them to the front.

This state of things was so painful that excellent people were not wanting who gave their whole genius to reproducing here the original Bull, whether by gaiters, the cut of their whiskers, by a factitious brutality in their tone, or by an accent that was forever tripping and failing flat over the tangled roots of our common tongue. Martyrs to a false ideal, it never occurred to them that nothing is more hateful to gods and men than a second-rate Englishman, and for the very reason that this planet never produced a more splendid creature than the first-rate one, witness Shakespeare and the Indian Mutiny. Witness that truly sublime self-abnegation of those prisoners lately among the bandits of Greece, where average men gave an example of quiet fortitude for which all the stoicism of antiquity can show no match. If we could contrive to be not too unobtrusively our simple selves, we should be the most delightful of human beings, and the most original; whereas, when the plating of Anglicism rubs off, as it always will in points that come to much wear, we are liable to very unpleasing conjectures about the quality of the metal underneath. Perhaps one reason why the average Briton spreads himself here with such an easy air of superiority may be owing to the fact that he meets with so many bad imitations as to conclude himself the only real thing in a wilderness of shams. He fancies himself moving through an endless Bloomsbury, where his mere apparition confers honor as an avatar of the court-end of the universe. Not a Bull of them all but is persuaded he bears Europa upon his back. This is the sort of fellow whose patronage is so divertingly insufferable. Thank Heaven he is not the only specimen of cater-cousinship from the dear old Mother Island that is shown to us! Among genuine things, I know nothing more genuine than the better men whose limbs were made in England. So manly-tender, so brave, so true, so warranted to wear, they make us proud to feel that blood is thicker than water.

But it is not merely the Englishman ; every European candidly admits in himself some right of primogeniture in respect to us, and pats this shaggy continent on the back with a lively sense of generous unbending. The German who plays the bass-viol has a well-founded contempt, which he is not always nice in concealing, for a country so few of whose children ever take that noble instrument between their knees. His cousin, the Ph. D. from Göttingen, cannot help despising a people who do not grow loud and red over Aryans and Turanians, and are indifferent about their descent from either. The Frenchman feels an easy mastery in speaking his mother tongue, and attributes it to some native superiority of parts that lifts him high above us barbarians of the West. The Italian *prima donna* sweeps a courtesy of careless pity to the over-facile pit which unsexes her with the *bravo !* innocently meant to show a familiarity with foreign usage. But all without exception make no secret of regarding us as the goose bound to deliver them a golden egg in return for *their* cackle. Such men as Agassiz, Guyot, and Goldwin Smith come with gifts in their hands ; but since it is commonly European failures who bring hither their remarkable gifts and acquirements, this view of the case is sometimes just the least bit in the world provoking. To think what a delicious seclusion of contempt we enjoyed till California and our own ostentatious *parvenus,* flinging gold away in Europe that might have endowed libraries at home, gave us the ill repute of riches ! What a shabby downfall from the Arcadia which the French officers of our Revolutionary War fancied they saw here through Rousseau-tinted spectacles ! Something of Arcadia there really was, something of the Old Age ; and that divine provincialism were cheaply repurchased could we have it back again in exchange for the tawdry upholstery that has taken its place.

For some reason or other, the European has rarely been able to see America except in caricature. Would the first Review of the world have printed the *niaiseries* of Mr. Maurice Sand as a picture of society in any civilized country? Mr. Sand, to be sure, has inherited nothing of his famous mother's literary outfit, except the pseudonyme. But since the conductors of the *Revue* could not have published his story because it was clever, they must have thought it valuable for its truth. As true as the last-century Englishman's picture of Jean Crapaud! We do not ask to be sprinkled with rosewater, but may perhaps fairly protest against being drenched with the rinsings of an unclean imagination. The next time the *Revue* allows such ill-bred persons to throw their slops out of its first-floor windows, let it honestly preface the discharge with a *gare de l'eau!* that we may run from under in season. And Mr. Duvergier d'Hauranne, who knows how to be entertaining! I know *le Français est plutôt indiscret que confiant,* and the pen slides too easily when indiscretions will fetch so much a page; but should we not have been *tant-soit-peu* more cautious had we been writing about people on the other side of the Channel? But then it is a fact in the natural history of the American long familiar to Europeans, that he abhors privacy, knows not the meaning of reserve, lives in hotels because of their greater publicity, and is never so pleased as when his domestic affairs (if he may be said to have any) are paraded in the newspapers. Barnum, it is well known, represents perfectly the average national sentiment in this respect. However it be, we are not treated like other people, or perhaps I should say like people who are ever likely to be met with in society.

Is it in the climate ? Either I have a false notion of European manners, or else the atmosphere affects them strangely when exported hither. Perhaps they suffer from the sea-voyage like some of the more delicate wines. During our Civil War an English gentleman of the highest description was kind enough to call upon me, mainly, as it seemed, to inform me how entirely he sympathized with the Confederates, and how sure he felt that we could never subdue them, — " they were the *gentlemen* of the country, you know." Another, the first greetings hardly over, asked me hcw I accounted for the universal meagreness of my countrymen. To a thinner man than I, or from a stouter man than he, the question *might* have been offensive. The Marquis of Hartington * wore a secession badge at a public ball in New York. In a civilized country he might have been roughly handled ; but here, where the *biensèances* are not so well understood, of course nobody minded it. A French traveller told me he had been a good deal in the British colonies, and had been astonished to see how soon the people became Americanized. He added, with delightful *bonhomie*, and as if he were sure it would charm me, that " they even began to talk through their noses, just like you ! " I was naturally ravished with this testimony to the assimilating power of democracy, and could only reply that I hoped they would never adopt our democratic patent-method of seeming to settle one's honest debts, for they would find it paying through the nose in the long-run. I am a man of the New

---

* One of Mr. Lincoln's neatest strokes of humor was his treatment of this gentleman when a laudable curiosity induced him to be presented to the President of the Broken Bubble. Mr. Lincoln persisted in calling him Mr. Partington. Surely the refinement of good-breeding could go no further. Giving the young man his real name (already notorious in the newspapers) would have made his visit an insult. Had Henri IV. done this, it would have been famous.

World, and do not know precisely the present fashion of
May-Fair, but I have a kind of feeling that if an American (*mutato nomine, de te* is always frightfully possible)
were to do this kind of thing under a European roof, it
would induce some disagreeable reflections as to the
ethical results of democracy. I read the other day in
print the remark of a British tourist who had eaten
large quantities of our salt, such as it is (I grant it has
not the European savor), that the Americans were
hospitable, no doubt, but that it was partly because they
longed for foreign visitors to relieve the tedium of their
dead-level existence, and partly from ostentation. What
shall we do? Shall we close our doors? Not I, for one,
if I should so have forfeited the friendship of L. S.,
most lovable of men. He somehow seems to find us
human, at least, and so did Clough, whose poetry will
one of these days, perhaps, be found to have been the
best utterance in verse of this generation. And T. H.
the mere grasp of whose manly hand carries with it the
pledge of frankness and friendship, of an abiding simplicity of nature as affecting as it is rare !

The fine old Tory aversion of former times was not
hard to bear. There was something even refreshing in
it, as in a northeaster to a hardy temperament. When
a British parson, travelling in Newfoundland while the
slash of our separation was still raw, after prophesying a
glorious future for an island that continued to dry its
fish under the ægis of Saint George, glances disdainfully
over his spectacles in parting at the U. S. A., and fore-
bodes for them a " speedy relapse into barbarism," now
that they have madly cut themselves off from the
humanizing influences of Britain, I smile with barbarian
self-conceit. But this kind of thing became by degrees
an unpleasant anachronism. For meanwhile the young
giant was growing, was beginning indeed to feel tight in

his clothes, was obliged to let in a gore here and there in Texas, in California, in New Mexico, in Alaska, and had the scissors and needle and thread ready for Canada when the time came. His shadow loomed like a Brocken-spectre over against Europe, — the shadow of what they were coming to, that was the unpleasant part of it. Even in such misty image as they had of him, it was painfully evident that his clothes were not of any cut hitherto fashionable, nor conceivable by a Bond Street tailor, — and this in an age, too, when everything depends upon clothes, when, if we do not keep up appearances, the seeming-solid frame of this universe, nay, your very God, would slump into himself, like a mockery king of snow, being nothing, after all, but a prevailing mode. From this moment the young giant assumed the respectable aspect of a phenomenon, to be got rid of if possible, but at any rate as legitimate a subject of human study as the glacial period or the silurian what-d'ye-call-ems. If the man of the primeval drift-heaps is so absorbingly interesting, why not the man of the drift that is just beginning, of the drift into whose irresistible current we are just being sucked whether we will or no? If I were in their place, I confess I should not be frightened. Man has survived so much, and contrived to be comfortable on this planet after surviving so much! I am something of a protestant in matters of government also, and am willing to get rid of vestments and ceremonies and to come down to bare benches, if only faith in God take the place of a general agreement to profess confidence in ritual and sham. Every mortal man of us holds stock in the only public debt that is absolutely sure of payment, and that is the debt of the Maker of this Universe to the Universe he has made. I have no notion of selling out my stock in a panic.

It was something to have advanced even to the dignity

of a phenomenon, and yet I do not know that the relation of the individual American to the individual European was bettered by it ; and that, after all, must adjust itself comfortably before there can be a right understanding between the two. We had been a desert, we became a museum. People came hither for scientific and not social ends. The very cockney could not complete his education without taking a vacant stare at us in passing. But the sociologists (I think they call themselves so) were the hardest to bear. There was no escape. I have even known a professor of this fearful science to come disguised in petticoats. We were cross-examined as a chemist cross-examines a new substance. Human ? yes, all the elements are present, though abnormally combined. Civilized? Hm ! that needs a stricter assay. No entomologist could take a more friendly interest in a strange bug. After a few such experiences, I, for one, have felt as if I were merely one of those horrid things preserved in spirits (and very bad spirits, too) in a cabinet. I was not the fellow-being of these explorers : I was a curiosity ; I was a *specimen.* Hath not an American organs, dimensions, senses, affections, passions even as a European hath ? If you prick us, do we not bleed ? If you tickle us, do we not laugh ? I will not keep on with Shylock to his next question but one.

Till after our Civil War it never seemed to enter the head of any foreigner, especially of any Englishman, that an American had what could be called a country, except as a place to eat, sleep, and trade in. Then it seemed to strike them suddenly. "By Jove, you know, fellahs don't fight like that for a shop-till ! " No, I rather think not. To Americans America is something more than a promise and an expectation. It has a past and traditions of its own. A descent from men who sacrificed everything and came hither, not to better their fortunes, but to plant their idea in virgin soil, should be a good pedigree. There was never colony save this that went forth, not to seek gold, but God. Is it not as well to have sprung from such as these as from some burly beggar who came over with Wilhelmus Conquestor, unless, indeed, a line grow better as it runs farther away from stalwart ancestors? And for history, it is dry enough, no doubt, in the books, but, for all that, is of a kind that tells in the blood. I have admitted that Carlyle's sneer had a show of truth in it. But what does he himself, like a true Scot, admire in the Hohenzollerns? First of all, that they were *canny*, a thrifty, forehanded race. Next, that they made a good fight from generation to generation with the chaos around them. That is precisely the battle which the English race on this continent has been carrying doughtily on for two centuries and a half. Doughtily and silently, for you cannot hear in Europe "that crash, the death-song of the perfect tree," that has been going on here from sturdy father to sturdy son, and making this continent habitable for the weaker Old World breed that has swarmed to it during the last half-century. If ever men did a good stroke of work on this planet, it was the forefathers of those whom you are wondering whether it would not be prudent to acknowledge as far-off cousins. Alas, man of genius, to whom we owe so much, could you see nothing more than the burning of a foul chimney in that clash of Michael and Satan which flamed up under your very eyes?

Before our war we were to Europe but a huge mob of adventurers and shop-keepers. Leigh Hunt expressed it well enough when he said that he could never think of America without seeing a gigantic counter stretched all along the seaboard. Feudalism had by degrees made commerce, the great civilizer, contemptible. But a tradesman with sword on thigh and very prompt of stroke was not only redoubtable, he had become respectable also. Few people, I suspect, alluded twice to a needle in Sir John Hawkwood's presence, after that doughty fighter had exchanged it for a more dangerous tool of the same metal. Democracy had been hitherto only a ludicrous effort to reverse the laws of nature by thrusting Cleon into the place of Pericles. But a democracy that could fight for an abstraction, whose members held life and goods cheap compared with that larger life which we call country, was not merely unheard-of, but portentous. It was the nightmare of the Old World taking upon itself flesh and blood, turning out to be substance and not dream. Since the Norman crusader clanged down upon the throne of the *porphyro-geniti*, carefully-draped appearances had never received such a shock, had never been so rudely called on to produce their titles to the empire of the world. Authority has had its periods not unlike those of geology, and at last comes Man claiming kingship in right of his mere manhood. The world of the Saurians might be in some respects more picturesque, but the march of events is inexorable, and it is bygone.

The young giant had certainly got out of long-clothes. He had become the *enfant terrible* of the human household. It was not and will not be easy for the world (especially for our British cousins) to look upon us as grown up. The youngest of nations, its people must also be young and to be treated accordingly, was the syllogism, — as if libraries did not make all nations equally old in all those respects, at least, where age is an advantage and not a defect. Youth, no doubt, has its good qualities, as people feel who are losing it, but boyishness is another thing. We had been somewhat boyish as a

nation, a little loud, a little pushing, a little braggart.
But might it not partly have been because we felt that
we had certain claims to respect that were not admitted?
The war which established our position as a vigorous
nationality has also sobered us. A nation, like a man,
cannot look death in the eye for four years, without some
strange reflections, without arriving at some clearer consciousness of the stuff it is made of, without some great
moral change. Such a change, or the beginning of it,
no observant person can fail to see here. Our thought
and our politics, our bearing as a people, are assuming a
manlier tone. We have been compelled to see what was
weak in democracy as well as what was strong. We
have begun obscurely to recognize that things do not go
of themselves, and that popular government is not in
itself a panacea, is no better than any other form except
as the virtue and wisdom of the people make it so, and
that when men undertake to do their own kingship, they
enter upon the dangers and responsibilities as well as
the privileges of the function. Above all, it looks as if
we were on the way to be persuaded that no government
can be carried on by declamation. It is noticeable also
that facility of communication has made the best English and French thought far more directly operative
here than ever before. Without being Europeanized,
our discussion of important questions in statesmanship,
political economy, in æsthetics, is taking a broader scope
and a higher tone. It had certainly been provincial,
one might almost say local, to a very unpleasant extent.
Perhaps our experience in soldiership has taught us to
value training more than we have been popularly wont.
We may possibly come to the conclusion, one of these
days, that self-made men may not be always equally
skilful in the manufacture of wisdom, may not be
divinely commissioned to fabricate the higher qualities
of opinion on all possible topics of human interest.

So long as we continue to be the most common-schooled and the least cultivated people in the world, I suppose we must consent to endure this condescending manner of foreigners toward us. The more friendly they mean to be the more ludicrously prominent it becomes. They can never appreciate the immense amount of silent work that has been done here, making this continent slowly fit for the abode of man, and which will demonstrate itself, let us hope, in the character of the people. Outsiders can only be expected to judge a nation by the amount it has contributed to the civilization of the world ; the amount, that is, that can be seen and handled. A great place in history can only be achieved by competitive examinations, nay, by a long course of them. How much new thought have we contributed to the common stock ? Till that question can be triumphantly answered, or needs no answer, we must continue to be simply interesting as an experiment, to be studied as a problem, and not respected as an attained result or an accomplished solution. Perhaps, as I have hinted, their patronizing manner toward us is the fair result of their failing to see here anything more than a poor imitation, a plaster-cast of Europe. And are they not partly right ? If the tone of the uncultivated American has too often the arrogance of the barbarian, is not that of the cultivated as often vulgarly apologetic ? In the America they meet with is there the simplicity, the manliness, the absence of sham, the sincere human nature. the sensitiveness to duty and implied obligation, that in any way distinguishes us from what our orators call "the effete civilization of the Old World"? Is there a politician among us daring enough (except a Dana here and there) to risk his future on the chance of our keeping our word with the exactness of superstitious communities like England ? Is it certain that we shall be ashamed of a bankruptcy of honor, if we can only keep the letter of our bond ? I hope we shall be able to answer all these questions with a frank *yes*. At any rate, we would advise our visitors that we are not merely curious creatures, but belong to the family of man, and that, as individuals, we are not to be always subjected to the competitive examination above mentioned, even if we acknowledged their competence as an examining board. Above all, we beg them to remember that America is not to us, as to them, a mere object of external interest to be discussed and analyzed, but *in* us, part of our very marrow. Let them not suppose that we conceive of ourselves as exiles from the graces and amenities of an older date than we, though very much at home in a state of things not yet all it might be or should be, but which we mean to make so, and which we find both wholesome and pleasant for men (though perhaps not for *dilettanti*) to live in. "The full tide of human existence" may be felt here as keenly as Johnson felt it at Charing Cross, and in a larger sense. I know one person who is singular enough to think Cambridge the very best spot on the habitable globe. " Doubtless God *could* have made a better, but doubtless he never did."

It will take England a great while to get over her airs of patronage toward us, or even passably to conceal them. She cannot help confounding the people with the country, and regarding us as lusty juveniles. She has a conviction that whatever good there is in us is wholly English, when the truth is that we are worth nothing except so far as we have disinfected ourselves of Anglicism. She is especially condescending just now, and lavishes sugar-plums on us as if we had not outgrown them. I am no believer in sudden conversions, especially in sudden conversions to a favorable opinion of people who have just proved you to be mistaken in judgment and therefore unwise in policy. I never blamed her for not wishing well to democracy, — how should she? — but Alabamas are not wishes. Let her not be too hasty in believing Mr. Reverdy Johnson's pleasant words. Though there is no thoughtful man in America who would not consider a war with England the greatest of calamities, yet the feeling towards her here is very far from cordial, whatever our Minister may say in the effusion that comes after ample dining. Mr. Adams, with his famous " My Lord, this means war," perfectly represented his country. Justly or not, we have a feeling that we have been wronged, not merely insulted. The only sure way of bringing about a healthy relation between the two countries is for Englishmen to clear their minds of the notion that we are always to be treated as a kind of inferior and deported Englishman whose nature they perfectly understand, and whose back they accordingly stroke the wrong way of the fur with amazing persever- ance. Let them learn to treat us naturally on our merits as human beings, as they would a German or a Frenchman, and not as if we were a kind of counterfeit Briton whose crime appeared in every shade of difference, and before long there would come that right feeling which we naturally call a good understanding. The common blood, and still more the common language, are fatal instruments of misapprehension. Let them give up *trying* to understand us, still more thinking that they do, and acting in various absurd ways as the necessary consequence, for they will never arrive at that devoutly-to-be-wished consummation, till they learn to look at us as we are and not as they suppose us to be. Dear old long-estranged mother-in-law, it is a great many years since we parted. Since 1660, when you married again, you have been a step-mother to us. Put on your

spectacles, dear madam. Yes, we *have* grown, and
changed likewise. You would not let us darken your
doors, if you could help it. We know that perfectly
well. But pray, when we look to be treated as men,
don't shake that rattle in our faces, nor talk baby to us
any longer.

> " Do, child, go to it grandam, child;
> Give grandam kingdom, and it grandam will
> Give it a plum, a cherry, and a fig! "

A GREAT PUBLIC CHARACTER.*

IT is the misfortune of American biography that it must needs be more or less provincial, and that, contrary to what might have been predicted, this quality in it predominates in proportion as the country grows larger. Wanting any great and acknowledged centre of national life and thought, our expansion has hitherto been rather aggregation than growth ; reputations must be hammered out thin to cover so wide a surface, and the substance of most hardly holds out to the boundaries of a single State. Our very history wants unity, and down to the Revolution the attention is wearied and confused by having to divide itself among thirteen parallel threads, instead of being concentred on a single clew. A sense of remoteness and seclusion comes over us as we read, and we cannot help asking ourselves, " Were *not* these things done in a corner ?" Notoriety may be achieved in a narrow sphere, but fame demands for its evidence a more distant and prolonged reverberation. To the world at large we were but a short column of figures in the corner of a bluebook, New England exporting so much salt-fish, timber, and Medford rum, Virginia so many hogsheads of tobacco, and buying with the proceeds a certain amount of English manufactures. The story of our early colonization had a certain moral interest, to be sure, but was altogether inferior in picturesque fascination to that of

* The Life of Josiah Quincy by his son.

Mexico or Peru. The lives of our worthies, like that of our nation, are bare of those foregone and far-reaching associations with names, the divining-rods of fancy, which the soldiers and civilians of the Old World get for nothing by the mere accident of birth. Their historians and biographers have succeeded to the good-will, as well as to the long-established stand, of the shop of glory. Time is, after all, the greatest of poets, and the sons of Memory stand a better chance of being the heirs of Fame. The philosophic poet may find a proud solace in saying,

> " Avia Pieridum peragro loca nullius ante
>   Trita solo ";

but all the while he has the splendid centuries of Greece and Rome behind him, and can begin his poem with invoking a goddess from whom legend derived the planter of his race. His eyes looked out on a landscape saturated with glorious recollections ; he had seen Cæsar, and heard Cicero. But who shall conjure with Saugus or Cato Four Corners, — with Israel Putnam or Return Jonathan Meigs? We have been transplanted, and for us the long hierarchical succession of history is broken. The Past has not laid its venerable hands upon us in consecration, conveying to us that mysterious influence whose force is in its continuity. We are to Europe as the Church of England to her of Rome. The latter old lady may be the Scarlet Woman, or the Beast with ten horns, if you will, but hers are all the heirlooms, hers that vast spiritual estate of tradition, nowhere yet everywhere, whose revenues are none the less fruitful for being levied on the imagination. We may claim that England's history is also ours, but it is a *de jure,* and not a *de facto* property that we have in it, — something that may be proved indeed, yet is a merely intellectual satisfaction, and does not savor of the realty. Have we not seen the mockery crown and sceptre of the exiled Stuarts in St. Peter's? the medal struck so lately as 1784 with its legend, HEN IX MAG BRIT ET HIB REX, whose contractions but faintly typify the scantness of the fact?

As the novelist complains that our society wants that sharp contrast of character and costume which comes of caste, so in the narrative of our historians we miss what may be called background and perspective, as if the events and the actors in them failed of that cumulative interest which only a long historical entail can give. Relatively, the crusade of Sir William Pepperell was of more consequence than that of St. Louis, and yet forgive us, injured shade of the second American baronet, if we find the narrative of Joinville more interesting than your despatches to Governor Shirley. Relatively, the insurrection of that Daniel whose Irish patronymic Shea was euphonized into Shays, as a set-off for the debasing of French *chaise* into *shay*, was more dangerous than that of Charles Edward; but for some reason or other (as vice sometimes has the advantage of virtue) the latter is more enticing to the imagination, and the least authentic relic of it in song or story has a relish denied to the painful industry of Minot. Our events seem to fall short of that colossal proportion which befits the monumental style. Look grave as we will, there is something ludicrous in Counsellor Keane's pig being the pivot of a revolution. We are of yesterday, and it is to no purpose that our political augurs divine from the flight of our eagles that to-morrow shall be ours, and flatter us with an all-hail hereafter. Things do really gain in greatness by being acted on a great and cosmopolitan stage, because there is inspiration in the thronged audience, and the nearer match that puts men on their mettle. Webster was more largely endowed by nature than Fox, and Fisher Ames not much below Burke as a talker; but what a

difference in the intellectual training, in the literary culture and associations, in the whole social outfit, of the
men who were their antagonists and companions! It
should seem that, if it be collision with other minds and
with events that strikes or draws the fire from a man, then
the quality of those might have something to do with
the quality of the fire, — whether it shall be culinary or
electric. We have never known the varied stimulus, the
inexorable criticism, the many-sided opportunity of a
great metropolis, the inspiring reinforcement of an un-
divided national consciousness. In everything but trade
we have missed the invigoration of foreign rivalry. We
may prove that we are this and that and the other, —
our Fourth-of-July orators have proved it time and again,
— the census has proved it ; but the Muses are women,
and have no great fancy for statistics, though easily
silenced by them. We are great, we are rich, we are all
kinds of good things ; but did it never occur to you that
somehow we are not interesting, except as a phenomenon?
It may safely be affirmed that for one cultivated man in
this country who studies American, there are fifty who
study European history, ancient or modern.

Till within a year or two we have been as distant and
obscure to the eyes of Europe as Ecuador to our own.
Every day brings us nearer, enables us to see the Old
World more clearly, and by inevitable comparison to
judge ourselves with some closer approach to our real
value. This has its advantage so long as our culture is,
as for a long time it must be, European ; for we shall be
little better than apes and parrots till we are forced to
measure our muscle with the trained and practised cham-
pions of that elder civilization. We have at length established our claim to the noblesse of the sword, the first
step still of every nation that would make its entry into
the best society of history. To maintain ourselves there,

we must achieve an equality in the more exclusive circle
of culture, and to that end must submit ourselves to the
European standard of intellectual weights and measures-
That we have made the hitherto biggest gun might excite apprehension (were there a dearth of iron), but can
never exact respect.   That our pianos and patent reapers
have won medals does but confirm us in our mechanic
and material measure of merit.   We must contribute
something more than mere contrivances for the saving
of labor, which we have been only too ready to misapply
in the domain of thought and the higher kinds of invention.   In those Olympic games where nations contend for
truly immortal wreaths, it may well be questioned whether
a mowing-machine would stand much chance in the
chariot-races, — whether a piano, though made by a chev-
alier, could compete successfully for the prize of music.

We shall have to be content for a good while yet with
our provincialism, and must strive to make the best of it.
In it lies the germ of nationality, and that is, after all,
the prime condition of all thorough-bred greatness of
character.   To this choicest fruit of a healthy life, well
rooted in native soil, and drawing prosperous juices
thence, nationality gives the keenest flavor.   Mr. Lincoln
was an original man, and in so far a great man ; yet it
was the Americanism of his every thought, word, and act
which not only made his influence equally at home in
East and West, but drew the eyes of the outside world,
and was the pedestal that lifted him where he could be
seen by them.   Lincoln showed that native force may
transcend local boundaries, but the growth of such
nationality is hindered and hampered by our division
into so many half-independent communities, each with its
objects of county ambition, and its public men great to
the borders of their district.   In this way our standard
of greatness is insensibly debased.   To receive any na-

tional appointment, a man must have gone through precisely the worst training for it; he must have so far narrowed and belittled himself with State politics as to be acceptable at home. In this way a man may become chairman of the Committee on Foreign Affairs, because he knows how to pack a caucus in Catawampus County, or be sent ambassador to Barataria, because he has drunk bad whiskey with every voter in Wildcat City. Should we ever attain to a conscious nationality, it will have the advantage of lessening the number of our great men, and widening our appreciation to the larger scale of the two or three that are left, — if there should be so many. Meanwhile we offer a premium to the production of great men in a small way, by inviting each State to set up the statues of two of its immortals in the Capitol. What a niggardly percentage ! Already we are embarrassed, not to find the two, but to choose among the crowd of candidates. Well, seventy-odd heroes in about as many years is pretty well for a young nation. We do not envy most of them their eternal martyrdom in marble, their pillory of indiscrimination. We fancy even native tourists pausing before the greater part of the effigies, and, after reading the names, asking desperately, "Who was *he* ?" Nay, if they should say, "Who the devil was *he* ?" it were a pardonable invocation, for none so fit as the Prince of Darkness to act as *cicerone* among such palpable obscurities. We recall the court-yard of the Uffizj at Florence. That also is not free of parish celebrities ; but Dante, Galileo, Michael Angelo, Macchiavelli, — shall the inventor of the sewing-machine, even with the button-holing improvement, let us say, match with these, or with far lesser than these ? Perhaps he was more practically useful than any one of these, or all of them together, but the soul is sensible of a sad difference somewhere. These also were citizens of a provincial capital ;

so were the greater part of Plutarch's heroes. Did they
have a better chance than we moderns, — than we
Americans ?   At any rate they have the start of us, and
we must confess that

> " By bed and table they lord it o'er us,
>   Our elder brothers, but one in blood."

Yes, one in blood ; that is the hardest part of it. Is
our provincialism then in some great measure due to
our absorption in the practical, as we politely call it,
meaning the material, — to our habit of estimating
greatness by the square mile and the hundred weight ?
Even during our war, in the midst of that almost unrivalled stress of soul, were not our speakers and newspapers so enslaved to the vulgar habit as to boast ten
times of the thousands of square miles it covered with
armed men, for once that they alluded to the motive
that gave it all its meaning and its splendor ?   Perhaps
it was as well that they did not exploit that passion of
patriotism as an advertisement in the style of Barnum
or Perham.   " I scale one hundred and eighty pounds,
but when I 'm mad I weigh two ton," said the Ken-
tuckian, with a true notion of moral avoirdupois.   That
ideal kind of weight is wonderfully increased by a national feeling, whereby one man is conscious that thirty
millions of men go into the balance with him.   The
Roman in ancient, and the Englishman in modern times,
have been most conscious of this representative solidity,
and wherever one of them went there stood Rome or
England in his shoes.   We have made some advance in
the right direction.   Our civil war, by the breadth of its
proportions and the implacability of its demands, forced
us to admit a truer valuation, and gave us, in our own
despite, great soldiers and sailors, allowed for such by all
the world.   The harder problems it has left behind may
in time compel us to have great statesmen, with views

capable of reaching beyond the next election. The
criticism of Europe alone can rescue us from the provincialism of an over or false estimate of ourselves.   Let us
be thankful, and not angry, that we must accept it as
our touchstone.   Our stamp has so often been impressed
upon base metal, that we cannot expect it to be taken
on trust, but we may be sure that true gold will be
equally persuasive the world over.   Real manhood and
honest achievement are nowhere provincial, but enter
the select society of all time on an even footing.

Spanish America might be a good glass for us to look
into.   Those Catharine-wheel republics, always in revolution while the powder lasts, and sure to burn the fingers
of whoever attempts intervention, have also their great
men, as placidly ignored by us as our own by jealous
Europe.   The following passage from the life of Don
Simon Bolivar might allay many *motus animorum*, if
rightly pondered.   Bolivar, then a youth, was travelling in
Italy, and his biographer tells us that "near Castiglione
he was present at the grand review made by Napoleon of
the columns defiling into the plain large enough to contain sixty thousand men.   The throne was situated on
an eminence that overlooked the plain, and Napoleon on
several occasions looked through a glass at Bolivar and
his companions, who were at the base of the hill.   The
hero Cæsar could not imagine that he beheld the liberator of the world of Columbus ! "   And small blame to
him, one would say.   We are not, then, it seems, the
only foundling of Columbus, as we are so apt to take for
granted.   The great Genoese did not, as we supposed,
draw that first star-guided furrow across the vague of
waters with a single eye to the future greatness of the
United States.   And have we not sometimes, like the
enthusiastic biographer, fancied the Old World staring
through all its telescopes at us, and wondered that it did

not recognize in us what we were fully persuaded we were *going* to be and do?

Our American life is dreadfully barren of those elements of the social picturesque which give piquancy to anecdote. And without anecdote, what is biography, or even history, which is only biography on a larger scale? Clio, though she take airs on herself, and pretend to be "philosophy teaching by example," is, after all, but a gossip who has borrowed Fame's speaking-trumpet, and should be figured with a tea-cup instead of a scroll in her hand. How much has she not owed of late to the tittle-tattle of her gillflirt sister Thalia? In what gutters has not Macaulay raked for the brilliant bits with which he has put together his admirable mosaic picture of England under the last two Stuarts? Even Mommsen himself, who dislikes Plutarch's method as much as Montaigne loved it, cannot get or give a lively notion of ancient Rome, without running to the comic poets and the anecdote-mongers. He gives us the very beef-tea of history, nourishing and even palatable enough, excellently portable for a memory that must carry her own packs, and can afford little luggage; but for our own part, we prefer a full, old-fashioned meal, with its side-dishes of spicy gossip, and its last relish, the Stilton of scandal, so it be not too high. One volume of contemporary memoirs, stuffed though it be with lies, (for lies to be good for anything must have a potential probability, must even be true so far as their moral and social setting is concerned,) will throw more light into the dark backward of time than the gravest Camden or Thuanus. If St. Simon is not accurate, is he any the less essentially *true?* No history gives us so clear an understanding of the moral condition of average men after the restoration of the Stuarts as the unconscious blabbings of the Puritan tailor's son, with his two con-

sciences, as it were, — an inward, still sensitive in spots,
though mostly toughened to India-rubber, and good
rather for rubbing out old scores than retaining them,
and an outward, alert, and termagantly effective in Mrs.
Pepys.   But we can have no St. Simons or Pepyses
till we have a Paris or London to delocalize our gossip
and give it historic breadth.   All our capitals are frac-
tional, merely greater or smaller gatherings of men,
centres of business rather than of action or influence.
Each contains so many souls, but is not, as the word
" capital " implies, the true head of a community and
seat of its common soul.

Has not life itself perhaps become a little more prosaic
than it once was?   As the clearing away of the woods
scants the streams, may not our civilization have dried
up some feeders that helped to swell the current of
individual and personal force?   We have sometimes
thought that the stricter definition and consequent
seclusion from each other of the different callings in
modern times, as it narrowed the chance of developing
and giving variety to character, lessened also the interest
of biography.   Formerly arts and arms were not divided
by so impassable a barrier as now.   There was hardly
such a thing as a *pékin*.   Cæsar gets up from writing
his Latin Grammar to conquer Gaul, change the course
of history, and make so many things possible, — among
the rest our English language and Shakespeare.   Horace
had been a colonel ; and from Æschylus, who fought at
Marathon, to Ben Jonson, who trailed a pike in the Low
Countries, the list of martial civilians is a long one.   A
man's education seems more complete who has smelt
hostile powder from a less æsthetic distance than Goethe.
It raises our confidence in Sir Kenelm Digby as a physi-
cist, that he is able to illustrate some theory of acous-
tics in his Treatise of Bodies by instancing the effect of

his guns in a sea-fight off Scanderoon. One would expect the proportions of character to be enlarged by such variety and contrast of experience. Perhaps it will by and by appear that our own Civil War has done something for us in this way. Colonel Higginson comes down from his pulpit to draw on his jack-boots, and thenceforth rides in our imagination alongside of John Bunyan and Bishop Compton. To have stored moral capital enough to meet the drafts of Death at sight, must be an unmatched tonic. We saw our light-hearted youth come back with the modest gravity of age, as if they had learned to throw out pickets against a surprise of any weak point in their temperament. Perhaps that American shiftiness, so often complained of, may not be so bad a thing, if, by bringing men acquainted with every humor of fortune and human nature, it puts them in fuller possession of themselves.

But with whatever drawbacks in special circumstances, the main interest of biography must always lie in the amount of character or essential manhood which the subject of it reveals to us, and events are of import only as means to that end. It is true that lofty and far-seen exigencies may give greater opportunity to some men, whose energy is more sharply spurred by the shout of a multitude than by the grudging *Well done !* of conscience. Some theorists have too hastily assumed that, as the power of public opinion increases, the force of private character, or what we call originality, is absorbed into and diluted by it. But we think Horace was right in putting tyrant and mob on a level as the trainers and tests of a man's solid quality. The amount of resistance of which one is capable to whatever lies outside the conscience, is of more consequence than all other faculties together; and democracy, perhaps, tries this by pressure in more directions, and with a more

continuous strain, than any other form of society. In
Josiah Quincy we have an example of character trained
and shaped, under the nearest approach to a pure
democracy the world has ever seen, to a firmness, unity,
and self-centred poise that recall the finer types of antiquity, in whom the public and private man were so
wholly of a piece that they were truly everywhere at
home, for the same sincerity of nature that dignified the
hearth carried also a charm of homeliness into the forum.
The phrase "a great public character," once common,
seems to be going out of fashion, perhaps because there
are fewer examples of the thing. It fits Josiah Quincy
exactly. Active in civic and academic duties till beyond
the ordinary period of man, at fourscore and ten his pen,
voice, and venerable presence were still efficient in public affairs. A score of years after the energies of even
vigorous men are declining or spent, his mind and character made themselves felt as in their prime. A true
pillar of house and state, he stood unflinchingly upright
under whatever burden might be laid upon him. The
French Revolutionists aped what was itself but a parody
of the elder republic, with their hair à la Brutus and
their pedantic moralities à la Cato Minor, but this man
unconsciously was the antique Roman they laboriously
went about to be. Others have filled places more conspicuous, few have made the place they filled so conspicuous by an exact and disinterested performance of duty.

In the biography of Mr. Quincy by his son there is
something of the provincialism of which we have spoken
as inherent in most American works of the kind. His
was a Boston life in the strictest sense. But provincialism is relative, and where it has a flavor of its own, as
in Scotland, it is often agreeable in proportion to its
very intensity. The Massachusetts in which Mr. Quincy's habits of thought were acquired was a very different

Massachusetts from that in which we of later generations have been bred. Till after he had passed middle life, Boston was more truly a capital than any other city in America, before or since, except possibly Charleston. The acknowledged head of New England, with a population of wellnigh purely English descent, mostly derived from the earlier emigration, with ancestral traditions and inspiring memories of its own, it had made its name familiar in both worlds, and was both historically and politically more important than at any later period. The Revolution had not interrupted, but rather given a freer current to the tendencies of its past. Both by its history and position, the town had what the French call a solidarity, an almost personal consciousness, rare anywhere, rare especially in America, and more than ever since our enormous importation of fellow-citizens to whom America means merely shop, or meat three times a day. Boston has been called the "American Athens." Æsthetically, the comparison is ludicrous, but politically it was more reasonable. Its population was homogeneous, and there were leading families; while the form of government by town-meeting, and the facility of social and civic intercourse, gave great influence to popular personal qualities and opportunity to new men. A wide commerce, while it had insensibly softened the asperities of Puritanism and imported enough foreign refinement to humanize, not enough foreign luxury to corrupt, had not essentially qualified the native tone of the town. Retired sea-captains (true brothers of Chaucer's Shipman), whose exploits had kindled the imagination of Burke, added a not unpleasant savor of salt to society. They belonged to the old school of Gilbert, Hawkins, Frobisher, and Drake, parcel-soldiers all of them, who had commanded armed ships and had tales to tell of gallant fights with privateers or pirates, truest representatives of those Vikings who, if trade in lumber or peltry was dull, would make themselves Dukes of Dublin or Earls of Orkney. If trade pinches the mind, commerce liberalizes it; and Boston was also advantaged with the neighborhood of the country's oldest College, which maintained the wholesome traditions of culture, — where Homer and Horace are familiar there is a certain amount of cosmopolitanism, — and would not allow bigotry to become despotism. Manners were more self-respectful, and therefore more respectful of others, and personal sensitiveness was fenced with more of that ceremonial with which society armed itself when it surrendered the ruder protection of the sword. We had not then seen a Governor in his chamber at the State-House with his hat on, a cigar in his mouth, and his feet upon the stove. Domestic service, in spite of the proverb, was not seldom an inheritance, nor was household peace dependent on the whim of a foreign armed neutrality in the kitchen. Servant and master were of one stock; there was decent authority and becoming respect; the tradition of the Old World lingered after its superstition had passed away. There was an aristocracy such as is healthful in a well-ordered community, founded on public service, and hereditary so long as the virtue which was its patent was not escheated. The clergy, no longer hedged by the reverence exacted by sacerdotal caste, were more than repaid by the consideration willingly paid to superior culture. What changes, many of them for the better, some of them surely for the worse, and all of them inevitable, did not Josiah Quincy see in that wellnigh secular life which linked the war of independence to the war of nationality! We seemed to see a type of them the other day in a colored man standing with an air of comfortable self-possession while his boots were brushed by a youth of catholic neutral tint, but whom nature had planned for white. The same eyes that had looked on Gage's red-coats, saw Colonel Shaw's negro regiment march out of Boston in the national blue. Seldom has a life, itself actively associated with public affairs, spanned so wide a chasm for the imagination. Oglethorpe's offers a parallel, — the aide-de-camp of Prince Eugene calling on John Adams, American Ambassador to England. Most long lives resemble those threads of gossamer, the nearest approach to nothing unmeaningly prolonged, scarce visible pathway of some worm from his cradle to his grave; but Quincy's was strung with seventy active years, each one a rounded bead of usefulness and service.

Mr. Quincy was a Bostonian of the purest type. Since the settlement of the town, there had been a colonel of the Boston regiment in every generation of his family. He lived to see a grandson brevetted with the same title for gallantry in the field. Only child of one among the most eminent advocates of the Revolution, and who but for his untimely death would have been a leading actor in it, his earliest recollections belonged to the heroic period in the history of his native town. With that history his life was thenceforth intimately united by offices of public trust, as Representative in Congress, State Senator, Mayor, and President of the University, to a period beyond the ordinary span of mortals. Even after he had passed ninety, he would not claim to be *emeritus*, but came forward to brace his townsmen with a courage and warm them with a fire younger than their own. The legend of Colonel Goffe at Deerfield became a reality to the eyes of this generation. The New England breed is running out, we are told! This was in all ways a beautiful and fortunate life, — fortunate in the goods of this world, — fortunate, above all, in the force of character which makes fortune

secondary and subservient. We are fond in this country
of what are called self-made men (as if real success could
ever be other) ; and this is all very well, provided they
make something worth having of themselves. Otherwise
it is not so well, and the examples of such are at best
but stuff for the Alnaschar dreams of a false democracy.
The gist of the matter is, not where a man starts from,
but where he comes out. We are glad to have the
biography of one who, beginning as a gentleman, kept
himself such to the end, — who, with no necessity of
labor, left behind him an amount of thoroughly done
work such as few have accomplished with the mighty
help of hunger. Some kind of pace may be got out of
the veriest jade by the near prospect of oats ; but the
thorough-bred has the spur in his blood.

Mr. Edmund Quincy has told the story of his father's
life with the skill and good taste that might have been
expected from the author of " Wensley." Considering
natural partialities, he has shown a discretion of which
we are oftener reminded by missing than by meeting it.
He has given extracts enough from speeches to show
their bearing and quality, — from letters, to recall bygone modes of thought and indicate many-sided friendly
relations with good and eminent men ; above all, he has
lost no opportunity to illustrate that life of the past,
near in date, yet alien in manners, whose current glides
so imperceptibly from one generation into another that
we fail to mark the shiftings of its bed or the change in
its nature wrought by the affluents that discharge into
it on all sides, — here a stream bred in the hills to
sweeten, there the sewerage of some great city to corrupt. We cannot but lament that Mr. Quincy did not
earlier begin to keep a diary.   " Miss not the discourses
of the elders," though put now in the Apocrypha, is a
wise precept, but incomplete unless we add, " Nor cease

from recording whatsoever thing thou hast gathered therefrom," — so ready is Oblivion with her fatal shears. The somewhat greasy heap of a literary rag-and-bone-picker, like Athenæus, is turned to gold by time. Even the *Virgilium vidi tantum* of Dryden about Milton, and of Pope again about Dryden, is worth having, and gives a pleasant fillip to the fancy. There is much of this quality in Mr. Edmund Quincy's book, enough to make us wish there were more. We get a glimpse of President Washington, in 1795, who reminded Mr. Quincy "of the gentlemen who used to come to Boston in those days to attend the General Court from Hampden or Franklin County, in the western part of the State. A little stiff in his person, not a little formal in his manners, not particularly at ease in the presence of strangers. He had the air of a country-gentleman not accustomed to mix much in society, perfectly polite, but not easy in his address and conversation, and not graceful in his gait and movements." Our figures of Washington have been so long equestrian, that it is pleasant to meet him dismounted for once. In the same way we get a card of invitation to a dinner of sixty covers at John Hancock's, and see the rather light-weighted great man wheeled round the room (for he had adopted Lord Chatham's convenient trick of the gout) to converse with his guests. In another place we are presented, with Mr. Merry, the English Minister, to Jefferson, whom we find in an unofficial costume of studied slovenliness, intended as a snub to haughty Albion. Slippers down at the heel and a dirty shirt become weapons of diplomacy and threaten more serious war. Thus many a door into the past, long irrevocably shut upon us, is set ajar, and we of the younger generation on the landing catch peeps of distinguished men, and bits of their table-talk. We drive in from Mr. Lyman's beautiful seat at Waltham (unique

at that day in its stately swans and half-shy, half-familiar
deer) with John Adams, who tells us that Dr. Priestley
looked on the French monarchy as the tenth horn of the
Beast in Revelation, — a horn that has set more sober
wits dancing than that of Huon of Bordeaux. Those
were days, we are inclined to think, of more solid and
elegant hospitality than our own, — the elegance of
manners, at once more courtly and more frugal, of men
who had better uses for wealth than merely to display it.
Dinners have more courses now, and, like the Gascon in
the old story, who could not see the town for the houses,
we miss the real dinner in the multiplicity of its details.
We might seek long before we found so good cheer, so
good company, or so good talk as our fathers had at
Lieutenant-Governor Winthrop's or Senator Cabot's.

We shall not do Mr. Edmund Quincy the wrong of
picking out in advance all the plums in his volume,
leaving to the reader only the less savory mixture that
held them together, — a kind of filling unavoidable in
books of this kind, and too apt to be what boys at
boarding-school call *stick-jaw*, but of which there is no
more than could not be helped here, and that light and
palatable. But here and there is a passage where we
cannot refrain, for there is a smack of Jack Horner in all
of us, and a reviewer were nothing without it. Josiah
Quincy was born in 1772. His father, returning from a
mission to England, died in sight of the dear New England shore three years later. His young widow was
worthy of him, and of the son whose character she was
to have so large a share in forming. There is something very touching and beautiful in this little picture
of her which Mr. Quincy drew in his extreme old age.

"My mother imbibed, as was usual with the women
of the period, the spirit of the times. Patriotism was
not then a profession, but an energetic principle beating

in the heart and active in the life. The death of my father, under circumstances now the subject of history, had overwhelmed her with grief. She viewed him as a victim in the cause of freedom, and cultivated his memory with veneration, regarding him as a martyr, falling, as did his friend Warren, in the defence of the liberties of his country. These circumstances gave a pathos and vehemence to her grief, which, after the first violence of passion had subsided, sought consolation in earnest and solicitous fulfilment of duty to the representative of his memory and of their mutual affections. Love and reverence for the memory of his father was early impressed on the mind of her son, and worn into his heart by her sadness and tears. She cultivated the memory of my father in my heart and affections, even in my earliest childhood, by reading to me passages from the poets, and obliging me to learn by heart and repeat such as were best adapted to her own circumstances and feelings. Among others, the whole leave-taking of Hector and Andromache, in the sixth book of Pope's Homer, was one of her favorite lessons, which she made me learn and frequently repeat. Her imagination, probably, found consolation in the repetition of lines which brought to mind and seemed to typify her own great bereavement.

> ' And think'st thou not how wretched we shall be, —
> A widow I, a helpless orphan he? '

These lines, and the whole tenor of Andromache's address and circumstances, she identified with her own sufferings, which seemed relieved by the tears my repetition of them drew from her."

Pope's Homer is not Homer, perhaps ; but how many noble natures have felt its elation, how many bruised spirits the solace of its bracing, if monotonous melody ! To us there is something inexpressibly tender in this instinct of the widowed mother to find consolation in the

idealization of her grief by mingling it with those sor-
rows which genius has turned into the perennial delight
of mankind.   This was a kind of sentiment that was
healthy for her boy, refining without unnerving, and associating his father's memory with a noble company un-
assailable by time.   It was through this lady, whose
image looks down on us out of the past, so full of
sweetness and refinement, that Mr. Quincy became of
kin with Mr. Wendell Phillips, so justly eminent as a
speaker.   There is something nearer than cater-cousinship in a certain impetuous audacity of temper common
to them both.

When six years old, Mr. Quincy was sent to Phillips
Academy at Andover, where he remained till he entered
college.   His form-fellow here was a man of thirty, who
had been a surgeon in the Continental Army, and
whose character and adventures might almost seem borrowed from a romance of Smollett.   Under Principal
Pearson, the lad, though a near relative of the founder
of the school, seems to have endured all that severity of
the old *a posteriori* method of teaching which still
smarted in Tusser's memory when he sang,

> " From Paul's I went, to Eton sent,
>   To learn straightways the Latin phrase,
>   Where fifty-three stripes given to me
>   At once I had."

The young victim of the wisdom of Solomon was boarded
with the parish minister, in whose kindness he found a
lenitive for the scholastic discipline he underwent.   This
gentleman had been a soldier in the Colonial service, and
Mr. Quincy afterwards gave as a reason for his mildness,
that, " while a sergeant at Castle William, he had seen
something of mankind."   This, no doubt, would be a
better preparative for successful dealing with the young
than is generally thought.   However, the birch was

then the only classic tree, and every round in the ladder
of learning was made of its inspiring wood. Dr. Pearson, perhaps, thought he was only doing justice to his
pupil's claims of kindred by giving him a larger share of
the educational advantages which the neighboring forest
afforded. The vividness with which this system is always remembered by those who have been subjected to it
would seem to show that it really enlivened the attention,
and thereby invigorated the memory, nay, might even
raise some question as to what part of the person is chosen
by the mother of the Muses for her residence. With
an appetite for the classics quickened by "Cheever's
Accidence," and such other preliminary whets as were
then in vogue, young Quincy entered college, where he
spent the usual four years, and was graduated with the
highest honors of his class. The amount of Latin and
Greek imparted to the students of that day was not
very great. They were carried through Horace, Sallust,
and the *De Oratoribus* of Cicero, and read portions of
Livy, Xenophon, and Homer. Yet the chief end of classical studies was perhaps as often reached then as now,
in giving young men a love for something apart from
and above the more vulgar associations of life. Mr.
Quincy, at least, retained to the last a fondness for
certain Latin authors. While he was President of the
College, he told a gentleman, from whom we received
the story, that, "if he were imprisoned, and allowed
to choose one book for his amusement, that should
be Horace."

In 1797 Mr. Quincy was married to Miss Eliza Susan
Morton of New York, a union which lasted in unbroken
happiness for more than fifty years. His case might be
cited among the leading ones in support of the old poet's
axiom, that

"He never loved, that loved not at first sight";

for he saw, wooed, and won in a week.   In later life he
tried in a most amusing way to account for this rash-
ness, and to find reasons of settled gravity for the happy
inspiration of his heart.   He cites the evidence of Judge
Sedgwick, of Mr. and Mrs. Oliver Wolcott, of the Rev.
Dr. Smith, and others, to the wisdom of his choice.
But it does not appear that he consulted them beforehand.   If love were not too cunning for that, what
would become of the charming idyl, renewed in all its
wonder and freshness for every generation ?   Let us be
thankful that in every man's life there is a holiday of
romance, an illumination of the senses by the soul, that
makes him a poet while it lasts.   Mr. Quincy caught
the enchantment through his ears, a song of Burns
heard from the next room conveying the infection, — a
fact still inexplicable to him after lifelong meditation
thereon, as he "was not very impressible by music " !
To us there is something very characteristic in this
rapid energy of Mr. Quincy, something very delightful
in his naïve account of the affair.   It needs the magic
of no Dr. Heidegger to make these dried roses, that
drop from between the leaves of a volume shut for
seventy years, bloom again in all their sweetness.   Mr.
Edmund Quincy tells us that his mother was "not handsome " ; but those who remember the gracious dignity
of her old age will hardly agree with him.   She must
always have had that highest kind of beauty which
grows more beautiful with years, and keeps the eyes
young, as if with the partial connivance of Time.

We do not propose to follow Mr. Quincy closely
through his whole public life, which, beginning with his
thirty-second, ended with his seventy-third year.   He
entered Congress as the representative of a party pri-
vately the most respectable, publicly the least sagacious,
among all those which under different names have

divided the country. The Federalists were the only proper tories our politics have ever produced, whose conservatism truly represented an idea, and not a mere selfish interest, — men who honestly distrusted democracy, and stood up for experience, or the tradition which they believed for such, against empiricism. During his Congressional career, the government was little more than an *attaché* of the French legation, and the opposition to which he belonged a helpless *revenant* from the dead and buried Colonial past. There are some questions whose interest dies the moment they are settled; others, into which a moral element enters that hinders them from being settled, though they may be decided. It is hard to revive any enthusiasm about the *Embargo*, though it once could inspire the boyish Muse of Bryant, or in the impressment quarrel, though the Trent difficulty for a time rekindled its old animosities. The stars in their courses fought against Mr. Quincy's party, which was not in sympathy with the instincts of the people, groping about for some principle of nationality, and finding a substitute for it in hatred of England. But there are several things which still make his career in Congress interesting to us, because they illustrate the personal character of the man. He prepared himself honestly for his duties, by a thorough study of whatever could make him efficient in them. It was not enough that he could make a good speech; he wished also to have something to say. In Congress, as everywhere else, *quod voluit valde voluit;* and he threw a fervor into the most temporary topic, as if his eternal salvation depended upon it. He had not merely, as the French say, the courage of his opinions, but his opinions became principles, and gave him that gallantry of fanaticism which made him always ready to head a forlorn hope, — the more ready, perhaps, that it was a forlorn hope.

This is not the humor of a statesman, — no, unless he holds a position like that of Pitt, and can charge a whole people with his own enthusiasm, and then we call it genius.   Mr. Quincy had the moral firmness which enabled him to decline a duel without any loss of personal *prestige*.   His opposition to the Louisiana purchase illustrates that Roman quality in him to which we have alluded.   He would not conclude the purchase till each of the old thirteen States had signified its assent.   He was reluctant to endow a Sabine city with the privilege of Roman citizenship.   It is worth noting, that while in Congress, and afterwards in the State Senate, many of his phrases became the catchwords of party politics.   He always dared to say what others deemed it more prudent only to think, and whatever he said he intensified with the whole ardor of his temperament.   It is this which makes Mr. Quincy's speeches good reading still, even when the topics they discussed were ephemeral.   In one respect he is distinguished from the politicians, and must rank with the far-seeing statesmen of his time.   He early foresaw and denounced the political danger with which the Slave Power threatened the Union.   His fears, it is true, were aroused for the balance of power between the old States, rather than by any moral sensitiveness, which would, indeed, have been an anachronism at that time.   But the Civil War justified his prescience.

It was as Mayor of his native city that his remarkable qualities as an administrator were first called into requisition and adequately displayed.   He organized the city government, and put it in working order.   To him we owe many reforms in police, in the management of the poor, and other kindred matters, — much in the way of cure, still more in that of prevention.   The place demanded a man of courage and firmness, and found

5 *

those qualities almost superabundantly in him. His virtues lost him his office, as such virtues are only too apt to do in peaceful times, where they are felt more as a restraint than a protection. His address on laying down the mayoralty is very characteristic. We quote the concluding sentences : —

" And now, gentlemen, standing as I do in this relation for the last time in your presence and that of my fellow-citizens, about to surrender forever a station full of difficulty, of labor and temptation, in which I have been called to very arduous duties, affecting the rights, property, and at times the liberty of others ; concerning which the perfect line of rectitude — though desired — was not always to be clearly discerned ; in which great interests have been placed within my control, under circumstances in which it would have been easy to advance private ends and sinister projects ; — under these circumstances, I inquire, as I have a right to inquire, — for in the recent contest insinuations have been cast against my integrity, — in this long management of your affairs, whatever errors have been committed, — and doubtless there have been many, — have you found in me anything selfish, anything personal, anything mercenary? In the simple language of an ancient seer, I say, ' Behold, here I am ; witness against me. Whom have I defrauded ? Whom have I oppressed ? At whose hands have I received any bribe ?'

" Six years ago, when I had the honor first to address the City Council, in anticipation of the event which has now occurred, the following expressions were used : ' In administering the police, in executing the laws, in protecting the rights and promoting the prosperity of the city, its first officer will be necessarily beset and assailed by individual interests, by rival projects, by personal influences, by party passions. The more firm and inflexible he is in maintaining the rights and in pursuing the interests of the city, the greater is the probability of his becoming obnoxious to the censure of all whom he causes to be prosecuted or punished, of all whose passions he thwarts, of all whose interests he opposes.'

"The day and the event have come. I retire — as in that first address I told my fellow-citizens, 'If, in conformity with the experience of other republics, faithful exertions should be followed by loss of favor and confidence,' I should retire — 'rejoicing, not, indeed, with a public and patriotic, but with a private and individual joy'; for I shall retire with a consciousness weighed against which all *human suffrages* are but as the light dust of the balance."

Of his mayoralty we have another anecdote quite Roman in color. He was in the habit of riding early in the morning through the various streets that he might look into everything with his own eyes. He was once arrested on a malicious charge of violating the city ordinance against fast driving. He might have resisted, but he appeared in court and paid the fine, because it would serve as a good example "that no citizen was above the law."

Hardly had Mr. Quincy given up the government of the city, when he was called to that of the College. It is here that his stately figure is associated most intimately and warmly with the recollections of the greater number who hold his memory dear. Almost everybody looks back regretfully to the days of some Consul Plancus. Never were eyes so bright, never had wine so much wit and good-fellowship in it, never were we ourselves so capable of the various great things we have never done. Nor is it merely the sunset of life that casts such a ravishing light on the past, and makes the western windows of those homes of fancy we have left

forever tremble with a sentiment of such sweet regret.
We set great store by what we had, and cannot have
again, however indifferent in itself, and what is past is
infinitely past. This is especially true of college life,
when we first assume the titles without the responsibilities of manhood, and the President of our year is apt to
become our Plancus very early. Popular or not while
in office, an ex-president is always sure of enthusiastic
cheers at every college festival. Mr. Quincy had many
qualities calculated to win favor with the young, — that
one above all which is sure to do it, indomitable pluck.
With him the dignity was in the man, not in the office.
He had some of those little oddities, too, which afford
amusement without contempt, and which rather tend to
heighten than diminish personal attachment to superiors
in station. His punctuality at prayers, and in dropping
asleep there, his forgetfulness of names, his singular in-
ability to make even the shortest off-hand speech to the
students, — all the more singular in a practised orator, — his occasional absorption of mind, leading him to
hand you his sand-box instead of the leave of absence he
had just dried with it, — the old-fashioned courtesy of
his, "Sir, your servant," as he bowed you out of his
study, — all tended to make him popular. He had also
a little of what is somewhat contradictorily called dry
humor, not without influence in his relations with the
students. In taking leave of the graduating class, he
was in the habit of paying them whatever honest compliment he could. Who, of a certain year which shall
be nameless, will ever forget the gravity with which he
assured them that they were "the *best-dressed* class that
had passed through college during his administration"?
How sincerely kind he was, how considerate of youthful
levity, will always be gratefully remembered by whoever
had occasion to experience it. A visitor not long before

his death found him burning some memoranda of college peccadilloes, lest they should ever rise up in judgment against the men eminent in Church and State who had been guilty of them. One great element of his popularity with the students was his *esprit de corps*. However strict in discipline, he was always on *our* side as respected the outside world. Of his efficiency, no higher testimony could be asked than that of his successor, Dr. Walker. Here also many reforms date from his time. He had that happiest combination for a wise vigor in the conduct of affairs, — he was a conservative with an open mind.

One would be apt to think that, in the various offices which Mr. Quincy successively filled, he would have found enough to do. But his indefatigable activity overflowed. Even as a man of letters, he occupies no inconsiderable place. His " History of Harvard College " is a valuable and entertaining treatment of a subject not wanting in natural dryness. His " Municipal History of Boston," his " History of the Boston Athenæum," and his " Life of Colonel Shaw " have permanent interest and value. All these were works demanding no little labor and research, and the thoroughness of their workmanship makes them remarkable as the by-productions of a busy man. Having consented, when more than eighty, to write a memoir of John Quincy Adams, to be published in the " Proceedings " of the Massachusetts Historical Society, he was obliged to excuse himself. On account of his age? Not at all, but because the work had grown to be a volume under his weariless hand. *Ohne Hast ohne Rast*, was as true of him as of Goethe. We find the explanation of his accomplishing so much in a rule of life which he gave, when President, to a young man employed as his secretary, and who was a little behindhand with his work : " When you have a number of duties to perform, always do the most disagreeable one first." No advice could have been more in character, and it is perhaps better than the great German's, "Do the duty that lies nearest thee."

Perhaps the most beautiful part of Mr. Quincy's life was his old age. What in most men is decay, was in him but beneficent prolongation and adjournment. His interest in affairs unabated, his judgment undimmed, his fire unchilled, his last years were indeed "lovely as a Lapland night." Till within a year or two of its fall, there were no signs of dilapidation in that stately edifice. Singularly felicitous was Mr. Winthrop's application to him of Wordsworth's verses : —

> " The monumental pomp of age
> Was in that goodly personage."

Everything that Macbeth foreboded the want of, he had in deserved abundance, — the love, the honor, the obedience, the troops of friends. His equanimity was beautiful. He loved life, as men of large vitality always do, but he did not fear to lose life by changing the scene of it. Visiting him in his ninetieth year with a friend, he said to us, among other things : "I have no desire to die, but also no reluctance. Indeed, I have a considerable curiosity about the other world. I have never been to Europe, you know." Even in his extreme senescence there was an April mood somewhere in his nature "that put a spirit of youth in everything." He seemed to feel that he could draw against an unlimited credit of years. When eighty-two, he said smilingly to a young man just returned from a foreign tour, "Well, well, I mean to go myself when I am old enough to profit by it." We have seen many old men whose lives were mere waste and desolation, who made longevity disreputable by their untimely persistence in it; but in Mr. Quincy's length of years there was nothing that was not venerable. To him it was fulfilment, not deprivation; the days were marked to the last for what they brought, not for what they took away.

The memory of what Mr. Quincy did will be lost in the crowd of newer activities; it is the memory of what he was that is precious to us. *Bonum virum facile crederes, magnum libenter.* If John Winthrop be the highest type of the men who shaped New England, we can find no better one of those whom New England has shaped than Josiah Quincy. It is a figure that we can contemplate with more than satisfaction, — a figure of admirable example in a democracy as that of a model citizen. His courage and high-mindedness were personal to him; let us believe that his integrity, his industry, his love of letters, his devotion to duty, go in some sort to the credit of the society which gave him birth and formed his character. In one respect he is especially interesting to us, as belonging to a class of men of whom he was the last representative, and whose like we shall never see again. Born and bred in an age of greater social distinctions than ours, he was an aristocrat in a sense that is good even in a republic. He had the sense of a certain personal dignity *inherent* in him, and which could not be alienated by any whim of the popular will. There is no stouter buckler than this for independence of spirit, no surer guaranty of that courtesy which, in its consideration of others, is but paying a debt of self-respect. During his presidency, Mr. Quincy was once riding to Cambridge in a crowded omnibus. A colored woman got in, and could nowhere find a seat. The President instantly gave her his own, and stood the rest of the way, a silent rebuke of the general rudeness. He was a man of quality in the true sense, — of quality not hereditary, but personal. Position might be taken from him, but *he* remained where he was. In what he valued most, his sense of personal worth, the world's opinion could neither help nor hinder. We do not mean that this was conscious in him; if it had been, it would have been a weakness. It was an instinct, and acted with the force and promptitude proper to such. Let us hope that the scramble of democracy will give us something as good; anything of so classic dignity we shall not look to see again.

Josiah Quincy was no seeker of office; from first to last he and it were drawn together by the mutual attraction of need and fitness, and it clung to him as most men cling to it. The people often make blunders in their choice; they are apt to mistake presence of speech for presence of mind; they love so to help a man rise from the ranks, that they will spoil a good demagogue to make a bad general; a great many faults may be laid at their door, but they are not fairly to be charged with fickleness. They are constant to whoever is constant to his real self, to the best manhood that is in him, and not to the mere selfishness, the *antica lupa* so cunning to hide herself in the sheep's fleece even from ourselves. It is true, the contemporary world is apt to be the gull of brilliant parts, and the maker of a lucky poem or picture or statue, the winner of a lucky battle, gets perhaps more than is due to the solid result of his triumph. It is time that fit honor should be paid also to him who shows a genius for public usefulness, for the achievement of character, who shapes his life to a certain classic proportion, and comes off conqueror on those inward fields where something more than mere talent is demanded for victory. The memory of such men should be cherished as the most precious inheritance which one generation can bequeath to the next. However it might be with popular favor, public respect followed Mr. Quincy unwaveringly for seventy years, and it was because he had never forfeited his own. In this, it appears to us, lies the lesson of his life, and his claim upon our grateful recollection. It is this which makes him an example, while the careers of so many of our prominent men are only useful for warning. As regards history, his greatness was narrowly provincial; but if the measure of deeds be the spirit in which they are done, that fidelity to instant duty, which, according to Herbert, makes an action fine, then his length of years should be very precious to us for its lesson. Talleyrand, whose life may be compared with his for the strange vicissitude which it witnessed, carried with him out of the world the respect of no man, least of all his own; and how many of our own public men have we seen whose old age but accumulated a disregard which they would gladly have exchanged for oblivion! In Quincy the public fidelity was loyal to the private, and the withdrawal of his old age was into a sanctuary, — a diminution of publicity with addition of influence.

> " Conclude we, then, felicity consists
> Not in exterior fortunes. . . . .
> Sacred felicity doth ne'er extend
> Beyond itself. . . . .
> The swelling of an outward fortune can
> Create a prosperous, not a happy man."

CARLYLE.*

A FEELING of comical sadness is likely to come over the mind of any middle-aged man who sets himself to recollecting the names of different authors that have been famous, and the number of contemporary immortalities whose end he has seen since coming to manhood. Many a light, hailed by too careless observers as a fixed star, has proved to be only a short-lived lantern at the tail of a newspaper kite. That literary heaven which our youth saw dotted thick with rival glories, we find now to have been a stage-sky merely, artificially enkindled from behind; and the cynical daylight which is sure to follow all theatrical enthusiasms shows us ragged holes where once were luminaries, sheer vacancy instead of lustre. Our earthly reputations, says a great poet, are the color of grass, and the same sun that makes the green bleaches it out again. But next morning is not the time to criticise the scene-painter's firmament, nor is it quite fair to examine coldly a part of some general illusion in the absence of that sympathetic enthusiasm, that self-surrender of the fancy, which made it what it was. It would not be safe for all neglected authors to comfort themselves in Wordsworth's fashion, inferring genius in an inverse proportion to public favor, and a high and solitary merit from the world's indifference. On the contrary, it would be more just to argue from popularity a certain amount of real value,

* Apropos of his Frederick the Great.

though it may not be of that permanent quality which insures enduring fame. The contemporary world and Wordsworth were both half right. He undoubtedly owned and worked the richest vein of his period; but he offered to his contemporaries a heap of gold-bearing quartz where the baser mineral made the greater show, and the purchaser must do his own crushing and smelting, with no guaranty but the bare word of the miner. It was not enough that certain bolder adventurers should now and then show a nugget in proof of the success of their venture. The gold of the poet must be refined, moulded, stamped with the image and superscription of his time, but with a beauty of design and finish that are of no time. The work must surpass the material. Wordsworth was wholly void of that shaping imagination which is the highest criterion of a poet.

Immediate popularity and lasting fame, then, would seem to be the result of different qualities, and not of mere difference in degree. It is safe to prophesy a certain durability of recognition for any author who gives evidence of intellectual force, in whatever kind, above the average amount. There are names in literary history which are only names; and the works associated with them, like acts of Congress already agreed on in debate, are read by their titles and passed. What is it that insures what may be called living fame, so that a book shall be at once famous and read? What is it that relegates divine Cowley to that remote, uncivil Pontus of the "British Poets," and keeps garrulous Pepys within the cheery circle of the evening lamp and fire? Originality, eloquence, sense, imagination, not one of them is enough by itself, but only in some happy mixture and proportion. Imagination seems to possess in itself more of the antiseptic property than any other single quality; but, without less showy and more substantial allies, it can at best give only deathlessness, without the perpetual youth that makes it other than dreary. It were easy to find examples of this Tithonus immortality, setting its victims apart from both gods and men; helpless duration, undying, to be sure, but sapless and voiceless also, and long ago deserted by the fickle Hemera. And yet chance could confer that gift on Glaucus, which love and the consent of Zeus failed to secure for the darling of the Dawn. Is it mere luck, then? Luck may, and often does, have some share in ephemeral successes, as in a gambler's winnings spent as soon as got, but not in any lasting triumph over time. Solid success must be based on solid qualities and the honest culture of them.

The first element of contemporary popularity is undoubtedly the power of entertaining. If a man have anything to tell, the world cannot be expected to listen to him unless he have perfected himself in the best way of telling it. People are not to be argued into a pleasurable sensation, nor is taste to be compelled by any syllogism, however stringent. An author may make himself very popular, however, and even justly so, by appealing to the passion of the moment, without having anything in him that shall outlast the public whim which he satisfies. Churchill is a remarkable example of this. He had a surprising extemporary vigor of mind; his phrase carries great weight of blow; he undoubtedly surpassed all contemporaries, as Cowper says of him, in a certain rude and earth-born vigor; but his verse is dust and ashes now, solemnly inurned, of course, in the Chalmers columbarium, and without danger of violation. His brawn and muscle are fading traditions, while the fragile, shivering genius of Cowper is still a good life on the books of the Critical Insurance Office. " Is it not, then, loftiness of mind that puts one by the

side of Virgil?" cries poor old Cavalcanti at his wits'
end. Certainly not altogether that. There must be
also the great Mantuan's art; his power, not only of
being strong in parts, but of making those parts coherent in an harmonious whole, and tributary to it. Gray,
if we may believe the commentators, has not an idea,
scarcely an epithet, that he can call his own; and yet
he is, in the best sense, one of the classics of English
literature. He had exquisite felicity of choice; his
dictionary had no vulgar word in it, no harsh one, but
all culled from the luckiest moods of poets, and with a
faint but delicious aroma of association; he had a perfect sense of sound, and one idea without which all the
poetic outfit (*si absit prudentia*) is of little avail, — that
of combination and arrangement, in short, of art. The
poets from whom he helped himself have no more claim
to any of his poems as wholes, than the various beauties
of Greece (if the old story were true) to the Venus of
the artist.

Imagination, as we have said, has more virtue to keep
a book alive than any other single faculty. Burke is
rescued from the usual doom of orators, because his
learning, his experience, his sagacity are rimmed with a
halo by this bewitching light behind the intellectual eye
from the highest heaven of the brain. Shakespeare has
impregnated his common sense with the steady glow of
it, and answers the mood of youth and age, of high and
low, immortal as that dateless substance of the soul he
wrought in. To have any chance of lasting, a book
must satisfy, not merely some fleeting fancy of the day,
but a constant longing and hunger of human nature;
and it needs only a superficial study of literature to be
convinced that real fame depends rather on the sum of
an author's powers than on any brilliancy of special
parts. There must be wisdom as well as wit, sense no

less than imagination, judgment in equal measure with fancy, and the fiery rocket must be bound fast to the poor wooden stick that gives it guidance if it would mount and draw all eyes. There are some who think that the brooding patience which a great work calls for belonged exclusively to an earlier period than ours. Others lay the blame on our fashion of periodical publication, which necessitates a sensation and a crisis in every number, and forces the writer to strive for startling effects, instead of that general lowness of tone which is the last achievement of the artist. The simplicity of antique passion, the homeliness of antique pathos, seem not merely to be gone out of fashion, but out of being as well. Modern poets appear rather to tease their words into a fury, than to infuse them with the deliberate heats of their matured conception, and strive to replace the rapture of the mind with a fervid intensity of phrase. Our reaction from the decorous platitudes of the last century has no doubt led us to excuse this, and to be thankful for something like real fire, though of stubble; but our prevailing style of criticism, which regards parts rather than wholes, which dwells on the beauty of passages, and, above all, must have its languid nerves pricked with the expected sensation at whatever cost, has done all it could to confirm us in our evil way. Passages are good when they lead to something, when they are necessary parts of the building, but they are not good to dwell in. This taste for the startling reminds us of something which happened once at the burning of a country meeting-house. The building stood on a hill, and, apart from any other considerations, the fire was as picturesque as could be desired. When all was a black heap, licking itself here and there with tongues of fire, there rushed up a farmer gasping anxiously, "Hez the bell fell yit?" An ordinary fire was no more to him than that on his hearthstone; even the burning of a meeting-house, in itself a vulcanic rarity, (so long as he was of another parish,) could not tickle his outworn palate; but he had hoped for a certain *tang* in the downcome of the bell that might recall the boyish flavor of conflagration. There was something dramatic, no doubt, in this surprise of the brazen sentinel at his post, but the breathless rustic has always seemed to us a type of the prevailing delusion in æsthetics. Alas! if the bell must fall in every stanza or every monthly number, how shall an author contrive to stir us at last, unless with whole Moscows, crowned with the tintinnabulary crash of the Kremlin? For ourselves, we are glad to feel that we are still able to find contentment in the more conversational and domestic tone of our old-fashioned wood-fire. No doubt a great part of our pleasure in reading is unexpectedness, whether in turn of thought or of phrase; but an emphasis out of place, an intensity of expression not founded on sincerity of moral or intellectual conviction, reminds one of the underscorings in young ladies' letters, a wonder even to themselves under the colder north-light of matronage. It is the part of the critic, however, to keep cool under whatever circumstances, and to reckon that the excesses of an author will be at first more attractive to the many than that average power which shall win him attention with a new generation of men. It is seldom found out by the majority, till after a considerable interval, that he was the original man who contrived to be simply natural, — the hardest lesson in the school of art and the latest learned, if, indeed, it be a thing capable of acquisition at all. The most winsome and wayward of brooks draws now and then some lover's foot to its intimate reserve, while the spirt of a bursting water-pipe gathers a gaping crowd forthwith.

Mr. Carlyle is an author who has now been so long before the world, that we may feel toward him something of the unprejudice of posterity. It has long been evident that he had no more ideas to bestow upon us, and that no new turn of his kaleidoscope would give us anything but some variation of arrangement in the brilliant colors of his style. It is perhaps possible, then, to arrive at some not wholly inadequate estimate of his place as a writer, and especially of the value of the ideas whose advocate he makes himself, with a bitterness and violence that increase, as it seems to us, in proportion as his inward conviction of their truth diminishes.

The leading characteristics of an author who is in any sense original, that is to say, who does not merely reproduce, but modifies the influence of tradition, culture, and contemporary thought upon himself by some admixture of his own, may commonly be traced more or less clearly in his earliest works. This is more strictly true, no doubt, of poets, because the imagination is a fixed quantity, not to be increased by any amount of study and reflection. Skill, wisdom, and even wit are cumulative; but that diviner faculty, which is the spiritual eye, though it may be trained and sharpened, cannot be added to by taking thought. This has always been something innate, unaccountable, to be laid to a happy conjunction of the stars. Goethe, the last of the *great* poets, accordingly takes pains to tell us under what planets he was born; and in him it is curious how uniform the imaginative quality is from the beginning to the end of his long literary activity. His early poems show maturity, his mature ones a youthful freshness. The apple already lies potentially in the blossom, as that may be traced also in the ripened fruit. With a mere change of emphasis, Goethe might be called an old boy at both ends of his career.

6

In the earliest authorship of Mr. Carlyle we find some not obscure hints of the future man. Nearly fifty years ago he contributed a few literary and critical articles to the Edinburgh Encyclopædia. The outward fashion of them is that of the period; but they are distinguished by a certain security of judgment remarkable at any time, remarkable especially in one so young. British criticism has been always more or less parochial; has never, indeed, quite freed itself from sectarian cant, and planted itself honestly on the æsthetic point of view. It cannot quite persuade itself that truth is of immortal essence, totally independent of all assistance from quarterly journals or the British army and navy. Carlyle, in these first essays, already shows the influence of his master, Goethe, the most widely receptive of critics. In a compact notice of Montaigne, there is not a word as to his religious scepticism. The character is looked at purely from its human and literary sides. As illustrating the bent of the author's mind, the following passage is most to our purpose : "A modern reader will not easily cavil at the patient and good-natured, though exuberant egotism which brings back to our view 'the form and pressure' of a time long past. *The habits and humors, the mode of acting and thinking, which characterized a Gascon gentleman in the sixteenth century, cannot fail to amuse an inquirer of the nineteenth; while the faithful delineation of human feelings, in all their strength and weakness, will serve as a mirror to every mind capable of self-examination.*" We find here no uncertain indication of that eye for the moral picturesque, and that sympathetic appreciation of character, which within the next few years were to make Carlyle the first in insight of English critics and the most vivid of English historians. In all his earlier writing he never loses sight of his master's great rule, *Den Gegenstand fest zu halten.*

He accordingly gave to Englishmen the first humanly possible likeness of Voltaire, Diderot, Mirabeau, and others, who had hitherto been measured by the usual British standard of their respect for the geognosy of Moses and the historic credibility of the Books of Chronicles. What was the real meaning of this phenomenon? what the amount of this man's honest performance in the world? and in what does he show that family-likeness, common to all the sons of Adam, which gives us a fair hope of being able to comprehend him? These were the questions which Carlyle seems to have set himself honestly to answer in the critical writings which fill the first period of his life as a man of letters. In this mood he rescued poor Boswell from the unmerited obloquy of an ungrateful generation, and taught us to see something half-comically beautiful in the poor, weak creature, with his pathetic instinct of reverence for what was nobler, wiser, and stronger than himself. Everything that Mr. Carlyle wrote during this first period thrills with the purest appreciation of whatever is brave and beautiful in human nature, with the most vehement scorn of cowardly compromise with things base; and yet, immitigable as his demand for the highest in us seems to be, there is always something reassuring in the humorous sympathy with mortal frailty which softens condemnation and consoles for shortcoming. The remarkable feature of Mr. Carlyle's criticism (see, for example, his analysis and exposition of Goethe's "Helena") is the sleuth-hound instinct with which he presses on to the *matter* of his theme, — never turned aside by a false scent, regardless of the outward beauty of form, sometimes almost contemptuous of it, in his hunger after the intellectual nourishment which it may hide. The delicate skeleton of admirably articulated and related parts which underlies and sustains every true work of art, and

keeps it from sinking on itself a shapeless heap, he
would crush remorselessly to come at the marrow of
meaning. With him the ideal sense is secondary to the
ethical and metaphysical, and he has but a faint conception of their possible unity.

By degrees the humorous element in his nature gains
ground, till it overmasters all the rest. Becoming always more boisterous and obtrusive, it ends at last, as
such humor must, in cynicism. In "Sartor Resartus"
it is still kindly, still infused with sentiment ; and the
book, with its mixture of indignation and farce, strikes
one as might the prophecies of Jeremiah, if the marginal
comments of the Rev. Mr. Sterne in his wildest mood
had by some accident been incorporated with the text.
In "Sartor" the marked influence of Jean Paul is undeniable, both in matter and manner. It is curious for
one who studies the action and reaction of national liter-
atures on each other, to see the humor of Swift and
Sterne and Fielding, after filtering through Richter, reappear in Carlyle with a tinge of Germanism that makes
it novel, alien, or even displeasing, as the case may be,
to the English mind. Unhappily the bit of *mother* from
Swift's vinegar-barrel has had strength enough to sour
all the rest. The whimsicality of "Tristram Shandy,"
which, even in the original, has too often the effect
of forethought, becomes a deliberate artifice in Richter,
and at last a mere mannerism in Carlyle.

Mr. Carlyle in his critical essays had the advantage
of a well-defined theme, and of limits both in the
subject and in the space allowed for its treatment, which
kept his natural extravagance within bounds, and compelled some sort of discretion and compactness. The
great merit of these essays lay in a criticism based on
wide and various study, which, careless of tradition,
applied its standard to the real and not the contem-

porary worth of the literary or other performance to be judged, and in an unerring eye for that fleeting expression of the moral features of character, a perception of which alone makes the drawing of a coherent likeness possible. Their defect was a tendency, gaining strength with years, to confound the moral with the æsthetic standard, and to make the value of an author's work dependent on the general force of his nature rather than on its special fitness for a given task. In proportion as his humor gradually overbalanced the other qualities of his mind, his taste for the eccentric, amorphous, and violent in men became excessive, disturbing more and more his perception of the more commonplace attributes which give consistency to portraiture. His " French Revolution " is a series of lurid pictures, unmatched for vehement power, in which the figures of such sons of earth as Mirabeau and Danton loom gigantic and terrible as in the glare of an eruption, their shadows swaying far and wide grotesquely awful. But all is painted by eruption-flashes in violent light and shade. There are no half-tints, no gradations, and we find it impossible to account for the continuance in power of less Titanic actors in the tragedy like Robespierre, on any theory whether of human nature or of individual character supplied by Mr. Carlyle. Of his success, however, in accomplishing what he aimed at, which was to haunt the mind with memories of a horrible political nightmare, there can be no doubt.

Goethe says, apparently thinking of Richter, " The worthy Germans have persuaded themselves that the essence of true humor is formlessness." Heine had not yet shown that a German might combine the most airy humor with a sense of form as delicate as Goethe's own, and that there was no need to borrow the bow of Philoctetes for all kinds of game. Mr. Carlyle's own tendency was toward the lawless, and the attraction of Jean Paul made it an overmastering one. Goethe, we think, might have gone farther, and affirmed that nothing but the highest artistic sense can prevent humor from degenerating into the grotesque, and thence downwards to utter anarchy. Rabelais is a striking example of it. The moral purpose of his book cannot give it that unity which the instinct and forethought of art only can bring forth. Perhaps we owe the masterpiece of humorous literature to the fact that Cervantes had been trained to authorship in a school where form predominated over substance, and the most convincing proof of the supremacy of art at the highest period of Greek literature is to be found in Aristophanes. Mr. Carlyle has no artistic sense of form or rhythm, scarcely of proportion. Accordingly he looks on verse with contempt as something barbarous, — a savage ornament which a higher refinement will abolish, as it has tattooing and nose-rings. With a conceptive imagination vigorous beyond any in his generation, with a mastery of language equalled only by the greatest poets, he wants altogether the plastic imagination, the shaping faculty, which would have made him a poet in the highest sense. He is a preacher and a prophet, — anything you will, — but an artist he is not, and never can be. It is always the knots and gnarls of the oak that he admires, never the perfect and balanced tree.

It is certainly more agreeable to be grateful for what we owe an author, than to blame him for what he cannot give us. But it is sometimes the business of a critic to trace faults of style and of thought to their root in character and temperament, — to show their necessary relation to, and dependence on, each other, — and to find some more trustworthy explanation than mere wantonness of will for the moral obliquities of a man so largely moulded and gifted as Mr. Carlyle. So long as he was merely an exhorter or dehorter, we were thankful for such eloquence, such humor, such vivid or grotesque images, and such splendor of illustration as only he could give; but when he assumes to be a teacher of moral and political philosophy, when he himself takes to compounding the social panaceas he has made us laugh at so often, and advertises none as genuine but his own, we begin to inquire into his qualifications and his defects, and to ask ourselves whether his patent pill differs from others except in the larger amount of aloes, or has any better recommendation than the superior advertising powers of a mountebank of genius. Comparative criticism teaches us that moral and æsthetic defects are more nearly related than is commonly supposed. Had Mr. Carlyle been fitted out completely by nature as an artist, he would have had an ideal in his work which would have lifted his mind away from the muddier part of him, and trained him to the habit of seeking and seeing the harmony rather than the discord and contradiction of things. His innate love of the picturesque, (which is only another form of the sentimentalism he so scoffs at, perhaps as feeling it a weakness in himself,) or ce turned in the direction of character, and finding its chief satisfaction there, led him to look for that ideal of human nature in individual men which is but fragmentarily represented in the entire race, and is rather divined from the aspiration, forever disenchanted to be forever renewed, of the immortal part in us, than found in any example of actual achievement. A wiser temper would have found something more consoling than disheartening in the continual failure of men eminently endowed to reach the standard of this spiritual requirement, would perhaps have found in it an inspiring hint that it is mankind, and not special men, that are to be shaped at

last into the image of God, and that the endless life of
the generations may hope to come nearer that goal of
which the short-breathed threescore years and ten fall
too unhappily short.

But Mr. Carlyle has invented the Hero-cure, and all
who recommend any other method, or see any hope of
healing elsewhere, are either quacks and charlatans or
their victims. His lively imagination conjures up the
image of an impossible he, as contradictorily endowed
as the chief personage in a modern sentimental novel,
and who, at all hazards, must not lead mankind like a
shepherd, but bark, bite, and otherwise worry them
toward the fold like a truculent sheep-dog.   If Mr.
Carlyle would only now and then recollect that men are
men, and not sheep, — nay, that the farther they are
from being such, the more well grounded our hope of
one day making something better of them!   It is indeed
strange that one who values Will so highly in the
greatest, should be blind to its infinite worth in the least
of men ; nay, that he should so often seem to confound
it with its irritable and purposeless counterfeit, Wilful-
ness.   The natural impatience of an imaginative temperament, which conceives so vividly the beauty and
desirableness of a nobler manhood and a diviner political
order, makes him fret at the slow moral processes by
which the All-Wise brings about his ends, and turns the
very foolishness of men to his praise and glory.   Mr.
Carlyle is for calling down fire from Heaven whenever
he cannot readily lay his hand on the match-box.   No
doubt it is somewhat provoking that it should be so easy
to build castles in the air, and so hard to find tenants
for them.   It is a singular intellectual phenomenon to
see a man, who earlier in life so thoroughly appreciated
the innate weakness and futile tendency of the " storm
and thrust " period of German literature, constantly

assimilating, as he grows older, more and more nearly to its principles and practice. It is no longer the sagacious and moderate Goethe who is his type of what is highest in human nature, but far rather some Götz of the Iron Hand, some assertor of the divine legitimacy of *Faustrecht*. It is odd to conceive the fate of Mr. Carlyle under the sway of any of his heroes, — how Cromwell would have scorned him as a babbler more long-winded than Prynne, but less clear and practical, — how Friedrich would have scoffed at his tirades as *dummes Zeug* not to be compared with the romances of Crébillon *fils*, or possibly have clapped him in a marching regiment as a fit subject for the cane of the sergeant. Perhaps something of Mr. Carlyle's irritability is to be laid to the account of his early schoolmastership at Ecclefechan. This great booby World is such a dull boy, and will not learn the lesson we have taken such pains in expounding for the fiftieth time. Well, then, if eloquence, if example, if the awful warning of other little boys who neglected their accidence and came to the gallows, if none of these avail, the birch at least is left, and we will try that. The dominie spirit has become every year more obtrusive and intolerant in Mr. Carlyle's writing, and the rod, instead of being kept in its place as a resource for desperate cases, has become the alpha and omega of all successful training, the one divinely-appointed means of human enlightenment and progress, — in short, the final hope of that absurd animal who fancies himself a little lower than the angels. Have we feebly taken it for granted that the distinction of man was reason ? Never was there a more fatal misconception. It is in the gift of unreason that we are unenviably distinguished from the brutes, whose nobler privilege of instinct saves them from our blunders and our crimes.

But since Mr. Carlyle has become possessed with the

6 *   I

hallucination that he is head-master of this huge boys'
school which we call the world, his pedagogic birch has
grown to the taller proportions and more ominous aspect of a gallows.   His article on Dr. Francia was a
panegyric of the halter, in which the gratitude of mankind is invoked for the self-appointed dictator who had
discovered in Paraguay a tree more beneficent than that
which produced the Jesuits' bark.   Mr. Carlyle seems to
be in the condition of a man who uses stimulants, and
must increase his dose from day to day as the senses
become dulled under the spur.   He began by admiring
strength of character and purpose, and the manly self-
denial which makes a humble fortune great by steadfast
loyalty to duty.   He has gone on till mere strength has
become such washy weakness that there is no longer any
titillation in it; and nothing short of downright violence
will rouse his nerves now to the needed excitement.   At
first he made out very well with remarkable men; then,
lessening the water and increasing the spirit, he took to
Heroes : and now he must have downright *in*humanity,
or the draught has no savor; — so he gets on at last to
Kings, types of remorseless Force, who maintain the
political views of Berserkers by the legal principles of
Lynch.   Constitutional monarchy is a failure, representative government is a gabble, democracy a birth of the
bottomless pit; there is no hope for mankind except in
getting themselves under a good driver who shall not
spare the lash.   And yet, unhappily for us, these drivers
are providential births not to be contrived by any cunning of ours, and Friedrich II. is hitherto the last of
them.   Meanwhile the world's wheels have got fairly
stalled in mire and other matter of every vilest consistency and most disgustful smell.   What are we to do?
Mr. Carlyle will not let us make a lever with a rail from
the next fence, or call in the neighbors.   That would be

too commonplace and cowardly, too anarchical. No; he would have us sit down beside him in the slough, and shout lustily for Hercules. If that indispensable demigod will not or cannot come, we can find a useful and instructive solace, during the intervals of shouting, in a hearty abuse of human nature, which, at the long last, is always to blame.

Since "Sartor Resartus" Mr. Carlyle has done little but repeat himself with increasing emphasis and heightened shrillness. Warning has steadily heated toward denunciation, and remonstrance soured toward scolding. The image of the Tartar prayer-mill, which he borrowed from Richter and turned to such humorous purpose, might be applied to himself. The same phrase comes round and round, only the machine, being a little crankier, rattles more, and the performer is called on for a more visible exertion. If there be not something very like cant in Mr. Carlyle's later writings, then cant is not the repetition of a creed after it has become a phrase by the cooling of that white-hot conviction which once made it both the light and warmth of the soul. We do not mean intentional and deliberate cant, but neither is that which Mr. Carlyle denounces so energetically in his fellow-men of that conscious kind. We do not mean to blame him for it, but mention it rather as an interesting phenomenon of human nature. The stock of ideas which mankind has to work with is very limited, like the alphabet, and can at best have an air of freshness given it by new arrangements and combinations, or by application to new times and circumstances. Montaigne is but Ecclesiastes writing in the sixteenth century, Voltaire but Lucian in the eighteenth. Yet both are original, and so certainly is Mr. Carlyle, whose borrowing is mainly from his own former works. But he does this so often and so openly, that we may at least be sure that he ceased growing a number of years ago, and is a remarkable example of arrested development.

The cynicism, however, which has now become the prevailing temper of his mind, has gone on expanding with unhappy vigor. In Mr. Carlyle it is not, certainly, as in Swift, the result of personal disappointment, and of the fatal eye of an accomplice for the mean qualities by which power could be attained that it might be used for purposes as mean. It seems rather the natural corruption of his exuberant humor. Humor in its first analysis is a perception of the incongruous, and in its highest development, of the incongruity between the actual and the ideal in men and life. With so keen a sense of the ludicrous contrast between what men might be, nay, wish to be, and what they are, and with a vehement nature that demands the instant realization of his vision of a world altogether heroic, it is no wonder that Mr. Carlyle, always hoping for a thing and always disappointed, should become bitter. Perhaps if he expected less he would find more. Saul seeking his father's asses found himself turned suddenly into a king; but Mr. Carlyle, on the lookout for a king, always seems to find the other sort of animal. He sees nothing on any side of him but a procession of the Lord of Misrule, in gloomier moments, a Dance of Death, where everything is either a parody of whatever is noble, or an aimless jig that stumbles at last into the annihilation of the grave, and so passes from one nothing to another. Is a world, then, which buys and reads Mr. Carlyle's works distinguished only for its "fair, large ears"? If he who has read and remembered so much would only now and then call to mind the old proverb, *Nec deus, nec lupus, sed homo!* If he would only recollect that, from the days of the first grandfather, everybody has remembered a golden age behind him!

The very qualities, it seems to us, which came so near making a great poet of Mr. Carlyle, disqualify him for the office of historian. The poet's concern is with the appearances of things, with their harmony in that whole which the imagination demands for its satisfaction, and their truth to that ideal nature which is the proper object of poetry. History, unfortunately, is very far from being ideal, still farther from an exclusive interest in those heroic or typical figures which answer all the wants of the epic and the drama and fill their utmost artistic limits. Mr. Carlyle has an unequalled power and vividness in painting detached scenes, in bringing out in their full relief the oddities or peculiarities of character; but he has a far feebler sense of those gradual changes of opinion, that strange communication of sympathy from mind to mind, that subtile influence of very subordinate actors in giving a direction to policy or action, which we are wont somewhat vaguely to call the progress of events. His scheme of history is purely an epical one, where only leading figures appear by name and are in any strict sense operative. He has no conception of the people as anything else than an element of mere brute force in political problems, and would sniff scornfully at that unpicturesque common-sense of the many, which comes slowly to its conclusions, no doubt, but compels obedience even from rulers the most despotic when once its mind is made up. His history of Frederick is, of course, a Fritziad; but next to his hero, the cane of the drill-sergeant and iron ramrods appear to be the conditions which to his mind satisfactorily account for the result of the Seven Years War. It is our opinion, which subsequent events seem to justify, that, had there not been in the Prussian people a strong instinct of nationality, Protestant nationality too, and an intimate conviction of its advantages, the war might have ended quite otherwise. Frederick II. left the machine of war which he received from his father even more perfect than he found it, yet within a few years of his death it went to pieces before the shock of French armies animated by an idea. Again a few years, and the Prussian soldiery, inspired once more by the old national fervor, were victorious. Were it not for the purely picturesque bias of Mr. Carlyle's genius, for the necessity which his epical treatment lays upon him of always having a protagonist, we should be astonished that an idealist like him should have so little faith in ideas and so much in matter.

Mr. Carlyle's manner is not so well suited to the historian as to the essayist. He is always great in single figures and striking episodes, but there is neither gradation nor continuity. He has extraordinary patience and conscientiousness in the gathering and sifting of his material, but is scornful of commonplace facts and characters, impatient of whatever will not serve for one of his clever sketches, or group well in a more elaborate figure-piece. He sees history, as it were, by flashes of lightning. A single scene, whether a landscape or an interior, a single figure or a wild mob of men, whatever may be snatched by the eye in that instant of intense illumination, is minutely photographed upon the memory. Every tree and stone, almost every blade of grass ; every article of furniture in a room ; the attitude or expression, nay, the very buttons and shoe-ties of a principal figure ; the gestures of momentary passion in a wild throng, — everything leaps into vision under that sudden glare with a painful distinctness that leaves the retina quivering. The intervals are absolute darkness. Mr. Carlyle makes us acquainted with the isolated spot where we happen to be when the flash comes, as if by actual eyesight, but there is no possibility of a comprehensive view. No other writer compares with him for vividness.

He is himself a witness, and makes us witnesses of what ever he describes. This is genius beyond a question, and of a very rare quality, but it is not history. He has not the cold-blooded impartiality of the historian; and while he entertains us, moves us to tears or laughter, makes us the unconscious captives of his ever-changeful mood, we find that he has taught us comparatively little. His imagination is so powerful that it makes him the contemporary of his characters, and thus his history seems to be the memoirs of a cynical humorist, with hearty likes and dislikes, with something of acridity in his partialities whether for or against, more keenly sensitive to the grotesque than the simply natural, and who enters in his diary, even of what comes within the range of his own observation, only so much as amuses his fancy, is congenial with his humor, or feeds his prejudice. Mr. Carlyle's method is accordingly altogether pictorial, his hasty temper making narrative wearisome to him. In his Friedrich, for example, we get very little notion of the civil administration of Prussia; and when he comes, in the last volume, to his hero's dealings with civil reforms, he confesses candidly that it would tire him too much to tell us about it, even if he knew anything at all satisfactory himself.

Mr. Carlyle's historical compositions are wonderful prose poems, full of picture, incident, humor, and character, where we grow familiar with his conception of certain leading personages, and even of subordinate ones, if they are necessary to the scene, so that they come out living upon the stage from the dreary limbo of names; but this is no more history than the historical plays of Shakespeare. There is nothing in imaginative literature superior in its own way to the episode of Voltaire in the Fritziad. It is delicious in humor, masterly in minute characterization. We feel as if the principal victim (for we cannot help feeling all the while that he is so) of this mischievous genius had been put upon the theatre before us by some perfect mimic like Foote, who had studied his habitual gait, gestures, tones, turn of thought, costume, trick of feature, and rendered them with the slight dash of caricature needful to make the whole composition tell. It is in such things that Mr. Carlyle is beyond all rivalry, and that we must go back to Shakespeare for a comparison. But the mastery of Shakespeare is shown perhaps more strikingly in his treatment of the ordinary than of the exceptional. His is the gracious equality of Nature herself. Mr. Carlyle's gift is rather in the representation than in the evolution of character; and it is a necessity of his art, therefore, to exaggerate slightly his heroic, and to caricature in like manner his comic parts. His appreciation is less psychological than physical and external. Grimm relates that Garrick, riding once with Préville, proposed to him that they should counterfeit drunkenness. They rode through Passy accordingly, deceiving all who saw them. When beyond the town Préville asked how he had succeeded. "Excellently," said Garrick, "as to your body; but your legs were not tipsy." Mr. Carlyle would be as exact in his observation of nature as the great actor, and would make us *see* a drunken man as well; but we doubt whether he could have conceived that unmatchable scene in Antony and Cleopatra, where the tipsiness of Lepidus pervades the whole metaphysical no less than the physical part of the triumvir. If his sympathies bore any proportion to his instinct for catching those traits which are the expression of character, but not character itself, we might have had a great historian in him instead of a history-painter. But that which is a main element in Mr. Carlyle's talent, and does perhaps more than anything else to make it effective, is a defect

of his nature. The cynicism which renders him so entertaining precludes him from any just conception of
men and their motives, and from any sane estimate of
the relative importance of the events which concern
them. We remember a picture of Hamon's, where before a Punch's theatre are gathered the wisest of mankind in rapt attention. Socrates sits on a front bench,
absorbed in the spectacle, and in the corner stands Dante
making entries in his note-book. Mr. Carlyle as an
historian leaves us in somewhat such a mood. The
world is a puppet-show, and when we have watched the
play out, we depart with a half-comic consciousness of
the futility of all human enterprise, and the ludicrous-
ness of all man's action and passion on the stage of the
world. Simple, kindly, blundering Oliver Goldsmith
was after all wiser, and his Vicar, ideal as Hector and
not less immortal, is a demonstration of the perennial
beauty and heroism of the homeliest human nature.
The cynical view is congenial to certain moods, and is so
little inconsistent with original nobleness of mind, that
it is not seldom the acetous fermentation of it ; but it
is the view of the satirist, not of the historian, and takes
in but a narrow arc in the circumference of truth.
Cynicism in itself is essentially disagreeable. It is the
intellectual analogue of the truffle ; and though it may
be very well in giving a relish to thought for certain
palates, it cannot supply the substance of it. Mr. Carlyle's cynicism is not that polished weariness of the out-
sides of life which we find in Ecclesiastes. It goes much
deeper than that to the satisfactions, not of the body or
the intellect, but of the very soul itself. It vaunts
itself ; it is noisy and aggressive. What the wise master
puts into the mouth of desperate ambition, thwarted of
the fruit of its crime, as the fitting expression of passionate sophistry, seems to have become an article of his
creed. With him

> " Life *is* a tale
> Told by an idiot, full of sound and fury,
> Signifying nothing."

He goes about with his Diogenes dark-lantern, professing to seek a man, but inwardly resolved to find a monkey. He loves to flash it suddenly on poor human nature in some ridiculous or degrading posture. He admires still, or keeps affirming that he admires, the doughty, silent, hard-working men who, like Cromwell, go honestly about their business; but when we come to his later examples, we find that it is not loyalty to duty or to an inward ideal of high-mindedness that he finds admirable in them, but a blind unquestioning vassalage to whomsoever it has pleased him to set up for a hero. He would fain replace the old feudalism with a spiritual counterpart, in which there shall be an obligation to soul-service. He who once popularized the word *flunkey* by ringing the vehement changes of his scorn upon it, is at last forced to conceive an ideal flunkeyism to squire the hectoring Don Belianises of his fancy about the world. Failing this, his latest theory of Divine government seems to be the cudgel. Poets have sung all manner of vegetable loves; Petrarch has celebrated the laurel, Chaucer the daisy, and Wordsworth the gallows-tree; it remained for the ex-pedagogue of Ecclefechan to become the volunteer laureate of the rod, and to imagine a world created and directed by a divine Dr. Busby. We cannot help thinking that Mr. Carlyle might have learned something to his advantage by living a few years in the democracy which he scoffs at as heartily *a priori* as if it were the demagogism which Aristophanes derided from experience. The Hero, as Mr. Carlyle understands him, was a makeshift of the past; and the ideal of manhood is to be found hereafter in free communities, where the state shall at length sum up and exemplify in itself all those qualities which poets were forced to imagine and typify because they could not find them in the actual world.

In the earlier part of his literary career, Mr. Carlyle was the denouncer of shams, the preacher up of sincerity, manliness, and of a living faith, instead of a droning ritual. He had intense convictions, and he made disciples. With a compass of diction unequalled by any other public performer of the time, ranging as it did from the unbooked freshness of the Scottish peasant to the most far-sought phrase of literary curiosity, with humor, pathos, and eloquence at will, it was no wonder that he found eager listeners in a world longing for a sensation, and forced to put up with the West-End gospel of " Pelham." If not a profound thinker, he had what was next best, — he felt profoundly, and his cry came out of the depths. The stern Calvinism of his early training was rekindled by his imagination to the old fervor of Wishart and Brown, and became a new phenomenon as he reproduced it subtilized by German transcendentalism and German culture. Imagination, if it lays hold of a Scotchman, possesses him in the old demoniac sense of the word, and that hard logical nature, if the Hebrew fire once gets fair headway in it, burns unquenchable as an anthracite coal-mine. But to utilize these sacred heats, to employ them, as a literary man is always tempted, to keep the domestic pot a-boiling, — is such a thing possible? Only too possible, we fear; and Mr. Carlyle is an example of it. If the languid public long for a sensation, the excitement of making one becomes also a necessity of the successful author, as the intellectual nerves grow duller and the old inspiration that came unbidden to the bare garret grows shier and shier of the comfortable parlor. As he himself said thirty years ago of Edward Irving, " Unconsciously, for the most part in deep unconsciousness, there was now the impossibility to live neglected, — to walk on the quiet paths where alone it is well with us. Singularity must henceforth succeed singularity. O foulest Circean draught, thou poison of Popular Applause! madness is in thee and death; thy end is Bedlam and the grave." Mr. Carlyle won his first successes as a kind of preacher in print. His fervor, his oddity of manner, his pugnacious paradox, drew the crowd; the truth, or, at any rate, the faith that underlay them all, brought also the fitter audience, though fewer. But the curse was upon him; he must attract, he must astonish. Thenceforth he has done nothing but revamp his telling things; but the oddity has become always odder, the paradoxes more paradoxical. No very large share of truth falls to the apprehension of any one man; let him keep it sacred, and beware of repeating it till it turn to falsehood on his lips by becoming ritual. Truth always has a bewitching savor of newness in it, and novelty at the first taste recalls that original sweetness to the tongue; but alas for him who would make the one a substitute for the other! We seem to miss of late in Mr. Carlyle the old sincerity. He has become the purely literary man, less concerned about what he says than about how he shall say it to best advantage. The Muse should be the companion, not the guide, says he whom Mr. Carlyle has pronounced "the wisest of this generation." What would be a virtue in the poet is a vice of the most fatal kind in the teacher, and, alas that we should say it! the very Draco of shams, whose code contained no penalty milder than capital for the most harmless of them, has become at last something very like a sham himself. Mr. Carlyle continues to be a voice crying in the wilderness, but no longer a voice with any earnest conviction behind it.

Hearing him rebuke us for being humbugs and impos-
tors, we are inclined to answer, with the ambassador of
Philip II., when his master reproached him with forgetting substance in ceremony, "Your Majesty forgets
that you are only a ceremony yourself." And Mr. Carlyle's teaching, moreover, — if teaching we may call it,
— belongs to what the great German, whose disciple he
is, condemned as the "literature of despair." An apostle
to the gentiles might hope for some fruit of his preaching; but of what avail an apostle who shouts his
message down the mouth of the pit to poor lost souls,
whom he can positively assure only that it is impossible
to get out? Mr. Carlyle lights up the lanterns of his
Pharos after the ship is already rolling between the
tongue of the sea and the grinders of the reef. It is
very brilliant, and its revolving flashes touch the crests
of the breakers with an awful picturesqueness ; but in
so desperate a state of things, even Dr. Syntax might
be pardoned for being forgetful of the picturesque. The
Toryism of Scott sprang from love of the past ; that of
Carlyle is far more dangerously infectious, for it is logi-
cally deduced from a deep disdain of human nature.

Browning has drawn a beautiful picture of an old king
sitting at the gate of his palace to judge his people in
the calm sunshine of that past which never existed outside a poet's brain. It is the sweetest of waking dreams,
this of absolute power and perfect wisdom in one supreme ruler ; but it is as pure a creation of human
want and weakness, as clear a witness of mortal limitation and incompleteness, as the shoes of swiftness, the
cloak of darkness, the purse of Fortunatus, and the
elixir vitæ. It is the natural refuge of imaginative temperaments impatient of our blunders and shortcomings,
and, given a complete man, all would submit to the
divine right of his despotism. But alas ! to every the

most fortunate human birth hobbles up that malign fairy who has been forgotten, with her fatal gift of imperfection! So far as our experience has gone, it has been the very opposite of Mr. Carlyle's. Instead of finding men disloyal to their natural leader, nothing has ever seemed to us so touching as the gladness with which they follow him, when they are sure they have found him at last. But a natural leader of the ideal type is not to be looked for *nisi dignus vindice nodus.* The Divine Forethought had been cruel in furnishing one for every petty occasion, and thus thwarting in all inferior men that priceless gift of reason, to develop which, and to make it one with free-will, is the highest use of our experience on earth. Mr. Carlyle was hard bestead and very far gone in his idolatry of mere *pluck*, when he was driven to choose Friedrich as a hero. A poet — and Mr. Carlyle is nothing else — is unwise who yokes Pegasus to a prosaic theme which no force of wing can lift from the dull earth. Charlemagne would have been a wiser choice, far enough in the past for ideal treatment, more manifestly the Siegfried of Anarchy, and in his rude way the refounder of that empire which is the ideal of despotism in the Western world.

Friedrich was doubtless a remarkable man, but surely very far below any lofty standard of heroic greatness. He was the last of the European kings who could look upon his kingdom as his private patrimony; and it was this estate of his, this piece of property, which he so obstinately and successfully defended. He had no idea of country as it was understood by an ancient Greek or Roman, as it is understood by a modern Englishman or American; and there is something almost pitiful in seeing a man of genius like Mr. Carlyle fighting painfully over again those battles of the last century which settled nothing but the continuance of the Prussian monarchy, while he saw only the "burning of a dirty chimney" in the war which a great people was waging under his very eyes for the idea of nationality and orderly magistrature, and which fixed, let us hope forever, a boundary-line on the map of history and man's advancement toward self-conscious and responsible freedom. The true historical genius, to our thinking is that which can see the nobler meaning of events that are near him, as the true poet is he who detects the divine in the casual; and we somewhat suspect the depth of his insight into the past, who cannot recognize the godlike of to-day under that disguise in which it always visits us. Shall we hint to Mr. Carlyle that a man may look on an heroic age, as well as an heroic master, with the eyes of a valet, as misappreciative certainly, though not so ignoble?

What Goethe says of a great poet, that he must be a citizen of his age as well as of his country, may be said inversely of a great king. He should be a citizen of his country as well as of his age. Friedrich was certainly the latter in its fullest sense; whether he was, or could have been, the former, in any sense, may be doubted. The man who spoke and wrote French in preference to his mother-tongue, who, dying when Goethe was already drawing toward his fortieth year, Schiller toward his thirtieth, and Lessing had been already five years in his grave, could yet see nothing but barbarism in German literature, had little of the old Teutonic fibre in his nature. The man who pronounced the Nibelungen Lied not worth a pinch of priming, had little conception of the power of heroic traditions in making heroic men, and especially in strengthening that instinct made up of so many indistinguishable associations which we call love of country. Charlemagne, when he caused the old songs of his people to be gathered and written down, showed a truer sense of the sources of national feeling and a

deeper political insight. This want of sympathy points
to the somewhat narrow limits of Friedrich's nature.
In spite of Mr. Carlyle's adroit statement of the case,
and the whole book has an air of being the plea of
a masterly advocate in mitigation of sentence, we feel
that his hero was essentially hard, narrow, and selfish.
His popularity will go for little with any one who has
studied the trifling and often fabulous elements that
make up that singular compound. A bluntness of speech,
a shabby uniform, a frugal camp equipage, a timely
familiarity, may make a man the favorite of an army or
a nation, — above all, if he have the knack of success.
Moreover, popularity is much more easily won from
above downward, and is bought at a better bargain by
kings and generals than by other men. We doubt if
Friedrich would have been liked as a private person, or
even as an unsuccessful king. He apparently attached
very few people to himself, fewer even than his brutal
old Squire Western of a father. His sister Wilhelmina
is perhaps an exception. We say perhaps, for we do not
know how much the heroic part he was called on to
play had to do with the matter, and whether sisterly
pride did not pass even with herself for sisterly affection.
Moreover she was far from him; and Mr. Carlyle waves
aside, in his generous fashion, some rather keen comments of hers on her brother's character when she visited
Berlin after he had become king. Indeed, he is apt
to deal rather contemptuously with all adverse criticism
of his hero. We sympathize with his impulse in this respect, agreeing heartily as we do in Chaucer's scorn of
those who "*gladlie* demen to the baser end" in such
matters. But we are not quite sure if this be a safe
method with the historian. He must doubtless be the
friend of his hero if he would understand him, but he
must be more the friend of truth if he would understand

history. Mr. Carlyle's passion for truth is intense, as befits his temper, but it is that of a lover for his mistress. He would have her all to himself, and has a lover's conviction that no one is able, or even fit, to appreciate her but himself. He does well to despise the tittle-tattle of vulgar minds, but surely should not ignore *all* testimony on the other side. For ourselves, we think it not unimportant that Goethe's friend Knebel, a man not incapable of admiration, and who had served a dozen years or so as an officer of Friedrich's guard, should have bluntly called him "the tyrant."

Mr. Carlyle's history traces the family of his hero down from its beginnings in the picturesque chiaro-scuro of the Middle Ages. It was an able and above all a *canny* house, a Scotch version of the word *able*, which implies thrift and an eye to the main chance, the said main chance or chief end of man being altogether of this world. Friedrich, inheriting this family faculty in full measure, was driven, partly by ambition, partly by necessity, to apply it to war. He did so, with the success to be expected where a man of many expedients has the good luck to be opposed by men with few. He adds another to the many proofs that it is possible to be a great general without a spark of that divine fire which we call genius, and that good fortune in war results from the same prompt talent and unbending temper which lead to the same result in the peaceful professions. Friedrich had certainly more of the temperament of genius than Marlborough or Wellington ; but not to go beyond modern instances, he does not impress us with the massive breadth of Napoleon, nor attract us with the climbing ardor of Turenne. To compare him with Alexander or Cæsar were absurd. The kingship that was in him, and which won Mr. Carlyle to be his biographer, is that of will merely, of rapid and relentless

7   J

command. For organization he had a masterly talent; but he could not apply it to the arts of peace, both because he wanted experience and because the rash decision of the battle-field will not serve in matters which are governed by natural laws of growth. He seems, indeed, to have had a coarse, soldier's contempt for all civil distinction, altogether unworthy of a wise king, or even of a prudent one. He confers the title of Hofrath on the husband of a woman with whom his General Walrave is living in what Mr. Carlyle justly calls " brutish polygamy," and this at Walrave's request, on the ground that " a general's drab ought to have a handle to her name." Mr. Carlyle murmurs in a mild parenthesis that " we rather regret this " ! (Vol. III. p. 559.) This is his usual way of treating unpleasant matters, sidling by with a deprecating shrug of the shoulders. Not that he ever wilfully suppresses anything. On the contrary, there is no greater proof of his genius than the way in which, while he seems to paint a character with all its disagreeable traits, he contrives to win our sympathy for it, nay, almost our liking. This is conspicuously true of his portrait of Friedrich's father; and that he does not succeed in making Friedrich himself attractive is a strong argument with us that the fault is in the subject and not the artist.

The book, we believe, has been comparatively unsuccessful as a literary venture. Nor do we wonder at it. It is disproportionately long, and too much made up of those descriptions of battles to read which seems even more difficult than to have won the victory itself, more disheartening than to have suffered the defeat. To an American, also, the warfare seemed Liliputian in the presence of a conflict so much larger in its proportions and significant in its results. The interest, moreover, flags decidedly toward the close, where the reader cannot

help feeling that the author loses breath somewhat painfully under the effort of so prolonged a course. Mr.
Carlyle has evidently devoted to his task a labor that
may be justly called prodigious. Not only has he sifted
all the German histories and memoirs, but has visited
every battle-field, and describes them with an eye for
country that is without rival among historians. The
book is evidently an abridgment of even more abundant
collections, and yet as it stands the matter overburdens
the work. It is a bundle of lively episodes rather than
a continuous narrative. In this respect it contrasts
oddly with the concinnity of his own earlier Life of
Schiller. But the episodes *are* lively, the humor and
pathos spring from a profound nature, the sketches of
character are masterly, the seizure of every picturesque
incident infallible, and the literary judgments those of a
thorough scholar and critic. There is, of course, the
usual amusing objurgation of Dryasdust and his rubbish-
heaps, the usual assumption of omniscience, and the
usual certainty of the lively French lady of being always in the right ; yet we cannot help thinking that a
little of Dryasdust's plodding exactness would have saved
Fouquet eleven years of the imprisonment to which Mr.
Carlyle condemns him, would have referred us to St.
Simon rather than to Voltaire for the character of the
brothers Belle-Ile, and would have kept clear of a
certain ludicrous etymology of the name Antwerp, not
to mention some other trifling slips of the like nature.
In conclusion, after saying, as honest critics must, that
" The History of Friedrich II. called Frederick the
Great" is a book to be read in with more satisfaction
than to be read through, after declaring that it is open
to all manner of criticism, especially in point of moral
purpose and tendency, we must admit with thankfulness, that it has the one prime merit of being the work

of a man who has every quality of a great poet except that supreme one of rhythm which shapes both matter and manner to harmonious proportion, and that where it is good, it is good as only genius knows how to be.

With the gift of song, Carlyle would have been the greatest of epic poets since Homer. Without it, to modulate and harmonize and bring parts into their proper relation, he is the most amorphous of humorists, the most shining avatar of whim the world has ever seen. Beginning with a hearty contempt for shams, he has come at length to believe in brute force as the only reality, and has as little sense of justice as Thackeray allowed to women. We say *brute force* because, though the theory is that this force should be directed by the supreme intellect for the time being, yet all inferior wits are treated rather as obstacles to be contemptuously shoved aside than as ancillary forces to be conciliated through their reason. But, with all deductions, he remains the profoundest critic and the most dramatic imagination of modern times. Never was there a more striking example of that *ingenium perfervidum* long ago said to be characteristic of his countrymen. His is one of the natures, rare in these latter centuries, capable of rising to a white heat; but once fairly kindled, he is like a three-decker on fire, and his shotted guns go off, as the glow reaches them, alike dangerous to friend or foe. Though he seems more and more to confound material with moral success, yet there is always something wholesome in his unswerving loyalty to reality, as he understands it. History, in the true sense, he does not and cannot write, for he looks on mankind as a herd without volition, and without moral force; but such vivid pictures of events, such living conceptions of character, we find nowhere else in prose. The figures of most historians seem like dolls stuffed with bran, whose whole sub-

stance runs out through any hole that criticism may
tear in them, but Carlyle's are so real in comparison,
that, if you prick them, they bleed. He seems a little
wearied, here and there, in his Friedrich, with the multiplicity of detail, and does his filling-in rather shabbily;
but he still remains in his own way, like his hero, the
Only, and such episodes as that of Voltaire would make
the fortune of any other writer. Though not the safest
of guides in politics or practical philosophy, his value as
an inspirer and awakener cannot be over-estimated. It
is a power which belongs only to the highest order of
minds, for it is none but a divine fire that can so kindle
and irradiate. The debt due him from those who listened to the teachings of his prime for revealing to them
what sublime reserves of power even the humblest may
find in manliness, sincerity, and self-reliance, can be paid
with nothing short of reverential gratitude. As a puri-
fier of the sources whence our intellectual inspiration is
drawn, his influence has been second only to that of
Wordsworth, if even to his.

ABRAHAM LINCOLN.

1864.

———•———

THERE have been many painful crises since the impatient vanity of South Carolina hurried ten prosperous Commonwealths into a crime whose assured retribution was to leave them either at the mercy of the nation they had wronged, or of the anarchy they had summoned but could not control, when no thoughtful American opened his morning paper without dreading to find that he had no longer a country to love and honor. Whatever the result of the convulsion whose first shocks were beginning to be felt, there would still be enough square miles of earth for elbow-room; but that ineffable sentiment made up of memory and hope, of instinct and tradition, which swells every man's heart and shapes his thought, though perhaps never present to his consciousness, would be gone from it, leaving it common earth and nothing more. Men might gather rich crops from it, but that ideal harvest of priceless associations would be reaped no longer; that fine virtue which sent up messages of courage and security from every sod of it would have evaporated beyond recall. We should be irrevocably cut off from our past, and be forced to splice the ragged ends of our lives upon whatever new conditions chance might leave dangling for us.

We confess that we had our doubts at first whether the patriotism of our people were not too narrowly provincial to embrace the proportions of national peril.

We felt an only too natural distrust of immense public meetings and enthusiastic cheers.

That a reaction should follow the holiday enthusiasm with which the war was entered-on, that it should follow soon, and that the slackening of public spirit should be proportionate to the previous over-tension, might well be foreseen by all who had studied human nature or history. Men acting gregariously are always in extremes; as they are one moment capable of higher courage, so they are liable, the next, to baser depression, and it is often a matter of chance whether numbers shall multiply confidence or discouragement. Nor does deception lead more surely to distrust of men, than self-deception to suspicion of principles. The only faith that wears well and holds its color in all weathers is that which is woven of conviction and set with the sharp mordant of experience. Enthusiasm is good material for the orator, but the statesman needs something more durable to work in, — must be able to rely on the deliberate reason and consequent firmness of the people, without which that presence of mind, no less essential in times of moral than of material peril, will be wanting at the critical moment. Would this fervor of the Free States hold out? Was it kindled by a just feeling of the value of constitutional liberty? Had it body enough to withstand the inevitable dampening of checks, reverses, delays? Had our population intelligence enough to comprehend that the choice was between order and anarchy, between the equilibrium of a government by law and the tussle of misrule by *pronunciamiento?* Could a war be maintained without the ordinary stimulus of hatred and plunder, and with the impersonal loyalty of principle? These were serious questions, and with no precedent to aid in answering them.

At the beginning of the war there was, indeed, occa-

sion for the most anxious apprehension. A President
known to be infected with the political heresies, and
suspected of sympathy with the treason, of the Southern
conspirators, had just surrendered the reins, we will not
say of power, but of chaos, to a successor known only as
the representative of a party whose leaders, with long
training in opposition, had none in the conduct of affairs;
an empty treasury was called on to supply resources
beyond precedent in the history of finance; the trees
were yet growing and the iron unmined with which a
navy was to be built and armored; officers without discipline were to make a mob into an army; and, above
all, the public opinion of Europe, echoed and reinforced
with every vague hint and every specious argument of
despondency by a powerful faction at home, was either
contemptuously sceptical or actively hostile. It would
be hard to over-estimate the force of this latter element
of disintegration and discouragement among a people
where every citizen at home, and every soldier in the
field, is a reader of newspapers. The pedlers of rumor
in the North were the most effective allies of the rebellion. A nation can be liable to no more insidious
treachery than that of the telegraph, sending hourly its
electric thrill of panic along the remotest nerves of the
community, till the excited imagination makes every
real danger loom heightened with its unreal double.

And even if we look only at more palpable difficulties,
the problem to be solved by our civil war was so vast,
both in its immediate relations and its future consequences; the conditions of its solution were so intricate
and so greatly dependent on incalculable and uncontrol-
lable contingencies; so many of the data, whether for
hope or fear, were, from their novelty, incapable of
arrangement under any of the categories of historical
precedent, that there were moments of crisis when the

firmest believer in the strength and sufficiency of the democratic theory of government might well hold his breath in vague apprehension of disaster. Our teachers of political philosophy, solemnly arguing from the precedent of some petty Grecian, Italian, or Flemish city, whose long periods of aristocracy were broken now and then by awkward parentheses of mob, had always taught us that democracies were incapable of the sentiment of loyalty, of concentrated and prolonged effort, of far-reaching conceptions; were absorbed in material interests; impatient of regular, and much more of exceptional restraint; had no natural nucleus of gravitation, nor any forces but centrifugal; were always on the verge of civil war, and slunk at last into the natural almshouse of bankrupt popular government, a military despotism. Here was indeed a dreary outlook for persons who knew democracy, not by rubbing shoulders with it lifelong, but merely from books, and America only by the report of some fellow-Briton, who, having eaten a bad dinner or lost a carpet-bag here, had written to the Times demanding redress, and drawing a mournful inference of democratic instability. Nor were men wanting among ourselves who had so steeped their brains in London literature as to mistake Cockneyism for European culture, and contempt of their country for cosmopolitan breadth of view, and who, owing all they had and all they were to democracy, thought it had an air of high-breeding to join in the shallow epicedium that our bubble had burst.

But beside any disheartening influences which might affect the timid or the despondent, there were reasons enough of settled gravity against any over-confidence of hope. A war — which, whether we consider the expanse of the territory at stake, the hosts brought into the field, or the reach of the principles involved, may fairly be

7 *

reckoned the most momentous of modern times — was to be waged by a people divided at home, unnerved by fifty years of peace, under a chief magistrate without experience and without reputation, whose every measure was sure to be cunningly hampered by a jealous and unscrupulous minority, and who, while dealing with unheard-of complications at home, must soothe a hostile neutrality abroad, waiting only a pretext to become war. All this was to be done without warning and without preparation, while at the same time a social revolution was to be accomplished in the political condition of four millions of people, by softening the prejudices, allaying the fears, and gradually obtaining the co-operation, of their unwilling liberators. Surely, if ever there were an occasion when the heightened imagination of the historian might see Destiny visibly intervening in human affairs, here was a knot worthy of her shears. Never, perhaps, was any system of government tried by so continuous and searching a strain as ours during the last three years; never has any shown itself stronger; and never could that strength be so directly traced to the virtue and intelligence of the people, — to that general enlightenment and prompt efficiency of public opinion possible only under the influence of a political framework like our own. We find it hard to understand how even a foreigner should be blind to the grandeur of the combat of ideas that has been going on here, — to the heroic energy, persistency, and self-reliance of a nation proving that it knows how much dearer greatness is than mere power; and we own that it is impossible for us to conceive the mental and moral condition of the American who does not feel his spirit braced and heightened by being even a spectator of such qualities and achievements. That a steady purpose and a definite aim have been given to the jarring forces which, at the beginning of the war, spent themselves in the discussion of schemes which could only become operative, if at all, after the war was over; that a popular excitement has been slowly intensified into an earnest national will; that a somewhat impracticable moral sentiment has been made the unconscious instrument of a practical moral end; that the treason of covert enemies, the jealousy of rivals, the unwise zeal of friends, have been made not only useless for mischief, but even useful for good; that the conscientious sensitiveness of England to the horrors of civil conflict has been prevented from complicating a domestic with a foreign war; — all these results, any one of which might suffice to prove greatness in a ruler, have been mainly due to the good sense, the good-humor, the sagacity, the large-mindedness, and the unselfish honesty of the unknown man whom a blind fortune, as it seemed, had lifted from the crowd to the most dangerous and difficult eminence of modern times. It is by presence of mind in untried emergencies that the native metal of a man is tested; it is by the sagacity to see, and the fearless honesty to admit, whatever of truth there may be in an adverse opinion, in order more convincingly to expose the fallacy that lurks behind it, that a reasoner at length gains for his mere statement of a fact the force of argument; it is by a wise forecast which allows hostile combinations to go so far as by the inevitable reaction to become elements of his own power, that a politician proves his genius for state-craft; and especially it is by so gently guiding public sentiment that he seems to follow it, by so yielding doubtful points that he can be firm without seeming obstinate in essential ones, and thus gain the advantages of compromise without the weakness of concession; by so instinctively comprehending the temper and prejudices of a people as to make them gradually conscious of the superior wisdom of his freedom from temper and prejudice, — it is by qualities such as these that a magistrate shows himself worthy to be chief in a commonwealth of freemen. And it is for qualities such as these that we firmly believe History will rank Mr. Lincoln among the most prudent of statesmen and the most successful of rulers. If we wish to appreciate him, we have only to conceive the inevitable chaos in which we should now be weltering, had a weak man or an unwise one been chosen in his stead.

"Bare is back," says the Norse proverb, "without brother behind it"; and this is, by analogy, true of an elective magistracy. The hereditary ruler in any critical emergency may reckon on the inexhaustible resources of *prestige*, of sentiment, of superstition, of dependent interest, while the new man must slowly and painfully create all these out of the unwilling material around him, by superiority of character, by patient singleness of purpose, by sagacious presentiment of popular tendencies and instinctive sympathy with the national character. Mr. Lincoln's task was one of peculiar and exceptional difficulty. Long habit had accustomed the American people to the notion of a party in power, and of a President as its creature and organ, while the more vital fact, that the executive for the time being represents the abstract idea of government as a permanent principle superior to all party and all private interest, had gradually become unfamiliar. They had so long seen the public policy more or less directed by views of party, and often even of personal advantage, as to be ready to suspect the motives of a chief magistrate compelled, for the first time in our history, to feel himself the head and hand of a great nation, and to act upon the fundamental maxim, laid down by all publicists, that the first duty of a government is to defend and maintain its own existence. Accordingly, a powerful weapon seemed to be put into the hands of the opposition by the necessity under which the administration found itself of applying this old truth to new relations. Nor were the opposition his only nor his most dangerous opponents.

The Republicans had carried the country upon an issue in which ethics were more directly and visibly mingled with politics than usual. Their leaders were trained to a method of oratory which relied for its effect rather on the moral sense than the understanding. Their arguments were drawn, not so much from experience as from general principles of right and wrong. When the war came, their system continued to be applicable and effective, for here again the reason of the people was to be reached and kindled through their sentiments. It was one of those periods of excitement, gathering, contagious, universal, which, while they last, exalt and clarify the minds of men, giving to the mere words *country, human rights, democracy,* a meaning and a force beyond that of sober and logical argument. They were convictions, maintained and defended by the supreme logic of passion. That penetrating fire ran in and roused those primary instincts that make their lair in the dens and caverns of the mind. What is called the great popular heart was awakened, that indefinable something which may be, according to circumstances, the highest reason or the most brutish unreason. But enthusiasm, once cold, can never be warmed over into anything better than cant, — and phrases, when once the inspiration that filled them with beneficent power has ebbed away, retain only that semblance of meaning which enables them to supplant reason in hasty minds. Among the lessons taught by the French Revolution there is none sadder or more striking than this, that you may make everything else out of the passions of men

except a political system that will work, and that there
is nothing so pitilessly and unconsciously cruel as sincerity formulated into dogma.   It is always demoralizing
to extend the domain of sentiment over questions where
it has no legitimate jurisdiction; and perhaps the
severest strain upon Mr. Lincoln was in resisting a tendency of his own supporters which chimed with his own
private desires while wholly opposed to his convictions
of what would be wise policy.

The change which three years have brought about is
too remarkable to be passed over without comment, too
weighty in its lesson not to be laid to heart.   Never did
a President enter upon office with less means at his
command, outside his own strength of heart and steadiness of understanding, for inspiring confidence in the
people, and so winning it for himself, than Mr. Lincoln.
All that was known of him was that he was a good
stump-speaker, nominated for his *availability*, — that is,
because he had no history, — and chosen by a party with
whose more extreme opinions he was not in sympathy.
It might well be feared that a man past fifty, against
whom the ingenuity of hostile partisans could rake up
no accusation, must be lacking in manliness of character, in decision of principle, in strength of will; that
a man who was at best only the representative of a
party, and who yet did not fairly represent even that,
would fail of political, much more of popular, support.
And certainly no one ever entered upon office with so
few resources of power in the past, and so many materials of weakness in the present, as Mr. Lincoln.   Even
in that half of the Union which acknowledged him as
President, there was a large, and at that time dangerous
minority, that hardly admitted his claim to the office,
and even in the party that elected him there was also a
large minority that suspected him of being secretly a

communicant with the church of Laodicea. All that he did was sure to be virulently attacked as ultra by one side ; all that he left undone, to be stigmatized as proof of lukewarmness and backsliding by the other. Meanwhile he was to carry on a truly colossal war by means of both ; he was to disengage the country from diplomatic entanglements of unprecedented peril undisturbed by the help or the hinderance of either, and to win from the crowning dangers of his administration, in the confidence of the people, the means of his safety and their own. He has contrived to do it, and perhaps none of our Presidents since Washington has stood so firm in the confidence of the people as he does after three years of stormy administration.

Mr. Lincoln's policy was a tentative one, and rightly so. He laid down no programme which must compel him to be either inconsistent or unwise, no cast-iron theorem to which circumstances must be fitted as they rose, or else be useless to his ends. He seemed to have chosen Mazarin's motto, *Le temps et moi*. The *moi*, to be sure, was not very prominent at first; but it has grown more and more so, till the world is beginning to be persuaded that it stands for a character of marked individuality and capacity for affairs. Time was his prime-minister, and, we began to think, at one period, his general-in-chief also. At first he was so slow that he tired out all those who see no evidence of progress but in blowing up the engine ; then he was so fast, that he took the breath away from those who think there is no getting on safely while there is a spark of fire under the boilers. God is the only being who has time enough; but a prudent man, who knows how to seize occasion, can commonly make a shift to find as much as he needs. Mr. Lincoln, as it seems to us in reviewing his career, though we have sometimes in our impatience thought

otherwise, has always waited, as a wise man should, till
the right moment brought up all his reserves. *Semper
nocuit differre paratis*, is a sound axiom, but the really
efficacious man will also be sure to know when he is *not*
ready, and be firm against all persuasion and reproach
till he is.

One would be apt to think, from some of the criticisms
made on Mr. Lincoln's course by those who mainly agree
with him in principle, that the chief object of a statesman should be rather to proclaim his adhesion to certain
doctrines, than to achieve their triumph by quietly accomplishing his ends. In our opinion, there is no more
unsafe politician than a conscientiously rigid *doctrinaire*,
nothing more sure to end in disaster than a theoretic
scheme of policy that admits of no pliability for contingencies. True, there is a popular image of an impossible He, in whose plastic hands the submissive destinies
of mankind become as wax, and to whose commanding
necessity the toughest facts yield with the graceful
pliancy of fiction; but in real life we commonly find
that the men who control circumstances, as it is called,
are those who have learned to allow for the influence of
their eddies, and have the nerve to turn them to account
at the happy instant. Mr. Lincoln's perilous task has
been to carry a rather shaky raft through the rapids,
making fast the unrulier logs as he could snatch opportunity, and the country is to be congratulated that he
did not think it his duty to run straight at all hazards,
but cautiously to assure himself with his setting-pole
where the main current was, and keep steadily to that.
He is still in wild water, but we have faith that his skill
and sureness of eye will bring him out right at last.

A curious, and, as we think, not inapt parallel, might
be drawn between Mr. Lincoln and one of the most
striking figures in modern history, — Henry IV. of

France. The career of the latter may be more picturesque, as that of a daring captain always is ; but in all
its vicissitudes there is nothing more romantic than that
sudden change, as by a rub of Aladdin's lamp, from the
attorney's office in a country town of Illinois to the helm
of a great nation in times like these. The analogy
between the characters and circumstances of the two
men is in many respects singularly close. Succeeding to
a rebellion rather than a crown, Henry's chief material
dependence was the Huguenot party, whose doctrines
sat upon him with a looseness distasteful certainly, if
not suspicious, to the more fanatical among them. King
only in name over the greater part of France, and with
his capital barred against him, it yet gradually became
clear to the more far-seeing even of the Catholic party
that he was the only centre of order and legitimate
authority round which France could reorganize itself.
While preachers who held the divine right of kings made
the churches of Paris ring with declamations in favor of
democracy rather than submit to the heretic dog of a
Béarnois, — much as our *soi-disant* Democrats have
lately been preaching the divine right of slavery, and
denouncing the heresies of the Declaration of Independence, — Henry bore both parties in hand till he was
convinced that only one course of action could possibly
combine his own interests and those of France. Meanwhile the Protestants believed somewhat doubtfully that
he was theirs, the Catholics hoped somewhat doubtfully
that he would be theirs, and Henry himself turned aside
remonstrance, advice, and curiosity alike with a jest
or a proverb (if a little *high*, he liked them none the
worse), joking continually as his manner was. We have
seen Mr. Lincoln contemptuously compared to Sancho
Panza by persons incapable of appreciating one of the
deepest pieces of wisdom in the profoundest romance

K

ever written; namely, that, while Don Quixote was incomparable in theoretic and ideal statesmanship, Sancho, with his stock of proverbs, the ready money of human experience, made the best possible practical governor. Henry IV. was as full of wise saws and modern instances as Mr. Lincoln, but beneath all this was the thoughtful, practical, humane, and thoroughly earnest man, around whom the fragments of France were to gather themselves till she took her place again as a planet of the first magnitude in the European system. In one respect Mr. Lincoln was more fortunate than Henry. However some may think him wanting in zeal, the most fanatical can find no taint of apostasy in any measure of his, nor can the most bitter charge him with being influenced by motives of personal interest. The leading distinction between the policies of the two is one of circumstances. Henry went over to the nation; Mr. Lincoln has steadily drawn the nation over to him. One left a united France; the other, we hope and believe, will leave a reunited America. We leave our readers to trace the further points of difference and resemblance for themselves, merely suggesting a general similarity which has often occurred to us. One only point of melancholy interest we will allow ourselves to touch upon. That Mr. Lincoln is not handsome nor elegant, we learn from certain English tourists who would consider similar revelations in regard to Queen Victoria as thoroughly American in their want of *bienséance*. It is no concern of ours, nor does it affect his fitness for the high place he so worthily occupies; but he is certainly as fortunate as Henry in the matter of good looks, if we may trust contemporary evidence. Mr. Lincoln has also been reproached with Americanism by some not unfriendly British critics; but, with all deference, we cannot say that we like him any the worse for it, or see in it any reason why he should govern Americans the less wisely.

People of more sensitive organizations may be shocked, but we are glad that in this our true war of independence, which is to free us forever from the Old World, we have had at the head of our affairs a man whom America made, as God made Adam, out of the very earth, unancestried, unprivileged, unknown, to show us how much truth, how much magnanimity, and how much statecraft await the call of opportunity in simple manhood when it believes in the justice of God and the worth of man. Conventionalities are all very well in their proper place, but they shrivel at the touch of nature like stubble in the fire. The genius that sways a nation by its arbitrary will seems less august to us than that which multiplies and reinforces itself in the instincts and convictions of an entire people. Autocracy may have something in it more melodramatic than this, but falls far short of it in human value and interest.

Experience would have bred in us a rooted distrust of improvised statesmanship, even if we did not believe politics to be a science, which, if it cannot always command men of special aptitude and great powers, at least demands the long and steady application of the best powers of such men as it can command to master even its first principles. It is curious, that, in a country which boasts of its intelligence, the theory should be so generally held that the most complicated of human contrivances, and one which every day becomes more complicated, can be worked at sight by any man able to talk for an hour or two without stopping to think.

Mr. Lincoln is sometimes claimed as an example of a ready-made ruler. But no case could well be less in point ; for, besides that he was a man of such fair-mindedness as is always the raw material of wisdom, he had in his profession a training precisely the opposite of that to which a partisan is subjected. His experience as a lawyer compelled him not only to see that there is a principle underlying every phenomenon in human affairs, but that there are always two sides to every question, both of which must be fully understood in order to understand either, and that it is of greater advantage to an advocate to appreciate the strength than the weakness of his antagonist's position. Nothing is more remarkable than the unerring tact with which, in his debate with Mr. Douglas, he went straight to the reason of the question; nor have we ever had a more striking lesson in political tactics than the fact, that, opposed to a man exceptionally adroit in using popular prejudice and bigotry to his purpose, exceptionally unscrupulous in appealing to those baser motives that turn a meeting of citizens into a mob of barbarians, he should yet have won his case before a jury of the people. Mr. Lincoln was as far as possible from an impromptu politician. His wisdom was made up of a knowledge of things as well as of men; his sagacity resulted from a clear perception and honest acknowledgment of difficulties, which enabled him to see that the only durable triumph of political opinion is based, not on any abstract right, but upon so much of justice, the highest attainable at any given moment in human affairs, as may be had in the balance of mutual concession. Doubtless he had an ideal, but it was the ideal of a practical statesman, — to aim at the best, and to take the next best, if he is lucky enough to get even that. His slow, but singularly masculine, intelligence taught him that precedent is only another name for embodied experience, and that it counts for even more in the guidance of communities of men than in that of the individual life. He was not a man who held it good public economy to pull down on the mere chance of rebuilding better. Mr. Lincoln's faith in God was qualified by a very well-founded distrust of the wisdom of man. Perhaps it was his want of self-confidence that more than anything else won him the unlimited confidence of the people, for they felt that there would be no need of retreat from any position he had deliberately taken. The cautious, but steady, advance of his policy during the war was like that of a Roman army. He left behind him a firm road on which public confidence could follow; he took America with him where he went; what he gained he occupied, and his advanced posts became colonies. The very homeliness of his genius was its distinction. His kingship was conspicuous by its workday homespun. Never was ruler so absolute as he, nor so little conscious of it; for he was the incarnate common-sense of the people. With all that tenderness of nature whose sweet sadness touched whoever saw him with something of its own pathos, there was no trace of sentimentalism in his speech or action. He seems to have had but one rule of conduct, always that of practical and successful politics, to let himself be guided by events, when they were sure to bring him out where he wished to go, though by what seemed to unpractical minds, which let go the possible to grasp at the desirable, a longer road.

Undoubtedly the highest function of statesmanship is by degrees to accommodate the conduct of communities to ethical laws, and to subordinate the conflicting self-interests of the day to higher and more permanent concerns. But it is on the understanding, and not on the sentiment, of a nation that all safe legislation must be based. Voltaire's saying, that " a consideration of petty circumstances is the tomb of great things," may be true of individual men, but it certainly is not true of governments. It is by a multitude of such considerations, each

in itself trifling, but all together weighty, that the framers
of policy can alone divine what is practicable and therefore wise.   The imputation of inconsistency is one to
which every sound politician and every honest thinker
must sooner or later subject himself. (The foolish and
the dead alone never change their opinion) The course
of a great statesman resembles that of navigable rivers,
avoiding immovable obstacles with noble bends of concession, seeking the broad levels of opinion on which men
soonest settle and longest dwell, following and marking
the almost imperceptible slopes of national tendency,
yet always aiming at direct advances, always recruited
from sources nearer heaven, and sometimes bursting
open paths of progress and fruitful human commerce
through what seem the eternal barriers of both.   It
is loyalty to great ends, even though forced to combine
the small and opposing motives of selfish men to accomplish them ; it is the anchored cling to solid principles of
duty and action, which knows how to swing with the
tide, but is never carried away by it, — that we demand
in public men, and not sameness of policy, or a conscientious persistency in what is impracticable.   For the impracticable, however theoretically enticing, is always politically unwise, sound statesmanship being the application of that prudence to the public business which is the
safest guide in that of private men.

No doubt slavery was the most delicate and embarrass-
ing question with which Mr. Lincoln was called on to deal,
and it was one which no man in his position, whatever his
opinions, could evade ; for, though he might withstand
the clamor of partisans, he must sooner or later yield to
the persistent importunacy of circumstances, which thrust
the problem upon him at every turn and in every shape.

It has been brought against us as an accusation
abroad, and repeated here by people who measure their

country rather by what is thought of it than by what it is, that our war has not been distinctly and avowedly for the extinction of slavery, but a war rather for the preservation of our national power and greatness, in which the emancipation of the negro has been forced upon us by circumstances and accepted as a necessity. We are very far from denying this; nay, we admit that it is so far true that we were slow to renounce our constitutional obligations even toward those who had absolved us by their own act from the letter of our duty. We are speaking of the government which, legally installed for the whole country, was bound, so long as it was possible, not to overstep the limits of orderly prescription, and could not, without abnegating its own very nature, take the lead in making rebellion an excuse for revolution. There were, no doubt, many ardent and sincere persons who seemed to think this as simple a thing to do as to lead off a Virginia reel. They forgot what should be forgotten least of all in a system like ours, that the administration for the time being represents not only the majority which elects it, but the minority as well, — a minority in this case powerful, and so little ready for emancipation that it was opposed even to war. Mr. Lincoln had not been chosen as general agent of an antislavery society, but President of the United States, to perform certain functions exactly defined by law. Whatever were his wishes, it was no less duty than policy to mark out for himself a line of action that would not further distract the country, by raising before their time questions which plainly would soon enough compel attention, and for which every day was making the answer more easy.

Meanwhile he must solve the riddle of this new Sphinx, or be devoured. Though Mr. Lincoln's policy in this critical affair has not been such as to satisfy those who demand an heroic treatment for even the most trifling occasion, and who will not cut their coat according to their cloth, unless they can borrow the scissors of Atropos, it has been at least not unworthy of the long-headed king of Ithaca. Mr. Lincoln had the choice of Bassanio offered him. Which of the three caskets held the prize that was to redeem the fortunes of the country? There was the golden one whose showy speciousness might have tempted a vain man; the silver of compromise, which might have decided the choice of a merely acute one; and the leaden, — dull and homely-looking, as prudence always is, — yet with something about it sure to attract the eye of practical wisdom. Mr. Lincoln dallied with his decision perhaps longer than seemed needful to those on whom its awful responsibility was not to rest, but when he made it, it was worthy of his cautious but sure-footed understanding. The moral of the Sphinx-riddle, and it is a deep one, lies in the childish simplicity of the solution. Those who fail in guessing it, fail because they are over-ingenious, and cast about for an answer that shall suit their own notion of the gravity of the occasion and of their own dignity, rather than the occasion itself.

In a matter which must be finally settled by public opinion, and in regard to which the ferment of prejudice and passion on both sides has not yet subsided to that equilibrium of compromise from which alone a sound public opinion can result, it is proper enough for the private citizen to press his own convictions with all possible force of argument and persuasion; but the popular magistrate, whose judgment must become action, and whose action involves the whole country, is bound to wait till the sentiment of the people is so far advanced toward his own point of view, that what he does shall find support in it, instead of merely confusing it with

new elements of division. It was not unnatural that
men earnestly devoted to the saving of their country,
and profoundly convinced that slavery was its only real
enemy, should demand a decided policy round which all
patriots might rally, — and this might have been the
wisest course for an absolute ruler. But in the then
unsettled state of the public mind, with a large party
decrying even resistance to the slaveholders' rebellion as
not only unwise, but even unlawful; with a majority,
perhaps, even of the would-be loyal so long accustomed
to regard the Constitution as a deed of gift conveying to
the South their own judgment as to policy and instinct
as to right, that they were in doubt at first whether
their loyalty were due to the country or to slavery ; and
with a respectable body of honest and influential men
who still believed in the possibility of conciliation, — Mr.
Lincoln judged wisely, that, in laying down a policy in
deference to one party, he should be giving to the other
the very fulcrum for which their disloyalty had been
waiting.

It behooved a clear-headed man in his position not to
yield so far to an honest indignation against the brokers
of treason in the North as to lose sight of the materials
for misleading which were their stock in trade, and
to forget that it is not the falsehood of sophistry which
is to be feared, but the grain of truth mingled with
it to make it specious, — that it is not the knavery of
the leaders so much as the honesty of the followers they
may seduce, that gives them power for evil. It was
especially his duty to do nothing which might help the
people to forget the true cause of the war in fruitless
disputes about its inevitable consequences.

The doctrine of State rights can be so handled by an
adroit demagogue as easily to confound the distinction
between liberty and lawlessness in the minds of ignorant

8

persons, accustomed always to be influenced by the sound of certain words, rather than to reflect upon the principles which give them meaning. For, though Secession involves the manifest absurdity of denying to a State the right of making war against any foreign power while permitting it against the United States ; though it supposes a compact of mutual concessions and guaranties among States without any arbiter in case of dissension ; though it contradicts common-sense in assuming that the men who framed our government did not know what they meant when they substituted Union for Confederation ; though it falsifies history, which shows that the main opposition to the adoption of the Constitution was based on the argument that it did not allow that independence in the several States which alone would justify them in seceding ; — yet, as slavery was universally admitted to be a reserved right, an inference could be drawn from any direct attack upon it (though only in self-defence) to a natural right of resistance, logical enough to satisfy minds untrained to detect fallacy, as the majority of men always are, and now too much disturbed by the disorder of the times, to consider that the order of events had any legitimate bearing on the argument. Though Mr. Lincoln was too sagacious to give the Northern allies of the Rebels the occasion they desired and even strove to provoke, yet from the beginning of the war the most persistent efforts have been made to confuse the public mind as to its origin and motives, and to drag the people of the loyal States down from the national position they had instinctively taken to the old level of party squabbles and antipathies. The wholly unprovoked rebellion of an oligarchy proclaiming negro slavery the corner-stone of free institutions, and in the first flush of over-hasty confidence venturing to parade the logical sequence of their leading dogma, "that slavery is right in principle, and has nothing to do with difference of complexion," has been represented as a legitimate and gallant attempt to maintain the true principles of democracy. The rightful endeavor of an established government, the least onerous that ever existed, to defend itself against a treacherous attack on its very existence, has been cunningly made to seem the wicked effort of a fanatical clique to force its doctrines on an oppressed population.

Even so long ago as when Mr. Lincoln, not yet convinced of the danger and magnitude of the crisis, was endeavoring to persuade himself of Union majorities at the South, and to carry on a war that was half peace in the hope of a peace that would have been all war, — while he was still enforcing the Fugitive Slave Law, under some theory that Secession, however it might absolve States from their obligations, could not escheat them of their claims under the Constitution, and that slaveholders in rebellion had alone among mortals the privilege of having their cake and eating it at the same time, — the enemies of free government were striving to persuade the people that the war was an Abolition crusade. To rebel without reason was proclaimed as one of the rights of man, while it was carefully kept out of sight that to suppress rebellion is the first duty of government. All the evils that have come upon the country have been attributed to the Abolitionists, though it is hard to see how any party can become permanently powerful except in one of two ways, — either by the greater truth of its principles, or the extravagance of the party opposed to it. To fancy the ship of state, riding safe at her constitutional moorings, suddenly engulfed by a huge kraken of Abolitionism, rising from unknown depths and grasping it with slimy tentacles, is to look at the natural history of the matter with the eyes of Pontoppidan. To believe that the leaders in the Southern treason feared any danger from Abolitionism, would be to deny them ordinary intelligence, though there can be little doubt that they made use of it to stir the passions and excite the fears of their deluded accomplices. They rebelled, not because they thought slavery weak, but because they believed it strong enough, not to overthrow the government, but to get possession of it ; for it becomes daily clearer that they used rebellion only as a means of revolution, and if they got revolution, though not in the shape they looked for, is the American people to save them from its consequences at the cost of its own existence ? The election of Mr. Lincoln, which it was clearly in their power to prevent had they wished, was the occasion merely, and not the cause, of their revolt. Abolitionism, till within a year or two, was the despised heresy of a few earnest persons, without political weight enough to carry the election of a parish constable ; and their cardinal principle was disunion, because they were convinced that within the Union the position of slavery was impregnable. In spite of the proverb, great effects do not follow from small causes, — that is, disproportionately small, — but from adequate causes acting under certain required conditions. To contrast the size of the oak with that of the parent acorn, as if the poor seed had paid all costs from its slender strong-box, may serve for a child's wonder ; but the real miracle lies in that divine league which bound all the forces of nature to the service of the tiny germ in fulfilling its destiny. Everything has been at work for the past ten years in the cause of antislavery, but Garrison and Phillips have been far less successful propagandists than the slaveholders themselves, with the constantly-growing arrogance of their pretensions and encroachments. They have forced the question upon the attention of every voter in the Free States, by defiantly putting freedom and democracy on the defensive. But, even after the Kansas outrages, there was no wide-spread desire on the part of the North to commit aggressions, though there was a growing determination to resist them. The popular unanimity in favor of the war three years ago was but in small measure the result of antislavery sentiment, far less of any zeal for abolition. But every month of the war, every movement of the allies of slavery in the Free States, has been making Abolitionists by the thousand. The masses of any people, however intelligent, are very little moved by abstract principles of humanity and justice, until those principles are interpreted for them by the stinging commentary of some infringement upon their own rights, and then their instincts and passions, once aroused, do indeed derive an incalculable reinforcement of impulse and intensity from those higher ideas, those sublime traditions, which have no motive political force till they are allied with a sense of immediate personal wrong or imminent peril. Then at last the stars in their courses begin to fight against Sisera. Had any one doubted before that the rights of human nature are unitary, that oppression is of one hue the world over, no matter what the color of the oppressed, — had any one failed to see what the real essence of the contest was, — the efforts of the advocates of slavery among ourselves to throw discredit upon the fundamental axioms of the Declaration of Independence and the radical doctrines of Christianity, could not fail to sharpen his eyes.

While every day was bringing the people nearer to the conclusion which all thinking men saw to be inevitable from the beginning, it was wise in Mr. Lincoln to leave the shaping of his policy to events. In this country, where the rough and ready understanding of the people is sure at last to be the controlling power, a profound common-sense is the best genius for statesmanship. Hitherto the wisdom of the President's measures has been justified by the fact that they have always resulted in more firmly uniting public opinion. One of the things particularly admirable in the public utterances of President Lincoln is a certain tone of familiar dignity, which, while it is perhaps the most difficult attainment of mere style, is also no doubtful indication of personal character. There must be something essentially noble in an elective ruler who can descend to the level of confidential ease without losing respect, something very manly in one who can break through the etiquette of his conventional rank and trust himself to the reason and intelligence of those who have elected him. No higher compliment was ever paid to a nation than the simple confidence, the fireside plainness, with which Mr. Lincoln always addresses himself to the reason of the American people. This was, indeed, a true democrat, who grounded himself on the assumption that a democracy can think. "Come, let us reason together about this matter," has been the tone of all his addresses to the people; and accordingly we have never had a chief magistrate who so won to himself the love and at the same time the judgment of his countrymen. To us, that simple confidence of his in the right-mindedness of his fellow-men is very touching, and its success is as strong an argument as we have ever seen in favor of the theory that men can govern themselves. He never appeals to any vulgar sentiment, he never alludes to the humbleness of his origin; it probably never occurred to him, indeed, that there was anything higher to start from than manhood; and he put himself on a level with those he addressed, not by going down to them, but only by taking it for granted that they had brains and would come up to a common ground of reason. In an article lately printed in "The Nation," Mr. Bayard Taylor mentions the striking fact, that in the foulest dens of the Five Points he found the portrait of Lincoln. The wretched population that makes its hive there threw all its votes and more against him, and yet paid this instinctive tribute to the sweet humanity of his nature. Their ignorance sold its vote and took its money, but all that was left of manhood in them recognized its saint and martyr.

Mr. Lincoln is not in the habit of saying, "This is *my* opinion, or *my* theory," but, "This is the conclusion to which, in my judgment, the time has come, and to which, accordingly, the sooner we come the better for us." His policy has been the policy of public opinion based on adequate discussion and on a timely recognition of the influence of passing events in shaping the features of events to come.

One secret of Mr. Lincoln's remarkable success in captivating the popular mind is undoubtedly an unconsciousness of self which enables him, though under the necessity of constantly using the capital *I*, to do it without any suggestion of egotism. There is no single vowel which men's mouths can pronounce with such difference of effect. That which one shall hide away, as it were, behind the substance of his discourse, or, if he bring it to the front, shall use merely to give an agreeable accent of individuality to what he says, another shall make an offensive challenge to the self-satisfaction of all his hearers, and an unwarranted intrusion upon each man's sense of personal importance, irritating every pore of his vanity, like a dry northeast wind, to a goose-flesh of opposition and hostility. Mr. Lincoln has never studied Quinctilian; but he has, in the earnest sim-

plicity and unaffected Americanism of his own character,
one art of oratory worth all the rest. He forgets himself so entirely in his object as to give his *I* the sympathetic and persuasive effect of *We* with the great body
of his countrymen. Homely, dispassionate, showing all
the rough-edged process of his thought as it goes along,
yet arriving at his conclusions with an honest kind of
every-day logic, he is so eminently our representative
man, that, when he speaks, it seems as if the people
were listening to their own thinking aloud. The dignity of his thought owes nothing to any ceremonial
garb of words, but to the manly movement that comes
of settled purpose and an energy of reason that knows
not what rhetoric means. There has been nothing of
Cleon, still less of Strepsiades striving to underbid him
in demagogism, to be found in the public utterances of
Mr. Lincoln. He has always addressed the intelligence
of men, never their prejudice, their passion, or their
ignorance.

On the day of his death, this simple Western attorney, who according to one party was a vulgar joker,
and whom the *doctrinaires* among his own supporters
accused of wanting every element of statesmanship,
was the most absolute ruler in Christendom, and this
solely by the hold his good-humored sagacity had
laid on the hearts and understandings of his countrymen. Nor was this all, for it appeared that he had
drawn the great majority, not only of his fellow-citizens,
but of mankind also, to his side. So strong and so
persuasive is honest manliness without a single quality
of romance or unreal sentiment to help it! A civilian
during times of the most captivating military achievement, awkward, with no skill in the lower technicalities

of manners, he left behind him a fame beyond that of any conqueror, the memory of a grace higher than that of outward person, and of a gentlemanliness deeper than mere breeding.   Never before that startled April morning did such multitudes of men shed tears for the death of one they had never seen, as if with him a friendly presence had been taken away from their lives, leaving them colder and darker.   Never was funeral panegyric so eloquent as the silent look of sympathy which strangers exchanged when they met on that day.   Their common manhood had lost a kinsman.

THE LIFE AND LETTERS OF JAMES
GATES PERCIVAL.

THIS is an interesting and in many respects instructive book. Mr. Ward has done his work, as is
fitting, in a loving spirit ; and if he over-estimates both
what Percival was and what he did, he enables us to
form our own judgment by letting him so far as possible
speak for himself. The book gives a rather curious
picture of what the life of a man of letters is likely to
be in a country not yet ripe for literary production,
especially if he be not endowed with the higher qualities
which command and can wait for that best of all successes which comes slowly. In a generation where
everybody can write verses, and where certain modes of
thought and turns of phrase have become so tyrannous
that it is as hard to distinguish between the productions of one minor poet and another as among those of
so many Minnesingers or Troubadours, there is a demand for only two things, — for what chimes with the
moment's whim of popular sentiment and is forgotten
when that has changed, or for what is never an anachronism, because it slakes or seems to slake the eternal thirst
of our nature for those ideal waters that glimmer before
us and still before us in ever-renewing mirage. Percival
met neither of these conditions. With a nature singularly unplastic, unsympathetic, and self-involved, he was
incapable of receiving into his own mind the ordinary
emotions of men and giving them back in music ; and

with a lofty conception of the object and purposes of poesy, he had neither the resolution nor the power which might have enabled him to realize it. He offers as striking an example as could be found of the poetic temperament unballasted with those less obvious qualities which make the poetic faculty. His verse carries every inch of canvas that diction and sentiment can crowd, but the craft is cranky, and we miss that deep-grasping keel of reason which alone can steady and give direction. His mind drifts, too waterlogged to answer the helm, and in his longer poems, like "Prometheus," half the voyage is spent in trying to make up for a lee-way which becomes at last irretrievable. If he had a port in view when he set out, he seems soon to give up all hope of ever reaching it; and wherever we open the log-book, we find him running for nowhere in particular, as the wind happens to lead, or lying-to in the merest gale of verbiage. The truth is, that Percival was led to the writing of verse by a sentimental desire of the mind, and not by that concurring instinct of all the faculties which is a self-forgetting passion of the entire man. Too excitable to possess his subject fully, as a man of mere talent may often do, he is not possessed by it as the man of genius is, and seems helplessly striving, the greater part of the time, to make out what, in the name of common or uncommon sense, he is after. With all the stock properties of verse whirling and dancing about his ears puffed out to an empty show of life, the reader of much of his blank verse feels as if a mob of well-draperied clothes-lines were rioting about him in all the unwilling ecstasy of a thunder-gust.

Percival, living from 1795 to 1856, arrived at manhood just as the last war with England had come to an end. Poor, shy, and proud, there is nothing in his earlier years that might not be paralleled in those of hundreds of sensitive boys who gradually get the nonsense shaken out of them in the rough school of life. The length of the schooling needful in his case is what makes it peculiar. Not till after he was fifty, if even then, did he learn that the world never takes a man at his own valuation, and never pays money for what it does not want, or think it wants. It did not want his poetry, simply because it was not, is not, and by no conceivable power of argument can be made, interesting, — the first duty of every artistic product. Percival, who would have thought his neighbors mad if they had insisted on his buying twenty thousand refrigerators merely because they had been at the trouble of making them, and found it convenient to turn them into cash, could never forgive the world for taking this business view of the matter in his own case. He went on doggedly, making refrigerators of every possible pattern, and comforted himself with the thought of a wiser posterity, which should have learned that the purpose of poetry is to cool and not to kindle. His "Mind," which is on the whole perhaps the best of his writings, vies in coldness with the writings of his brother doctor, Akenside, whose "Pleasures of Imagination" are something quite other than pleasing in reality. If there be here and there a semblance of pale fire, it is but the reflection of moonshine upon ice. Akenside is respectable, because he really had something new to say, in spite of his pompous, mouthing way of saying it; but when Percival says it over again, it is a little too much. In his more ambitious pieces, — and it is curious how literally the word "pieces" applies to all he did, — he devotes himself mainly to telling us what poetry ought to be, as if mankind were not always more than satisfied with any one who fulfils the true office of poet, by showing them, with the least possible fuss, what it is. Percival was a professor of poetry rather than a poet, and we are not surprised at the number of lectures he reads us, when we learn that in early life he was an excellent demonstrator of anatomy, whose subject must be dead before his business with it begins. His interest in poetry was always more or less scientific. He was forever trying experiments in matter and form, especially the latter. And these were especially unhappy, because it is plain that he had no musical ear, or at best a very imperfect one. His attempts at classical metres are simply unreadable, whether as verse or prose. He contrives to make even the Sapphic so, which when we read it in Latin moves featly to our modern accentuation. Let any one who wishes to feel the difference between ear and no ear compare Percival's specimens with those in the same kind of Coleridge, who had the finest metrical sense since Milton. We take this very experimenting to be a sufficient proof that Percival's faculty, such as it was, and we do not rate it highly, was artificial, and not innate. The true poet is much rather experimented upon by life and nature, by joy and sorrow, by beauty and defect, till it be found out whether he have any hidden music in him that can sing them into an accord with the eternal harmony which we call God.

It is easy to trace the literary influences to which the mind of Percival was in turn subjected. Early in life we find a taint of Byronism, which indeed does not wholly disappear to the last. There is among his poems "An Imprecation," of which a single stanza will suffice as a specimen : —

> " Wrapped in sheets of gory lightning,
> While cursed night-hags ring thy knell,
> May the arm of vengeance bright'ning,
> O'er thee wave the sword of hell ! "

If we could fancy Laura Matilda shut up tipsy in the

watch-house, we might suppose her capable of this melodious substitute for swearing. We confess that we cannot read it without laughing, after learning from Mr. Ward that its Salmoneus-thunderbolts were launched at the comfortable little city of Hartford, because the poet fancied that the inhabitants thereof did not like him or his verses so much as he himself did. There is something deliciously ludicrous in the conception of night-hags ringing the orthodox bell of the Second Congregational or First Baptist Meeting-house to summon the parishioners to witness these fatal consequences of not reading Percival's poems. Nothing less than the fear of some such catastrophe could compel the perusal of the greater part of them. Next to Byron comes Moore, whose cloying sentimentalism and too facile melody are recalled by the subject and treatment of very many of the shorter lyrics of Percival. In "Prometheus" it is Shelley who is paramount for the time, and Shelley at his worst period, before his unwieldy abundance of incoherent words and images, that were merely words and images without any meaning of real experience to give them solidity, had been compressed in the stricter moulds of thought and study. In the blank verse again, we encounter Wordsworth's tone and sentiment. These were no good models for Percival, who always improvised, and who seems to have thought verse the great distinction between poetry and prose. Percival got nothing from Shelley but the fatal copiousness which is his vice, nothing from Wordsworth but that tendency to preach at every corner about a sympathy with nature which is not his real distinction, and which becomes a wearisome cant at second-hand. Shelley and Wordsworth are both stilted, though in different ways. Shelley wreathed his stilts with flowers; while Wordsworth, protesting against the use of them as sinful, mounts his

solemnly at last, and stalks away conscientiously eschew-
ing whatever would serve to hide the naked wood, —
nay, was it not Gray's only that were scandalous, and
were not his own, modelled upon those of the sainted
Cowper, of strictly orthodox pattern after all ? Percival,
like all imitators, is caught by the defects of what he
copies, and exaggerates them. With him the stilts are
the chief matter; and getting a taller pair than either
of his predecessors, he lifts his commonplace upon them
only to make it more drearily conspicuous. Shelley has
his gleams of unearthly wildfire, Wordsworth is by fits
the most deeply inspired man of his generation; but
Percival has no lucid interval. He is pertinaciously and
unappeasably dull, — as dull as a comedy of Goethe.
He never in his life wrote a rememberable verse. We
should not have thought this of any consequence now,
for we need not try to read him, did not Mr. Ward with
amusing gravity all along assume that he was a great
poet. There was scarce timber enough in him for the
making of a Tiedge or a Hagedorn, both of whom he
somewhat resembles.

Percival came to maturity at an unfortunate time for
a man so liable to self-delusion. Leaving college with so
imperfect a classical training (in spite of the numerous
"testimonials" cited by Mr. Ward) that he was capable
of laying the accent on the second syllable of Pericles,
he seems never to have systematically trained even such
faculty as was in him, but to have gone on to the end
mistaking excitability of brain for wholesome exercise of
thought. The consequence is a prolonged immaturity,
which makes his latest volume, published in 1843, as
crude and as plainly wanting in enduring quality as the
first number of his "Clio." We have the same old com-
plaints of neglected genius, — as if genius could ever be
neglected so long as it has the perennial consolation of

its own divine society, — the same wilted sentiment, the same feeling about for topics of verse in which he may possibly find that inspiration from without which the true poet cannot flee from in himself. These tedious wailings about heavenly powers suffocating in the heavy atmosphere of an uncongenial, unrecognizing world, and Percival is profuse of them, are simply an advertisement to whoever has ears of some innate disability in the man who utters them. Heavenly powers know very well how to take care of themselves. The poor "World," meaning thereby that small fraction of society which has any personal knowledge of an author or his affairs, has had great wrong done it in such matters. It is not, and never was, the powers of a man that it neglects, — it could not if it would, — but his weaknesses, and especially the publication of them, of which it grows weary. It can never supply any man with what is wanting in himself, and the attempt to do it only makes bad worse. If a man can find the proof of his own genius only in public appreciation, still worse, if his vanity console itself with taking it as an evidence of rare qualities in himself that his fellow-mortals are unable to see them, it is all up with him. The "World" resolutely refused to find Wordsworth entertaining, and it refuses still, on good grounds; but the genius that was in him bore up unflinchingly, would take no denial, got its claim admitted on all hands, and impregnated at last the literature of an entire generation, though *habitans in sicco*, if ever genius did. But Percival seems to have satisfied himself with a syllogism something like this : Men of genius are neglected; the more neglect, the more genius; I am altogether neglected, — *ergo*, wholly made up of that priceless material.

The truth was that he suffered rather from over appreciation; and "when," says a nameless old French

man, " I see a man go up like a rocket, I expect before
long to see the stick come down." The times were
singularly propitious to mediocrity. As in Holland one
had only to

> " Invent a shovel and be a magistrate,"

so here to write a hundred blank verses was to be immortal, till somebody else wrote a hundred and fifty
blanker ones. It had been resolved unanimously that
we must and would have a national literature. England,
France, Spain, Italy, each already had one, Germany
was getting one made as fast as possible, and Ireland
vowed that she once had one far surpassing them all.
To be respectable, we must have one also, and that
speedily. That we were not yet, in any true sense, a
nation ; that we wanted that literary and social atmosphere which is the breath of life to all artistic production ; that our scholarship, such as it was, was mostly
of that theological sort which acts like a prolonged
drouth upon the brain ; that our poetic fathers were
Joel Barlow and Timothy Dwight, — was nothing to the
purpose ; a literature adapted to the size of the country was what we must and would have. Given the
number of square miles, the length of the rivers, the
size of the lakes, and you have the greatness of the literature we were bound to produce without further
delay. If that little dribble of an Avon had succeeded
in engendering Shakespeare, what a giant might we not
look for from the mighty womb of Mississippi ! Physical
Geography for the first time took her rightful place
as the tenth and most inspiring Muse. A glance at the
map would satisfy the most incredulous that she had
done her best for us, and should we be wanting to the
glorious opportunity ? Not we indeed ! So surely as
Franklin invented the art of printing, and Fulton the
steam-engine, we would invent us a great poet in time

to send the news by the next packet to England, and
teach her that we were her masters in arts as well as
arms.

Percival was only too ready to be invented, and he
forthwith produced his bale of verses from a loom capable of turning off a hitherto unheard-of number of yards
to the hour, and perfectly adapted to the amplitude of
our territory, inasmuch as it was manufactured on the
theory of covering the largest surface with the least
possible amount of meaning that would hold words
together. He was as ready to accept the perilous em-
prise, and as loud in asserting his claim thereto, as
Sir Kay used to be, and with much the same result.
Our critical journals — and America certainly *has* led
the world in a department of letters which of course
requires no outfit but the power to read and write, gra-
tuitously furnished by our public schools — received him
with a shout of welcome. Here came the true deliverer
at last, mounted on a steed to which he himself had
given the new name of " Pegāsus," — for we were to be
original in everything, — and certainly blowing his own
trumpet with remarkable vigor of lungs. Solitary enthusiasts, who had long awaited this sublime avatar,
addressed him in sonnets which he accepted with a
gravity beyond all praise. (To be sure, even Mr. Ward
seems to allow that his sense of humor was hardly equal
to his other transcendent endowments.) His path was
strewn with laurel — of the native variety, altogether
superior to that of the Old World, at any rate not precisely like it. Verses signed " P.," as like each other as
two peas, and as much like poetry as that vegetable
is like a peach, were watched for in the corner of a newspaper as an astronomer watches for a new planet. There
was never anything so comically unreal since the crowning in the Capitol of Messer Francesco Petrarca, Grand

Sentimentalist in Ordinary at the Court of King Robert of Naples. Unhappily, Percival took it all quite seriously. There was no praise too ample for the easy elasticity of his swallow. He believed himself as gigantic as the shadow he cast on these rolling mists of insubstantial adulation, and life-long he could never make out why *his* fine words refused to butter his parsnips for him, nay, to furnish both parsnips and sauce. While the critics were debating precisely how many of the prime qualities of the great poets of his own and preceding generations he combined in his single genius, and in what particular respects he surpassed them all, — a point about which he himself seems never to have had any doubts, — the public, which could read Scott and Byron with avidity, and which was beginning even to taste Wordsworth, found his verses inexpressibly wearisome. They would not throng and subscribe for a collected edition of those works which singly had been too much for them. With whatever dulness of sense they may be charged, they have a remarkably keen scent for tediousness, and will have none of it unless in a tract or sermon, where, of course, it is to be expected. Percival never forgave the public; but it was the critics that he never should have forgiven, for of all the maggots that can make their way into the brains through the ears, there is none so disastrous as the persuasion that you are a great poet. There is surely something in the construction of the ears of small authors which lays them specially open to the inroads of this pest. It tickles pleasantly while it eats away the fibre of will, and incapacitates a man for all honest commerce with realities. Unhappily its insidious titillation seems to have been Percival's one great pleasure during life.

We began by saying that the book before us was interesting and instructive; but we meant that it was so

not so much from any positive merits of its own as by
the lesson which almost every page of it suggests. To
those who have some knowledge of the history of literature, or some experience in life, it is from beginning
to end a history of weakness mistaking great desires for
great powers. If poetry, in Bacon's noble definition of
it, "adapt the shows of things to the desires of the mind,"
sentimentalism is equally skilful in making realities
shape themselves to the cravings of vanity. The theory
that the poet is a being above the world and apart from
it is true of him as an observer only who applies to the
phenomena about him the test of a finer and more spiritual sense. That he is a creature divinely set apart from
his fellow-men by a mental organization that makes
them mutually unintelligible to each other, is in flat
contradiction with the lives of those poets universally
acknowledged as greatest. Dante, Shakespeare, Cervantes, Calderon, Milton, Molière, Goethe, — in what
conceivable sense is it true of them that they wanted
the manly qualities which made them equal to the
demands of the world in which they lived? That a poet
should assume, as Victor Hugo used to do, that he is a
reorganizer of the moral world, and that works cunningly
adapted to the popular whim of the time form part of
some mysterious system which is to give us a new heaven
and a new earth, and to remodel laws of art which are
as unchangeable as those of astronomy, can do no very
great harm to any one but the author himself, who will
thereby be led astray from his proper function, and from
the only path to legitimate and lasting success. But
when the theory is carried a step further, and we are
asked to believe, as in Percival's case, that, because
a man can write verses, he is exempt from that inexorable logic of life and circumstance to which all other men
are subjected, and to which it is wholesome for them

that they should be, then it becomes mischievous, and calls for a protest from all those who have at heart the interests of good morals and healthy literature. It is the theory of idlers and *dilettanti*, of fribbles in morals and declaimers in verse, which a young man of real power may dally with during some fit of mental indigestion, but which when accepted by a mature man, and carried along with him through life, is a sure mark of feebleness and of insincere dealing with himself. Percival is a good example of a class of authors unhappily too numerous in these latter days. In Europe the natural growth of a world ill at ease with itself and still nervous with the frightful palpitation of the French Revolution, they are but feeble exotics in our healthier air. Without faith or hope, and deprived of that outward support in the habitual procession of events and in the authoritative limitations of thought which in ordinary times gives steadiness to feeble and timid intellects, they are turned inward, and forced, like Hudibras's sword,

> " To eat into themselves, for lack
> Of other thing to hew and hack."

Compelled to find within them that stay which had hitherto been supplied by creeds and institutions, they learned to attribute to their own consciousness the grandeur which belongs of right only to the mind of the human race, slowly endeavoring after an equilibrium between its desires and the external conditions under which they are attainable. Hence that exaggeration of the individual, and depreciation of the social man, which has become the cant of modern literature. Abundance of such phenomena accompanied the rise of what was called Romanticism in Germany and France, reacting to some extent even upon England, and consequently America. The smaller poets erected themselves into a kind of guild, into which all were admitted who gave proof of a certain feebleness of character which rendered them superior to their grosser fellow-men. It was a society of cripples undertaking to teach the new generation how to walk. Meanwhile, the object of their generous solicitude, what with clinging to Mother Past's skirts, and helping itself by every piece of household furniture it could lay hands on, learned, after many a tumble, to get on its legs, and to use them as other generations had done before it. Percival belonged to this new order of bards, weak in the knees, and thinking it healthy exercise to climb the peaks of Dreamland. To the vague and misty views attainable from those sublime summits into his own vast interior, his reports in blank verse and otherwise did ample justice, but failed to excite the appetite of mankind. He spent his life, like others of his class, in proclaiming himself a neglected Columbus, ever ready to start on his voyage when the public would supply the means of building his ships. Meanwhile, to be ready at a moment's warning, he packs his mind pellmell like a carpet-bag, wraps a geologist's hammer in a shirt with a Byron collar, does up Volney's "Ruins" with an odd volume of Wordsworth, and another of Bell's "Anatomy" in a loose sheet of Webster's Dictionary, jams Moore's poems between the leaves of Bopp's Grammer, — and forgets only such small matters as combs and brushes. It never seems to have entered his head that the gulf between genius and its new world is never too wide for ε stout swimmer. Like all sentimentalists, he reversed the process of nature, which makes it a part of greatness that it is a simple thing to itself, however much of a marvel it may be to other men. He discovered his own genius, as he supposed, — a thing impossible had the genius been real. Donne never wrote a profounder verse than

"Who knows his virtue's name and place, hath none."

Percival's life was by no means a remarkable one, except, perhaps, in the number of chances that seem to have been offered him to make something of himself, if anything were possibly to be made. He was never without friends, never without opportunities, if he could have availed himself of them. It is pleasant to see Mr. Ticknor treating him with that considerate kindness which many a young scholar can remember as shown so generously to himself. But nothing could help Percival, whose nature had defeat worked into its very composition. He was not a real, but an imaginary man. His early attempt at suicide (as Mr. Ward seems to think it) is typical of him. He is not the first young man who, when crossed in love, has spoken of " loupin o'er a linn," nor will he be the last. But that any one who really meant to kill himself should put himself resolutely in the way of being prevented, as Percival did, is hard to believe. Châteaubriand, the arch sentimentalist of these latter days, had the same harmless *velleity* of self-destruction, — enough to scare his sister and so give him a smack of sensation, — but a very different thing from the settled will which would be really perilous. Shakespeare, always true to Nature, makes Hamlet dally with the same exciting fancy. Alas ! self is the one thing the sentimentalist never truly wishes to destroy ! One remarkable gift Percival seems to have had, which may be called memory of the eye. What he saw he never forgot, and this fitted him for a good geological observer. How great his power of combination was, which alone could have made him a great geologist, we cannot determine. But he seems to have shown but little in other directions. His faculty of acquiring foreign tongues we do not value so highly as Mr. Ward. We have known many otherwise inferior men who possessed it. Indeed, the power to express the same nothing in ten different languages is something to be dreaded rather than admired. It gives a horrible advantage to dulness. The best thing to be learned from Percival's life is that he was happy for the first time when taken away from his vague pursuit of the ideal, and set to practical work.

THOREAU.

WHAT contemporary, if he was in the fighting period of his life, (since Nature sets limits about her conscription for spiritual fields, as the state does in physical warfare,) will ever forget what was somewhat vaguely called the "Transcendental Movement" of thirty years ago? Apparently set astirring by Carlyle's essays on the "Signs of the Times," and on "History," the final and more immediate impulse seemed to be given by "Sartor Resartus." At least the republication in Boston of that wonderful Abraham à Sancta Clara sermon on Lear's text of the miserable forked radish gave the signal for a sudden mental and moral mutiny. *Ecce nunc tempus acceptabile!* was shouted on all hands with every variety of emphasis, and by voices of every conceivable pitch, representing the three sexes of men, women, and Lady Mary Wortley Montagues. The nameless eagle of the tree Ygdrasil was about to sit at last, and wild-eyed enthusiasts rushed from all sides, each eager to thrust under the mystic bird that chalk egg from which the new and fairer Creation was to be hatched in due time. *Redeunt Saturnia regna,* — so far was certain, though in what shape, or by what methods, was still a matter of debate. Every possible form of intellectual and physical dyspepsia brought forth its gospel. Bran had its prophets, and the presartorial simplicity of Adam its martyrs, tailored impromptu from the tar-pot by incensed

9   M

neighbors, and sent forth to illustrate the "feathered Mercury," as defined by Webster and Worcester. Plainness of speech was carried to a pitch that would have taken away the breath of George Fox ; and even swearing had its evangelists, who answered a simple inquiry after their health with an elaborate ingenuity of imprecation that might have been honorably mentioned by Marlborough in general orders. Everybody had a mission (with a capital M) to attend to everybody-else's business. No brain but had its private maggot, which must have found pitiably short commons sometimes. Not a few impecunious zealots abjured the use of money (unless earned by other people), professing to live on the internal revenues of the spirit. Some had an assurance of instant millennium so soon as hooks and eyes should be substituted for buttons. Communities were established where everything was to be common but common-sense. Men renounced their old gods, and hesitated only whether to bestow their furloughed allegiance on Thor or Budh. Conventions were held for every hitherto inconceivable purpose. The belated gift of tongues, as among the Fifth Monarchy men, spread like a contagion, rendering its victims incomprehensible to all Christian men ; whether equally so to the most distant possible heathen or not was unexperimented, though many would have subscribed liberally that a fair trial might be made. It was the pentecost of Shinar. The day of utterances reproduced the day of rebuses and anagrams, and there was nothing so simple that uncial letters and the style of Diphilus the Labyrinth could not turn into a riddle. Many foreign revolutionists out of work added to the general misunderstanding their contribution of broken English in every most ingenious form of fracture. All stood ready at a moment's notice to reform everything but themselves. The general motto was : —

"And we'll *talk* with them, too,
And take upon's the mystery of things
As if we were God's spies."

Nature is always kind enough to give even her clouds a humorous lining. We have barely hinted at the comic side of the affair, for the material was endless. This was the whistle and trailing fuse of the shell, but there was a very solid and serious kernel, full of the most deadly explosiveness. Thoughtful men divined it, but the generality suspected nothing. The word "transcendental" then was the maid of all work for those who could not think, as "Pre-Raphaelite" has been more recently for people of the same limited housekeeping. The truth is, that there was a much nearer metaphysical relation and a much more distant æsthetic and literary relation between Carlyle and the Apostles of the Newness, as they were called in New England, than has commonly been supposed. Both represented the reaction and revolt against *Philisterei*, a renewal of the old battle begun in modern times by Erasmus and Reuchlin, and continued by Lessing, Goethe, and, in a far narrower sense, by Heine in Germany, and of which Fielding, Sterne, and Wordsworth in different ways have been the leaders in England. It was simply a struggle for fresh air, in which, if the windows could not be opened, there was danger that panes would be broken, though painted with images of saints and martyrs. Light colored by these reverend effigies was none the more respirable for being picturesque. There is only one thing better than tradition, and that is the original and eternal life out of which all tradition takes its rise. It was this life which the reformers demanded, with more or less clearness of consciousness and expression, life in politics, life in literature, life in religion. Of what use to import a gospel from Judæa, if we leave behind the soul that made it possible, the God who keeps it forever real and present? Surely Abana and Pharpar *are* better than Jordan, if a living faith be mixed with those waters and none with these.

Scotch Presbyterianism as a motive of spiritual progress was dead; New England Puritanism was in like manner dead; in other words, Protestantism had made its fortune and no longer protested; but till Carlyle spoke out in the Old World and Emerson in the New, no one had dared to proclaim, *Le roi est mort: vive le roi!* The meaning of which proclamation was essentially this : the vital spirit has long since departed out of this form once so kingly, and the great seal has been in commission long enough ; but meanwhile the soul of man, from which all power emanates and to which it reverts, still survives in undiminished royalty; God still survives, little as you gentlemen of the Commission seem to be aware of it, — nay, may possibly outlive the whole of you, incredible as it may appear. The truth is, that both Scotch Presbyterianism and New England Puritanism made their new avatar in Carlyle and Emerson, the heralds of their formal decease, and the tendency of the one toward Authority and of the other toward Independency might have been prophesied by whoever had studied history. The necessity was not so much in the men as in the principles they represented and the traditions which overruled them. The Puritanism of the past found its unwilling poet in Hawthorne, the rarest creative imagination of the century, the rarest in some ideal respects since Shakespeare ; but the Puritanism that cannot die, the Puritanism that made New England what it is, and is destined to make America what it should be, found its voice in Emerson. Though holding himself aloof from all active partnership in movements of reform, he has been the sleeping partner who has supplied a great part of their capital.

The artistic range of Emerson is narrow, as every well-read critic must feel at once ; and so is that of Æschylus, so is that of Dante, so is that of Montaigne, so is that of Schiller, so is that of nearly every one except Shakespeare ; but there is a gauge of height no less than of breadth, of individuality as well as of comprehensiveness, and, above all, there is the standard of genetic power, the test of the masculine as distinguished from the receptive minds. There are staminate plants in literature, that make no fine show of fruit, but without whose pollen, quintessence of fructifying gold, the garden had been barren. Emerson's mind is emphatically one of these, and there is no man to whom our æsthetic culture owes so much. The Puritan revolt had made us ecclesiastically, and the Revolution politically independent, but we were still socially and intellectually moored to English thought, till Emerson cut the cable and gave us a chance at the dangers and the glories of blue water. No man young enough to have felt it can forget, or cease to be grateful for, the mental and moral *nudge* which he received from the writings of his high-minded and brave-spirited countryman. That we agree with him, or that he always agrees with himself, is aside from the question ; but that he arouses in us something that we are the better for having awakened, whether that something be of opposition or assent, that he speaks always to what is highest and least selfish in us, few Americans of the generation younger than his own would be disposed to deny. His oration before the Phi Beta Kappa Society at Cambridge, some thirty years ago, was an event without any former parallel in our literary annals, a scene to be always treasured in the memory for its picturesqueness and its inspiration. What crowded and breathless aisles, what windows clustering with eager heads, what enthusiasm of approval, what grim silence of foregone dissent! It was our Yankee version of a lecture by Abelard, our Harvard parallel to the last public appearances of Schelling.

We said that the Transcendental Movement was the protestant spirit of Puritanism seeking a new outlet and an escape from forms and creeds which compressed rather than expressed it. In its motives, its preaching, and its results, it differed radically from the doctrine of Carlyle. The Scotchman, with all his genius, and his humor gigantesque as that of Rabelais, has grown shriller and shriller with years, degenerating sometimes into a common scold, and emptying very unsavory vials of wrath on the head of the sturdy British Socrates of worldly common-sense. The teaching of Emerson tended much more exclusively to self-culture and the independent development of the individual man. It seemed to many almost Pythagorean in its voluntary seclusion from commonwealth affairs. Both Carlyle and Emerson were disciples of Goethe, but Emerson in a far truer sense; and while the one, from his bias toward the eccentric, has degenerated more and more into mannerism, the other has clarified steadily toward perfection of style, — exquisite fineness of material, unobtrusive lowness of tone and simplicity of fashion, the most high-bred garb of expression. Whatever may be said of his thought, nothing can be finer than the delicious limpidness of his phrase. If it was ever questionable whether democracy could develop a gentleman, the problem has been affirmatively solved at last. Carlyle, in his cynicism and his admiration of force in and for itself, has become at last positively inhuman; Emerson, reverencing strength, seeking the highest outcome of the individual, has found that society and politics are also main elements in the attainment of the desired end, and has drawn steadily manward and worldward. The two men represent respectively those grand personifications in the drama of Æschylus, Βία and Κράτος.

Among the pistillate plants kindled to fruitage by the Emersonian pollen, Thoreau is thus far the most remarkable; and it is something eminently fitting that his posthumous works should be offered us by Emerson, for they are strawberries from his own garden. A singular mixture of varieties, indeed, there is; — alpine, some of them, with the flavor of rare mountain air; others wood, tasting of sunny roadside banks or shy openings in the forest; and not a few seedlings swollen hugely by culture, but lacking the fine natural aroma of the more modest kinds. Strange books these are of his, and interesting in many ways, — instructive chiefly as showing how considerable a crop may be raised on a comparatively narrow close of mind, and how much a man may make of his life if he will assiduously follow it, though perhaps never truly finding it at last.

We have just been renewing our recollection of Mr. Thoreau's writings, and have read through his six volumes in the order of their production. We shall try to give an adequate report of their impression upon us both as critic and as mere reader. He seems to us to have been a man with so high a conceit of himself that he accepted without questioning, and insisted on our accepting, his defects and weaknesses of character as virtues and powers peculiar to himself. Was he indolent, he finds none of the activities which attract or employ the rest of mankind worthy of him. Was he wanting in the qualities that make success, it is success that is contemptible, and not himself that lacks persistency and purpose. Was he poor, money was an unmixed evil. Did his life seem a selfish one, he condemns doing good as one of the weakest of superstitions. To be of use was with him the most killing bait of the wily

tempter Uselessness. He had no faculty of generalization from outside of himself, or at least no experience
which would supply the material of such, and he makes
his own whim the law, his own range the horizon of the
universe. He condemns a world, the hollowness of
whose satisfactions he had never had the means of testing, and we recognize Apemantus behind the mask of
Timon. He had little active imagination; of the receptive he had much. His appreciation is of the highest
quality; his critical power, from want of continuity of
mind, very limited and inadequate. He somewhere cites
a simile from Ossian, as an example of the superiority
of the old poetry to the new, though, even were the
historic evidence less convincing, the sentimental melancholy of those poems should be conclusive of their mod-
ernness. He had no artistic power such as controls a
great work to the serene balance of completeness, but
exquisite mechanical skill in the shaping of sentences
and paragraphs, or (more rarely) short bits of verse for
the expression of a detached thought, sentiment, or
image. His works give one the feeling of a sky full of
stars, — something impressive and exhilarating certainly,
something high overhead and freckled thickly with spots
of isolated brightness; but whether these have any
mutual relation with each other, or have any concern
with our mundane matters, is for the most part matter
of conjecture, — astrology as yet, and not astronomy.

It is curious, considering what Thoreau afterwards
became, that he was not by nature an observer. He
only saw the things he looked for, and was less poet
than naturalist. Till he built his Walden shanty, he
did not know that the hickory grew in Concord. Till
he went to Maine, he had never seen phosphorescent
wood, a phenomenon early familiar to most country
boys. At forty he speaks of the seeding of the pine as

a new discovery, though one should have thought that its gold-dust of blowing pollen might have earlier drawn his eye. Neither his attention nor his genius was of the spontaneous kind. He discovered nothing. He thought everything a discovery of his own, from moonlight to the planting of acorns and nuts by squirrels. This is a defect in his character, but one of his chief charms as a writer. Everything grows fresh under his hand. He delved in his mind and nature ; he planted them with all manner of native and foreign seeds, and reaped assiduously. He was not merely solitary, he would be isolated, and succeeded at last in almost persuading himself that he was autochthonous. He valued everything in proportion as he fancied it to be exclusively his own. He complains in "Walden," that there is no one in Concord with whom he could talk of Oriental literature, though the man was living within two miles of his hut who had introduced him to it. This intellectual selfishness becomes sometimes almost painful in reading him. He lacked that generosity of "communication" which Johnson admired in Burke. De Quincey tells us that Wordsworth was impatient when any one else spoke of mountains, as if he had a peculiar property in them. And we can readily understand why it should be so : no one is satisfied with another's appreciation of his mistress. But Thoreau seems to have prized a lofty way of thinking (often we should be inclined to call it a remote one) not so much because it was good in itself as because he wished few to share it with him. It seems now and then as if he did not seek to lure others up "above our lower region of turmoil," but to leave his own name cut on the mountain peak as the first climber. This itch of originality infects his thought and style. To be misty is not to be mystic. He turns commonplaces end for end, and fancies it makes something new

9 *

of them. As we walk down Park Street, our eye is caught by Dr. Windship's dumb-bells, one of which bears an inscription testifying that it is the heaviest ever put up at arm's length by any athlete; and in reading Mr. Thoreau's books we cannot help feeling as if he sometimes invited our attention to a particular sophism or paradox as the biggest yet maintained by any single writer. He seeks, at all risks, for perversity of thought, and revives the age of *concetti* while he fancies himself going back to a pre-classical nature. "A day," he says, "passed in the society of those Greek sages, such as described in the Banquet of Xenophon, would not be comparable with the dry wit of decayed cranberry-vines and the fresh Attic salt of the moss-beds." It is not so much the True that he loves as the Out-of-the-Way. As the Brazen Age shows itself in other men by exaggeration of phrase, so in him by extravagance of statement. He wishes always to trump your suit and to *ruff* when you least expect it. Do you love Nature because she is beautiful? He will find a better argument in her ugliness. Are you tired of the artificial man? He instantly dresses you up an ideal in a Penobscot Indian, and attributes to this creature of his otherwise-mindedness as peculiarities things that are common to all woodsmen, white or red, and this simply because he has not studied the pale-faced variety.

This notion of an absolute originality, as if one could have a patent-right in it, is an absurdity. A man cannot escape in thought, any more than he can in language, from the past and the present. As no one ever invents a word, and yet language somehow grows by general contribution and necessity, so it is with thought. Mr. Thoreau seems to us to insist in public on going back to flint and steel, when there is a match-box in his pocket which he knows very well how to use at a pinch. Originality consists in power of digesting and assimilating thought, so that they become part of our life and substance. Montaigne, for example, is one of the most original of authors, though he helped himself to ideas in every direction. But they turn to blood and coloring in his style, and give a freshness of complexion that is forever charming. In Thoreau much seems yet to be foreign and unassimilated, showing itself in symptoms of indigestion. A preacher-up of Nature, we now and then detect under the surly and stoic garb something of the sophist and the sentimentalizer. We are far from implying that this was conscious on his part. But it is much easier for a man to impose on himself when he measures only with himself. A greater familiarity with ordinary men would have done Thoreau good, by showing him how many fine qualities are common to the race. The radical vice of his theory of life was, that he confounded physical with spiritual remoteness from men. One is far enough withdrawn from his fellows if he keep himself clear of their weaknesses. He is not so truly withdrawn as exiled, if he refuse to share in their strength. "Solitude," says Cowley, "can be well fitted and set right but upon a very few persons. They must have enough knowledge of the world to see the vanity of it, and enough virtue to despise all vanity." It is a morbid self-consciousness that pronounces the world of men empty and worthless before trying it, the instinctive evasion of one who is sensible of some innate weakness, and retorts the accusation of it before any has made it but himself. To a healthy mind, the world is a constant challenge of opportunity. Mr. Thoreau had not a healthy mind, or he would not have been so fond of prescribing. His whole life was a search for the doctor. The old mystics had a wiser sense of what the world was worth. They or-

dained a severe apprenticeship to law, and even ceremonial, in order to the gaining of freedom and mastery over
these. Seven years of service for Rachel were to be
rewarded at last with Leah. Seven other years of faith-
fulness with her were to win them at last the true bride
of their souls. Active Life was with them the only path
to the Contemplative.

Thoreau had no humor, and this implies that he was
a sorry logician. Himself an artist in rhetoric, he confounds thought with style when he undertakes to speak
of the latter. He was forever talking of getting away
from the world, but he must be always near enough to
it, nay, to the Concord corner of it, to feel the impression he makes there. He verifies the shrewd remark of
Sainte-Beuve, "On touche encore à son temps et très-
fort, même quand on le repousse." This egotism of his
is a Stylites pillar after all, a seclusion which keeps him
in the public eye. The dignity of man is an excellent
thing, but therefore to hold one's self too sacred and
precious is the reverse of excellent. There is something
delightfully absurd in six volumes addressed to a world
of such "vulgar fellows" as Thoreau affirmed his fellow-
men to be. We once had a glimpse of a genuine solitary
who spent his winters one hundred and fifty miles beyond all human communication, and there dwelt with
his rifle as his only confidant. Compared with this, the
shanty on Walden Pond has something the air, it must
be confessed, of the Hermitage of La Chevrette. We do
not believe that the way to a true cosmopolitanism
carries one into the woods or the society of musquashes.
Perhaps the narrowest provincialism is that of Self ; that
of Kleinwinkel is nothing to it. The natural man, like
the singing birds, comes out of the forest as inevitably
as the natural bear and the wildcat stick there. To seek
to be natural implies a consciousness that forbids all

naturalness forever. It is as easy — and no easier — to be natural in a *salon* as in a swamp, if one do not aim at it, for what we call unnaturalness always has its spring in a man's thinking too much about himself. " It is impossible," said Turgot, " for a vulgar man to be simple."

We look upon a great deal of the modern sentimentalism about Nature as a mark of disease. It is one more symptom of the general liver-complaint. To a man of wholesome constitution the wilderness is well enough for a mood or a vacation, but not for a habit of life. Those who have most loudly advertised their passion for seclusion and their intimacy with nature, from Petrarch down, have been mostly sentimentalists, unreal men, misanthropes on the spindle side, solacing an uneasy suspicion of themselves by professing contempt for their kind. They make demands on the world in advance proportioned to their inward measure of their own merit, and are angry that the world pays only by the visible measure of performance. It is true of Rousseau, the modern founder of the sect, true of Saint Pierre, his intellectual child, and of Châteaubriand, his grandchild, the inventor, we might almost say, of the primitive forest, and who first was touched by the solemn falling of a tree from natural decay in the windless silence of the woods. It is a very shallow view that affirms trees and rocks to be healthy, and cannot see that men in communities are just as true to the laws of their organization and destiny; that can tolerate the puffin and the fox, but not the fool and the knave ; that would shun politics because of its demagogues, and snuff up the stench of the obscene fungus. The divine life of Nature is more wonderful, more various, more sublime in man than in any other of her works, and the wisdom that is gained by commerce with men, as Montaigne and Shakespeare gained it, or with one's own soul among men, as Dante, is the most delightful, as it is the most precious, of all. In outward nature it is still man that interests us, and we care far less for the things seen than the way in which poetic eyes like Wordsworth's or Thoreau's see them, and the reflections they cast there. To hear the to-do that is often made over the simple fact that a man sees the image of himself in the outward world, one is reminded of a savage when he for the first time catches a glimpse of himself in a looking-glass. " Venerable child of Nature," we are tempted to say, " to whose science in the invention of the tobacco-pipe, to whose art in the tattooing of thine undegenerate hide not yet enslaved by tailors, we are slowly striving to climb back, the miracle thou beholdest is sold in my unhappy country for a shilling ! " If matters go on as they have done, and everybody must needs blab of all the favors that have been done him by roadside and river-brink and woodland walk, as if to kiss and tell were no longer treachery, it will be a positive refreshment to meet a man who is as superbly indifferent to Nature as she is to him. By and by we shall have John Smith, of No. –12 –12th Street, advertising that he is not the J. S. who saw a cow-lily on Thursday last, as he never saw one in his life, would not see one if he could, and is prepared to prove an alibi on the day in question.

Solitary communion with Nature does not seem to have been sanitary or sweetening in its influence on Thoreau's character. On the contrary, his letters show him more cynical as he grew older. While he studied with respectful attention the minks and woodchucks, his neighbors, he looked with utter contempt on the august drama of destiny of which his country was the scene, and on which the curtain had already risen. He

was converting us back to a state of nature "so eloquently," as Voltaire said of Rousseau, "that he almost
persuaded us to go on all fours," while the wiser fates
were making it possible for us to walk erect for the first
time. Had he conversed more with his fellows, his
sympathies would have widened with the assurance that
his peculiar genius had more appreciation, and his writings a larger circle of readers, or at least a warmer one,
than he dreamed of. We have the highest testimony *
to the natural sweetness, sincerity, and nobleness of his
temper, and in his books an equally irrefragable one to
the rare quality of his mind. He was not a strong
thinker, but a sensitive feeler. Yet his mind strikes us
as cold and wintry in its purity. A light snow has
fallen everywhere in which he seems to come on the
track of the shier sensations that would elsewhere leave
no trace. We think greater compression would have done
more for his fame. A feeling of sameness comes over us
as we read so much. Trifles are recorded with an over-
minute punctuality and conscientiousness of detail. He
records the state of his personal thermometer thirteen
times a day. We cannot help thinking sometimes of the
man who

> " Watches, starves, freezes, and sweats
> To learn but catechisms and alphabets
> Of unconcerning things, matters of fact,"

and sometimes of the saying of the Persian poet, that
" when the owl would boast, he boasts of catching mice
at the edge of a hole." We could readily part with
some of his affectations. It was well enough for Py-
thagoras to say, once for all, "When I was Euphorbus
at the siege of Troy"; not so well for Thoreau to travesty it into " When I was a shepherd on the plains of

* Mr. Emerson, in the Biographical Sketch prefixed to the " Excur-
sions."

Assyria." A naive thing said over again is anything but naive. But with every exception, there is no writing comparable with Thoreau's in kind, that is comparable with it in degree where it is best; where it disengages itself, that is, from the tangled roots and dead leaves of a second-hand Orientalism, and runs limpid and smooth and broadening as it runs, a mirror for whatever is grand and lovely in both worlds.

George Sand says neatly, that "Art is not a study of positive reality," (*actuality* were the fitter word,) "but a seeking after ideal truth." It would be doing very inadequate justice to Thoreau if we left it to be inferred that this ideal element did not exist in him, and that too in larger proportion, if less obtrusive, than his nature-worship. He took nature as the mountain-path to an ideal world. If the path wind a good deal, if he record too faithfully every trip over a root, if he botanize somewhat wearisomely, he gives us now and then superb outlooks from some jutting crag, and brings us out at last into an illimitable ether, where the breathing is not difficult for those who have any true touch of the climbing spirit. His shanty-life was a mere impossibility, so far as his own conception of it goes, as an entire independency of mankind. The tub of Diogenes had a sounder bottom. Thoreau's experiment actually presupposed all that complicated civilization which it theoretically abjured. He squatted on another man's land; he borrows an axe; his boards, his nails, his bricks, his mortar, his books, his lamp, his fish-hooks, his plough, his hoe, all turn state's evidence against him as an accomplice in the sin of that artificial civilization which rendered it possible that such a person as Henry D. Thoreau should exist at all. *Magnis tamen excidit ausis.* His aim was a noble and a useful one, in the direction of "plain living and high thinking." It was a practical sermon on Emerson's text that "things

are in the saddle and ride mankind," an attempt to
solve Carlyle's problem (condensed from Johnson) of
"lessening your denominator." His whole life was a
rebuke of the waste and aimlessness of our American
luxury, which is an abject enslavement to tawdry upholstery. He had "fine translunary things" in him.
His better style as a writer is in keeping with the
simplicity and purity of his life. We have said that
his range was narrow, but to be a master is to be a master. ¹He had caught his English at its living source,
among the poets and prose-writers of its best days ; his
literature was extensive and recondite ; his quotations
are always nuggets of the purest ore : there are sentences
of his as perfect as anything in the language, and thoughts
as clearly crystallized ; his metaphors and images are always fresh from the soil ; he had watched Nature like a
detective who is to go upon the stand ; as we read him,
it seems as if all-out-of-doors had kept a diary and become its own Montaigne ; we look at the landscape as in
a Claude Lorraine glass ; compared with his, all other
books of similar aim, even White's "Selborne," seem dry
as a country clergyman's meteorological journal in an old
almanac. He belongs with Donne and Browne and No-
valis ; if not with the originally creative men, with the
scarcely smaller class who are peculiar, and whose leaves
shed their invisible thought-seed like ferns.

SWINBURNE'S TRAGEDIES.

A RE we really, then, to believe the newspapers for
once, and to doff our critical nightcaps, in which
we have comfortably overslept many similar rumors and
false alarms, to welcome the advent of a new poet? New
poets, to our thinking, are not very common, and the
soft columns of the press often make dangerous concessions, for which the marble ones of Horace's day were
too stony-hearted. Indeed, we have some well-grounded
doubts whether England is precisely the country from
which we have a right to expect that most precious of
gifts just now. There is hardly enough fervor of political
life there at present to ripen anything but the fruits of
the literary forcing-house, so fair outwardly and so flavor-
less compared with those which grow in the hardier open
air of a vigorous popular sentiment. Mere wealth of
natural endowment is not enough ; there must be also
the co-operation of the time, of the public genius roused
to a consciousness of itself by the necessity of 'asserting
or defending the vital principle on which that consciousness rests, in order that a poet may rise to the highest
level of his vocation. The great names of the last generation — Scott, Wordsworth, Byron — represent moods
of national thought and feeling, and are therefore more
or less truly British poets ; just as Goethe, in whose ca-
pacious nature, open to every influence of earth and sky,
the spiritual fermentation of the eighteenth century settled and clarified, is a European one. A sceptic might

say, we think, with some justice, that poetry in England
was passing now, if it have not already passed, into one
of those periods of mere art without any intense convictions to back it, which lead inevitably, and by no long
gradation, to the mannered and artificial.   Browning, by
far the richest nature of the time, becomes more difficult,
draws nearer to the all-for-point fashion of the *concettisti*,
with every poem he writes ; the dainty trick of Tennyson cloys when caught by a whole generation of versifiers, as the *style* of a great poet never can be ; and we
have a foreboding that Clough, imperfect as he was in
many respects, and dying before he had subdued his sensitive temperament to the sterner requirements of his
art, will be thought a hundred years hence to have been
the truest expression in verse of the moral and intellectual tendencies, the doubt and struggle towards settled
convictions, of the period in which he lived.   To make
beautiful conceptions immortal by exquisiteness of phrase,
is to be a poet, no doubt ; but to be a new poet is to feel
and to utter that immanent life of things without which
the utmost perfection of mere form is at best only wax
or marble.   He who can do both is the great poet.

Over " Chastelard, a Tragedy," we need not spend
much time.   It is at best but the school exercise of a
young poet learning to write, and who reproduces in his
copy-book, more or less travestied, the copy that has been
set for him at the page's head by the authors he most
admires.   Grace and even force of expression are not
wanting, but there is the obscurity which springs from
want of definite intention ; the characters are vaguely
outlined from memory, not drawn firmly from the living
and the nude in actual experience of life ; the working
of passion is an *a priori* abstraction from a scheme in the
author's mind ; and there is no thought, but only a vehement grasping after thought.   The hand is the hand

of Swinburne, but the voice is the voice of Browning. With here and there a pure strain of sentiment, a genuine touch of nature, the effect of the whole is unpleasant with the faults of the worst school of modern poetry, — the physically intense school, as we should be inclined to call it, of which Mrs. Browning's " Aurora Leigh " is the worst example, whose muse is a *fast* young woman with the lavish ornament and somewhat overpowering perfume of the *demi-monde,* and which pushes expression to the last gasp of sensuous exhaustion.   They forget that convulsion is not energy, and that words, to hold fire, must first catch it from vehement heat of thought, while no artificial fervors of phrase can make the charm work backward to kindle the mind of writer or reader.   An overmastering passion no longer entangles the spiritual being of its victim in the burning toils of a retribution foredoomed in its own nature, purifying us with the terror and pity of a soul in its extremity, as the great masters were wont to set it before us ; no, it must be fleshly, corporeal, must " bite with small white teeth " and draw blood, to satisfy the craving of our modern inquisitors, who torture language instead of wooing it to confess the secret of its witchcraft.   That books written on this theory should be popular, is one of the worst signs of the times ; that they should be praised by the censors of literature shows how seldom criticism goes back to first principles, or is even aware of them, — how utterly it has forgotten its most earnest function of demolishing the high places where the unclean rites of Baal and Ashtaroth usurp on the worship of the one only True and Pure.

"Atalanta in Calydon" is in every respect better than its forerunner.   It is a true poem, and seldom breaks from the maidenly reserve which should characterize the higher forms of poetry, even in the keenest energy of expression.   If the blank verse be a little mannered and

stiff, reminding one of Landor in his attempts to reproduce the antique, the lyrical parts are lyrical in the
highest sense, graceful, flowing, and generally simple in
sentiment and phrase.   There are some touches of nature
in the mother's memories of Althea, so sweetly pathetic
that they go as right to the heart as they came from it,
and are neither Greek nor English, but broadly human.
And yet, when we had read the book through, we felt as
if we were leaving a world of shadows, inhabited by less
substantial things than that nether realm of Homer
where the very eidolon of Achilles is still real to us in its
longings and regrets.   These are not characters, but outlines after the Elgin marbles in the thinnest manner of
Flaxman.   There is not so much blood in the whole of
them as would warm the little finger of one of Shakespeare's living and breathing conceptions.   We could
not help thinking of those exquisite verses addressed by
Schiller to Goethe, in which, while he expresses a half-
truth so eloquently as almost to make it seem a whole
one, he touches unconsciously the weak point of their
common striving after a Grecian instead of a purely human ideal.

> " Doch leicht gezimmert nur ist Thespis Wagen,
> Und er ist gleich dem acheront'schen Kahn;
> Nur Schatten und Idole kann er tragen,
> Und drängt das rohe Leben sich heran,
> So droht das leichte Fahrzeug umzuschlagen
> Das nur die flücht'gen Geister fassen kann;
> Der Schein soll nie die Wirklichkeit erreichen
> Und siegt Natur, so muss die Kunst entweichen."

The actors in the drama are unreal and shadowy, the
motives which actuate them alien to our modern modes
of thought and conceptions of character.   To a Greek,
the element of Fate, with which his imagination was
familiar, while it heightened the terror of the catastrophe,
would have supplied the place of that impulse in mere

human nature which our habit of mind demands for its satisfaction. The fulfilment of an oracle, the anger of a deity, the arbitrary doom of some blind and purposeless power superior to man, the avenging of blood to appease an injured ghost, any one of these might make that seem simply natural to a contemporary of Sophocles which is intelligible to us only by study and reflection. It is not a little curious that Shakespeare should have made the last of the motives we have just mentioned, and which was conclusive for Orestes, insufficient for Hamlet, who so perfectly typifies the introversion and complexity of modern thought as compared with ancient, in dealing with the problems of life and action. It was not perhaps without intention (for who may venture to assume a want of intention in the world's highest poetic genius at its full maturity?) that Shakespeare brings in his hero fresh from the University of Wittenberg, where Luther, who entailed upon us the responsibility of private judgment, had been Professor. The dramatic motive in the "Electra" and "Hamlet" is essentially the same, but what a difference between the straightforward bloody-mindedness of Orestes and the metaphysical punctiliousness of the Dane! Yet each was natural in his several way, and each would have been unintelligible to the audience for which the other was intended. That Fate which the Greeks made to operate from without, we recognize at work within in some vice of character or hereditary predisposition. Hawthorne, the most profoundly ideal genius of these latter days, was continually returning, more or less directly, to this theme; and his "Marble Faun," whether consciously or not, illustrates that invasion of the æsthetic by the moral which has confused art by dividing its allegiance, and dethroned the old dynasty without as yet firmly establishing the new in an acknowledged legitimacy.

"Atalanta in Calydon" shows that poverty of thought and profusion of imagery which are at once the defect and the compensation of all youthful poetry, even of Shakespeare's. It seems a paradox to say that there can be too much poetry in a poem, and yet this is a fault with which all poets begin, and which some never get over. But "Atalanta" is hopefully distinguished, in a rather remarkable way, from most early attempts, by a sense of form and proportion, which, if seconded by a seasonable ripening of other faculties, as we may fairly expect, gives promise of rare achievement hereafter. Mr. Swinburne's power of assimilating style, which is, perhaps, not so auspicious a symptom, strikes us as something marvellous. The argument of his poem, in its quaint archaism, would not need the change of a word or in the order of a period to have been foisted on Sir Thomas Malory as his own composition. The choosing a theme which Æschylus had handled in one of his lost tragedies is justified by a certain Æschylean flavor in the treatment. The opening, without deserving to be called a mere imitation, recalls that of the "Agamemnon," and the chorus has often an imaginative lift in it, an ethereal charm of phrase, of which it is the highest praise to say that it reminds us of him who soars over the other Greek tragedians like an eagle.

But in spite of many merits, we cannot help asking ourselves, as we close the book, whether "Atalanta" can be called a success, and if so, whether it be a success in the right direction. The poem reopens a question which in some sort touches the very life of modern literature. We do not mean to renew the old quarrel of Fontenelle's day as to the comparative merits of ancients and moderns. That is an affair of taste, which does not admit of any authoritative settlement. Our concern is about a principle which certainly demands a fuller discussion, and which is important enough to deserve it. Do we show our appreciation of the Greeks most wisely in attempting the mechanical reproduction of their forms, or by endeavoring to comprehend the thoughtful spirit of full-grown manhood in which they wrought, to kindle ourselves by the emulation of it, and to bring it to bear with all its plastic force upon our wholly new conditions of life and thought? It seems to us that the question is answered by the fact, patent in the history of all the fine arts, that every attempt at reproducing a bygone excellence by external imitation of it, or even by applying the rules which analytic criticism has formulated from the study of it, has resulted in producing the artificial, and not the artistic. That most subtile of all essences in physical organization, which eludes chemist, anatomist, and microscopist, the life, is in æsthetics not less shy of the critic, and will not come forth in obedience to his most learned spells, for the very good reason that it cannot, because in all works of art it is the joint product of the artist and of the time. Faust may believe he is gazing on "the face that launched a thousand ships," but Mephistopheles knows very well that it is only shadows that he has the skill to conjure. He is not merely the spirit that ever denies, but the spirit also of discontent with the present, that material in which every man shall work who will achieve realities and not their hollow semblance. The true anachronism, in our opinion, is not in Shakespeare's making Ulysses talk as Lord Bacon might, but in attempting to make him speak in a dialect of thought utterly dead to all present comprehension. Ulysses was the type of long-headedness; and the statecraft of an Ithacan cateran would have seemed as childish to the age of Elizabeth and Burleigh as it was naturally sufficing to the first hearers of Homer. Ulysses, living in Florence during the fifteenth century, might have been Macchiavelli; in France, during the seventeenth, Cardinal Richelieu; in America, during the nineteenth, Abraham Lincoln, but not Ulysses. Truth to nature can be reached ideally, never historically; it must be a study from the life, and not from the scholiasts. Theocritus lets us into the secret of his good poetry, when he makes Daphnis tell us that he preferred his rock with a view of the Siculian Sea to the kingdom of Pelops.

It is one of the marvels of the human mind, this sorcery which the fiend of technical imitation weaves about his victims, giving a phantasmal Helen to their arms, and making an image of the brain seem substance. Men still pain themselves to write Latin verses, matching their wooden bits of phrase together as children do dissected maps, and measuring the value of what they have done, not by any standard of intrinsic merit, but by the difficulty of doing it. Petrarch expected to be known to posterity by his Africa. Gray hoped to make a Latin poem his monument. Goethe, who was classic in the only way it is now possible to be classic, in his "Hermann and Dorothea," and at least Propertian in his "Roman Idyls," wasted his time and thwarted his creative energy on the mechanical mock-antique of an unreadable "Achilleis." Landor prized his waxen "Gebirus Rex" above all the natural fruits of his mind; and we have no doubt that, if some philosopher should succeed in accomplishing Paracelsus's problem of an artificial *homunculus*, he would dote on this misbegotten babe of his science, and think him the only genius of the family. We cannot over-estimate the value of some of the ancient classics, but a certain amount of superstition about Greek and Latin has come down to us from the revival of learning, and seems to hold in mortmain the intellects of whoever has, at some time, got a smattering

10

of them. Men quote a platitude in either of those tongues with a relish of conviction as droll to the uninitiated as the knighthood of free-masonry. Horace Walpole's nephew, the Earl of Orford, when he was in his cups, used to have Statius read aloud to him every night for two hours by a tipsy tradesman, whose hiccupings threw in here and there a kind of cæsural pause, and found some strange mystery of sweetness in the disquantitied syllables. So powerful is this hallucination that we can conceive of *festina lente* as the favorite maxim of a Mississippi steamboat captain, and ἄριστον μὲν ὕδωρ cited as conclusive by a gentleman for whom the bottle before him reversed the wonder of the stereoscope, and substituted the Gascon *v* for the *b* in binocular.

Something of this singular superstition has infected the minds of those who confound the laws of conventional limitation which governed the practice of Greek authors in dramatic composition — laws adapted to the habits and traditions and preconceptions of their audience — with that sense of ideal form which made the Greeks masters in art to all succeeding generations. Aristophanes is beyond question the highest type of pure comedy, etherealizing his humor by the infusion, or intensifying it by the contrast of poetry, and deodorizing the personality of his sarcasm by a sprinkle from the clearest springs of fancy. His satire, aimed as it was at typical characteristics, is as fresh as ever; but we doubt whether an Aristophanic drama, retaining its exact form, but adapted to present events and personages, would keep the stage as it is kept by "The Rivals," for example, immeasurably inferior as that is in every element of genius except the prime one of liveliness. Something similar in purpose to the parabasis was essayed in one, at least, of the comedies of Beaumont and Fletcher, and in our time by Tieck; but it took, of necessity, a differ

ent form of expression, and does not seem to have been
successful. Indeed, the fact that what is called the
legitimate drama of modern times in England, Spain,
and France has been strictly a growth, and not a manufacture, that in each country it took a different form,
and that, in all, the period of its culminating and beginning to decline might be measured by a generation,
seems to point us toward some natural and inevitable
law of human nature, and to show that, while the principles of art are immutable, their application must accommodate itself to the material supplied them by the
time and by the national character and traditions. The
Spanish tragedy inclines more toward the lyrical, the
French toward the epical, the English toward the historical, in the representation of real life ; the Spanish and
English agree in the Teutonic peculiarity of admitting
the humorous offset of the clown, though in the one
case he parodies the leading motive of the drama, and
represents the self-consciousness of the dramatist, while
in the other he heightens the tragic effect by contrast,
(as in the grave-digging scene of Hamlet,) and suggests
that stolid but wholesome indifference of the general
life — of what, for want of a better term, we call Nature
— to the sin and suffering, the weakness and misfortunes
of the individual man. All these nations had the same
ancient examples before them, had the same reverence
for antiquity, yet they involuntarily deviated, more or
less happily, into originality, success, and the freedom
of a living creativeness. The higher kinds of literature,
the only kinds that live on because they had life at the
start, are not, then, it should seem, the fabric of scholarship, of criticism, diligently studying and as diligently
copying the best models, but are much rather born of
some genetic principle in the character of the people and
the age which produce them. One drop of ruddy human

blood puts more life into the veins of a poem, than all the delusive *aurum potabile* that can be distilled out of the choicest library.

The opera is the closest approach we have to the ancient drama in the essentials of structure and presentation; and could we have a *libretto* founded on a national legend and written by one man of genius to be filled out and accompanied by the music of another, we might hope for something of the same effect upon the stage. But themes of universal familiarity and interest are rare, — Don Giovanni and Faust, perhaps, most nearly, though not entirely, fulfilling the required conditions, — and men of genius rarer. The oratorio seeks to evade the difficulty by choosing Scriptural subjects, and it may certainly be questioned whether the day of popular mythology, in the sense in which it subserves the purposes of epic or dramatic poetry, be not gone by forever. Longfellow is driven to take refuge among the red men, and Tennyson in the Cambro-Breton cyclus of Arthur; but it is impossible that such themes should come so intimately home to us as the semi-fabulous stories of their own ancestors did to the Greeks. The most successful attempt at reproducing the Greek tragedy, both in theme and treatment, is the "Samson Agonistes," as it is also the most masterly piece of English versification. Goethe admits that it alone, among modern works, has caught life from the breath of the antique spirit. But he failed to see, or at least to give, the reason of it; probably failed to see it, or he would never have attempted the "Iphigenia." Milton not only subjected himself to the structural requirements of the Attic tragedy, but with a true poetic instinct availed himself of the striking advantage it had in the choice of a subject. No popular tradition lay near enough to him for his purpose; none united in itself the essential requisites of human interest and universal belief. He accordingly chose a Jewish mythus, very near to his own heart as a blind prisoner, betrayed by his wife, among the Philistines of the Restoration, and familiar to the earliest associations of his hearers. This subject, and this alone, met all the demands both of living poetic production and of antique form, — the action grandly simple, the personages few, the protagonist at once a victim of divine judgment and an executor of divine retribution, an intense personal sympathy in the poet himself, and no strangeness to the habitual prepossessions of those he addressed to be overcome before he could touch their hearts or be sure of aid from their imaginations. To compose such a drama on such a theme was to *be* Greek, and not to counterfeit it ; for Samson was to Milton traditionally just what Herakles was to Sophocles, and personally far more. The "Agonistes" is still fresh and strong as morning, but where are "Caractacus" and "Elfrida"? Nay, where is the far better work of a far abler man, — where is "Merope"? If the frame of mind which performs a deliberate experiment were the same as that which produces poetry vitalized through and through by the conspiring ardors of every nobler passion and power of the soul, then "Merope" might have had some little space of life. But without color, without harmonious rhythm of movement, with less passion than survived in an average Grecian ghost, and all this from the very theory of her creation, she has gone back, a shadow, to join her shadowy Italian and French namesakes in that limbo of things that would be and cannot be. Mr. Arnold but retraces, in his Preface to "Merope," the arguments of Mason in the letters prefixed to his classical experiments. What finds defenders, but not readers, may be correct, classic, right in principle, but it is not

poetry of that absolute kind which may and does help
men, but needs no help of theirs; and such surely we
have a right to demand in tragedy, if nowhere else.   We
should not speak so unreservedly if we did not set a
high value on Mr. Arnold and his poetic gift.   But
" Merope " has that one fault against which the very
gods, we are told, strive in vain.   It is dull, and the
seed of this dulness lay in the system on which it was
written.

Pseudo-classicism takes two forms.   Sometimes, as
Mr. Landor has done, it attempts truth of detail to
ancient scenery and manners, which may be attained
either by hard reading and good memory, or at a cheaper
rate from such authors as Becker.   The " Moretum,"
once attributed to Virgil, and the idyl of Theocritus
lately chosen as a text by Mr. Arnold, are interesting,
because they describe real things; but the mock-antique,
if not true, is nothing, and how true such poems are
likely to be we can judge by "Punch's" success at
Yankeeisms, by all England's accurate appreciation of
the manners and minds of a contemporary people one
with herself in language, laws, religion, and literature.
The eye is the only note-book of the true poet; but a
patchwork of second-hand memories is a laborious futility, hard to write and harder to read, with about as much
nature in it as a dialogue of the Deipnosophists.   Alexander's bushel of peas was a criticism worthy of Aristotle's
pupil.   We should reward such writing with the gift of
a classical dictionary.   In this idyllic kind of poetry
also we have a classic, because Goldsmith went to nature
for his " Deserted Village," and borrowed of tradition
nothing but the poetic diction in which he described it.
This is the only method by which a poet may surely
reckon on ever becoming an ancient himself.   When we
heard it said once that a certain poem might have been

written by Simonides, we could not help thinking that, if it were so, then it was precisely what Simonides could never have written, since he looked at the world through his own eyes, not through those of Linus or Hesiod, and thought his own thoughts, not theirs, or we should never have had him to imitate.

Objections of the same nature, but even stronger, lie against a servile copying of the form and style of the Greek tragic drama, and yet more against the selection of a Greek theme. As we said before, the life we lead, and the views we take of it, are more complex than those of men who lived five centuries before Christ. They may be better or worse, but, at any rate, they are different, and irremediably so. The idea and the form in which it naturally embodies itself, mutually sustaining and invigorating each other, cannot be divided without endangering the lives of both. For in all real poetry the form is not a garment, but a body. Our very passion has become metaphysical, and speculates upon itself. Their simple and downright way of thinking loses all its savor when we assume it to ourselves by an effort of thought. Human nature, it is true, remains always the same, but the displays of it change; the habits which are a second nature modify it inwardly as well as outwardly, and what moves it to passionate action in one age may leave it indifferent in the next. Between us and the Greeks lies the grave of their murdered paganism, making our minds and theirs irreconcilable. Christianity as steadily intensifies the self-consciousness of man as the religion of the Greeks must have turned their thoughts away from themselves to the events of this life and the phenomena of nature. We cannot even conceive of their conception of Phoibos with any plausible assurance of coming near the truth. To take lesser matters, since the invention of printing and the cheapening of books have made the thought of all ages and nations the common property of educated men, we cannot so dis-saturate our minds of it as to be keenly thrilled in the modern imitation with those commonplaces of proverbial lore in which the chorus and secondary characters are apt to indulge, though in the original they may interest us as being natural and characteristic. In the German-silver of the modern we get something of this kind, which does not please us the more by being cut up into single lines that recall the outward semblance of some pages in Sophocles. We find it cheaper to make a specimen than to borrow one.

CHORUS. Foolish who bites off nose, his face to spite.
OUTIS. Who fears his fate, him Fate shall one day spurn.
CHORUS. The gods themselves are pliable to Fate.
OUTIS. The strong self-ruler dreads no other sway.
CHORUS. Sometimes the shortest way goes most about.
OUTIS. Why fetch a compass, having stars within?
CHORUS. A shepherd once, I know that stars may set.
OUTIS. That thou led'st sheep fits not for leading men.
CHORUS. To sleep-sealed eyes the wolf-dog barks in vain.

We protest that we have read something very like this, we will not say where, and we might call it the battle-door and shuttlecock style of dialogue, except that the players do not seem to have any manifest relation to each other, but each is intent on keeping his own bit of feathered cork continually in the air.

The first sincerely popular yearning toward antiquity, the first germ of Schiller's "Götter Griechenland's" is to be found in the old poem of Tanhäuser, very nearly coincident with the beginnings of the Reformation. And if we might allegorize it, we should say that it typified precisely that longing after Venus, under her other name of Charis, which represents the relation in which modern should stand to ancient art. It is the grace of the Greeks, their sense of proportion, their dis-

taste for the exaggerated, their exquisite propriety of
phrase, which steadies imagination without cramping it,
— it is these that we should endeavor to assimilate
without the loss of our own individuality. We should
quicken our sense of form by intelligent sympathy with
theirs, and not stiffen it into formalism by a servile surrender of what is genuine in us to what *was* genuine
in them. "A pure form," says Schiller, "helps and
sustains, an impure one hinders and shatters." But we
should remember that the spirit of the age must enter
as a modifying principle, not only into ideas, but into
the best manner of their expression. The old bottles
will not always serve for the new wine. A principle of
life is the first requirement of all art, and it can only be
communicated by the touch of the time and a simple
faith in it; all else is circumstantial and secondary.
The Greek tragedy passed through the three natural
stages of poetry, — the imaginative in Æschylus, the
thoughtfully artistic in Sophocles, the sentimental in
Euripides, — and then died. If people could only learn
the general applicability to periods and schools of what
young Mozart says of Gellert, that "he had written no
poetry *since* his death"! No effort to raise a defunct
past has ever led to anything but just enough galvanic
twitching of the limbs to remind us unpleasantly of life.
The romantic movement of the school of German poets
which succeeded Goethe and Schiller ended in extravagant unreality, and Goethe himself with his enerring
common-sense, has given us, in the second part of Faust,
the result of his own and Schiller's common striving
after a Grecian ideal. Euphorion, the child of Faust
and Helen, falls dead at their feet; and Helen herself
soon follows him to the shades, leaving only her mantle
in the hands of her lover. This, he is told, shall lift
him above the earth. We fancy we can interpret the

symbol. Whether we can or not, it is certainly suggestive of thought that the only immortal production of
the greatest of recent poets was conceived and carried
out in that Gothic spirit and form from which he was all
his life struggling to break loose.

CHAUCER.*

WILL it *do* to say anything more about Chaucer?
Can any one hope to say anything, not new, but
even fresh, on a topic so well worn? It may well be
doubted; and yet one is always the better for a walk in
the morning air, — a medicine which may be taken over
and over again without any sense of sameness, or any
failure of its invigorating quality. There is a pervading
wholesomeness in the writings of this man, — a vernal
property that soothes and refreshes in a way of which no
other has ever found the secret. I repeat to myself a
thousand times, —

> " Whan that Aprilë with his showrës sotë
> The droughte of March hath percëd to the rotë,
> And bathëd every veine in swich licour
> Of which vertue engendered is the flour, —
> When Zephyrus eek with his swetë breth
> Enspirëd hath in every holt and heth
> The tender croppës, and the yongë sonne
> Hath in the ram his halfë cors yronne,
> And smalë foulës maken melodië," —

and still at the thousandth time a breath of uncontami-

* *Publications of the Chaucer Society.* London. 1869–70.
Étude sur G. Chaucer considéré comme imitateur des Trouvères. Par
E. G. SANDRAS, Agrégé de l'Université. Paris: Auguste Dusand.
1859. 8vo. pp. 298.
*Geoffrey Chaucer's Canterbury-Geschichten, uebersetzt in den Vers-
massen der Urschrift, und durch Einleitung und Anmerkungen erläutert.*
Von WILHELM HERTZBERG. Hildburghausen. 1866. 12mo. pp. 674.
*Chaucer in Seinen Beziehungen zur italienischen Literatur. Inaugu-
ral-Dissertation zur Erlangung der Doctorwürde.* Von ALFONS KISS-
NER. Bonn. 1867. 8vo pp. 81.

nate springtide seems to lift the hair upon my forehead.
If here be not the *largior ether*, the serene and motionless
atmosphere of classical antiquity, we find at least the
seclusum nemus, the *domos placidas*, and the *oubliance*,
as Froissart so sweetly calls it, that persuade us we are
in an Elysium none the less sweet that it appeals to our
more purely human, one might almost say domestic, sympathies. We may say of Chaucer's muse, as Overbury of
his milkmaid, "her breath is her own, which scents all
the year long of *June* like a new-made haycock." The
most hardened *roué* of literature can scarce confront these
simple and winning graces without feeling somewhat of
the unworn sentiment of his youth revive in him. Modern imaginative literature has become so self-conscious,
and therefore so melancholy, that Art, which should be
"the world's sweet inn," whither we repair for refreshment and repose, has become rather a watering-place,
where one's own private touch of the liver-complaint is
exasperated by the affluence of other sufferers whose talk
is a narrative of morbid symptoms. Poets have forgotten that the first lesson of literature, no less than of life,
is the learning how to burn your own smoke; that the
way to be original is to be healthy; that the fresh color,
so delightful in all good writing, is won by escaping from
the fixed air of self into the brisk atmosphere of universal
sentiments; and that to make the common marvellous,
as if it were a revelation, is the test of genius. It is good
to retreat now and then beyond earshot of the introspec-
tive confidences of modern literature, and to lose ourselves in the gracious worldliness of Chaucer. Here was
a healthy and hearty man, so genuine that he need not
ask whether he were genuine or no, so sincere as quite to
forget his own sincerity, so truly pious that he could be
happy in the best world that God chose to make, so humane that he loved even the foibles of his kind. Here

was a truly epic poet, without knowing it, who did not waste time in considering whether his age were good or bad, but quietly taking it for granted as the best that ever was or could be for *him*, has left us such a picture of contemporary life as no man ever painted.   "A perpetual fountain of good-sense," Dryden calls him, yes, and of good-humor, too, and wholesome thought. He was one of those rare authors whom, if we had met him under a porch in a shower, we should have preferred to the rain. He could be happy with a crust and spring-water, and could see the shadow of his benign face in a flagon of Gascon wine without fancying Death sitting opposite to cry *Supernaculum !* when he had drained it. He could look to God without abjectness, and on man without contempt. The pupil of manifold experience, — scholar, courtier, soldier, ambassador, who had known poverty as a housemate and been the companion of princes, — his was one of those happy temperaments that could equally enjoy both halves of culture, — the world of books and the world of men.

> " Unto this day it doth mine hertë boote,
>   That I have had my world as in my time! "

The portrait of Chaucer, which we owe to the loving regret of his disciple Occleve, confirms the judgment of him which we make from his works.   It is, I think, more engaging than that of any other poet. The downcast eyes, half sly, half meditative, the sensuous mouth, the broad brow, drooping with weight of thought, and yet with an inexpugnable youth shining out of it as from the morning forehead of a boy, are all noticeable, and not less so their harmony of placid tenderness. We are struck, too, with the smoothness of the face as of one who thought easily, whose phrase flowed naturally, and who had never puckered his brow over an unmanageable verse.

Nothing has been added to our knowledge of Chaucer's

life since Sir Harris Nicholas, with the help of original
records, weeded away the fictions by which the few facts
were choked and overshadowed. We might be sorry that
no confirmation has been found for the story, fathered
on a certain phantasmal Mr. Buckley, that Chaucer was
" fined two shillings for beating a Franciscan friar in
Fleet Street," if it were only for the alliteration ; but we
refuse to give up the meeting with Petrarch. All the
probabilities are in its favor. That Chaucer, being at
Milan, should not have found occasion to ride across so
far as Padua, for the sake of seeing the most famous literary man of the day, is incredible. If Froissart could
journey on horseback through Scotland and Wales, surely
Chaucer, whose curiosity was as lively as his, might have
ventured what would have been a mere pleasure-trip in
comparison. I cannot easily bring myself to believe that
he is not giving some touches of his own character in
that of the Clerk of Oxford : —

> " For him was liefer have at his bed's head
> A twenty bookës clothed in black and red
> Of Aristotle and his philosophië
> Than robës rich, or fiddle or psaltrië :
> But although that he were a philosòpher
> Yet had he but a little gold in coffer:
> Of study took he mostë care and heed;
> Not one word spake he morë than was need:
> All that he spake it was of high prudèncë,
> And short and quick, and full of great sentencë;
> Sounding in moral virtue was his speech
> And gladly would he learn and gladly teach."

That, himself as plump as Horace, he should have
described the Clerk as being lean, will be no objection to
those who remember how carefully Chaucer effaces his
own personality in his great poem. Our chief debt to
Sir Harris Nicholas is for having disproved the story that
Chaucer, imprisoned for complicity in the insurrection of
John of Northampton, had set himself free by betraying

his accomplices. That a poet, one of whose leading
qualities is his good sense and moderation, and who
should seem to have practised his own rule, to

> " Fly from the press and dwell with soothfastness;
> Sufficë thee thy good though it be small,"

should have been concerned in any such political excesses,
was improbable enough ; but that he should add to this
the baseness of broken faith was incredible except to
such as in a doubtful story

> " Demen gladly to the badder end."

Sir Harris Nicholas has proved by the records that the
fabric is baseless, and we may now read the poet's fine
verse,

> " Truth is the highest thing a man may keep,"

without a pang. We are thankful that Chaucer's shoulders are finally discharged of that weary load, " The
Testament of Love." * The later biographers seem inclined to make Chaucer a younger man at his death in
1400 than has hitherto been supposed. Herr Hertzberg
even puts his birth so late as 1340. But, till more conclusive evidence is produced, we shall adhere to the received dates as on the whole more consonant with the
probabilities of the case. The monument is clearly right
as to the year of his death, and the chances are at least
even that both this and the date of birth were copied
from an older inscription. The only counter-argument
that has much force is the manifestly unfinished condition of the " Canterbury Tales." That a man of seventy
odd could have put such a spirit of youth into those

---

* Tyrwhitt doubted the authenticity of " The Flower and the Leaf"
and " The Cuckoo and the Nightingale." To these Mr. Bradshaw
(and there can be no higher authority) would add " The Court of Love,"
the " Dream," the " Praise of Woman," the " Romaunt of the Rose,"
and several of the shorter poems. To these doubtful productions there
is strong ground, both moral and æsthetic, for adding the " Parson's
Tale."

matchless prologues will not, however, surprise those who remember Dryden's second spring-time. It is plain that the notion of giving unity to a number of disconnected stories by the device which Chaucer adopted was an afterthought. These stories had been written, and some of them even published, at periods far asunder, and without any reference to connection among themselves. The prologues, and those parts which internal evidence justifies us in taking them to have been written after the thread of plan to string them on was conceived, are in every way more mature, — in knowledge of the world, in easy mastery of verse and language, and in the overpoise of sentiment by judgment. They may with as much probability be referred to a green old age as to the middle-life of a man who, upon any theory of the dates, was certainly slow in ripening.

The formation of a Chaucer Society, now four centuries and a half after the poet's death, gives suitable occasion for taking a new observation of him, as of a fixed star, not only in our own, but in the European literary heavens, "whose worth's unknown although his height be taken." The admirable work now doing by this Society, whose establishment was mainly due to the pious zeal of Mr. Furnivall, deserves recognition from all who know how to value the too rare union of accurate scholarship with minute exactness in reproducing the text. The six-text edition of the "Canterbury Tales," giving what is practically equivalent to six manuscript copies, is particularly deserving of gratitude from this side the water, as it for the first time affords to Americans the opportunity of independent critical study and comparison. This beautiful work is fittingly inscribed to our countryman, Professor Child, of Harvard, a lover of Chaucer, "so proved by his wordës and his werke,"

who has done more for the great poet's memory than
any man since Tyrwhitt. We earnestly hope that the
Society may find enough support to print all the remaining manuscript texts of importance, for there can
hardly be any one of them that may not help us to a
valuable hint. The works of Mr. Sandras and Herr
Hertzberg show that this is a matter of interest not
merely or even primarily to English scholars. The introduction to the latter is one of the best essays on
Chaucer yet written, while the former, which is an in-
vestigation of the French and Italian sources of the
poet, supplies us with much that is new and worth
having as respects the training of the poet, and the
obstacles of fashion and taste through which he had to
force his way before he could find free play for his native
genius or even so much as arrive at a consciousness
thereof. M. Sandras is in every way a worthy pupil of
the accomplished M. Victor Leclerc, and, though he lays
perhaps a little too much stress on the indebtedness of
Chaucer in particulars, shows a singularly intelligent
and clear-sighted eye for the general grounds of his
claim to greatness and originality. It is these grounds
which I propose chiefly to examine here.

The first question we put to any poet, nay, to any
so-called national literature, is that which Farinata
addressed to Dante, *Chi fur li maggior tui?* Here is no
question of plagiarism, for poems are not made of words
and thoughts and images, but of that something in the
poet himself which can compel them to obey him and
move to the rhythm of his nature. Thus it is that the
new poet, however late he come, can never be forestalled,
and the ship-builder who built the pinnace of Columbus
has as much claim to the discovery of America as he
who suggests a thought by which some other man opens
new worlds to us has to a share in that achievement by

him unconceived and inconceivable.   Chaucer undoubtedly began as an imitator, perhaps as mere translator,
serving the needful apprenticeship in the use of his
tools.   Children learn to speak by watching the lips and
catching the words of those who know how already, and
poets learn in the same way from their elders.   They
import their raw material from any and everywhere, and
the question at last comes down to this, — whether an
author have original force enough to assimilate all he
has acquired, or that be so overmastering as to assimilate *him*.   If the poet turn out the stronger, we allow
him to help himself from other people with wonderful
equanimity.   Should a man discover the art of transmuting metals and present us with a lump of gold as
large as an ostrich-egg, would it be in human nature to
inquire too nicely whether he had stolen the lead?

Nothing is more certain than that great poets are not
sudden prodigies, but slow results.   As an oak profits
by the foregone lives of immemorial vegetable races
that have worked-over the juices of earth and air into
organic life out of whose dissolution a soil might gather
fit to maintain that nobler birth of nature, so we may
be sure that the genius of every remembered poet drew
the forces that built it up out of the decay of a long
succession of forgotten ones.   Nay, in proportion as the
genius is vigorous and original will its indebtedness be
greater, will its roots strike deeper into the past and
grope in remoter fields for the virtue that must sustain
it.   Indeed, if the works of the great poets teach anything, it is to hold mere invention somewhat cheap.   It
is not the finding of a thing, but the making something
out of it after it is found, that is of consequence.   Accordingly, Chaucer, like Shakespeare, invented almost
nothing.   Wherever he found anything directed to
Geoffrey Chaucer, he took it and made the most of it.

It was not the subject treated, but himself, that was the new thing. *Cela m'appartient de droit,* Molière is reported to have said when accused of plagiarism. Chaucer pays that "usurious interest which genius," as Coleridge says, "always pays in borrowing." The characteristic touch is his own. In the famous passage about the caged bird, copied from the "Romaunt of the Rose," the "gon eten wormes" was added by him. We must let him, if he will, eat the heart out of the literature that had preceded him, as we sacrifice the mulberry-leaves to the silkworm, because he knows how to convert them into something richer and more lasting. The question of originality is not one of form, but of substance, not of cleverness, but of imaginative power. Given your material, in other words the life in which you live, how much can you see in it? For on that depends how much you can make of it. Is it merely an arrangement of man's contrivance, a patchwork of expediencies for temporary comfort and convenience, good enough if it last your time, or is it so much of the surface of that ever-flowing deity which we call Time, wherein we catch such fleeting reflection as is possible for us, of our relation to perdurable things? This is what makes the difference between Æschylus and Euripides, between Shakespeare and Fletcher, between Goethe and Heine, between literature and rhetoric. Something of this depth of insight, if not in the fullest, yet in no inconsiderable measure, characterizes Chaucer. We must not let his playfulness, his delight in the world as mere spectacle, mislead us into thinking that he was incapable of serious purpose or insensible to the deeper meanings of life.

There are four principal sources from which Chaucer may be presumed to have drawn for poetical suggestion or literary culture, — the Latins, the Troubadours, the

Trouvères, and the Italians. It is only the two latter who can fairly claim any immediate influence in the direction of his thought or the formation of his style. The only Latin poet who can be supposed to have influenced the spirit of mediæval literature is Ovid. In his sentimentality, his love of the marvellous and the picturesque, he is its natural precursor. The analogy between his Fasti and the versified legends of saints is more than a fanciful one. He was certainly popular with the poets of the thirteenth and fourteenth centuries. Virgil had wellnigh become mythical. The chief merit of the Provençal poets is in having been the first to demonstrate that it was possible to write with elegance in a modern dialect, and their interest for us is mainly as forerunners, as indications of tendency. Their literature is prophecy, not fulfilment. Its formal sentiment culminated in Laura, its ideal aspiration in Beatrice. Shakespeare's hundred and sixth sonnet, if, for the imaginary mistress to whom it was addressed, we substitute the muse of a truer conception and more perfected utterance, represents exactly the feeling with which we read Provençal poetry : —

> " When in the chronicle of wasted Time
> I see descriptions of the fairest wights
> And beauty making beautiful old rhyme
> In praise of ladies dead and lovely knights,
>
> . . .
>
> I see their antique pen would have expressed
> Even such a beauty as you master now;
> So all their praises are but prophecies
> Of this our time, all you prefiguring,
> And, for they looked but with divining eyes,
> They had not skill enough your worth to sing."

It is astonishing how little of the real life of the time we learn from the Troubadours except by way of inference and deduction. Their poetry is purely lyric in its most narrow sense, that is, the expression of personal and

momentary moods. To the fancy of critics who take
their cue from tradition, Provençe is a morning sky of
early summer, out of which innumerable larks rain a
faint melody (the sweeter because rather half divined
than heard too distinctly) over an earth where the dew
never dries and the flowers never fade. But when we
open Raynouard it is like opening the door of an aviary.
We are deafened and confused by a hundred minstrels
singing the same song at once, and more than suspect
that the flowers they welcome are made of French cambric spangled with dewdrops of prevaricating glass.
Bernard de Ventadour and Bertrand de Born are wellnigh the only ones among them in whom we find an
original type. Yet the Troubadours undoubtedly led
the way to refinement of conception and perfection of
form. They were the conduit through which the failing
stream of Roman literary tradition flowed into the new
channel which mediæval culture was slowly shaping for
itself. Without them we could not understand Petrarca,
who carried the manufacture of artificial bloom and fic-
titious dew-drop to a point of excellence where artifice,
if ever, may claim the praise of art. Without them we
could not understand Dante, in whom their sentiment
for woman was idealized by a passionate intellect and
a profound nature, till Beatrice becomes a half-human,
half-divine abstraction, a woman still to memory and
devotion, a disembodied symbol to the ecstasy of thought.
The Provençal love-poetry was as abstracted from all
sensuality as that of Petrarca, but it stops short of that
larger and more gracious style of treatment which has
secured him a place in all gentle hearts and refined
imaginations forever. In it also woman leads her servants upward, but it is along the easy slopes of conventional sentiment, and no Troubadour so much as dreamed
of that loftier region, native to Dante, where *the* woman

is subtilized into *das Ewig-Weibliche,* type of man's finer
conscience and nobler aspiration made sensible to him
only through her.

On the whole, it would be hard to find anything more
tediously artificial than the Provençal literature, except
the reproduction of it by the Minnesingers.   The *Tedes-
chi lurchi* certainly *did* contrive to make something heavy
as dough out of what was at least light, if not very satisfying, in the canorous dialect of Southern Gaul.   But its
doom was inevitably predicted in its nature and position,
nay, in its very name.   It was, and it continues to be, a
strictly *provincial* literature, imprisoned within extremely narrow intellectual and even geographical limits.   It
is not race or language that can inflict this leprous isolation, but some defect of sympathy with the simpler and
more universal relations of human nature.   You cannot
shut up Burns in a dialect bristling with archaisms, nor
prevent Béranger from setting all pulses a-dance in the
least rhythmic and imaginative of modern tongues.   The
healthy temperament of Chaucer, with its breadth of interest in all ranks and phases of social life, could have found
little that was sympathetic in the evaporated sentiment
and rhetorical punctilios of a school of poets which, with
rare exceptions, began and ended in courtly dilettantism.

The refined formality with which the literary product
of Provençe is for the most part stamped, as with a
trademark, was doubtless the legacy of Gallo-Roman culture, itself at best derivative and superficial.   I think,
indeed, that it may well be doubted whether Roman
literature, always a half-hardy exotic, could ripen the
seeds of living reproduction.   The Roman genius was
eminently practical, and far more apt for the triumphs
of politics and jurisprudence than of art.   Supreme elegance it could and did arrive at in Virgil, but, if I may
trust my own judgment, it produced but one original

poet, and that was Horace, who has ever since continued the favorite of men of the world, an apostle to the Gentiles of the mild cynicism of middle-age and an after-dinner philosophy. Though in no sense national, he was, more truly than any has ever been since, till the same combination of circumstances produced Béranger, an urbane or city poet. Rome, with her motley life, her formal religion, her easy morals, her spectacles, her luxury, her suburban country-life, was his muse. The situation was new, and found a singer who had wit enough to turn it to account. There are a half-dozen pieces of Catullus unsurpassed (unless their Greek originals should turn up) for lyric grace and fanciful tenderness. The sparrow of Lesbia still pecks the rosy lips of his mistress, immortal as the eagle of Pindar. One profound imagination, one man, who with a more prosperous subject might have been a great poet, lifted Roman literature above its ordinary level of tasteful common-sense. The invocation of Venus, as the genetic force of nature, by Lucretius, seems to me the one sunburst of purely poetic inspiration which the Latin language can show. But this very force, without which *neque fit lætum neque amabile quicquam* was wholly wanting in those poets of the post-classic period, through whom the literary influences of the past were transmitted to the romanized provincials. The works of Ausonius interest us as those of our own Dwights and Barlows do. The "Conquest of Canaan" and the "Columbiad" were Connecticut epics no doubt, but still were better than nothing in their day. If not literature, they were at least memories of literature, and such memories are not without effect in reproducing what they regret. The provincial writers of Latin devoted themselves with a dreary assiduity to the imitation of models which they deemed classical, but which were truly so only in the sense that they

were the more decorously respectful of the dead form in
proportion as the living spirit had more utterly gone out
of it.   It is, I suspect, to the traditions of this purely
rhetorical influence, indirectly exercised, that we are to
attribute the rapid passage of the new Provençal poetry
from what must have been its original popular character
to that highly artificial condition which precedes total
extinction.   It was the alienation of the written from
the spoken language (always, perhaps, more or less ma-
lignly operative in giving Roman literature a cold-blooded
turn as compared with Greek), which, ending at length
in total divorce, rendered Latin incapable of supplying
the wants of new men and new ideas.   The same thing,
I am strongly inclined to think, was true of the language
of the Troubadours.   It had become literary, and so far
dead.   It is true that no language is ever so far gone in
consumption as to be beyond the great-poet-cure.   Undoubtedly a man of genius can out of his own super-
abundant vitality compel life into the most decrepit
vocabulary.   But it is by the infusion of his own blood,
as it were, and not without a certain sacrifice of power.
No such rescue came for the *langue d'oc*, which, it should
seem, had performed its special function in the development of modern literature, and would have perished
even without the Albigensian war.   The position of the
Gallo-Romans of the South, both ethical and geographical, precluded them from producing anything really great
or even original in literature, for that must have its root
in a national life, and this they never had.   After the
Burgundian invasion their situation was in many respects
analogous to our own after the Revolutionary War.   They
had been thoroughly romanized in language and culture,
but the line of their historic continuity had been broken.
The Roman road, which linked them with the only past
they knew, had been buried under the great barbarian

land-slide. In like manner we, inheriting the language, the social usages, the literary and political traditions of Englishmen, were suddenly cut adrift from our historical anchorage. Very soon there arose a demand for a native literature, nay, it was even proposed that, as a first step toward it, we should adopt a lingo of our own to be called the Columbian or Hesperian. This, to be sure, was never accomplished, though our English cousins seem to hint sometimes that we have made very fair advances toward it; but if it could have been, our position would have been precisely that of the Provençals when they began to have a literature of their own. They had formed a language which, while it completed their orphanage from their imperial mother, continually recalled her, and kept alive their pride of lineage. Such reminiscences as they still retained of Latin culture were pedantic and rhetorical,* and it was only natural that out of these they should have elaborated a code of poetical jurisprudence with titles and subtitles applicable to every form of verse and tyrannous over every mode of sentiment. The result could not fail to be artificial and wearisome, except where some man with a truly lyrical genius could breathe life into the rigid formula and make it pliant to his more passionate feeling. The great service of the Provençals was that they kept in mind the fact that poetry was not merely an amusement, but an art, and long after their literary activity had ceased their influence reacted beneficially upon Europe through their Italian pupils. They are interesting as showing the tendency of the Romanic races to a scientific treatment of what, if it be not spontaneous, becomes a fashion and erelong an impertinence. Fauriel has endeavored to prove that they were the first to treat the mediæval heroic legends epically, but the evidence is strongly against him. The testimony

* Fauriel, *Histoire de la Gaule Meridionale*, Vol. I *passim*.

of Dante on this point is explicit,* and moreover not a
single romance of chivalry has come down to us in a
dialect of the pure Provencal.

The Trouvères, on the other hand, are apt to have
something naive and vigorous about them, something
that smacks of race and soil. Their very coarseness
is almost better than the Troubadour delicacy, because
it was not an affectation. The difference between the
two schools is that between a culture pedantically transmitted and one which grows and gathers strength from
natural causes. Indeed, it is to the North of France and
to the Trouvères that we are to look for the true origins
of our modern literature. I do not mean in their epical poetry, though there is something refreshing in the
mere fact of their choosing native heroes and legends as
the subjects of their song. It was in their *Fabliaux* and
Lais that, dealing with the realities of the life about
them, they became original and delightful in spite of
themselves. Their *Chansons de Geste* are fine specimens
of fighting Christianity, highly inspiring for men like
Peire de Bergerac, who sings

> " Bel m'es can aug lo resso
> Que fai l'ausbercs ab l'arso,
> Li bruit e il crit e il masan
> Que il corn e las trombas fan ";

but who after reading them — even the best of them,

---

* Allegat ergo pro se lingua *Oil* quod propter sui faciliorem et delec-
tabiliorem vulgaritatem, quicquid redactum sive inventum est ad vul-
gare prosaicum, suum est; videlicet biblia cum Trojanorum, Roman-
orumque gestibus compilata et Arturi regis ambages pulcherrimæ et
quamplures aliæ historiæ ac doctrinæ. That Dante by *prosaicum* did
not mean prose, but a more inartificial verse, *numeros lege solutos*, is
clear. Cf. Wolf, Ueber die Lais, pp. 92 *seq.* and notes. It has not, I
think, been remarked that Dante borrows his *faciliorem et delectabilio-
rem* from the *plus diletable et comune* of his master Brunetto Latini.

† " My ears no sweeter music know
> Than hauberk's clank with saddlebow,
> The noise, the cries, the tumult blown
> From trumpet and from clarion."

the Song of Roland — can remember much more than a
cloud of battle-dust, through which the paladins loom
dimly gigantic, and a strong verse flashes here and there
like an angry sword? What are the *Roman d'avantures*,
the cycle of Arthur and his knights, but a procession of
armor and plumes, mere spectacle, not vision like their
Grecian antitype, the Odyssey, whose pictures of life,
whether domestic or heroic, are among the abiding consolations of the mind? An element of disproportion, of
grotesqueness,* earmark of the barbarian, disturbs us,
even when it does not disgust, in them all. Except the
Roland, they all want adequate motive, and even in that
we may well suspect a reminiscence of the Iliad. They
are not without a kind of dignity, for manliness is always
noble, and there are detached scenes that are striking,
perhaps all the more so from their rarity, like the combat of Oliver and Fierabras, and the leave-taking of
Parise la Duchesse. But in point of art they are far
below even Firdusi, whose great poem is of precisely the
same romantic type. The episode of Sohrab and Rustem
as much surpasses the former of the passages just alluded
to in largeness and energy of treatment, in the true
epical quality, as the lament of Tehmine over her son
does the latter of them in refined and natural pathos.
In our revolt against pseudo-classicism we must not let
our admiration for the vigor and freshness which are the
merit of this old poetry tempt us to forget that our
direct literary inheritance comes to us from an ancestry
who would never have got beyond the Age of Iron but
for the models of graceful form and delicate workmanship which they found in the tombs of an earlier race.

I recall but one passage (from *Jourdain de Blaivies*)
which in its simple movement of the heart can in any
way be compared with Chaucer. I translate it freely,

* Compare Floripar in *Fierabras* with Nausikää, for example.

merely changing the original assonance into rhyme. Eremborc, to save the son of her liege-lord, has passed-off her own child for his, only stipulating that he shall pass the night before his death with her in the prison where she is confined by the usurper Fromond. The time is just as the dreaded dawn begins to break.

> " ' Garnier, fair son,' the noble lady said,
> ' To save thy father's life must thou be dead;
> And mine, alas, must be with sorrow spent,
> Since thou must die, albeit so innocent!
> Evening thou shalt not see that see'st the morn!
> Woe worth the hour that I beheld thee born,
> Whom nine long months within my side I bore!
> Was never babe desired so much before.
> Now summer will the pleasant days recall
> When I shall take my stand upon the wall
> And see the fair young gentlemen thy peers
> That come and go, and, as beseems their years
> Run at the quintain, strive to pierce the shield,
> And in the tourney keep their sell or yield;
> Then must my heart be tearswoln for thy sake
> That 't will be marvel if it do not break.'
> At morning, when the day began to peer,
> Matins rang out from minsters far and near,
> And the clerks sang full well with voices high.
> ' God,' said the dame, 'thou glorious in the sky,
> These lingering nights were wont to tire me so!
> And this, alas, how swift it hastes to go!
> These clerks and cloistered folk, alas, in spite
> So early sing to cheat me of my night!' "

The great advantages which the *langue d'oil* had over its sister dialect of the South of France were its wider distribution, and its representing the national and unitary tendencies of the people as opposed to those of provincial isolation. But the Trouvères had also this superiority, that they gave a voice to real and not merely conventional emotions. In comparison with the Troubadours their sympathies were more human, and their expression more popular. While the tiresome ingenuity of the latter busied itself chiefly in the filigree of wire-drawn sentiment and supersubtilized conceit, the former took their subjects from the street and the market as well as from the château. In the one case language had become a mere material for clever elaboration; in the other, as always in live literature, it was a soil from which the roots of thought and feeling unconsciously drew the coloring of vivid expression. The writers of French, by the greater pliancy of their dialect and the simpler forms of their verse, had acquired an ease which was impossible in the more stately and sharply angled vocabulary of the South. Their octosyllabics have not seldom a careless facility not unworthy of Swift in his best mood. They had attained the highest skill and grace in narrative, as the lays of Marie de France and the *Lai de l'Oiselet* bear witness.* Above all, they had learned how to brighten the hitherto monotonous web of story with the gayer hues of fancy.

It is no improbable surmise that the sudden and surprising development of the more strictly epical poetry in the North of France, and especially its growing partiality for historical in preference to mythical subjects, were due to the Normans. The poetry of the Danes was much of it authentic history, or what was believed to be so; the heroes of their Sagas were real men, with wives and children, with relations public and domestic, on the common levels of life, and not mere creatures of imagination, who dwell apart like stars from the vulgar cares and interests of men. If we compare Havelok with the least idealized figures of Carlovingian or Arthurian romance, we shall have a keen sense of this difference. Manhood has taken the place of caste, and homeliness of exaggeration. Havelok says, —

> " Godwot, I will with thee gang
> For to learn some good to get;

* If internal evidence may be trusted, the *Lai de l'Espine* is not hers.

> Swinken would I for my meat;
> It is no shame for to swinken."

This Dane, we see, is of our own make and stature, a being much nearer our kindly sympathies than his compatriot Ogier, of whom we are told,

> " Dix piès de lonc avoit le chevalier."

But however large or small share we may allow to the Danes in changing the character of French poetry and supplanting the Romance with the Fabliau, there can be little doubt either of the kind or amount of influence which the Normans must have brought with them into England. I am not going to attempt a definition of the Anglo-Saxon element in English literature, for generalizations are apt to be as dangerous as they are tempting. But as a painter may draw a cloud so that we recognize its general truth, though the boundaries of real clouds never remain the same for two minutes together, so amid the changes of feature and complexion brought about by commingling of race, there still remains a certain cast of physiognomy which points back to some one ancestor of marked and peculiar character. It is toward this type that there is always a tendency to revert, to borrow Mr. Darwin's phrase, and I think the general belief is not without some adequate grounds which in France traces this predominant type to the Kelt, and in England to the Saxon. In old and stationary communities, where tradition has a chance to take root, and where several generations are present to the mind of each inhabitant, either by personal recollection or transmitted anecdote, everybody's peculiarities, whether of strength or weakness, are explained and, as it were, justified upon some theory of hereditary bias. Such and such qualities he got from a grandfather on the spear or a great-uncle on the spindle side. This gift came in a right line from

So-and-so ; that failing came in by the dilution of the family blood with that of Such-a-one. In this way a certain allowance is made for every aberration from some assumed normal type, either in the way of reinforcement or defect, and that universal desire of the human mind to have everything accounted for — which makes the moon responsible for the whimsies of the weathercock — is cheaply gratified. But as mankind in the aggregate is always wiser than any single man, because its experience is derived from a larger range of observation and experience, and because the springs that feed it drain a wider region both of time and space, there is commonly some greater or smaller share of truth in all popular prejudices. The meteorologists are beginning to agree with the old women that the moon *is* an accessary before the fact in our atmospheric fluctuations. Now, although to admit this notion of inherited good or ill to its fullest extent would be to abolish personal character, and with it all responsibility, to abdicate freewill, and to make every effort at self-direction futile, there is no inconsiderable alloy of truth in it, nevertheless. No man can look into the title-deeds of what may be called his personal estate, his faculties, his predilections, his failings, — whatever, in short, sets him apart as a capital I, — without something like a shock of dread to find how much of him is held in mortmain by those who, though long ago mouldered away to dust, are yet fatally alive and active in him for good or ill. What is true of individual men is true also of races, and the prevailing belief in a nation as to the origin of certain of its characteristics has something of the same basis in facts of observation as the village estimate of the traits of particular families. *Interdum vulgus rectum videt.*

We are apt, it is true, to talk rather loosely about our Anglo-Saxon ancestors, and to attribute to them in a vague way all the pith of our institutions and the motive power of our progress. For my own part, I think there is such a thing as being too Anglo-Saxon, and the warp and woof of the English national character, though undoubtedly two elements mainly predominate in it, is quite too complex for us to pick out a strand here and there, and affirm that the *body* of the fabric is of this or that. Our present concern with the Saxons is chiefly a literary one ; but it leads to a study of general characteristics. What, then, so far as we can make it out, seems to be their leading mental feature? Plainly, understanding, common-sense, — a faculty which never carries its possessor very high in creative literature, though it may make him great as an acting and even thinking man. Take Dr. Johnson as an instance. The Saxon, as it appears to me, has never shown any capacity for art, nay, commonly commits ugly blunders when he is tempted in that direction. He has made the best working institutions and the ugliest monuments among the children of men. He is wanting in taste, which is as much as to say that he has no true sense of proportion. His genius is his *solidity*, — an admirable foundation of national character. He is healthy, in no danger of liver-complaint, with digestive apparatus of amazing force and precision. He is the best farmer and best grazier among men, raises the biggest crops and the fattest cattle, and consumes proportionate quantities of both. He settles and sticks like a diluvial deposit on the warm, low-lying levels, physical and moral. He has a prodigious talent, to use our Yankee phrase, of *staying put*. You cannot move him ; he and rich earth have a natural sympathy of cohesion. Not quarrelsome, but with indefatigable durability of fight in him, sound of stomach, and not too refined in nervous texture, he is capable of indefinitely prolonged punishment, with a singularly obtuse sense of propriety in acknowledging himself beaten. Among all races perhaps none has shown so acute a sense of the side on which its bread is buttered, and so great a repugnance for having fine phrases take the place of the butyraceous principle. They invented the words " humbug," " cant," " sham," "gag," " soft-sodder," " flapdoddle," and other disenchanting formulas whereby the devil of falsehood and unreality gets his effectual *apage Satana !*

An imperturbable perception of the *real* relations of things is the Saxon's leading quality, — no sense whatever, or at best small, of the ideal in him. He has no notion that two and two ever make five, which is the problem the poet often has to solve. Understanding, that is, equilibrium of mind, intellectual good digestion, this, with unclogged biliary ducts, makes him mentally and physically what we call a very fixed fact ; but you shall not find a poet in a hundred thousand square miles, — in many prosperous centuries of such. But one element of incalculable importance we have not mentioned. In this homely nature, the idea of God, and of a simple and direct relation between the All-Father and his children, is deeply rooted. There, above all, will he have honesty and simplicity ; less than anything else will he have the sacramental wafer, — that beautiful emblem of our dependence on Him who giveth the daily bread ; less than anything will he have this smeared with that Barmecide butter of fair words. This is the lovely and noble side of his character. Indignation at this will make him forget crops and cattle ; and this, after so many centuries, will give him at last a poet in the monk of Eisleben, who shall cut deep on the memory of mankind that brief creed of conscience, — " Here am I . God help me : I cannot otherwise." This, it seems to me, with dogged sense of justice, — both results of that

11 *

equilibrium of thought which springs from clear-sighted understanding,— makes the beauty of the Saxon nature.

He believes in another world, and conceives of it without metaphysical subtleties as something very much after the pattern of this, but infinitely more desirable. Witness the vision of John Bunyan. Once beat it into him that his eternal *well-being*, as he calls it, depends on certain conditions, that only so will the balance in the ledger of eternity be in his favor, and the man who seemed wholly of *this* world will give all that he has, even his life, with a superb simplicity and scorn of the theatric, for a chance in the next. Hard to move, his very solidity of nature makes him terrible when once fairly set agoing. He is the man of all others slow to admit the thought of revolution ; but let him once admit it, he will carry it through and make it *stick*, — a secret hitherto undiscoverable by other races.

But poetry is not made out of the understanding ; that is not the sort of block out of which you can carve wing-footed Mercuries. The question of common-sense is always, "What is it good for?" — a question which would abolish the rose and be answered triumphantly by the cabbage. The danger of the prosaic type of mind lies in the stolid sense of superiority which blinds it to everything ideal, to the use of anything that does not serve the practical purposes of life. Do we not remember how the all-observing and all-fathoming Shakespeare has typified this in Bottom the weaver? Surrounded by all the fairy creations of fancy, he sends one to fetch him the bag of a humble-bee, and can find no better employment for Mustard-seed than to help Cavalero Cobweb scratch his ass's head between the ears. When Titania, queen of that fair ideal world, offers him a feast of beauty, he says he has a good stomach to a pottle of hay !

The Anglo-Saxons never had any real literature of their own. They produced monkish chronicles in bad Latin, and legends of saints in worse metre. Their earlier poetry is essentially Scandinavian. It was that *gens inclytissima Northmannorum* that imported the divine power of imagination, — that power which, mingled with the solid Saxon understanding, produced at last the miracle of Stratford. It was to this adventurous race, which found America before Columbus, which, for the sake of freedom of thought, could colonize inhospitable Iceland, which, as it were, typifying the very action of the imaginative faculty itself, identified itself always with what it conquered, that we owe whatever aquiline features there are in the national physiognomy of the English race. It was through the Normans that the English mind and fancy, hitherto provincial and uncouth, were first infused with the lightness, grace, and self-confidence of Romance literature. They seem to have opened a window to the southward in that solid and somewhat sombre insular character, and it was a painted window all aglow with the figures of tradition and poetry. The old Gothic volume, grim with legends of devilish temptation and satanic lore, they illuminated with the gay and brilliant inventions of a softer climate and more genial moods. Even the stories of Arthur and his knights, toward which the stern Dante himself relented so far as to call them *gratissimas ambages,* most delightful circumlocutions, though of British original, were first set free from the dungeon of a barbarous dialect by the French poets, and so brought back to England, and made popular there by the Normans.

Chaucer, to whom French must have been almost as truly a mother tongue as English, was familiar with all that had been done by Troubadour or Trouvère. In him we see the first result of the Norman yeast upon the home-baked Saxon loaf. The flour had been honest, the paste well kneaded, but the inspiring leaven was wanting till the Norman brought it over. Chaucer works still in the solid material of his race, but with what airy lightness has he not infused it? Without ceasing to be English, he has escaped from being insular. But he was something more than this; he was a scholar, a thinker, and a critic. He had studied the *Divina Commedia* of Dante, he had read Petrarca and Boccaccio, and some of the Latin poets. He calls Dante the great poet of Italy, and Petrarch a learned clerk. It is plain that he knew very well the truer purpose of poetry, and had even arrived at the higher wisdom of comprehending the aptitudes and limitations of his own genius. He saw clearly and felt keenly what were the faults and what the wants of the prevailing literature of his country. In the "Monk's Tale" he slyly satirizes the long-winded morality of Gower, as his prose antitype, Fielding, was to satirize the prolix sentimentality of Richardson. In the rhyme of Sir Thopas he gives the *coup de grace* to the romances of Chivalry, and in his own choice of a subject he heralds that new world in which the actual and the popular were to supplant the fantastic and the heroic.

Before Chaucer, modern Europe had given birth to one great poet, Dante; and contemporary with him was one supremely elegant one, Petrarch. Dante died only seven years before Chaucer was born, and, so far as culture is derived from books, the moral and intellectual influences they had been subjected to, the speculative stimulus that may have given an impulse to their minds, — there could have been no essential difference between them. Yet there are certain points of resemblance and of contrast, and those not entirely fanciful, which seem to me of considerable interest. Both were of mixed race, Dante certainly, Chaucer presumably so. Dante seems to have inherited on the Teutonic side the strong moral sense, the almost nervous irritability of conscience, and the tendency to mysticism which made him the first of Christian poets, — first in point of time and first in point of greatness. From the other side he seems to have received almost in overplus a feeling of order and proportion, sometimes wellnigh hardening into mathematical precision and formalism, — a tendency which at last brought the poetry of the Romanic races to a dead-lock of artifice and decorum. Chaucer, on the other hand, drew from the South a certain airiness of sentiment and expression, a felicity of phrase, and an elegance of turn hitherto unprecedented and hardly yet matched in our literature, but all the while kept firm hold of his native soundness of understanding, and that genial humor which seems to be the proper element of worldly wisdom. With Dante, life represented the passage of the soul from a state of nature to a state of grace ; and there would have been almost an even chance whether (as Burns says) the *Divina Commedia* had turned out a song or a sermon, but for the wonderful genius of its author, which has compelled the sermon to sing and the song to preach, whether they would or no. With Chaucer, life is a pilgrimage, but only that his eye may be delighted with the varieties of costume and character. There are good morals to be found in Chaucer, but they are always incidental. With Dante the main question is the saving of the soul, with Chaucer it is the conduct of life. The distance between them is almost that between holiness and prudence. Dante applies himself to the realities and Chaucer to the scenery of life, and the former is consequently the more universal poet, as the latter is the more truly national one. Dante represents the justice of God, and Chaucer his loving-kindness. If there is anything that may properly be called satire in the one, it is like a blast of the divine wrath, before which the wretches cower and tremble, which rends away their cloaks of hypocrisy and their masks of worldly propriety, and leaves them shivering in the cruel nakedness of their shame. The satire of the other is genial with the broad sunshine of humor, into which the victims walk forth with a delightful unconcern, laying aside of themselves the disguises that seem to make them uncomfortably warm, till they have made a thorough betrayal of themselves so unconsciously that we almost pity while we laugh. Dante shows us the punishment of sins against God and one's neighbor, in order that we may shun them, and so escape the doom that awaits them in the other world. Chaucer exposes the cheats of the transmuter of metals, of the begging friars, and of the pedlers of indulgences, in order that we may be on our guard against them in this world. If we are to judge of what is national only by the highest and most characteristic types, surely we cannot fail to see in Chaucer the true forerunner and prototype of Shakespeare, who, with an imagination of far deeper grasp, a far wider reach of thought, yet took the same delight in the pageantry of the actual world, and whose moral is the moral of worldly wisdom only heightened to the level of his wide-viewing mind, and made typical by the dramatic energy of his plastic nature.

Yet if Chaucer had little of that organic force of life which so inspires the poem of Dante that, as he himself says of the heavens, part answers to part with mutual interchange of light, he had a structural faculty which distinguishes him from all other English poets, his contemporaries, and which indeed is the primary distinction of poets properly so called. There is, to be sure, only

one other English writer coeval with himself who deserves in any way to be compared with him, and that
rather for contrast than for likeness.

With the single exception of Langland, the English
poets, his contemporaries, were little else than bad
versifiers of legends classic or mediæval, as happened,
without selection and without art. Chaucer is the first
who broke away from the dreary traditional style, and
gave not merely stories, but lively *pictures* of real life as
the ever-renewed substance of poetry. He was a reformer, too, not only in literature, but in morals. But
as in the former his exquisite tact saved him from all
eccentricity, so in the latter the pervading sweetness of
his nature could never be betrayed into harshness and
invective. He seems incapable of indignation. He
mused good-naturedly over the vices and follies of men,
and, never forgetting that he was fashioned of the same
clay, is rather apt to pity than condemn. There is no
touch of cynicism in all he wrote. Dante's brush seems
sometimes to have been smeared with the burning pitch
of his own fiery lake. Chaucer's pencil is dipped in the
cheerful color-box of the old illuminators, and he has
their patient delicacy of touch, with a freedom far beyond their somewhat mechanic brilliancy.

English narrative poetry, as Chaucer found it, though
it had not altogether escaped from the primal curse of
long-windedness so painfully characteristic of its prototype, the French Romance of Chivalry, had certainly
shown a feeling for the picturesque, a sense of color, a
directness of phrase, and a simplicity of treatment which
give it graces of its own and a turn peculiar to itself.
In the easy knack of story-telling, the popular minstrels
cannot compare with Marie de France. The lightsome-
ness of fancy, that leaves a touch of sunshine and is
gone, is painfully missed in them all. Their incidents

enter dispersedly, as the old stage directions used to say, and they have not learned the art of concentrating their force on the key-point of their hearers' interest. They neither get fairly hold of their subject, nor, what is more important, does it get hold of them. But they sometimes yield to an instinctive hint of leaving-off at the right moment, and in their happy negligence achieve an effect only to be matched by the highest successes of art.

> " That lady heard his mourning all
> Right under her chamber wall,
> In her oriel where she was,
> Closëd well with royal glass;
> Fulfilled it was with imagery
> Every window, by and by;
> On each side had there a gin
> Sperred with many a divers pin;
> Anon that lady fair and free
> Undid a pin of ivory
> And wide the window she open set,
> The sun shone in at her closet."

It is true the old rhymer relapses a little into the habitual drone of his class, and shows half a mind to bolt into their common inventory style when he comes to his *gins* and *pins,* but he withstands the temptation manfully, and his sunshine fills our hearts with a gush as sudden as that which illumines the lady's oriel. Coleridge and Keats have each in his way felt the charm of this winsome picture, but have hardly equalled its hearty honesty, its economy of material, the supreme test of artistic skill. I admit that the phrase " *had* there a gin " is suspicious, and suggests a French original, but I remember nothing altogether so good in the romances from the other side of the Channel. One more passage occurs to me, almost incomparable in its simple straightforward force and choice of the right word.

> " Sir Graysteel to his death thus thraws,
> He welters [wallows] and the grass updraws;

> A little while then lay he still,
> (Friends that saw him liked full ill,)
> And bled into his armor bright."

The last line, for suggestive reticence, almost deserves to be put beside the famous

> " Quel giorno più non vi leggemmo avante "

of the great master of laconic narration. In the same poem * the growing love of the lady, in its maidenliness of unconscious betrayal, is touched with a delicacy and tact as surprising as they are delightful. But such passages, which are the despair of poets who have to work in a language that has faded into diction, are exceptional. They are to be set down rather to good luck than to art. Even the stereotyped similes of these fortunate illiterates, like "weary as water in a weir," or "glad as grass is of the rain," are new, like nature, at the thousandth repetition. Perhaps our palled taste overvalues the wild flavor of these wayside treasure-troves. They are wood-strawberries, prized in proportion as we must turn over more leaves ere we find one. This popular literature is of value in helping us toward a juster estimate of Chaucer by showing what the mere language was capable of, and that all it wanted was a poet to put it through its paces. For though the poems I have quoted be, in their present form, later than he, they are, after all, but modernized versions of older copies, which they doubtless reproduce with substantial fidelity.

It is commonly assumed that Chaucer did for English what Dante is supposed to have done for Italian and Luther for German, that he, in short, in some hitherto inexplicable way, created it. But this is to speak loosely and without book. Languages are never made in any

* *Sir Eger and Sir Grine* in the Percy Folio. The passage quoted is from Ellis.

such fashion, still less are they the achievement of any single man, however great his genius, however powerful his individuality.   They shape themselves by laws as definite as those which guide and limit the growth of other living organisms.   Dante, indeed, has told us that he chose to write in the tongue that might be learned of nurses and chafferers in the market.   His practice shows that he knew perfectly well that poetry has needs which cannot be answered by the vehicle of vulgar commerce between man and man.   What he instinctively felt was, that there was the living heart of all speech, without whose help the brain were powerless to send will, motion, meaning, to the limbs and extremities.   But it is true that a language, as respects the uses of literature, is liable to a kind of syncope.   No matter how complete its vocabulary may be, how thorough an outfit of inflections and case-endings it may have, it is a mere dead body without a soul till some man of genius set its arrested pulses once more athrob, and show what wealth of sweetness, scorn, persuasion, and passion lay there awaiting its liberator.   In this sense it is hardly too much to say that Chaucer, like Dante, found his native tongue a dialect and left it a language.   But it was not what he did with deliberate purpose of reform, it was his kindly and plastic genius that wrought this magic of renewal and inspiration.   It was not the new words he introduced,* but his way of using the old ones, that surprised them into grace, ease, and dignity in their own despite.   In order to feel fully how much he achieved, let any one subject himself to a penitential course of reading in his contemporary, Gower, who worked in a material to all intents and purposes the same, or listen for a moment to the barbarous jangle which Lydgate and Occleve contrive to draw from the instrument their master had tuned

---

* I think he tried one now and then, like " even *columbine*."

so deftly. Gower has positively raised tediousness to the precision of science, he has made dulness an heirloom for the students of our literary history. As you slip to and fro on the frozen levels of his verse, which give no foot-hold to the mind, as your nervous ear awaits the inevita-ble recurrence of his rhyme, regularly pertinacious as the tick of an eight-day clock and reminding you of Wordsworth's

> " Once more the ass did lengthen out
> The hard, dry, seesaw of his horrible bray,"

you learn to dread, almost to respect, the powers of this indefatigable man. He is the undertaker of the fair mediæval legend, and his style has the hateful gloss, the seemingly unnatural length, of a coffin. Love, beauty, passion, nature, art, life, the natural and theological vir-tues, — there is nothing beyond his power to disenchant, nothing out of which the tremendous hydraulic press of his allegory (or whatever it is, for I am not sure if it be not something even worse) will not squeeze all feeling and freshness and leave it a juiceless pulp. It matters not where you try him, whether his story be Christian or pagan, borrowed from history or fable, you cannot escape him. Dip in at the middle or the end, dodge back to the beginning, the patient old man is there to take you by the button and go on with his imperturba-ble narrative. You may have left off with Clytemnes-tra, and you begin again with Samson ; it makes no odds, for you cannot tell one from tother. His tedious-ness is omnipresent, and like Dogberry he could find in his heart to bestow it all (and more if he had it) on your worship. The word *lengthy* has been charged to our American account, but it must have been invented by the first reader of Gower's works, the only inspiration of which they were ever capable. Our literature had to lie by and recruit for more than four centuries ere it could give us an equal vacuity in Tupper, so persistent a uniformity of commonplace in the "Recreations of a Country Parson." Let us be thankful that the industrious Gower never found time for recreation !

But a fairer as well as more instructive comparison lies between Chaucer and the author of "Piers Ploughman." Langland has as much tenderness, as much interest in the varied picture of life, as hearty a contempt for hypocrisy, and almost an equal sense of fun. He has the same easy abundance of matter. But what a difference! It is the difference between the poet and the man of poetic temperament. The abundance of the one is a continual fulness within the fixed limits of good taste ; that of the other is squandered in overflow. The one can be profuse on occasion ; the other is diffuse whether he will or no. The one is full of talk ; the other is garrulous. What in one is the refined *bonhomie* of a man of the world, is a rustic shrewdness in the other. Both are kindly in their satire, and have not (like too many reformers) that vindictive love of virtue which spreads the stool of repentance with thistle-burrs before they invite the erring to seat themselves therein. But what in "Piers Ploughman" is sly fun, has the breadth and depth of humor in Chaucer ; and it is plain that while the former was taken up by his moral purpose, the main interest of the latter turned to perfecting the form of his work. In short, Chaucer had that fine literary sense which is as rare as genius, and, united with it, as it was in him, assures an immortality of fame. It is not merely what he has to say, but even more the agreeable way he has of saying it, that captivates our attention and gives him an assured place in literature. Above all, it is not in detached passages that his charm lies, but in the entirety of expression and the cumulative effect of many particulars working toward a common end. Now though *ex ungue leonem* be a good rule in comparative anatomy, its application, except in a very limited way, in criticism is sure to mislead ; for we should always bear in mind that the really great writer is great in the mass, and is to be tested less by his cleverness in the elaboration of parts than by that *reach* of mind which is incapable of random effort, which selects, arranges, combines, rejects, denies itself the cheap triumph of immediate effects, because it is absorbed by the controlling charm of proportion and unity. A careless good-luck of phrase is delightful ; but criticism cleaves to the teleological argument, and distinguishes the creative intellect, not so much by any happiness of natural endowment as by the marks of design. It is true that one may sometimes discover by a single verse whether an author have imagination, or may make a shrewd guess whether he have style or no, just as by a few spoken words you may judge of a man's accent; but the true artist in language is never spotty, and needs no guide-boards of admiring italics, a critical method introduced by Leigh Hunt, whose feminine temperament gave him acute perceptions at the expense of judgment. This is the Bœotian method, which offers us a brick as a sample of the house, forgetting that it is not the goodness of the separate bricks, but the way in which they are put together, that brings them within the province of art, and makes the difference between a heap and a house. A great writer does not reveal himself here and there, but everywhere. Langland's verse runs mostly like a brook, with a beguiling and wellnigh slumberous prattle, but he, more often than any writer of his class, flashes into salient lines, gets inside our guard with the home-thrust of a forthright word, and he gains if taken piecemeal. His imagery is naturally and vividly picturesque, as where he says of Old Age, —

> " Eld the hoar
> That was in the vauntward,
> And bare the banner before death," —

and he softens to a sweetness of sympathy beyond Chaucer when he speaks of the poor or tells us that Mercy is "sib of all sinful"; but to compare "Piers Ploughman" with the "Canterbury Tales" is to compare sermon with song.

Let us put a bit of Langland's satire beside one of Chaucer's. Some people in search of Truth meet a pilgrim and ask him whence he comes. He gives a long list of holy places, appealing for proof to the relics on his hat : —

> " 'I have walked full wide in wet and in dry
> And sought saints for my soul's health.'
> 'Know'st thou ever a relic that is called Truth?
> Couldst thou show us the way where that wight dwelleth?'
> 'Nay, so God help me,' said the man then,
> 'I saw never palmer with staff nor with scrip
> Ask after him ever till now in this place.' "

This is a good hit, and the poet is satisfied ; but, in what I am going to quote from Chaucer, everything becomes picture, over which lies broad and warm the sunshine of humorous fancy.

> " In oldë dayës of the King Artour
> Of which that Britouns speken gret honour,
> All was this lond fulfilled of fayerie:
> The elf-queen with her joly compaignie
> Dancëd ful oft in many a grenë mede:
> This was the old opinion as I rede;
> I speke of many hundrid yer ago:
> But now can no man see none elvës mo,
> For now the gretë charite and prayëres
> Of lymytours and other holy freres
> That sechen every lond and every streem,
> As thick as motis in the sonnëbeam,
> Blessyng halles, chambres, kichenës, and boures,
> Citees and burghës, castels hihe and toures,
> Thorpës and bernes, shepnes and dayeries,
> This makith that ther ben no fayeries.
> For ther as wont to walken was an elf

> There walkith none but the lymytour himself,
> In undermelës and in morwenynges,
> And sayth his matyns and his holy thinges,
> As he goth in his lymytatioun.
> Wommen may now go saufly up and doun;
> In every bush or under every tre
> There is none other incubus but he,
> And he ne wol doon hem no dishonóur."

How cunningly the contrast is suggested here between the Elf-queen's jolly company and the unsocial limiters, thick as motes in the sunbeam, yet each walking by himself! And with what an air of innocent unconsciousness is the deadly thrust of the last verse given, with its contemptuous emphasis on the *he* that seems so well-meaning! Even Shakespeare, who seems to come in after everybody has done his best with a "Let me take hold a minute and show you how to do it," could not have bettered this.

"Piers Ploughman" is the best example I know of what is called popular poetry, — of compositions, that is, which contain all the simpler elements of poetry, but still in solution, not crystallized around any thread of artistic purpose. In it appears at her best the Anglo-Saxon Muse, a first cousin of Poor Richard, full of proverbial wisdom, who always brings her knitting in her pocket, and seems most at home in the chimney-corner. It is genial; it plants itself firmly on human nature with its rights and wrongs; it has a surly honesty, prefers the downright to the gracious, and conceives of speech as a tool rather than a musical instrument. If we should seek for a single word that would define it most precisely, we should not choose simplicity, but homeliness. There is more or less of this in all early poetry, to be sure; but I think it especially proper to English poets, and to the most English among them, like Cowper, Crabbe, and one is tempted to add Wordsworth, — where he forgets Coleridge's private lectures. In reading such poets as Lang-

land, also, we are not to forget a certain charm of distance in the very language they use, making it unhack-
neyed without being alien. As it is the chief function
of the poet to make the familiar novel, these fortunate
early risers of literature, who gather phrases with the
dew still on them, have their poetry done for them, as
it were, by their vocabulary. But in Chaucer, as in all
great poets, the language gets its charm from him. The
force and sweetness of his genius kneaded more kindly
together the Latin and Teutonic elements of our mother
tongue, and made something better than either. The
necessity of writing poetry, and not mere verse, made
him a reformer whether he would or no ; and the instinct
of his finer ear was a guide such as none before him or
contemporary with him, nor indeed any that came after
him, till Spenser, could command. Gower had no notion
of the uses of rhyme except as a kind of crease at the
end of every eighth syllable, where the verse was to be
folded over again into another layer. He says, for example,

> " This maiden Canacee was hight,
> Both in the day and eke by night,"

as if people commonly changed their names at dark.
And he could not even contrive to say this without the
clumsy pleonasm of *both* and *eke*. Chaucer was put to
no such shifts of piecing out his metre with loose-woven
bits of baser stuff. He himself says, in the "Man of
Law's Tale," —

> " Me lists not of the chaff nor of the straw
> To make so long a tale as of the corn."

One of the world's three or four great story-tellers, he
was also one of the best versifiers that ever made English trip and sing with a gayety that seems careless, but
where every foot beats time to the tune of the thought.
By the skilful arrangement of his pauses he evaded the

monotony of the couplet, and gave to the rhymed pentameter, which he made our heroic measure, something
of the architectural repose of blank verse. He found
our language lumpish, stiff, unwilling, too apt to speak
Saxonly in grouty monosyllables; he left it enriched
with the longer measure of the Italian and Provençal
poets. He reconciled, in the harmony of his verse, the
English bluntness with the dignity and elegance of the
less homely Southern speech. Though he did not and
could not create our language (for he who writes to be
read does not write for linguisters), yet it is true that he
first made it easy, and to that extent modern, so that
Spenser, two hundred years later, studied his method
and called him master. He first wrote *English;* and it
was a feeling of this, I suspect, that made it fashionable
in Elizabeth's day to "talk pure Chaucer." Already we
find in his works verses that might pass without question
in Milton or even Wordsworth, so mainly unchanged
have the language of poetry and the movement of verse
remained from his day to our own.

> "Thou Polymnia
> On Pérnaso, that, with * thy sisters glade,
> By Helicon, not far from Cirrea,
> Singest with voice memorial in the shade,
> Under the laurel which that may not fade."

> "And downward from a hill under a bent
> There stood the temple of Mars omnipotent
> Wrought all of burnëd steel, of which th' entrée
> Was long and strait and ghastly for to see:
> The northern light in at the doorës shone
> For window in the wall ne was there none
> Through which men mighten any light discerne;
> The dore was all of adamant eterne."

And here are some lines that would not seem out of
place in the "Paradise of Dainty Devises":—

> "Hide, Absolom, thy giltë [gilded] tresses clear,
> Esther lay thou thy meekness all adown.

* Commonly printed *hath.*

12

Make of your wifehood no comparison ;
Hide ye your beauties Ysoude and Elaine,
My lady cometh, that all this may distain."

When I remember Chaucer's malediction upon his scriv-
ener, and consider that by far the larger proportion of
his verses (allowing always for change of pronunciation)
are perfectly accordant with our present accentual system, I cannot believe that he ever wrote an imperfect
line. His ear would never have tolerated the verses of
nine syllables, with a strong accent on the first, attributed to him by Mr. Skeate and Mr. Morris. Such
verses seem to me simply impossible in the pentameter
iambic as Chaucer wrote it. A great deal of misapprehension would be avoided in discussing English metres,
if it were only understood that quantity in Latin and
quantity in English mean very different things. Perhaps
the best quantitative verses in our language (better even
than Coleridge's) are to be found in Mother Goose, composed by nurses wholly by ear and beating time as they
danced the baby on their knee. I suspect Chaucer and
Shakespeare would be surprised into a smile by the
learned arguments which supply their halting verses
with every kind of excuse except that of being readable.
When verses were written to be chanted, more license
could be allowed, for the ear tolerates the widest devia-
tions from habitual accent in words that are sung.
Segnius irritant demissa per aurem. To some extent the
same thing is true of anapæstic and other tripping
measures, but we cannot admit it in marching tunes like
those of Chaucer. He wrote for the eye more than for
the voice, as poets had begun to do long before.* Some

---

* Froissart's description of the book of traités amoureux et de
moralité, which he had had engrossed for presentation to Richard II.
in 1394, is enough to bring tears to the eyes of a modern author. "Et
lui plut très grandement; et plaire bien lui devoit car il était enluminé

loose talk of Coleridge, loose in spite of its affectation of scientific precision, about "retardations" and the like, has misled many honest persons into believing that they can make good verse out of bad prose. Coleridge himself, from natural fineness of ear, was the best metrist among modern English poets, and, read with proper allowances, his remarks upon versification are always instructive to whoever is not rhythm-deaf. But one has no patience with the dyspondæuses, the pæon primuses, and what not, with which he darkens verses that are to be explained only by the contemporary habits of pronunciation. Till after the time of Shakespeare we must always bear in mind that it is not a language of books but of living speech that we have to deal with. Of this language Coleridge had little knowledge, except what could be acquired through the ends of his fingers as they lazily turned the leaves of his haphazard reading. If his eye was caught by a single passage that gave him a chance to theorize he did not look farther. Speaking of Massinger, for example, he says, "When a speech is interrupted, or one of the characters speaks aside, the last syllable of the former speech and first of the succeeding Massinger counts for one, because both are supposed to be spoken at the same moment.

> ' And felt the sweetness *of* ' *t*
>   ' *How* her mouth runs over.' "

Now fifty instances may be cited from Massinger which

écrit et historié et couvert de vermeil velours à dis cloux d'argent dorés d'or, et roses d'or au milieu, et à deux grands fremaulx dorés et richement ouvrés au milieu de rosiers d'or." How lovingly he lingers over it, hooking it together with *et* after *et !* But two centuries earlier, while the *jongleurs* were still in full song, poems were also read aloud.

> " Pur remembrer des ancessours
>   Les faits et les dits et les mours,
>   Deit l'en les livres et les gestes
>   Et les estoires *lire a festes*." — *Roman du Rou.*

But Chaucer wrote for the private reading of the closet.

tell against this fanciful notion, for one that seems, and
only seems, in its favor. Any one tolerably familiar with
the dramatists knows that in the passage quoted by
Coleridge, the *how* being emphatic, "*how her*" was pronounced *how'r*. He tells us that "Massinger is fond of
the anapæst in the first and third foot, as : —

'Tŏ yoŭr mōre | thăn mās|cŭlĭnĕ rēa|sŏn thāt | cŏmmānds 'ĕm ‖.'

Likewise of the second pæon (‿ — ‿ ‿) in the first foot,
followed by four trochees (— ‿), as : —

'Sŏ grēēdĭlў | lōng fŏr, | knōw theĭr | tĭtĭll|ātĭŏns.' "

In truth, he was no fonder of them than his brother
dramatists who, like him, wrote for the voice by the ear.
"To your" is still one syllable in ordinary speech, and
"masculine" and "greedily" were and are dissyllables
or trisyllables according to their place in the verse.
Coleridge was making pedantry of a very simple matter.
Yet he has said with perfect truth of Chaucer's verse,
"Let a few plain rules be given for sounding the final *è*
of syllables, and for expressing the terminations of such
words as *ocëan* and *natiön*, &c., as dissyllables, — or let
the syllables to be sounded in such cases be marked by
a competent metrist. This simple expedient would, with
a very few trifling exceptions, where the errors are in-
veterate, enable any one to feel the perfect smoothness
and harmony of Chaucer's verse." But let us keep widely clear of Latin and Greek terms of prosody ! It is also
more important here than even with the dramatists of
Shakespeare's time to remember that we have to do with
a language caught more from the ear than from books.
The best school for learning to understand Chaucer's
elisions, compressions, slurrings-over and runnings-to
gether of syllables is to listen to the habitual speech of
rustics with whom language is still plastic to meaning, and
hurries or prolongs itself accordingly. Here is a contrac-

tion frequent in Chaucer, and still common in New England : —

> " But me were lever than [lever 'n] all this town, quod he."

Let one example suffice for many. To Coleridge's rules
another should be added by a wise editor ; and that is to
restore the final *n* in the infinitive and third person plural
of verbs, and in such other cases as can be justified by
the authority of Chaucer himself. Surely his ear could
never have endured the sing-song of such verses as

> " I couthe telle for a gowne-cloth,"

or

> " Than ye to me schuld breke youre trouthe."

Chaucer's measure is so uniform (making due allowances)
that words should be transposed or even omitted where
the verse manifestly demands it, — and with copyists so
long and dull of ear this is often the case. Sometimes
they leave out a needful word : —

> " But er [the] thunder stynte, there cometh rain,"
> " When [that] we ben yflattered and ypraised,"
> " Tak [ye] him for the greatest gentleman."

Sometimes they thrust in a word or words that hobble
the verse : —

> " She trowed he were yfel in [some] maladie,"
> " Ye faren like a man [that] had lost his wit,"
> " Then have I got of you the maystrie, quod she,"
> ! (Then have I got the maystery, quod she,)
> " And quod the jugë [also] thou must lose thy head."

Sometimes they give a wrong word identical in meaning : —

> " And therwithal he knew [couthë] mo proverbes."

Sometimes they change the true order of the words : —

> " Therefore no woman of clerkës is [is of clerkës] praised "
> " His felaw lo, here he stont [stont he] hool on live."

> " He that covèteth is a porë wight
> For he wold have that is not in his might;
> But he that nought hath ne coveteth nought to have."

Here the "but" of the third verse belongs at the head of the first, and we get rid of the anomaly of "coveteth" differently accented within two lines. Nearly all the seemingly unmetrical verses may be righted in this way. I find a good example of this in the last stanza of "Troilus and Creseide." As it stands, we read, —

> " Thou one, two, and three, eterne on live
> That raignast aie in three, two and one."

It is plain that we should read "one *and* two" in the first verse, and "three *and* two" in the second. Remembering, then, that Chaucer was here translating Dante, I turned (after making the correction) to the original, and found as I expected

> " Quell' uno *e* due e tre che sempre vive
> E regna sempre in tre *e* due ed uno." (Par. xiv. 28, 29.)

In the stanza before this we have, —

> " To thee and to the philosophic*all* strode,
> To vouchsafe [vouchësafe] there need is, to correct " ;

and further on, —

> " With all mine herte' of mercy ever I pray
> And to the Lord aright thus I speake and say,"

where we must either strike out the second "I" or put it after "speake."

One often finds such changes made by ear justified by the readings in other texts, and we cannot but hope that the Chaucer Society will give us the means of at last settling upon a version which shall make the poems of one of the most fluent of metrists at least readable. Let any one compare the "Franklin's Tale" in the Aldine edition* with the text given by Wright, and he will find both sense and metre clear themselves up in a surprising way. A careful collation of texts, by the way, con

* One of the very worst, be it said in passing.

firms one's confidence in Tyrwhitt's good taste and thoroughness.

A writer in the "Proceedings of the Philological Society" has lately undertaken to prove that Chaucer did not sound the final or medial *e*, and throws us back on the old theory that he wrote "riding-rime," that is, verse to the eye and not the ear. This he attempts to do by showing that the Anglo-Norman poets themselves did not sound the *e*, or, at any rate, were not uniform in so doing. It should seem a sufficient answer to this merely to ask whence modern French poetry derived its rules of pronunciation so like those of Chaucer, so different from those of prose. But it is not enough to prove that some of the Anglo-Norman rhymers were bad versifiers. Let us look for examples in the works of the best poet among them all, Marie de France, with whose works Chaucer was certainly familiar. What was *her* practice? I open at random and find enough to overthrow the whole theory : —

> " Od sa fillë * ke le cela —
> Tut li curagës li fremi —
> Di mei, fet-elë par ta fei —
> La Dameiselë l'aporta —
> Kar ne li sembla mië boens —
> La damë l'aveit apelée —
> Et la merë l'areisuna."

But how about the elision ?

> " Le palï' esgardë sur le lit —
> Et ele' est devant li alée —
> Bele' amië [cf. mië, above] ne'il me celez
> La dame' ad sa fille' amenée."

These are all on a single page †, and there are some to

---

* Whence came, pray, the Elizabethan *commandĕment, chapĕlain, surĕty,* and a score of others? Whence the Scottish *bonny,* and so many English words of Romance derivation ending in *y*?

† Poésies de Marie de France, Tome I. p. 168.

spare.   How about the *hiatus?*   On the same page
I find, —

> " Kar l'Ercëveskë *i* estoit —
> Pur eus beneistre' *e* enseiner."

What was the practice of Wace?   Again I open at ran·
dom.

> " N'osa remaindre' en Normandië,
> Maiz, quant la guerrë fu finië,
> Od sou herneiz en Puille' *ala*—
> Cil de Baienës lungëment —
> Ne *il* nes pout par forcë prendre —
> Dunc la vilë mult amendout,
> Prisons e preiës amenout." *

Again we have the sounded final *e*, the elision, and the
hiatus.   But what possible reason is there for supposing
that Chaucer would go to obscure minstrels to learn the
rules of French versification?   Nay, why are we to sup·
pose that he followed them at all?   In his case as in
theirs, as in that of the Italians, with the works of whose
two greater poets he was familiar, it was the language
itself and the usages of pronunciation that guided the
poet, and not arbitrary laws laid down by a synod of
versemakers.   Chaucer's verse differs from that of Gower
and Lydgate precisely as the verse of Spenser differs
from that of Gascoigne, and for the same reason, — that
he was a great poet, to whom measure was a natural ve·
hicle.   But admitting that he must have formed his
style on the French poets, would he not have gone for
lessons to the most famous and popular among them, —
the authors of the " Roman de la Rose"?   Wherever
you open that poem, you find Guillaume de Lorris and
Jean de Meung following precisely the same method, — a
method not in the least arbitrary, but inherent in the
material which they wrought.   The *e* sounded or ab·
sorbed under the same conditions, the same slurring of

---

* Le Roman de la Rose, Tome II. p. 390.

diphthongs, the same occasional *hiatus*, the same compression of several vowels into one sound where they immediately follow each other. Shakespeare and Milton would supply examples enough of all these practices that seem so incredible to those who write about versification without sufficient fineness of sense to feel the difference between Ben Jonson's blank verse and Marlow's. Some men are verse-deaf as others are color-blind, — Messrs. Malone and Guest, for example.

I try Rutebeuf in the same haphazard way, and chance brings me upon his "Pharisian." This poem is in stanzas, the verses of the first of which have all of them masculine rhymes, those of the second feminine ones, and so on in such continual alternation to the end, as to show that it was done with intention to avoid monotony. Of feminine rhymes we find ypocrisië, famë, justicë, mesurë, yglisë. But did Rutebeuf mean so to pronounce them? I open again at the poem of the *Secrestain*, which is written in regular octosyllabics, and read, —

> " Envië fet homë tuer,
> Et si fait bonnë remuer —
> Envië greve', envië blecë,
> Envië confont charitë
> Envie' ocist humilitë, —
> Estoit en ce païs en vië
> Sanz orgueil ere' et sanz envië —
> La glorieusë, damë, chierë." *

Froissart was Chaucer's contemporary. What was his usage?

> " J'avoië fait en ce voiaigë
> Et je li di, ' Ma damë s'ai-je
> Pour vous ëu maint souvenir';
> Mais je ne sui pas bien hardis
> De vous remonstrer, damë chierë,
> Par quel art ne par quel manierë,
> J'ai ëu ce comencëment
> De l'amourous atouchëment.' "

* Rutebeuf, Tome I. pp. 203 seqq. 304 seqq.

If we try Philippe Mouskes, a mechanical rhymer, if ever there was one, and therefore the surer not to let go the leading-strings of rule, the result is the same.

But Chaucer, it is argued, was not uniform in his practice. Would this be likely? Certainly not with those terminations (like *courtesië*) which are questioned, and in diphthongs generally. Dante took precisely the same liberties.

> "Facea le stelle a noi parer più radi,"
> "Nè fu per fantasia giammai compreso"
> "Poi piovve dentro all 'alta fantasia,"
> "Solea valor e cortesia trovarsi,"
> "Che ne 'nvogliava amor e cortesia."

Here we have *fantasi'* and *fantasiä*, *cortesi'* and *cortesiä*. Even Pope has *promiscuous*, *obsequious*, as trisyllables, *individual* as a quadrisyllable, and words like *tapestry*, *opera*, indifferently as trochees or dactyls according to their place in the verse. Donne even goes so far as to make Cain a monosyllable and dissyllable in the same verse : —

> "Sister and wife to Cain, Caïn that first did plough."

The cæsural pause (a purely imaginary thing in accentual metres) may be made to balance a line like this of Donne's,

> "Are they not like | singers at doors for meat,"

but we defy any one by any trick of voice to make it supply a missing syllable in what is called our heroic measure, so mainly used by Chaucer.

Enough and far more than enough on a question about which it is as hard to be patient as about the authorship of Shakespeare's plays. It is easy to find all manner of bad metres among these versifiers, and plenty of inconsistencies, many or most of them the fault of careless or ignorant transcribers, but whoever has read them thoroughly, and with enough philological knowledge of cognate languages to guide him, is sure that they at least aimed at regularity, precisely as he is convinced that Raynouard's rule about singular and plural terminations has plenty of evidence to sustain it, despite the numerous exceptions. To show what a bad versifier *could* make out of the same language that Chaucer used, I copy one stanza from a contemporary poem.

> " When Phebus fresh was in chare resplendent,
> In the moneth of May erly in a morning,
> I hard two lovers profer this argument
> In the yeere of our Lord a M. by rekening,
> CCCXL. and VIII. yeere following.
> O potent princesse conserve true lovers all
> And grant them thy region and blisse celestial." *

Here is riding-rhyme, and on a very hard horse too. Can any one be insensible to the difference between such stuff as this and the measure of Chaucer? Is it possible that with him the one halting verse should be the rule, and the twenty musical ones the exception? Let us take heed to his own words : —

> " And, for there is so great diversitè
> In English, and in writing of our tong,
> So pray I God † that none miswritè the
> Ne the mismetre for defaut of tong,
> And redde whereso thou be or ellès song
> That thou be understood God I beseech."

Yet more. Boccaccio's *ottava rima* is almost as regular as that of Tasso. Was Chaucer unconscious of this? It will be worth while to compare a stanza of the original with one of the translation.

> " Era cortese Ettore di natura
> Però vedendo di costei il gran pianto,
> Ch'era più bella ch'altra creatura,
> Con pio parlare confortolla alquanto,

* From the " Craft of Lovers," attributed by Ritson to Lydgate, but too bad even for him.

† Here the received texts give " So pray I *to* God." Cf. " But Reason said him." T. & C.

Dicendo, lascia con la ria ventura
Tuo padre andar che tulti ha offeso tanto,
E tu, sicura e lieta, senza noia,
Mentre t 'aggrada, con noi resta in Troia." *

" Now was this Hector pitous of naturë,
And saw that she was sorrowful begon
And that she was so faire a creaturë,
Of his goodnesse he gladed her anon
And said [saidë] let your father's treason gon
Forth with mischance, and ye yourself in joy
Dwelleth with us while [that] you list in Troy."

If the Italian were read with the same ignorance that
has wreaked itself on Chaucer, the riding-rhyme would
be on its high horse in almost every line of Boccaccio's
stanza. The same might be said of many a verse in
Donne's satires. Spenser in his eclogues for February,
May, and September evidently took it for granted that
he had caught the measure of Chaucer, and it would be
rather amusing, as well as instructive, to hear the main-
tainers of the hop-skip-and-jump theory of versification
attempt to make the elder poet's verses dance to the tune
for which one of our greatest metrists (in his philological
deafness) supposed their feet to be trained.

I will give one more example of Chaucer's verse, again
making my selection from one of his less mature works.
He is speaking of Tarquin : —

" And ay the morë he was in despair
The more he coveted and thought her fair;
His blindë lust was all his coveting.
On morrow when the bird began to sing
Unto the siege he cometh full privily
And by himself he walketh soberly
The imáge of her recording alway new:
Thus lay her hair, and thus fresh was her hue,
Thus sate, thus spake, thus span, this was her cheer,
Thus fair she was, and this was her manére.
All this conceit his heart hath new ytake,
And as the sea, with tempest all toshake,

* Corrected from Kissner, p. 18.

> That after, when the storm is all ago,
> Yet will the water quap a day or two,
> Right so, though that her forme were absént,
> The pleasance of her forme was presént."

And this passage leads me to say a few words of Chaucer as a descriptive poet; for I think it a great mistake to attribute to him any properly dramatic power, as some have done. Even Herr Hertzberg, in his remarkably intelligent essay, is led a little astray on this point by his enthusiasm. Chaucer is a great narrative poet; and, in this species of poetry, though the author's personality should never be obtruded, it yet unconsciously pervades the whole, and communicates an individual quality, — a kind of flavor of its own. This very quality, and it is one of the highest in its way and place, would be fatal to all dramatic force. The narrative poet is occupied with his characters as picture, with their grouping, even their costume, it may be, and he feels for and with them instead of being they for the moment, as the dramatist must always be. The story-teller must possess the situation perfectly in all its details, while the imagination of the dramatist must be possessed and mastered by it. The latter puts before us the very passion or emotion itself in its utmost intensity; the former gives them, not in their primary form, but in that derivative one which they have acquired by passing through his own mind and being modified by his reflection. The deepest pathos of the drama, like the quiet " no more but so ? " with which Shakespeare tells us that Ophelia's heart is bursting, is sudden as a stab, while in narrative it is more or less suffused with pity, — a feeling capable of prolonged sustention. This presence of the author's own sympathy is noticeable in all Chaucer's pathetic passages, as, for instance, in the lamentation of Constance over her child in the " Man of

Law's Tale." When he comes to the sorrow of his story, he seems to croon over his thoughts, to soothe them and dwell upon them with a kind of pleased compassion, as a child treats a wounded bird which he fears to grasp too tightly, and yet cannot make up his heart wholly to let go. It is true also of his humor that it pervades his comic tales like sunshine, and never dazzles the attention by a sudden flash. Sometimes he brings it in parenthetically, and insinuates a sarcasm so slyly as almost to slip by without our notice, as where he satirizes provincialism by the cock

> " Who knew by nature each ascensiön
> Of the equinoctial in his native town."

Sometimes he turns round upon himself and smiles at a trip he has made into fine writing : —

> " Till that the brightë sun had lost his hue,
> For th' orisont had reft the sun his light,
> (This is as much to sayen as ' it was night.') "

Nay, sometimes it twinkles roguishly through his very tears, as in the

> " ' Why wouldest thou be dead,' these women cry,
> ' Thou haddest gold enough — and Emily ? ' "

that follows so close upon the profoundly tender despair of Arcite's farewell : —

> " What is this world ? What asken men to have ?
> Now with his love now in the coldë grave
> Alone withouten any company ! "

The power of diffusion without being diffuse would seem to be the highest merit of narration, giving it that easy flow which is so delightful. Chaucer's descriptive style is remarkable for its lowness of tone, — for that combination of energy with simplicity which is among the rarest gifts in literature. Perhaps all is said in saying that he has style at all, for that consists mainly in the absence of undue emphasis and exaggeration, in the clear uniform pitch which penetrates our interest and retains it, where mere loudness would only disturb and irritate.

Not that Chaucer cannot be intense, too, on occasion; but it is with a quiet intensity of his own, that comes in as it were by accident.

> "Upon a thickë palfrey, paper-white,
> With saddle red embroidered with delight,
> Sits Dido:
> And she is fair as is the brightë morrow
> That healeth sickë folk of nightës sorrow.
> Upon a courser startling as the fire,
> Æneas sits."

Pandarus, looking at Troilus,

> "Took up a light and found his countenance
> As for to look upon an old romance."

With Chaucer it is always the thing itself and not the description of it that is the main object. His picturesque bits are incidental to the story, glimpsed in passing; they never stop the way. His key is so low that his high lights are never obtrusive. His imitators, like Leigh Hunt, and Keats in his "Endymion," missing the nice gradation with which the master toned everything down, become streaky. Hogarth, who reminds one of him in the variety and natural action of his figures, is like him also in the subdued brilliancy of his coloring. When Chaucer condenses, it is because his conception is vivid. He does not need to personify Revenge, for personification is but the subterfuge of unimaginative and professional poets; but he embodies the very passion itself in a verse that makes us glance over our shoulder as if we heard a stealthy tread behind us : —

> "The smiler with the knife hid under the cloak." *

And yet how unlike is the operation of the imaginative faculty in him and Shakespeare! When the latter de-

* Compare this with the Mumbo-Jumbo Revenge in Collins's Ode.

scribes, his epithets imply always an impression on the moral sense (so to speak) of the person who hears or sees. The sun "flatters the mountain-tops with sovereign eye"; the bending "weeds lacquey the dull stream"; the shadow of the falcon "coucheth the fowl below"; the smoke is "helpless"; when Tarquin enters the chamber of Lucrece "the threshold grates the door to have him heard." His outward sense is merely a window through which the metaphysical eye looks forth, and his mind passes over at once from the simple sensation to the complex *meaning* of it, — feels *with* the object instead of merely feeling it. His imagination is forever dramatizing. Chaucer gives only the direct impression made on the eye or ear. He was the first great poet who really loved outward nature as the source of conscious pleasurable emotion. The Troubadour hailed the return of spring; but with him it was a piece of empty ritualism. Chaucer took a true delight in the new green of the leaves and the return of singing birds, — a delight as simple as that of Robin Hood : —

> "In summer when the shaws be sheen,
> And leaves be large and long,
> It is full merry in fair forest
> To hear the small birds' song."

He has never so much as heard of the "burthen and the mystery of all this unintelligible world." His flowers and trees and birds have never bothered themselves with Spinoza. He himself sings more like a bird than any other poet, because it never occurred to him, as to Goethe, that he ought to do so. He pours himself out in sincere joy and thankfulness. When we compare Spenser's imitations of him with the original passages, we feel that the delight of the later poet was more in the expression than in the thing itself. Nature with him is only good to be transfigured by art. We walk among Chaucer's sights and sounds ; we listen to Spenser's musical reproduction of them. In the same way, the pleasure which Chaucer takes in telling his stories has in itself the effect of consummate skill, and makes us follow all the windings of his fancy with sympathetic interest. His best tales run on like one of our inland rivers, sometimes hastening a little and turning upon themselves in eddies that dimple without retarding the current ; sometimes loitering smoothly, while here and there a quiet thought, a tender feeling, a pleasant image, a golden-hearted verse, opens quietly as a water-lily, to float on the surface without breaking it into ripple. The vulgar intellectual palate hankers after the titillation of foaming phrase, and thinks nothing good for much that does not go off with a pop like a champagne cork. The mellow suavity of more precious vintages seems insipid : but the taste, in proportion as it refines, learns to appreciate the indefinable flavor, too subtile for analysis. A manner has prevailed of late in which every other word seems to be underscored as in a school-girl's letter. The poet seems intent on showing his sinew, as if the power of the slim Apollo lay in the girth of his biceps. Force for the mere sake of force ends like Milo, caught and held mockingly fast by the recoil of the log he undertook to rive. In the race of fame, there are a score capable of brilliant *spurts* for one who comes in winner after a steady pull with wind and muscle to spare. Chaucer never shows any signs of effort, and it is a main proof of his excellence that he can be so inadequately sampled by detached passages, — by single lines taken away from the connection in which they contribute to the general effect. He has that continuity of thought, that evenly prolonged power, and that delightful equanimity, which characterize the higher orders of mind. There is something in him of the disinterestedness that made the Greeks masters in art. His

phrase is never importunate. His simplicity is that of
elegance, not of poverty.   The quiet unconcern with
which he says his best things is peculiar to him among
English poets, though Goldsmith, Addison, and Thackeray have approached it in prose.   He prattles inadvertently away, and all the while, like the princess in the
story, lets fall a pearl at every other word.   It is such a
piece of good luck to be natural !   It is the good gift
which the fairy godmother brings to her prime favorites
in the cradle.   If not genius, it is alone what makes
genius amiable in the arts.   If a man have it not, he will
never find it, for when it is sought it is gone.

When Chaucer describes anything, it is commonly by
one of those simple and obvious epithets or qualities that
are so easy to miss.   Is it a woman ?   He tells us she
is *fresh ;* that she has *glad* eyes ; that " every day her
beauty newed " ; that

> " Methought all fellowship as naked
> Withouten her that I saw once,
> As a coróne without the stones."

Sometimes he describes amply by the merest hint, as
where the Friar, before setting himself softly down,
drives away the cat.   We know without need of more
words that he has chosen the snuggest corner.   In some
of his early poems he sometimes, it is true, falls into the
catalogue style of his contemporaries ; but after he had
found his genius he never particularizes too much, — a
process as deadly to all effect as an explanation to a pun.
The first stanza of the " Clerk's Tale " gives us a landscape whose stately choice of objects shows a skill in
composition worthy of Claude, the last artist who painted
nature epically : —

> " There is at the west endë of Itaile,
> Down at the foot of Vesulus the cold,
> A lusty plain abundant of vitaile,

> Where many a tower and town thou may'st behold
> That founded were in time of fathers old,
> And many another delîtable sight;
> And Sàlucës this noble country hight."

The Pre-Raphaelite style of landscape entangles the eye among the obtrusive weeds and grass-blades of the foreground which, in looking at a real bit of scenery, we overlook; but what a sweep of vision is here! and what happy generalization in the sixth verse as the poet turns away to the business of his story! The whole is full of open air.

But it is in his characters, especially, that his manner is large and free; for he is painting history, though with the fidelity of portrait. He brings out strongly the essential traits, characteristic of the genus rather than of the individual. The Merchant who keeps so steady a countenance that

> " There wist no wight that he was e'er in debt,"

the Sergeant at Law, " who seemëd busier than he was," the Doctor of Medicine, whose " study was but little on the Bible," — in all these cases it is the type and not the personage that fixes his attention. William Blake says truly, though he expresses his meaning somewhat clumsily, " the characters of Chaucer's Pilgrims are the characters which compose all ages and nations. Some of the names and titles are altered by time, but the characters remain forever unaltered, and consequently they are the physiognomies and lineaments of universal human life, beyond which Nature never steps. Names alter, things never alter. As Newton numbered the stars, and as Linnæus numbered the plants, so Chaucer numbered the classes of men." In his outside accessaries, it is true, he sometimes seems as minute as if he were illuminating a missal. Nothing escapes his sure eye for the picturesque, — the cut of the beard, the soil of armor on the buff jerkin, the rust on the sword, the expression of the eye. But in this he has an artistic purpose. It is here that he individualizes, and, while every touch harmonizes with and seems to complete the moral features of the character, makes us feel that we are among living men, and not the abstracted images of men. Crabbe adds particular to particular, scattering rather than deepening the impression of reality, and making us feel as if every man were a species by himself; but Chaucer, never forgetting the essential sameness of human nature, makes it possible, and even probable, that his motley characters should meet on a common footing, while he gives to each the *expression* that belongs to him, the result of special circumstance or training. Indeed, the absence of any suggestion of *caste* cannot fail to strike any reader familiar with the literature on which he is supposed to have formed himself. No characters are at once so broadly human and so definitely outlined as his. Belonging, some of them, to extinct types, they continue contemporary and familiar forever. So wide is the difference between knowing a great many men and that knowledge of human nature which comes of sympathetic insight and not of observation alone.

It is this power of sympathy which makes Chaucer's satire so kindly, — more so, one is tempted to say, than the panegyric of Pope. Intellectual satire gets its force from personal or moral antipathy, and measures offences by some rigid conventional standard. Its mouth waters over a galling word, and it loves to say *Thou*, pointing out its victim to public scorn. *Indignatio facit versus*, it boasts, though they might as often be fathered on envy or hatred. But imaginative satire, warmed through and through with the genial leaven of humor, smiles half sadly and murmurs *We*. Chaucer either makes one knave betray another, through a natural jealousy of competition, or else expose himself with a *naïveté* of good-humored cynicism which amuses rather than disgusts. In the former case the butt has a kind of claim on our sympathy; in the latter, it seems nothing strange if the sunny atmosphere which floods that road to Canterbury should tempt anybody to throw off one disguise after another without suspicion. With perfect tact, too, the Host is made the *choragus* in this diverse company, and the coarse jollity of his temperament explains, if it does not excuse, much that would otherwise seem out of keeping. Surely nobody need have any scruples with *him*.

Chaucer seems to me to have been one of the most purely original of poets, as much so in respect of the world that is about us as Dante in respect of that which is within us. There had been nothing like him before, there has been nothing since. He is original, not in the sense that he thinks and says what nobody ever thought and said before, and what nobody can ever think and say again, but because he is always natural, because, if not always absolutely new, he is always delightfully fresh, because he sets before us the world as it honestly appeared to Geoffrey Chaucer, and not a world as it seemed proper to certain people that it ought to appear. He found that the poetry which had preceded him had been first the expression of individual feeling, then of class feeling as the vehicle of legend and history, and at last had wellnigh lost itself in chasing the mirage of allegory. Literature seemed to have passed through the natural stages which at regular intervals bring it to decline. Even the lyrics of the *jongleurs* were all run in one mould, and the Pastourelles of Northern France had become as artificial as the Pastorals of Pope. The Romances of chivalry had been made over into prose, and the *Melusine* of his contemporary Jehan d'Arras is

the forlorn hope of the modern novel. Arrived thus far
in their decrepitude, the monks endeavored to give them
a religious and moral turn by allegorizing them. Their
process reminds one of something Ulloa tells us of the
fashion in which the Spaniards converted the Mexicans :
" Here we found an old man in a cavern so extremely
aged as it was wonderful, which could neither see nor
go because he was so lame and crooked. The Father,
Friar Raimund, said it were good (seeing he was so
aged) to make him a Christian ; whereupon we baptized
him." The monks found the Romances in the same
stage of senility, and gave them a saving sprinkle with
the holy water of allegory. Perhaps they were only
trying to turn the enemy's own weapons against himself, for it was the free-thinking " Romance of the Rose "
that more than anything else had made allegory fashionable. Plutarch tells us that an allegory is to say one
thing where another is meant, and this might have been
needful for the personal security of Jean de Meung, as
afterwards for that of his successor, Rabelais. But,
except as a means of evading the fagot, the method has
few recommendations. It reverses the true office of
poetry by making the real unreal. It is imagination
endeavoring to recommend itself to the understanding
by means of cuts. If an author be in such deadly
earnest, or if his imagination be of such creative vigor
as to project real figures when it meant to cast only a
shadow upon vapor ; if the true spirit come, at once
obsequious and terrible, when the conjurer has drawn
his circle and gone through with his incantations merely
to produce a proper frame of mind in his audience, as
was the case with Dante, there is no longer any ques
tion of allegory as the word and thing are commonly
understood. But with all secondary poets, as with
Spenser for example, the allegory does not become of

one substance with the poetry, but is a kind of carven frame for it, whose figures lose their meaning, as they cease to be contemporary. It was not a style that could have much attraction for a nature so sensitive to the actual, so observant of it, so interested by it as that of Chaucer. He seems to have tried his hand at all the forms in vogue, and to have arrived in his old age at the truth, essential to all really great poetry, that his own instincts were his safest guides, that there is nothing deeper in life than life itself, and that to conjure an allegorical significance into it was to lose sight of its real meaning. He of all men could not say one thing and mean another, unless by way of humorous contrast.

In thus turning frankly and gayly to the actual world, and drinking inspiration from sources open to all; in turning away from a colorless abstraction to the solid earth and to emotions common to every pulse; in discovering that to make the best of nature, and not to grope vaguely after something better than nature, was the true office of Art; in insisting on a definite purpose, on veracity, cheerfulness, and simplicity, Chaucer shows himself the true father and founder of what is characteristically *English* literature. He has a hatred of cant as hearty as Dr. Johnson's, though he has a slier way of showing it; he has the placid common-sense of Franklin, the sweet, grave humor of Addison, the exquisite taste of Gray; but the whole texture of his mind, though its substance seem plain and grave, shows itself at every turn iridescent with poetic feeling like shot silk. Above all, he has an eye for character that seems to have caught at once not only its mental and physical features, but even its expression in variety of costume, — an eye, indeed, second only, if it should be called second in some respects, to that of Shakespeare.

I know of nothing that may be compared with the

prologue to the "Canterbury Tales," and with that to the story of the "Chanon's Yeoman" before Chaucer. Characters and portraits from real life had never been drawn with such discrimination, or with such variety, never with such bold precision of outline, and with such a lively sense of the picturesque. His Parson is still unmatched, though Dryden and Goldsmith have both tried their hands in emulation of him. And the humor also in its suavity, its perpetual presence and its shy unobtrusiveness, is something wholly new in literature. For anything that deserves to be called like it in English we must wait for Henry Fielding.

Chaucer is the first great poet who has treated To-day as if it were as good as Yesterday, the first who held up a mirror to contemporary life in its infinite variety of high and low, of humor and pathos. But he reflected life in its large sense as the life of *men*, from the knight to the ploughman, — the life of every day as it is made up of that curious compound of human nature with manners. The very form of the "Canterbury Tales" was imaginative. The garden of Boccaccio, the supper-party of Grazzini, and the voyage of Giraldi make a good enough thread for their stories, but exclude all save equals and friends, exclude consequently human nature in its wider meaning. But by choosing a pilgrimage, Chaucer puts us on a plane where all men are equal, with souls to be saved, and with another world in view that abolishes all distinctions. By this choice, and by making the Host of the Tabard always the central figure, he has happily united the two most familiar emblems of life, — the short journey and the inn. We find more and more as we study him that he rises quietly from the conventional to the universal, and may fairly take his place with Homer in virtue of the breadth of his humanity.

In spite of some external stains, which those who

have studied the influence of manners will easily account for without imputing them to any moral depravity, we feel that we can join the pure-minded Spenser in calling him "most sacred, happy spirit." If character may be divined from works, he was a good man, genial, sincere, hearty, temperate of mind, more wise, perhaps, for this world than the next, but thoroughly humane, and friendly with God and men. I know not how to sum up what we feel about him better than by saying (what would have pleased most one who was indifferent to fame) that we love him more even than we admire. We are sure that here was a true brother-man so kindly that, in his "House of Fame," after naming the great poets, he throws in a pleasant word for the oaten-pipes

> " Of the little herd-grooms
> That keepen beasts among the brooms."

No better inscription can be written on the first page of his works than that which he places over the gate in his "Assembly of Fowls," and which contrasts so sweetly with the stern lines of Dante from which they were imitated : —

> " Through me men go into the blissful place
> Of the heart's heal and deadly woundës' cure;
> Through me men go unto the well of Grace,
> Where green and lusty May doth ever endure;
> This is the way to all good aventure;
> Be glad, thou Reader, and thy sorrow offcast,
> All open am I, pass in, and speed thee fast!"

LIBRARY OF OLD AUTHORS.*

————◆————

MANY of our older readers can remember the anticipation with which they looked for each successive volume of the late Dr. Young's excellent series
of old English prose-writers, and the delight with which
they carried it home, fresh from the press and the bind-
ery in its appropriate livery of evergreen.   To most of
us it was our first introduction to the highest society
of letters, and we still feel grateful to the departed
scholar who gave us to share the conversation of such
men as Latimer, More, Sidney, Taylor, Browne, Fuller,
and Walton.   What a sense of security in an old book
which Time has criticised for us !   What a precious feeling of seclusion in having a double wall of centuries
between us and the heats and clamors of contemporary
literature !   How limpid seems the thought, how pure
the old wine of scholarship that has been settling for so
many generations in those silent crypts and Falernian
amphoræ of the Past !   No other writers speak to us
with the authority of those whose ordinary speech was
that of our translation of the Scriptures ; to no modern
is that frank unconsciousness possible which was natural
to a period when yet reviews were not ; and no later
style breathes that country charm characteristic of days
ere the metropolis had drawn all literary activity to itself, and the trampling feet of the multitude had banished
the lark and the daisy from the fresh privacies of lan

* London : John Russell Smith. 1856 – 64.

guage. Truly, as compared with the present, these old voices seem to come from the morning fields and not the paved thoroughfares of thought.

Even the "Retrospective Review" continues to be good reading, in virtue of the antique aroma (for wine only acquires its *bouquet* by age) which pervades its pages. Its sixteen volumes are so many tickets of admission to the vast and devious vaults of the sixteenth and seventeenth centuries, through which we wander, tasting a thimbleful of rich Canary, honeyed Cyprus, or subacidulous Hock, from what dusty butt or keg our fancy chooses. The years during which this review was published were altogether the most fruitful in genuine appreciation of old English literature. Books were prized for their imaginative and not their antiquarian value by young writers who sate at the feet of Lamb and Coleridge. Rarities of style, of thought, of fancy, were sought, rather than the barren scarcities of typography. But another race of men seems to have sprung up, in whom the futile enthusiasm of the collector predominates, who substitute archæologic perversity for fine-nerved scholarship, and the worthless profusion of the curiosity-shop for the sifted exclusiveness of the cabinet of Art. They forget, in their fanaticism for antiquity, that the dust of never so many centuries is impotent to transform a curiosity into a gem, that only good books absorb mellowness of tone from age, and that a baptismal register which proves a patriarchal longevity (if existence be life) cannot make mediocrity anything but a bore, or garrulous commonplace entertaining. There are volumes which have the old age of Plato, rich with gathering experience, meditation, and wisdom, which seem to have sucked color and ripeness from the genial autumns of all the select intelligences that have steeped them in the sunshine of their love and appreciation; — these quaint freaks of russet tell of Montaigne; these stripes of crimson fire, of Shakespeare; this sober gold, of Sir Thomas Browne; this purpling bloom, of Lamb; in such fruits we taste the legendary gardens of Alcinoüs and the orchards of Atlas; and there are volumes again which can claim only the inglorious senility of Old Parr or older Jenkins, which have outlived their half-dozen of kings to be the prize of showmen and treasuries of the born-to-be-forgotten trifles of a hundred years ago.

We confess a bibliothecarian avarice that gives all books a value in our eyes; there is for us a recondite wisdom in the phrase, "A book is a book"; from the time when we made the first catalogue of our library, in which "Bible, large, 1 vol.," and "Bible, small, 1 vol.," asserted their alphabetic individuality and were the sole *B*s in our little hive, we have had a weakness even for those checker-board volumes that only fill up; we cannot breathe the thin air of that Pepysian self-denial, that Himalayan selectness, which, content with one book-case, would have no tomes in it but *porphyrogeniti*, books of the bluest blood, making room for choicer new-comers by a continuous ostracism to the garret of present incumbents. There is to us a sacredness in a volume, however dull; we live over again the author's lonely labors and tremulous hopes; we see him, on his first appearance after parturition, " as well as could be expected," a nervous sympathy yet surviving between the late-severed umbilical cord and the wondrous offspring, doubtfully entering the Mermaid, or the Devil Tavern, or the Coffee-house of Will or Button, blushing under the eye of Ben or Dryden or Addison, as if they must needs know him for the author of the " Modest Enquiry into the Present State of Dramatique Poetry," or of the " Unities briefly considered by Philomusus," of which they have never heard and never will hear so much as

the names ; we see the country-gentlemen (sole cause of
its surviving to our day) who buy it as a book no gentleman's library can be complete without ; we see the
spendthrift heir, whose horses and hounds and Pharaonic
troops of friends, drowned in a Red Sea of claret, bring
it to the hammer, the tall octavo in tree-calf following
the ancestral oaks of the park. Such a volume is sacred
to us. But it must be the original foundling of the
book-stall, the engraved blazon of some extinct baron-
etcy within its cover, its leaves enshrining memorial-
flowers of some passion which the churchyard smothered
ere the Stuarts were yet discrowned, suggestive of the
trail of laced ruffles, burnt here and there with ashes
from the pipe of some dozing poet, its binding worn
and weather-stained, that has felt the inquisitive finger,
perhaps, of Malone, or thrilled to the touch of Lamb,
doubtful between desire and the odd sixpence. When
it comes to a question of reprinting, we are more choice.
The new duodecimo is bald and bare, indeed, compared
with its battered prototype that could draw us with a
single hair of association.

It is not easy to divine the rule which has governed
Mr. Smith in making the selections for his series. A
choice of old authors should be a *florilegium*, and not a
botanist's *hortus siccus*, to which grasses are as important
as the single shy blossom of a summer. The old-maid-
enly genius of antiquarianism seems to have presided
over the editing of the "Library." We should be inclined to surmise that the works to be reprinted had
been commonly suggested by gentlemen with whom they
were especial favorites, or who were ambitious that their
own names should be signalized on the title-pages with
the suffix of EDITOR. The volumes already published
are : Increase Mather's "Remarkable Providences";
the poems of Drummond of Hawthornden ; the "Vis-

ions of Piers Ploughman;" the works in prose and verse of Sir Thomas Overbury; the "Hymns and Songs" and the "Hallelujah" of George Wither; the poems of Southwell; Selden's "Table-Talk"; the "Enchiridion" of Quarles; the dramatic works of Marston, Webster, and Lilly; Chapman's translation of Homer; Lovelace, and four volumes of "Early English Poetry"! The volume of Mather is curious and entertaining, and fit to stand on the same shelf with the "Magnalia" of his book-suffocated son. Cunningham's comparatively recent edition, we should think, might satisfy for a long time to come the demand for Drummond, whose chief value to posterity is as the Boswell of Ben Jonson. Sir Thomas Overbury's "Characters" are interesting illustrations of contemporary manners, and a mine of footnotes to the works of better men, — but, with the exception of "The Fair and Happy Milkmaid," they are dull enough to have pleased James the First; his "Wife" is a *cento* of far-fetched conceits, — here a tom-tit, and there a hen mistaken for a pheasant, like the contents of a cockney's game-bag, and his chief interest for us lies in his having been mixed up with an inexplicable tragedy and poisoned in the Tower, not without suspicion of royal complicity. The "Piers Ploughman" is a reprint, with very little improvement that we can discover, of Mr. Wright's former edition. It would have been very well to have republished the "Fair Virtue," and "Shepherd's Hunting" of George Wither, which contain all the true poetry he ever wrote; but we can imagine nothing more dreary than the seven hundred pages of his "Hymns and Songs," whose only use, that we can conceive of, would be as penal reading for incorrigible poetasters. If a steady course of these did not bring them out of their nonsenses, nothing short of hanging would. Take this as a sample, hit on by opening at random : —

> " Rottenness my bones possest;
> Trembling fear possessèd me;
> I that troublous day might rest:
> For, when his approaches be
> Onward to the people made,
> His strong troops will them invade."

Southwell is, if possible, worse. He paraphrases David, putting into his mouth such punning conceits as "fears are my feres," and in his "Saint Peter's Complaint" makes that rashest and shortest-spoken of the Apostles drawl through thirty pages of maudlin repentance, in which the distinctions between the north and northeast sides of a sentimentality are worthy of Duns Scotus. It does not follow, that, because a man is hanged for his faith, he is able to write good verses. We would almost match the fortitude that quails not at the good Jesuit's poems with his own which carried him serenely to the fatal tree. The stuff of which poets are made, whether finer or not, is of a very different fibre from that which is used in the tough fabric of martyrs. It is time that an earnest protest should be uttered against the wrong done to the religious sentiment by the greater part of what is called religious poetry, and which is commonly a painful something misnamed by the noun and misqualified by the adjective. To dilute David, and make doggerel of that majestic prose of the Prophets which has the glow and wide-orbited metre of constellations, may be a useful occupation to keep country-gentlemen out of litigation or retired clergymen from polemics; but to regard these metrical mechanics as sacred because nobody wishes to touch them, as meritorious because no one can be merry in their company, — to rank them in the same class with those ancient songs of the Church, sweet with the breath of saints, sparkling with the tears of forgiven penitents, and warm with the fervor of martyrs, — nay, to set them up beside such poems as those of Herbert, composed in the upper chambers of the soul that open toward the sun's rising, is to confound piety with dulness, and the manna of heaven with its sickening namesake from the apothecary's drawer. The "Enchiridion" of Quarles is hardly worthy of the author of the "Emblems," and is by no means an unattainable book in other editions, — nor a matter of heartbreak, if it were. Of the dramatic works of Marston and Lilly it is enough to say that they are truly *works* to the reader, but in no sense dramatic, nor, as literature, worth the paper they blot. They seem to have been deemed worthy of republication because they were the contemporaries of true poets ; and if all the Tuppers of the nineteenth century will buy their plays on the same principle, the sale will be a remunerative one. It was worth while, perhaps, to reprint Lovelace, if only to show what dull verses may be written by a man who has made one lucky hit. Of the "Early English Poetry," nine tenths had better never have been printed at all, and the other tenth reprinted by an editor who had some vague suspicion, at least, of what they meant. The Homer of Chapman is so precious a gift, that we are ready to forgive all Mr. Smith's shortcomings in consideration of it. It is a vast *placer*, full of nuggets for the philologist and the lover of poetry.

Having now run cursorily through the series of Mr. Smith's reprints, we come to the closer question of *How are they edited ?* Whatever the merit of the original works, the editors, whether self-elected or chosen by the publisher, should be accurate and scholarly. The editing of the Homer we can heartily commend ; and Dr. Rimbault, who carried the works of Overbury through the press, has done his work well ; but the other volumes of the Library are very creditable neither to English scholarship nor to English typography. The Intro-

ductions to some of them are enough to make us think
that we are fallen to the necessity of reprinting our old
authors because the art of writing correct and graceful
English has been lost. William B. Turnbull, Esq., of
Lincoln's Inn, Barrister at Law, says, for instance, in his
Introduction to Southwell : " There was resident at
Uxendon, near Harrow on the Hill, in Middlesex, a
Catholic family of the name of Bellamy whom [which]
Southwell was in the habit of visiting and providing
with religious instruction when he exchanged his ordinary [ordinarily] close confinement for a purer atmosphere." (p. xxii.) Again, (p. xxii,) " He had, in this
manner, for six years, pursued, with very great success,
the objects of his mission, when these were abruptly
terminated by his foul betrayal into the hands of his
enemies in 1592." We should like to have Mr. Turnbull explain how the *objects* of a mission could be terminated by a betrayal, however it might be with the mission itself. From the many similar flowers in the Introduction to Mather's " Providences," by Mr. George
Offor, (in whom, we fear, we recognize a countryman,)
we select the following : " It was at this period when,
[that,] oppressed by the ruthless hand of persecu-
tion, our Pilgrim Fathers, threatened with torture and
death, succumbed not to man, but trusting on [in] an
almighty arm, braved the dangers of an almost unknown ocean, and threw themselves into the arms of
men called savages, who proved more beneficent than
national Christians." To whom or what our Pilgrim
Fathers *did* succumb, and what " national Christians "
are, we leave, with the song of the Sirens, to conjecture.
Speaking of the " Providences," Mr. Offor says, that
" they faithfully delineate the state of public opinion
two hundred years ago, the most striking feature being
an implicit faith in the power of the [in-]visible world to

13 *

hold visible intercourse with man : — not the angels to bless poor erring mortals, but of demons imparting power to witches and warlocks to injure, terrify and destroy," — a sentence which we defy any witch or warlock, though he were Michael Scott himself, to parse with the astutest demonic aid. On another page, he says of Dr. Mather, that "he was one of the first divines who discovered that very many strange events, which were considered preternatural, had occurred in the course of nature or by deceitful juggling; that the Devil could not speak English, nor prevail with Protestants; the smell of herbs alarms the Devil; that medicine drives out Satan!" We do not wonder that Mr. Offor put a mark of exclamation at the end of this surprising sentence, but we do confess our astonishment that the vermilion pencil of the proof-reader suffered it to pass unchallenged. Leaving its bad English out of the question, we find, on referring to Mather's text, that he was never guilty of the absurdity of believing that Satan was less eloquent in English than in any other language; that it was the British (Welsh) tongue which a certain demon whose education had been neglected (not *the* Devil) could not speak; that Mather is not fool enough to say that the Fiend cannot prevail with Protestants, nor that the smell of herbs alarms him, nor that medicine drives him out. Anything more helplessly inadequate than Mr. Offor's preliminary dissertation on Witchcraft we never read; but we could hardly expect much from an editor whose citations from the book he is editing show that he had either not read or not understood it.

Mr. Offor is superbly Protestant and iconoclastic, — not sparing, as we have seen, even Priscian's head among the rest; but, *en revanche*, Mr. Turnbull is ultramontane beyond the editors of the *Civiltà Cattolica.*

He allows himself to say, that, "after Southwell's death, one of his sisters, a Catholic in heart, but timidly and blamably simulating heresy, wrought, with some relics of the martyr, several cures on persons afflicted with desperate and deadly diseases, which had baffled the skill of all physicians." Mr. Turnbull is, we suspect, a recent convert, or it would occur to him that doctors are still secure of a lucrative practice in countries full of the relics of greater saints than even Southwell. That father was hanged (according to Protestants) for treason, and the relic which put the whole pharmacopœia to shame was, if we mistake not, his neckerchief. But whatever the merits of the Jesuit himself, and however it may gratify Mr. Turnbull's catechumenical enthusiasm to exalt the curative properties of this integument of his, even at the expense of Jesuits' bark, we cannot but think that he has shown a credulity that unfits him for writing a fair narrative of his hero's life, or making a tolerably just estimate of his verses. It is possible, however, that these last seem prosaic as a necktie only to heretical readers.

We have singled out the Introductions of Messrs. Turnbull and Offor for special animadversion because they are on the whole the worst, both of them being offensively sectarian, while that of Mr. Offor in particular gives us almost no information whatever. Some of the others are not without grave faults, chief among which is a vague declamation, especially out of place in critical essays, where it serves only to weary the reader and awaken his distrust. In his Introduction to Wither's "Hallelujah," for instance, Mr. Farr informs us that "nearly all the best poets of the latter half of the sixteenth century — for that was the period when the Reformation was fully established — and the whole of the seventeenth century were sacred poets," and that "even

Shakespeare and the contemporary dramatists of his age sometimes attuned their well-strung harps to the songs of Zion." Comment on statements like these would be as useless as the assertions themselves are absurd.

We have quoted these examples only to justify us in saying that Mr. Smith must select his editors with more care if he wishes that his "Library of Old Authors" should deserve the confidence and thereby gain the good word of intelligent readers, — without which such a series can neither win nor keep the patronage of the public. It is impossible that men who cannot construct an English sentence correctly, and who do not know the value of clearness in writing, should be able to disentangle the knots which slovenly printers have tied in the thread of an old author's meaning ; and it is more than doubtful whether they who assert carelessly, cite inaccurately, and write loosely are not by nature disqualified for doing thoroughly what they undertake to do. If it were unreasonable to demand of every one who assumes to edit one of our early poets the critical acumen, the genial sense, the illimitable reading, the philological scholarship, which in combination would alone make the ideal editor, it is not presumptuous to expect some one of these qualifications singly, and we have the right to insist upon patience and accuracy, which are within the reach of every one, and without which all the others are wellnigh vain. Now to this virtue of accuracy Mr. Offor specifically lays claim in one of his remarkable sentences : " We are bound to admire," he says, " the accuracy and beauty of this specimen of typography. Following in the path of my late friend William Pickering, our publisher rivals the Aldine and Elzevir presses, which have been so universally admired." We should think that it was the product of those presses which had been admired, and that Mr. Smith presents a still worthier object of admiration when he contrives to follow a path and rival a press at the same time. But let that pass ; — it is the claim to accuracy which we dispute ; and we deliberately affirm, that, so far as we are able to judge by the volumes we have examined, no claim more unfounded was ever set up. In some cases, as we shall show presently, the blunders of the original work have been followed with painful accuracy in the reprint; but many others have been added by the carelessness of Mr. Smith's printers or editors. In the thirteen pages of Mr. Offor's own Introduction we have found as many as seven typographical errors, — unless some of them are to be excused on the ground that Mr. Offor's studies have not yet led him into those arcana where we are taught such recondite mysteries of language as that verbs agree with their nominatives. In Mr. Farr's Introduction to the "Hymns and Songs" nine short extracts from other poems of Wither are quoted, and in these we have found no less than seven misprints or false readings which materially affect the sense. Textual inaccuracy is a grave fault in the new edition of an old poet; and Mr. Farr is not only liable to this charge, but also to that of making blundering misstatements which are calculated to mislead the careless or uncritical reader. Infected by the absurd cant which has been prevalent for the last dozen years among literary sciolists, he says, — "The language used by Wither in all his various works — whether secular or sacred — is pure Saxon." Taken literally, this assertion is manifestly ridiculous, and, allowing it every possible limitation, it is not only untrue of Wither, but of every English poet, from Chaucer down. The translators of our Bible made use of the German version, and a poet versifying the English Scriptures would therefore be likely to use more words of Teutonic origin than in his original compositions. But no English poet can write English poetry except in English, — that is, in that compound of Teutonic and Romanic which derives its heartiness and strength from the one and its canorous elegance from the other. The Saxon language does not sing, and, though its tough mortar serve to hold together the less compact Latin words, porous with vowels, it is to the Latin that our verse owes majesty, harmony, variety, and the capacity for rhyme. A quotation of six lines from Wither ends at the top of the very page on which Mr. Farr lays down his extraordinary *dictum*, and we will let this answer him, Italicizing the words of Romance derivation : —

> " Her true *beauty* leaves behind
> *Apprehensions* in the mind,
> Of more sweetness than all *art*
> Or *inventions* can *impart* ;
> Thoughts too deep to be *expressed*,
> And too strong to be *suppressed*."

Mr. Halliwell, at the close of his Preface to the Works of Marston, (Vol. I. p. xxii,) says, " The dramas now collected together are reprinted absolutely from the early editions, which were placed in the hands of our printers, who thus had the advantage of following them without the intervention of a transcriber. They are given as nearly as possible in their original state, the only modernizations attempted consisting in the alternations of the letters *i* and *j*, and *u* and *v*, the retention of which " (does Mr. Halliwell mean the letters or the " alternations " ?) " would have answered no useful purpose, while it would have unnecessarily perplexed the modern reader."

This is not very clear ; but as Mr. Halliwell is a member of several learned foreign societies, and especially of the Royal *Irish* Academy, perhaps it would be unfair to demand that he should write clear English. As one of Mr. Smith's editors, it was to be expected that he should not write it idiomatically. Some malign constellation (Taurus, perhaps, whose infaust aspect may be supposed to preside over the makers of bulls and blunders) seems to have been in conjunction with heavy Saturn when the Library was projected. At the top of the same page from which we have made our quotation, Mr. Halliwell speaks of " conveying a favorable impression *on* modern readers." It was surely to no such phrase as this that Ensign Pistol alluded when he said, "*Convey* the *wise* it call."

A literal reprint of an old author may be of value in two ways : the orthography may in certain cases indicate the ancient pronunciation, or it may put us on a scent which shall lead us to the burrow of a word among the roots of language. But in order to this, it surely is not needful to undertake the reproduction of all the original errors of the press ; and even were it so, the proofs of carelessness in the editorial department are so glaring, that we are left in doubt, after all, if we may congratulate ourselves on possessing all these sacred blunders of the Elizabethan type-setters in their integrity, and without any debasement of modern alloy. If it be gratifying to know that there lived stupid men before our contemporary Agamemnons in that kind, yet we demand absolute accuracy in the report of the phenomena in order to arrive at anything like safe statistics. For instance, we find (Vol. I. p. 89) " ACTUS SECUNDUS, SCENA PRIMUS," and (Vol. III. p. 174) " *exit ambo*," and we are interested to know that in a London printing-house, two centuries and a half ago, there was a philanthropist who wished to simplify the study of the Latin language by reducing all the nouns to one gender and all the verbs to one

number.   Had his emancipated theories of grammar prevailed, how much easier would that part of boys which
cherubs want have found the school-room benches!
How would birchen bark, as an educational tonic, have
fallen in repute! How white would have been the (now
black-and-blue) memories of Dr. Busby and so many
other educational *lictors*, who, with their bundles of rods,
heralded not alone the consuls, but all other Roman antiquities to us! We dare not, however, indulge in the
grateful vision, since there are circumstances which lead
us to infer that Mr. Halliwell himself (member though
he be of so many learned societies) hâs those vague notions of the speech of ancient Rome which are apt to
prevail in regions which count not the *betula* in their
Flora.   On page xv of his Preface, he makes Drummond
say that Ben Jonson " was dilated" (*delated*, — Gifford
gives it in English, *accused*) " to the king by Sir James
Murray," — Ben, whose corpulent person stood in so
little need of that malicious increment!

What is Mr. Halliwell's conception of editorial duty?
As we read along, and the once fair complexion of the
margin grew more and more pitted with pencil-marks,
like that of a bad proof-sheet, we began to think that he
was acting on the principle of every man his own wash-
erwoman, — that he was making blunders of set purpose,
(as teachers of languages do in their exercises,) in order
that we might correct them for ourselves, and so fit us
in time to be editors also, and members of various learned
societies, even as Mr. Halliwell himself is.   We fancied,
that, magnanimously waving aside the laurel with which
a grateful posterity crowned General Wade, he wished
us "to see these roads *before* they were made," and develop our intellectual muscles in getting over them.
But no; Mr. Halliwell has appended notes to his edition, and among them are some which correct misprints,

and therefore seem to imply that he considers that service as belonging properly to the editorial function. We are obliged, then, to give up our theory that his intention was to make every reader an editor, and to suppose that he wished rather to show how disgracefully a book might be edited and yet receive the commendation of professional critics who read with the ends of their fingers. If this were his intention, Marston himself never published so biting a satire.

Let us look at a few of the intricate passages, to help us through which Mr. Halliwell lends us the light of his editorial lantern. In the Induction to "What you Will" occurs the striking and unusual phrase, " Now out uppont," and Mr. Halliwell favors us with the following note : " Page 221, line 10. *Up-pont.* — That is, upon 't." Again in the same play we find —

> " Let twattling fame cheatd others rest,
>   I um no dish for rumors feast."

Of course, it should read, —

> " Let twattling [twaddling] Fame cheate others' rest,
>   I am no dish for Rumor's feast."

Mr. Halliwell comes to our assistance thus : " Page 244, line 21, [22 it should be,] *I um,* — a printer's error for *I am.*" *Dignus vindice nodus !* Five lines above, we have "whole" for "who 'll," and four lines below, " helmeth " for " whelmeth " ; but Mr. Halliwell vouchsafes no note. In the " Fawn " we read, " Wise *neads* use few words," and the editor says in a note, "a misprint for *heads* " ! Kind Mr. Halliwell !

Having given a few examples of our " Editor's " corrections, we proceed to quote a passage or two which, it is to be presumed, he thought perfectly clear.

> " A man can skarce put on a tuckt-up cap,
>   A button'd frizado sute, skarce eate good meate
>   *Anchoves, caviare,* but hee's satyred

> And term'd phantasticall.   By the muddy spawne
> Of slymie neughtes, when troth, phantasticknesse
> That which the naturall sophysters tearme
> *Phantusia incomplexa* — is a function
> Even of the bright immortal part of man.
> It is the common passe, the sacred dore,
> Unto the prive chamber of the soule;
> That bar'd, nought passeth past the baser court
> Of outward scence by it th' inamorate
> Most lively thinkes he sees the absent beauties
> Of his lov'd mistres."   (Vol. I. p. 241.)

In this case, also, the true readings are clear enough : —

> " And termed fantastical by the muddy spawn
>   Of slimy newts ";

and

> " . . . . past the baser court
>   Of outward sense "; —

but, if anything was to be explained, why are we here
deserted by our *fida compagna?* Again, (Vol. II. pp.
55, 56,) we read, "This Granuffo is a right wise good
lord, a man of excellent discourse, and never speakes his
signes to me, and men of profound reach instruct aboun-
dantly ; hee begges suites with signes, gives thanks with
signes," etc.   This Granuffo is qualified among the " In-
terlocutors " as " a silent lord," and what fun there is in
the character (which, it must be confessed, is rather of a
lenten kind) consists in his genius for saying nothing.
It is plain enough that the passage should read, "a
man of excellent discourse, and never speaks; his
signs to me and men of profound reach instruct abun-
dantly," etc.

In both the passages we have quoted, it is not difficult
for the reader to set the text right.   But if not difficult
for the reader, it should certainly not have been so for
the editor, who should have done what Broome was said
to have done for Pope in his Homer, — "gone before
and swept the way."   An edition of an English author
ought to be intelligible to English readers, and, if the

editor do not make it so, he wrongs the old poet, for two
centuries lapt in lead, to whose works he undertakes to
play the gentleman-usher. A play written in our own
tongue should not be as tough to us as Æschylus to
a ten years' graduate, nor do we wish to be reduced to
the level of a chimpanzee, and forced to gnaw our way
through a thick shell of misprints and mispointings only
to find (as is generally the case with Marston) a rancid
kernel of meaning after all. But even Marston sometimes deviates into poetry, as a man who wrote in that
age could hardly help doing, and one of the few instances
of it is in a speech of *Erichtho,* in the first scene of the
fourth act of " Sophonisba," (Vol. I. p. 197,) which Mr.
Halliwell presents to us in this shape : —

> ———" hardby the reverent (!) ruines
> Of a once glorious temple rear'd to Jove
> Whose very rubbish . . .
> . . . . . yet beares
> A deathlesse majesty, though now quite rac'd, [razed,]
> Hurl'd down by wrath and lust of impious kings,
> So that where holy Flamins [Flamens] wont to sing
> Sweet hymnes to Heaven, there the daw and crow,
> The ill-voyc'd raven, and still chattering pye,
> Send out ungratefull sounds and loathsome filth;
> Where statues and Joves acts were vively limbs,
>
> . . . .
>
> Where tombs and beautious urnes of well dead men
> Stood in assured rest," etc.

The last verse and a half are worthy of Chapman; but
why did not Mr. Halliwell, who explains *up-pont* and *I
çtm,* change " Joves acts were vively limbs " to " Jove's
acts were lively limned," which was unquestionably what
Marston wrote ?

In the " Scourge of Villanie," (Vol. III. p. 252,) there
is a passage which till lately had a modern application in
America, though happily archaic in England, which Mr.
Halliwell suffers to stand thus : —

> " Once Albion lived in such a cruel age
>   Than man did hold by servile vilenage:
>   Poore brats were slaves of bondmen that were borne,
>   And marted, sold: but that rude law is torne
>   And disannuld, as too too inhumane."

This should read —

> " *Man* man did hold in servile villanage;
>   Poor brats were slaves (of bondmen that were born)";

and perhaps some American poet will one day write in the past tense similar verses of the barbarity of his fore-fathers.

We will give one more scrap of Mr. Halliwell's text :—

> " Yfaith, why then, caprichious mirth,
>   Skip, light moriscoes, in our frolick blond,
>   Flagg'd veines, sweete, plump with fresh-infused joyes ! "

which Marston, doubtless, wrote thus : —

> " I'faith, why then, capricious Mirth,
>   Skip light moriscoes in our frolic blood !
>   Flagg'd veins, swell plump with fresh-infused joys ! "

We have quoted only a few examples from among the scores that we had marked, and against such a style of " editing " we invoke the shade of Marston himself. In the Preface to the Second Edition of the " Fawn," he says, " Reader, know I have perused this coppy, *to make some satisfaction for the first faulty impression ; yet so urgent hath been my business that some errors have styll passed, which thy discretion may amend.*"

Literally, to be sure, Mr. Halliwell has availed himself of the permission of the poet, in leaving all emendation to the reader ; but certainly he has been false to the spirit of it in his self-assumed office of editor. The notes to explain *up-pont* and *I um* give us a kind of standard of the highest intelligence which Mr. Halliwell dares to take for granted in the ordinary reader. Supposing this *nousometer* of his to be a centigrade, in what hitherto unconceived depths of cold obstruction can he find his zero-point of entire idiocy ? The expansive force of average wits cannot be reckoned upon, as we see, to drive them up as far as the temperate degree of misprints in one syllable, and those, too, in their native tongue. *A fortiori*, then, Mr. Halliwell is bound to lend us the aid of his great learning wherever his author has introduced foreign words and the old printers have made *pie* of them. In a single case he has accepted his responsibility as dragoman, and the amount of his success is not such as to give us any poignant regret that he has everywhere else left us to our own devices. On p. 119, Vol. II., *Francischina*, a Dutchwoman, exclaims, "O, mine aderliver love." Here is Mr. Halliwell's note. "*Aderliver.* — This is the speaker's error for *alder-liever*, the best beloved by all." Certainly not "the *speaker's* error," for Marston was no such fool as intentionally to make a Dutchwoman blunder in her own language. But is it an error for *alderliever* ? No, but for *alderliefster*. Mr. Halliwell might have found it in many an old Dutch song. For example, No. 96 of Hoffmann von Fallersleben's " Niederländische Volkslieder " begins thus : —

> " Mijn hert altijt heeft verlanghen
> Naer u, die *alderliefste* mijn."

But does the word mean "best beloved by all"? No such thing, of course ; but " best beloved of all," — that is, by the speaker.

In "Antonio and Mellida" (Vol. I. pp. 50, 51) occur some Italian verses, and here we hoped to fare better ; for Mr. Halliwell (as we learn from the title-page of his Dictionary) is a member of the " *Reale Academia di Firenze.*" This is the *Accademia della Crusca*, founded for the conservation of the Italian language in its purity, and it is rather a fatal symptom that Mr. Halliwell should indulge in the heresy of spelling *Accademia* with only one *c*. But let us see what our Della Cruscan's notions of conserving are. Here is a specimen : —

> " Bassiammi, coglier l' aura odorata
> Che in sua neggia in quello dolce labra.
> Dammi pimpero del tuo gradit' amore."

It is clear enough that we ought to read,

> " Lasciami coglier, ... Che ha sua seggia, ... Dammi l' impero."

A Della Cruscan academician might at least have corrected by his dictionary the spelling and number of
labra.

We think that we have sustained our indictment of
Mr. Halliwell's text with ample proof. The title of the
book should have been, " The Works of John Marston,
containing all the Misprints of the Original Copies,
together with a few added for the First Time in this
Edition, the whole carefully let alone by James Orchard
Halliwell, F. R. S., F. S. A." It occurs to us that Mr.
Halliwell may be also a Fellow of the Geological Society,
and may have caught from its members the enthusiasm
which leads him to attach so extraordinary a value to
every goose-track of the Elizabethan formation. It is
bad enough to be, as Marston was, one of those middling
poets whom neither gods nor men nor columns (Horace
had never seen a newspaper) tolerate ; but, really, even
they do not deserve the frightful retribution of being
reprinted by a Halliwell.

We have said that we could not feel even the dubious
satisfaction of knowing that the blunders of the old copies had been faithfully followed in the reprinting. We
see reason for doubting whether Mr. Halliwell ever read
the proof-sheets. In his own notes we have found several mistakes. For instance, he refers to p. 159 when he
means p. 153 ; he cites " I, but her *life*," instead of
" *lip* " ; and he makes Spenser speak of " old Pithonus."
Marston is not an author of enough importance to make
it desirable that we should be put in possession of all
the corrupted readings of his text, were such a thing

possible even with the most minute painstaking, and Mr. Halliwell's edition loses its only claim to value the moment a doubt is cast upon the accuracy of its inaccuracies. It is a matter of special import to us (whose means of access to originals are exceedingly limited) that the English editors of our old authors should be faithful and trustworthy, and we have singled out Mr. Halliwell's Marston for particular animadversion only because we think it on the whole the worst edition we ever saw of any author.

Having exposed the condition in which our editor has left the text, we proceed to test his competency in another respect, by examining some of the emendations and explanations of doubtful passages which he proposes. These are very few ; but had they been even fewer, they had been too many.

Among the *dramatis personæ* of the "Fawn," as we said before, occurs " Granuffo, *a silent lord.*" He speaks only once during the play, and that in the last scene. In Act I. Scene 2, *Gonzago* says, speaking to *Granuffo*, —

> " Now, sure, thou art a man
> Of a most learned *scilence*, and one whose words
> Have bin most pretious to me."

This seems quite plain, but Mr. Halliwell annotates thus : " *Scilence.* — Query, *science ?* The common reading, *silence,* may, however, be what is intended.' That the spelling should have troubled Mr. Halliwell is remarkable ; for elsewhere we find " god-boy " for " goodbye," " seace " for " cease," " bodies " for " boddice," " pollice " for " policy," " pitittying " for " pitying," " scence " for " sense," " Misenzius " for " Mezentius," " Ferazes " for " Ferrarese," — and plenty beside, equally odd. That he should have doubted the meaning is no less strange ; for on p. 41 of the same play we read, " My Lord Granuffo, you may likewise stay, for I know *you'l say nothing,"* — on pp. 55, 56, " This Granuffo is a right wise good lord, *a man of excellent discourse and never speaks,"* — and on p. 94, we find the following dialogue : —

> " *Gon.* My Lord Granuffo, this Fawne is an excellent fellow.
> " *Don.* Silence.
> " *Gon. I warrant you for my lord here.*

In the same play (p. 44) are these lines : —

> " I apt for love?
> Let lazy idlenes fild full of wine
> Heated with meates, high fedde with lustfull ease
> Goe dote on culler [color]. As for me, why, death a sence,
> I court the ladie ? "

This is Mr. Halliwell's note : " *Death a sence.* — ' Earth a sense,' ed. 1633. Mr. Dilke suggests : ' For me, why, earth's as sensible.' The original is not necessarily corrupt. It may mean, — why, you might as well think Death was a sense, one of the senses. See a like phrase at p. 77." What help we should get by thinking Death one of the senses, it would demand another Œdipus to unriddle. Mr. Halliwell can astonish us no longer, but we are surprised at Mr. Dilke, the very competent editor of the " Old English Plays," 1815. From him we might have hoped for better things. " Death o' sense ! " is an exclama. on. Throughout these volumes we find *a* for *o'*, — as, " a clock " for " o'clock," " a the side " for " o' the side." A similar exclamation is to be found in three other places in the same play, where the sense is obvious. Mr. Halliwell refers to one of them on p. 77, — " Death a man ! is she delivered ? " The others are, — " Death a justice ! are we in Normandy ? " (p. 98) ; and " Death a discretion ! if I should prove a foole now," or, as given by Mr. Halliwell, " Death, a discretion ! " Now let us apply Mr. Halliwell's explanation. " Death a man ! " you might as well think Death was a man,

that is, one of the men ! — or a discretion, that is, one
of the discretions ! — or a justice, that is, one of the
quorum ! We trust Mr. Halliwell may never have the
editing of Bob Acres's imprecations. " Odd's triggers ! "
he would say, "that is, as odd as, or as strange as, triggers."

Vol. III. p. 77, "the vote-killing mandrake." Mr.
Halliwell's note is, " *vote-killing.* — ' Voice-killing,' ed.
1613. It may well be doubted whether either be the
correct reading." He then gives a familiar citation from
Browne's " Vulgar Errors." " Vote-killing " may be a mere
misprint for " note-killing," but " voice-killing" is certainly the better reading. Either, however, makes sense. Although Sir Thomas Browne does not allude to the deadly property of the mandrake's shriek, yet Mr. Halliwell,
who has edited Shakespeare, might have remembered
the

> " Would curses kill, *as doth the mandrake's groan.*"
> (Second Part of Henry VI., Act III. Scene 2.)

and the notes thereon in the *variorum* edition. In Ja-
cob Grimm's " Deutsche Mythologie," (Vol. II. p. 1154,)
under the word *Alraun,* may be found a full account of
the superstitions concerning the mandrake. " When it
is dug up, it groans and shrieks so dreadfully that the dig-
ger will surely die. One must, therefore, before sunrise
on a Friday, having first stopped one's ears with wax or
cotton-wool, take with him an entirely black dog without
a white hair on him, make the sign of the cross three
times over the *alraun,* and dig about it till the root
holds only by thin fibres. Then tie these by a string to
the tail of the dog, show him a piece of bread, and run
away as fast as possible. The dog runs eagerly after
the bread, pulls up the root, and falls stricken dead by
its groan of pain."

These, we believe, are the only instances in which Mr.
Halliwell has ventured to give any opinion upon the

14

text, except as to a palpable misprint, here and there.
Two of these we have already cited. There is one other,
— "p. 46, line 10. *Iuconstant.* — An error for *incon-
stant.*" Wherever there is a real difficulty, he leaves us
in the lurch. For example, in "What you Will," he
prints without comment, —

> " Ha! he mount Chirall on the wings of fame ! "
>
> (Vol. I. p. 239.)

which should be "mount cheval," as it is given in Mr.
Dilke's edition (Old English Plays, Vol. II. p. 222). We
cite this, not as the worst, but the shortest, example at
hand.

Some of Mr. Halliwell's notes are useful and interesting, — as that on "keeling the pot," and a few others,
— but the greater part are utterly useless. He thinks
it necessary, for instance, to explain that "*to speak pure
foole,* is in sense equivalent to 'I will speak like a pure
fool,'" — that "belkt up" means "belched up," — that
"aprecocks" means "apricots." He has notes also upon
"meal-mouthed," "luxuriousnesse," "termagant," "fico,"
"estro," "a nest of goblets," which indicate either that
the "general reader" is a less intelligent person in England than in America, or that Mr. Halliwell's standard of
scholarship is very low. We ourselves, from our limited
reading, can supply him with a reference which will explain the allusion to the "Scotch barnacle" much better than his citations from Sir John Maundeville and
Giraldus Cambrensis, — namely, note 8, on page 179
of a Treatise on Worms, by Dr. Ramesey, court physician
to Charles II.

We turn now to Mr. Hazlitt's edition of Webster. We
wish he had chosen Chapman ; for Mr. Dyce's Webster
is hardly out of print, and, we believe, has just gone
through a second and revised edition. Webster was a

far more considerable man than Marston, and infinitely above him in genius. Without the poetic nature of Marlowe, or Chapman's somewhat unwieldy vigor of thought, he had that inflammability of mind which, untempered by a solid understanding, made his plays a strange mixture of vivid expression, incoherent declamation, dramatic intensity, and extravagant conception of character. He was not, in the highest sense of the word, a great dramatist. Shakespeare is the only one of that age. Marlowe had a rare imagination, a delicacy of sense that made him the teacher of Shakespeare and Milton in versification, and was, perhaps, as purely a poet as any that England has produced; but his mind had no balance-wheel. Chapman abounds in splendid enthusiasms of diction, and now and then dilates our imaginations with suggestions of profound poetic depth. Ben Jonson was a conscientious and intelligent workman, whose plays glow, here and there, with the golden pollen of that poetic feeling with which his age impregnated all thought and expression; but his leading characteristic, like that of his great namesake, Samuel, was a hearty common sense, which fitted him rather to be a great critic than a great poet. He had a keen and ready eye for the comic in situation, but no humor. Fletcher was as much a poet as fancy and sentiment can make any man. Only Shakespeare wrote comedy and tragedy with truly ideal elevation and breadth. Only Shakespeare had that true sense of humor which, like the universal solvent sought by the alchemists, so fuses together all the elements of a character, (as in Falstaff,) that any question of good or evil, of dignified or ridiculous, is silenced by the apprehension of its thorough humanity. Rabelais shows gleams of it in Panurge; but, in our opinion, no man ever possessed it in an equal degree with Shakespeare, except Cervantes; no man has since

shown anything like an approach to it, (for Molière's quality was comic power rather than humor,) except Sterne,
Fielding, and perhaps Richter.   Only Shakespeare was
endowed with that healthy equilibrium of nature whose
point of rest was midway between the imagination and
the understanding, — that perfectly unruffled brain
which reflected all objects with almost inhuman impartiality, — that outlook whose range was eccliptical, dom-
inating all zones of human thought and action, — that
power of veri-similar conception which could take away
Richard III. from History, and Ulysses from Homer, —
and that creative faculty whose equal touch is alike vivi-
fying in Shallow and in Lear.   He alone never seeks in
abnormal and monstrous characters to evade the risks
and responsibilities of absolute truthfulness, nor to stim-
ulate a jaded imagination by Caligulan horrors of plot.
He is never, like many of his fellow-dramatists, confronted with unnatural Frankensteins of his own making,
whom he must get off his hands as best he may.   Given
a human foible, he can incarnate it in the nothingness
of Slender, or make it loom gigantic through the tragic
twilight of Hamlet.   We are tired of the vagueness
which classes all the Elizabethan playwrights together
as "great dramatists," — as if Shakespeare did not differ from them in kind as well as in degree.   Fine poets
some of them were; but though imagination and the
power of poetic expression are, singly, not uncommon
gifts, and even in combination not without secular examples, yet it is the rarest of earthly phenomena to find
them joined with those faculties of perception, arrangement, and plastic instinct in the loving union which
alone makes a great dramatic poet possible.   We suspect
that Shakespeare will long continue the only specimen
of the genus.   His contemporaries, in their comedies,
either force what they call "a humor" till it becomes

fantastical, or hunt for jokes, like rat-catchers, in the sewers of human nature and of language. In their tragedies they become heavy without grandeur, like Jonson, or mistake the stilts for the cothurnus, as Chapman and Webster too often do. Every new edition of an Elizabethan dramatist is but the putting of another witness into the box to prove the inaccessibility of Shakespeare's stand-point as poet and artist.

Webster's most famous works are " The Duchess of Malfy " and " Vittoria Corombona," but we are strongly inclined to call " The Devil's Law-Case " his best play. The two former are in a great measure answerable for the " spasmodic " school of poets, since the extravagances of a man of genius are as sure of imitation as the equable self-possession of his higher moments is incapable of it. Webster had, no doubt, the primal requisite of a poet, imagination, but in him it was truly untamed, and Aristotle's admirable distinction between the *Horrible* and the *Terrible* in tragedy was never better illustrated and confirmed than in the " Duchess" and "Vittoria." His nature had something of the sleuth-hound quality in it, and a plot, to keep his mind eager on the trail, must be sprinkled with fresh blood at every turn. We do not forget all the fine things that Lamb has said of Webster, but, when Lamb wrote, the Elizabethan drama was an El Dorado, whose micaceous sand, even, was treasured as auriferous, — and no wonder, in a generation which admired the " Botanic Garden." Webster is the Gherardo della Notte of his day, and himself calls his " Vittoria Corombona" a " night-piece." Though he had no conception of Nature in its large sense, as something pervading a whole character and making it consistent with itself, nor of Art, as that which dominates an entire tragedy and makes all the characters foils to each other and tributaries to the catastrophe, yet there are flashes of Nature in his plays, struck out by the collisions of passion, and dramatic intensities of phrase for which it would be hard to find the match. The "prithee, undo this button" of Lear, by which Shakespeare makes us feel the swelling of the old king's heart, and that the bodily results of mental anguish have gone so far as to deaden for the moment all intellectual consciousness and forbid all expression of grief, is hardly finer than the broken verse which Webster puts into the mouth of Ferdinand when he sees the body of his sister, murdered by his own procurement : —

> "Cover her face: mine eyes dazzle: she died young."

He has not the condensing power of Shakespeare, who squeezed meaning into a phrase with an hydraulic press, but he could carve a cherry-stone with any of the *concettisti*, and abounds in imaginative quaintnesses that are worthy of Donne, and epigrammatic tersenesses that remind us of Fuller. Nor is he wanting in poetic phrases of the purest crystallization. Here are a few examples : —

> "Oh, if there be another world i' th' moon,
> As some fantastics dream, I could wish all *men*,
> The whole race of them, for their inconstancy,
> Sent thither to people that!"

(Old Chaucer was yet slier. After saying that Lamech was the first faithless lover, he adds, —

> "And he invented *tents*, unless men lie," —

implying that he was the prototype of nomadic men.)

> "Virtue is ever sowing of her seeds:
> In the trenches, for the soldier; in the wakeful study,
> For the scholar; in the furrows of the sea,
> For men of our profession [merchants]; all of which
> Arise and spring up honor."

("Of all which," Mr. Hazlitt prints it.)

> "Poor Jolenta! should she hear of this,
> She would not after the report keep fresh
> So long as flowers on graves."

> "For sin and shame are ever tied together
> With Gordian knots of such a strong thread spun,
> They cannot without violence be undone."

> "One whose mind
> Appears more like a ceremonious chapel
> Full of sweet music, than a thronging presence."

> "What is death?
> The safest trench i' th' world to keep man free
> From Fortune's gunshot."

> "It has ever been my opinion
> That there are none love perfectly indeed,
> But those that hang or drown themselves for love,"

says Julio, anticipating Butler's

> "But he that drowns, or blows out 's brains,
> The Devil's in him, if he feigns."

He also anticipated La Rochefoucauld and Byron in their apophthegm concerning woman's last love. In "The Devil's Law-Case," Leonora says, —

> "For, as we love our youngest children best,
> So the last fruit of our affection,
> Wherever we bestow it, is most strong,
> Most violent, most unresistible;
> Since 't is, indeed, our latest harvest-home,
> Last merriment 'fore winter."

In editing Webster, Mr. Hazlitt had the advantage (except in a single doubtful play) of a predecessor in the Rev. Alexander Dyce, beyond all question the best living scholar of the literature of the times of Elizabeth and James I. If he give no proof of remarkable fitness for his task, he seems, at least, to have been diligent and painstaking. His notes are short and to the point, and — which we consider a great merit — at the foot of the page. If he had added a glossarial index, we should have been still better pleased. Mr. Hazlitt seems to have read over the text with some care, and he has had the good sense to modernize the orthography, or, as ne says, has "observed the existing standard of spelling

throughout." Yet — for what reason we cannot imagine
— he prints "I" for "ay," taking the pains to explain
it every time in a note, and retains "banquerout" and
"coram" apparently for the sake of telling us that
they mean "bankrupt" and "quorum." He does not
seem to have a quick ear for scansion, which would
sometimes have assisted him to the true reading. We
give an example or two : —

> " The obligation wherein we all stood bound
>   Cannot be concealed [*cancelled*] without great reproach."

>   " The realm, not they,
> Must be regarded.   Be [we] strong and bold,
> We are the people's factors."

> " Shall not be o'erburdened [*overburdened*] in our reign

>   " A merry heart
> And a good stomach to [a] feast are all."

> " Have her meat serv'd up by bawds and ruffians "   [*dele* " up."]

>   " Brother or father
> In [a] dishonest suit, shall be to me."

> " What's she in Rome your greatness cannot awe,
> Or your rich purse purchase? Promises and threats."   [*dele* the
>   second " your."]

>   " Through clouds of envy and disast [rous] change."

>   " The Devil drives; 'tis [it is] full time to go."

He has overlooked some strange blunders. What is the
meaning of

> " Laugh at your misery, as foredeeming you
>   An idle meteor, which drawn forth, the earth
>   Would soon be lost i' the air " ?

We hardly need say that it should be

> " An idle meteor, which, drawn forth the earth,
>   Would," &c.

"*For*wardness" for *fro*wardness," (Vol. II. p. 87,) "ten-
nis-balls struck and ban*ded*" for "ban*died*," (Ib. p. 275,)
may be errors of the press ; but

>   " Come, I'll love you wisely:
> That's jealousy,"

has crept in by editorial oversight for "wisely, that 's
jealously."   So have

       "Ay, the great emperor of [*or*] the mighty Cham";

and

       'This wit [*with*] taking long journeys";

and

      "Virginius, thou dost but supply my place,
        I thine: Fortune hath lift me [*thee*] to my chair,
        And thrown me headlong to thy pleading bar";

and

      "I'll pour my soul into my daughter's belly, [*body*,]
       And with my soldier's tears embalm her wounds."

We suggest that the change of an *a* to an *r* would
make sense of the following : "Come, my little punk,
with thy two compositors, to this unlawful painting-
house," [printing-house,] which Mr. Hazlitt awkwardly
endeavors to explain by this note on the word *compositors*, — "i. e. (conjecturally), making up the composition
of the picture" !   Our readers can decide for themselves ;
— the passage occurs Vol. I. p. 214.

We think Mr. Hazlitt's notes are, in the main, good ;
but we should like to know his authority for saying that
pench means "the hole in a bench by which it was taken
up," — that "descant" means "look askant on," — and
that "I wis" is equivalent to "I surmise, imagine,"
which it surely is not in the passage to which his note is
appended.   On page 9, Vol. I., we read in the text,

      "To whom, my lord, bends thus your awe,"

and in the note, "i. e. submission.   The original has
aue, which, if it mean *ave*, is unmeaning here."   Did Mr.
Hazlitt never see a picture of the Annunciation with *ave*
written on the scroll proceeding from the bending angel's
mouth ?   We find the same word in Vol. III. p. 217 : —

      "Whose station's built on avees and applause."

Vol. III. pp. 47, 48 : —

14 *

U

> " And then rest, gentle bones ; yet pray
> That when by the precise you are view'd,
> A supersedeas be not sued
> To remove you to a place more airy,
> That in your stead they may keep chary
> Stockfish or seacoal, for the abuses
> Of sacrilege have turned graves to viler uses."

To the last verse Mr. Hazlitt appends this note, "Than that of burning men's bones for fuel." There is no allusion here to burning men's bones, but simply to the desecration of graveyards by building warehouses upon them, in digging the foundations for which the bones would be thrown out. The allusion is, perhaps, to the "Churchyard of the Holy Trinity"; — see Stow's *Survey*, ed. 1603, p. 126. Elsewhere, in the same play, Webster alludes bitterly to " begging church-land."

Vol. I. p. 73, "And if he walk through the street, he ducks at the penthouses, like an ancient that dares not flourish at the oathtaking of the prætor for fear of the signposts." Mr. Hazlitt's note is, " *Ancient* was a standard or flag ; also an *ensign*, of which Skinner says it is a corruption. What the meaning of the simile is the present editor cannot suggest." We confess we find no difficulty. The meaning plainly is, that he ducks for fear of hitting the penthouses, as an ensign on the Lord Mayor's day dares not flourish his standard for fear of hitting the signposts. We suggest the query, whether *ancient*, in this sense, be not a corruption of the Italian word *anziano*.

Want of space compels us to leave many other passages, which we had marked for comment, unnoticed. We are surprised that Mr. Hazlitt, (see his Introduction to " Vittoria Corombona,") in undertaking to give us some information concerning the Dukedom and Castle of Bracciano, should uniformly spell it *Brachiano*. Shakespeare's *Petruchio* might have put him on his guard.

We should be glad also to know in what part of Italy he places *Malfi*.

Mr. Hazlitt's General Introduction supplies us with no new information, but this was hardly to be expected where Mr. Dyce had already gone over the field. We wish that he had been able to give us better means of distinguishing the three almost contemporary John Websters one from the other, for we think the internal evidence is enough to show that all the plays attributed to the author of the "Duchess" and "Vittoria" could not have been written by the same person. On the whole, he has given us a very respectable, and certainly a very pretty, edition of an eminent poet.

We could almost forgive all other shortcomings of Mr. Smith's *library* for the great gift it brings us in the five volumes of Chapman's translations. Coleridge, sending Chapman's Homer to Wordsworth, writes, "What is stupidly said of Shakespeare is really true and appropriate of Chapman ; mighty faults counterpoised by mighty beauties. . . . . It is as truly an original poem as the Faery Queene ; — it will give you small idea of Homer, though a far truer one than Pope's epigrams, or Cowper's cumbersome most anti-Homeric Miltonism. For Chapman writes and feels as a poet, — as Homer might have written had he lived in England in the reign of Queen Elizabeth. In short, it is an exquisite poem, in spite of its frequent and perverse quaintnesses and harshnesses, which are, however, amply repaid by almost unexampled sweetness and beauty of language, all over spirit and feeling." * From a passage of his Preface it would appear that Chapman had been criticised pretty sharply in his own day for amplifying his author. "And this one example I thought necessary to insert here to show

* Literary Remains, Vol. I. pp. 259, 260.

my detractors that they have no reason to vilify my circumlocution sometimes, when their most approved Grecians, Homer's interpreters generally, hold him fit to be so converted. Yet how much I differ, and with what authority, let my impartial and judicial reader judge. Always conceiving how pedantical and absurd an affectation it is in the interpretation of any author (much more of Homer) to turn him word for word, when (according to Horace and other best lawgivers to translators) it is the part of every knowing and judicial interpreter not to follow the number and order of words, but the material things themselves, and sentences to weigh diligently, and to clothe and adorn them with words and such a style and form of oration as are most apt for the language in which they are converted." Again in his verses *To the Reader*, he speaks of

> " The *ample transmigration* to be shown
>   By nature-loving Poesy,"

and defends his own use of " needful periphrases," and says that " word for word " translation is to

> " Make fish with fowl, camels with whales, engender."

> " For even as different a production
>   Ask Greek and English : since, as they in sounds
>   And letters shun one form and unison,
>   So have their sense and elegancy bounds
>   In their distinguished natures, and require
>   Only a judgment to make both consent
>   In sense and elocution."

There are two theories of translation, — literal paraphrase and free reproduction. At best, the translation of poetry is but an imitation of natural flowers in cambric or wax ; and however much of likeness there may be, the aroma, whose charm of indefinable suggestion in the association of ideas is so powerful, is precisely what is lost irretrievably. From where it lurked in the immortal verse, a presence divined rather than ascertained,

baffling the ear which it enchanted, escaping the grasp
which yet it thrilled, airy, evanescent, imperishable,
beckoning the imagination with promises better than
any fulfilment,

> " The parting *genius* is with sighing sent."

The paraphrase is a plaster-cast of the Grecian urn ; the
reproduction, if by a man of genius, is like Keats's ode,
which makes the figures move and the leaves tremble
again, if not with the old life, with a sorcery which de-
ceives the fancy.   Of all English poets, Keats was the
one to have translated Homer.

In any other than a mere prose version of a great
poem, we have a right to demand that it give us at
least an adequate impression of force and originality.
We have a right to ask, If this poem were published
now for the first time, as the work of a contemporary,
should we read it, not with the same, but with anything
like the same conviction of its freshness, vigor, and originality, its high level of style and its witchery of verse,
that Homer, if now for the first time discovered, would
infallibly beget in us ?   Perhaps this looks like asking for
a new Homer to translate the old one ; but if this be too
much, it is certainly not unfair to insist that the feeling
given us should be that of life, and not artifice.

The Homer of Chapman, whatever its defects, alone
of all English versions has this crowning merit of being,
where it is most successful, thoroughly alive.   He has
made for us the best poem that has yet been Englished
out of Homer, and in so far gives us a truer idea of him.
Of all translators he is farthest removed from the fault
with which he charges others, when he says that " our
divine master's most ingenious imitating the life of things
(which is the soul of a poem) is never respected nor perceived by his interpreters only standing pedantically on

the grammar and words, utterly ignorant of the sense and grace of him." His mastery of English is something wonderful even in an age of masters, when the language was still a mother-tongue, and not a contrivance of pedants and grammarians. He had a reverential sense of "our divine Homer's depth and gravity, which will not open itself to the curious austerity of belaboring art, but only to the natural and most ingenious soul of our thrice-sacred Poesy." His task was as holy to him as a version of Scripture ; he justifies the tears of Achilles by those of Jesus, and the eloquence of his horse by that of Balaam's less noble animal. He does not always keep close to his original, but he sins no more, even in this, than any of his rivals. He is especially great in the similes. Here he rouses himself always, and if his enthusiasm sometimes lead him to heighten a little, or even to add outright, he gives us a picture full of life and action, or of the grandeur and beauty of nature, as stirring to the fancy as his original. Of all who have attempted Homer, he has the topping merit of being inspired by him.

In the recent discussions of Homeric translation in England, it has always been taken for granted that we had or could have some adequate conception of Homer's metre. Lord Derby, in his Preface, plainly assumes this. But there can be no greater fallacy. No human ears, much less Greek ones, could have endured what, with our mechanical knowledge of the verse, ignorance of the accent, and English pronunciation, we blandly accept for such music as Homer chanted. We have utterly lost the tune and cannot reproduce it. Mr. Newman conjectures it to have been something like Yankee Doodle ; Mr. Arnold is sure it was the English hexameter ; and they are both partly right so far as we may trust our reasonable impressions ; for, after all, an impression

is all that we have. Cowper attempts to give the ring
of the ἀργυρέοιο βιοῖο by

> "Dread-sounding, bounding on the silver bow,"

which only too fatally recalls the old Scottish dancing·
tune, —

> " Amaisit I gaisit
> To see, led at command,
> A strampant and rampant
> Ferss lyon in his hand."

The attempt was in the right direction, however, for
Homer, like Dante and Shakespeare, like all who really
command language, seems fond of playing with asso-
nances. No doubt the Homeric verse consented at will
to an eager rapidity, and no doubt also its general character is that of prolonged but unmonotonous roll. Everybody says it is like the long ridges of the sea, some
overtopping their neighbors a little, each with an independent undulation of its crest, yet all driven by a
common impulse, and breaking, not with the sudden
snap of an unyielding material, but one after the other,
with a stately curve, to slide back and mingle with those
that follow. Chapman's measure has the disadvantage
of an association with Sternhold and Hopkins, but it has
the merit of length, and, where he is in the right mood,
is free, spirited, and sonorous. Above all, there is everywhere the movement of life and passion in it. Chapman was a master of verse, making it hurry, linger, or
stop short, to suit the meaning. Like all great versifiers
he must be read with study, for the slightest change of
accent loses the expression of an entire passage. His
great fault as a translator is that he takes fire too easily
and runs beyond his author. Perhaps he *intensifies* too
much, though this be a fault on the right side ; he certainly sometimes weakens the force of passages by crowd-
ing in particulars which Homer had wisely omitted, for

Homer's simplicity is by no means mere simplicity of thought, nor, as it is often foolishly called, of nature. It is the simplicity of consummate art, the last achievement of poets and the invariable characteristic of the greatest among them. To Chapman's mind once warmed to its work, the words are only a mist, suggesting, while it hides, the divine form of the original image or thought; and his imagination strives to body forth that, as he conceives it, in all its celestial proportions. Let us compare with Lord Derby's version, as the latest, a passage where Chapman merely intensifies (Book XIII., beginning at the 86th verse in Lord Derby, the 73d of Chapman, and the 76th of Homer) : —

> " Whom answered thus the son of Telamon:
> ' My hands, too, grasp with firmer hold the spear,
> My spirit, like thine, is stirred; I feel my feet
> Instinct with fiery life; nor should I fear
> With Hector, son of Priam, in his might
> Alone to meet, and grapple to the death.' "

Thus Lord Derby. Chapman renders : —

> " This Telamonius thus received: ' So, to my thoughts, my hands
> Burn with desire to toss my lance; *each foot beneath me stands*
> *Bare on bright fire to use his speed ;* my heart is raised so high,
> That to encounter Hector's self I long insatiately.' "

There is no question which version is the more energetic. Is Lord Derby's nearer the original in being tamer? He has taken the " instinct with fiery life " from Chapman's hint. The original has simply " restless," or more familiarly "in a fidget." There is nothing about " grappling to the death," and " nor should I fear " is feeble where Chapman with his " long insatiately " is literal. We will give an example where Chapman has amplified his original (Book XVI. v. 426 ; Derby, 494 ; Chapman, 405) : —

> " Down jumped he from his chariot; down leapt his foe as light;
> And as, on some far-looking rock, a cast of vultures fight,

> Fly on each other, strike and truss, part, meet, and then stick by,
> Tug both with crooked beaks and seres, cry, fight, and fight and cry,
> So fiercely fought these angry kings." *

Lord Derby's version is nearer : —

> " He said, and from his car, accoutred, sprang;
> Patroclus saw and he too leaped to earth.
> As on a lofty rock, with angry screams,
> Hook-beaked, with talons curved, two vultures fight,
> So with loud shouts these two to battle rushed."

Chapman has made his first line out of two in Homer, but, granting the license, how rapid and springy is the verse ! Lord Derby's "withs" are not agreeable, his "shouts" is an ill-chosen word for a comparison with vultures, " talons curved " is feeble, and his verse is, as usual, mainly built up of little blocks of four syllables each. " To battle " also is vague. With whom ? Homer says that they rushed each at other. We shall not discuss how much license is loyal in a translator, but, as we think his chief aim should be to give a feeling of that life and spirit which makes the immortality of his original, and is the very breath in the nostrils of all poetry, he has a right to adapt himself to the genius of his own language. If he would do justice to his author, he must make up in one passage for his unavoidable shortcomings in another. He may here and there take for granted certain exigencies of verse in his original which he feels in his own case. Even Dante, who boasted that no word had ever made him say what he did not wish, should have made an exception of rhyming ones, for these sometimes, even in so abundant a language as the Italian, have driven the most straightforward of poets into an awkward _détour_.

We give one more passage from Chapman : —

---

* Chapman himself was evidently pleased with this, for he cites it as a sample of his version.

> "And all in golden weeds
> He clothed himself; the golden scourge most elegantly done
> He took and mounted to his seat; and then the god begun
> To drive his chariot through the waves. From whirl-pits every way
> The whales exulted under him, and knew their king; the sea
> For joy did open, and his horse so swift and lightly flew
> The under axle-tree of brass no drop of water drew."

Here the first half is sluggish and inadequate, but what surging vigor, what tumult of the sea, what swiftness, in the last! Here is Lord Derby's attempt:—

> "All clad in gold, the golden lash he grasped
> Of curious work, and, mounting on his car,
> Skimmed o'er the waves; from all the depths below
> Gambolled around the monsters of the deep,
> Acknowledging their king; the joyous sea
> Parted her waves; swift flew the bounding steeds,
> Nor was the brazen axle wet with spray."

Chapman here is truer to his master, and the motion is in the verse itself. Lord Derby's is description, and not picture. "Monsters of the deep" is an example of the hackneyed periphrases in which he abounds, like all men to whom language is a literary tradition, and not a living gift of the Muses. "*Lash*" is precisely the wrong word. Chapman is always great at sea. Here is another example from the Fourteenth Book:—

> "And as, when with unwieldy waves *the great sea forefeels winds*
> That both ways murmur, and no way her certain current finds,
> But pants and swells confusedly, here goes, and there will stay,
> Till on it air casts one firm wind, and then it rolls away."

Observe how the somewhat ponderous movement of the first verse assists the meaning of the words.

He is great, too, in single phrases and lines:—

> "And as, from top of some steep hill, the Lightener strips a cloud
> *And lets a great sky out of Heaven*, in whose delightsome light
> All prominent foreheads, forests, towers, and temples cheer the sight."
> (Book XVI. v. 286.)

The lion "lets his rough brows down so low they hide his eyes"; the flames "wrastle" in the woods; "rude feet dim the day with a fog of dust ; " and so in a hundred other instances.

For an example of his more restrained vigor, take the speech of Sarpedon in the Twelfth Book of the Iliad, and for poetic beauty, the whole story of Ulysses and Nausikaa in the Odyssey. It was here that Keats made himself Grecian and learned to versify.

Mr. Hooper has done his work of editing well. But he has sometimes misapprehended his author, and distorted his meaning by faulty punctuation. In one of the passages already cited, Mr. Hooper's text stands thus : "Lest I be prejudiced with opinion, to dissent, of ignorance, or singularity."   All the commas which darken the sense should be removed. Chapman meant to say, "Lest I be condemned beforehand by people thinking I dissent out of ignorance or singularity." (Iliad Vol. I. p. 23.)   So on the next page the want of a hyphen makes nonsense : "And saw the round coming [round-coming] of this silver bow of our Phoebus," that is, the crescent coming to the full circle. In the translations, too, the pointing needs reformation now and then, but shows, on the whole, a praiseworthy fidelity. We will give a few examples of what we believe to be errors on the part of Mr. Hooper, who, by the way, is weakest on points which concern the language of Chapman's day. We follow the order of the text as most convenient.

" Bid " (Il. i.) is explained to mean "threaten, challenge," where "offer" would be the right word.

> " And cast
> The offal of all to the deep."   (Il. i. 309.)

Surely a slip of Chapman's pen. He must have intended to write "Of all the offal," a transversion common with him and needed here to avoid a punning jingle.

" So much I must affirm our power exceeds th' inhabitant." (Il. ii. 110.

Mr. Hooper's note is "inhabiters, viz. of Troy." "Inhabitant" is an adjective agreeing with "power." Our power without exceeds that within.

> "Yet all this time to stay,
> Out of our judgments, for our end, and now to take our way
> Without it were absurd and vile." (Il. ii. 257.)

A note on this passage tells us that "out of judgments" means "against our inclinations." It means simply "in accordance with our good judgment," just as we still say "out of his wisdom." Compare Il. iii. 63,

> "Hector, because thy sharp reproof is *out of justice* given,
> I take it well."

> "And as Jove, brandishing a star which men a comet call,
> Hurls out his curlèd hair abroad, that from his brand exhals
> A thousand sparks." (Il. iv. 85.)

Mr. Hooper's note is "'*Which men a comet call*'—so both the folios. Dr. Taylor has printed '*which man a comet calls.*' This certainly suits the rhyme, but I adhere to Chapman's text." Both editors have misunderstood the passage. The fault is not in "call" but in "exhals," a clear misprint for "exhall," the spelling, as was common, being conformed to the visible rhyme. "That" means "so that" (a frequent Elizabethan construction) and "exhall" is governed by "sparks." The meaning is, "As when Jove, brandishing a comet, hurls out its curled hair so that a thousand sparks exhale from its burning."

> "The *evicke* skipping from the rock."

Mr. Hooper tells us, "It is doubtful what this word really is. Dr. Taylor suggests that it may probably mean the *evict*, or doomed one—but? It is possible Chapman meant to Anglicize the Greek αἴξ; or should we read Ibex, as the αἴξ ἴξαλος was such?" The word means the *chamois*, and is merely the English form of the French *ibiche*. Dr. Taylor's reading would amaze us were we not familiar with the commentators on Shake-speare.

> " And now they *out-ray* to your fleet." (Il. v. 793.)

" *Out-ray* — spread out in array ; abbreviated from ar-ray. Dr. Taylor says 'rush out,' from the Anglo-Saxon ' *rean*,' to flow ; but there seems no necessity for such an etymology." We should think not ! Chapman, like Pope, made his first sketch from the French, and corrected it by the Greek. Those who would under-stand Chapman's English must allow for traces of his French guide here and there. This is one of them, per-haps. The word is etymologically unrelated to *array*. It is merely the old French *oultréer*, a derivative of *ultra*. It means " they pass beyond their gates even to your fleet." He had said just before that formerly " your foes durst not a foot address *without their ports*." The word occurs again Il. xxiii. 413.

> " When none, though many kings put on, could make his vaunt, he led
> Tydides to renewed assault or issued first the dike." (Il. viii. 217.)

" *Tydides*. — He led Tydides, i. e. Tydides he led. An unusual construction." Not in the least. The old print-ers or authors sometimes put a comma where some con-necting particle was left out. We had just now an in-stance where one took the place of *so*. Here it supplies *that*. " None could make his vaunt that he led (that is, was before) Tydides." We still use the word in the same sense, as the " leading " horse in a race.

> " And all did wilfully expect the silver-throned morn." (Il. viii. 497.)

" *Wilfully* — willingly, anxiously." *Wishfully*, as else-where in Chapman.

> " And as, upon a rich man's crop of barley or of wheat,
> Opposed for swiftness at their work, a sort of reapers sweat."

" *Opposed* — standing opposite to one another for expedi-tion's sake." We hope Mr. Hooper understood his own note, for it baffles us utterly. The meaning is simply "pitted against each other to see which will reap most swiftly." In a note (Il. xi. 417) we are told that "the etymology [of *lucern*] seems uncertain." It is nothing more than a corruption of the old French *leucerve* (*loup-cervier*).

> "I would then make-in in deed and steep
> My income in their bloods." (Il. xvii. 481.)

"*Income* — communication, or infusion, of courage from the Gods. The word in this sense Todd says was a favorite in Cromwell's time." A surprising note! *Income* here means nothing more than "onfall," as the context shows.

> "To put the best in *ure*." (Il. xvii. 545.)

"*Ure* — use. Skinner thinks it a contraction of *usura*. It is frequent in Chaucer. Todd gives examples from Hooker and L'Estrange." The word is common enough, but how Mr. Hooper could seriously quote good old Skinner for such an etymology we cannot conceive. It does not mean "in use," but "to work," being merely the English form of *en œuvre*, as "manure" is of *manœuvrer*.

> "So troop-meal Troy pursued a while." (Il. xvii. 634.)

"*Troop-meal* — in troops, troop by troop. So piece-meal. To *meal* was to mingle, mix together; from the French *mêler*. . . . . The reader would do well to consult Dr. Jamieson's excellent 'Dictionary of the Scottish Language' in voce '*mell*.'" No doubt the reader might profit by consulting it under any other word beginning with M, and any of them would be as much to the purpose as *mell*. *Troop-meal*, like *inch-meal*, *piece-meal*, implies separation, not mingling, and is from a Teutonic root. Mr. Hooper is always weak in his linguistic. In a note on Il. xviii. 144, he informs us that "To *sterve* is to *die*; and the sense of *starve*, with cold or hunger

originated in the 17th century." We would it had!
But we suspect that men had died of both these diseases
earlier. What he should have said was that the restric-
tion of meaning to dying with hunger was modern.

Il. xx. 239 we have " the God's " for " the Gods' " and
a few lines below " Anchisiades' " for " Anchisiades's ";
Il. xxi. 407, " press'd " for " prest."

We had noted a considerable number of other slips,
but we will mention only two more. " Treen broches "
is explained to mean "branches of trees." (Hymn to
Hermes, 227.) It means " wooden spits." In the
Bacchus (28, 29) Mr. Hooper restores a corrupt reading
which Mr. Singer (for a wonder) had set right. He
prints, —

> " Nay, which of all the Pow'r fully-divined
> Esteem ye him? "

Of course it should be powerfully-divined, for otherwise
we must read " Pow'rs." The five volumes need a very
careful revision in their punctuation, and in another edition we should advise Mr. Hooper to strike out every
note in which he has been tempted into etymology.

We come next to Mr. W. C. Hazlitt's edition of Lovelace. Three short pieces of Lovelace's have lived, and
deserved to live : " To Lucasta from Prison," " To Lucasta on going to the Wars," and " The Grasshopper."
They are graceful, airy, and nicely finished. The last
especially is a charming poem, delicate in expression,
and full of quaint fancy, which only in the latter half is
strained to conceit. As the verses of a gentleman they
are among the best, though not of a very high order as
poetry. He is to be classed with the *lucky* authors who,
without great powers, have written one or two pieces so
facile in thought and fortunate in phrase as to be carried
lightly in the memory, poems in which analysis finds lit-

tle, but which are charming in their frail completeness. This faculty of hitting on the precise *lilt* of thought and measure that shall catch the universal ear and sing themselves in everybody's memory, is a rare gift.   We have heard many ingenious persons try to explain the *cling* of such a poem as " The Burial of Sir John Moore," and the result of all seemed to be, that there were certain verses that were good, not because of their goodness, but because one could not forget them.   They have the great merit of being portable, and we have to carry so much luggage through life, that we should be thankful for what will pack easily and take up no room.

All that Lovelace wrote beside these three poems is utterly worthless, mere chaff from the threshing of his wits.   Take out the four pages on which they are printed, and we have two hundred and eighty-nine left of the sorriest stuff that ever spoiled paper.   The poems are obscure, without anything in them to reward perseverance, dull without being moral, and full of conceits so far-fetched that we could wish the author no worse fate than to carry them back to where they came from.   We are no enemies to what are commonly called conceits, but authors bear them, as heralds say, with a difference. And a terrible difference it is !   With men like Earle, Donne, Fuller, Butler, Marvell, and even Quarles, conceit means wit ; they would carve the merest cherry-stone of thought in the quaintest and delicatest fashion. But with duller and more painful writers, such as Gascoyne, Marston, Felltham, and a score of others, even with cleverer ones like Waller, Crashawe, and Suckling, where they insisted on being fine, their wit is conceit. Difficulty without success is perhaps the least tolerable kind of writing.   Mere stupidity is a natural failing ; we skip and pardon.   But the other is Dulness in a domino, that travesties its familiar figure, and lures us

only to disappoint.   These unhappy verses of Lovelace's
had been dead and lapt in congenial lead these two hundred years;—what harm had they done Mr. Hazlitt that
he should disinter them?   There is no such disenchant-
er of peaceable reputations as one of these resurrection-
men of literature, who will not let mediocrities rest in
the grave, where the kind sexton, Oblivion, had buried
them, but dig them up to make a profit on their lead.

Of all Mr. Smith's editors, Mr. W. Carew Hazlitt
is the worst.   He is at times positively incredible,
worse even than Mr. Halliwell, and that is saying a
good deal.   Worthless as Lovelace's poems were, they
should have been edited correctly, if edited at all.   Even
dulness and dirtiness have a right to fair play, and to
be dull and dirty in their own way.   Mr. Hazlitt has
allowed all the misprints of the original (or by far the
greater part of them) to stand, but he has ventured on
many emendations of the text, and in every important
instance has blundered, and that, too, even where the
habitual practice of his author in the use of words might
have led him right.   The misapprehension shown in some
of his notes is beyond the belief of any not familiar
with the way in which old books are edited in England by the job.   We have brought a heavy indictment,
and we proceed to our proof, choosing only cases where
there can be no dispute.   We should premise that Mr.
Hazlitt professes to have corrected the punctuation.

> " And though he sees it full of wounds,
>   Cruel one, still he wounds it.   (p. 34.)

Here the original reads, " Cruel still on," and the only
correction needed was a comma after " cruel."

> " And by the glorious light
> Of both those stars, which of their spheres bereft,
>   Only the jelly 's left."   (p. 41.)

The original has " of which," and rightly, for " their
15   ▼

spheres bereft" is parenthetic, and the sense is "of
which only the jelly's left." Lovelace is speaking of the
eyes of a mistress who has grown old, and his image, confused as it is, is based on the belief that stars shooting
from their spheres fell to the earth as jellies, — a belief,
by the way, still to be met with in New England.

Lovelace, describing a cow (and it is one of the few
pretty passages in the volume), says, —

> " She was the largest, goodliest beast
> That ever mead or altar blest,
> Round as her udder, and more white
> Than is the Milky-Way in night."   (p. 64.)

Mr. Hazlitt changes to "Round was her udder," thus
making that white instead of the cow, as Lovelace intended.   On the next page we read, —

> " She takes her leave o' th' mournful neat,
> Who, by her toucht, now prizeth her life,
> Worthy alone the hollowed knife."

Compare Chapman (Iliads, xviii. 480) : —

> " Slew all their white fleec'd sheep and *neat*."

The original was "prize their life," and the use of
" neat " as a singular in this way is so uncommon, if
not unprecedented, and the verse as corrected so halting, that we have no doubt Lovelace so wrote it.   Of
course "hollowed" should be "hallowed," though the
broader pronunciation still lingers in our country pul-
pits.

> " What need she other bait or charm
> But look? or angle but her arm?"   (p. 65.)

So the original, which Mr. Hazlitt, missing the sense,
has changed to "what hook or angle."

> " Fly Joy on wings of Popinjays
> To courts of fools *where* as your plays
> Die laught at and forgot."   (p. 67.)

The original has "there."   Read, —

> " Fly, Joy, on wings of popinjays
> To courts of fools; there, as your plays,
> Die," &c.

" Where as," as then used, would make it the "plays"
that were to die.

> " As he Lucasta nam'd, a groan
> Strangles the fainting passing tone;
> But as she heard, Lucasta smiles,
> Posses her round; she's slipt meanwhiles
> Behind the blind of a thick bush." (p. 68.)

Mr. Hazlitt's note on "posses" could hardly be matched
by any member of the *posse comitatus* taken at random : —

" This word does not appear to have any very exact
meaning. See Halliwell's *Dictionary of Archaic Words,* art.
Posse, and Worcester's Dict., *ibid.,* &c. The context here
requires *to turn sharply or quickly.*"

The "*ibid.,* &c." is delightful; in other words, "find
out the meaning of *posse* for yourself." Though dark to
Mr. Hazlitt, the word has not the least obscurity in it.
It is only another form of *push,* nearer the French
pousser, from Latin *pulsare,* and "the context here requires" nothing more than that an editor should read a
poem if he wish to understand it. The plain meaning
is, —

> " But, as she heard *Lucasta,* smiles
> Possess her round."

That is, when she heard the name *Lucasta,* — for thus
far in the poem she has passed under the pseudonyme
of *Amarantha.* " Possess her round " is awkward, but
mildly so for Lovelace, who also spells " commandress "
in the same way with a single *s.* *Process* is spelt *prosses*
in the report of those who absented themselves from
Church in Stratford.

> " O thou, that swing'st upon the waving eare,
> Of some well-filled oaten beard." (p. 94.)

Mr. Hazlitt, for some inscrutable reason, has changed
"haire" to "eare" in the first line, preferring the ear
of a *beard* to its hair !

Mr. Hazlitt prints, —

> " Poor verdant foole ! and now green ice, thy joys
> Large and as lasting as thy peirch of grass,
> Bid us lay in 'gainst winter raine and poize
> Their flouds with an o'erflowing glasse." (p. 95.)

Surely we should read : —

> " Poor verdant foole and now green ice, thy joys,
> Large and as lasting as thy perch of grass,
> *Bid*," &c.

i. e. " Poor fool now frozen, the shortness of thy joys,
who mad'st no provision against winter, warns us to do
otherwise."

> " The radiant gemme was brightly set
> In as divine a carkanet;
> Of which the clearer was not knowne
> Her minde or her complexion." (p. 101.)

The original reads rightly "for which," &c., and, the
passage being rightly pointed, we have, —

> " For which the clearer was not known,
> Her mind or her complexion."

Of course "complexion" had not its present limited
meaning.

> " . . . . my future daring bayes
> Shall bow itself." (p. 107.)

"We should read *themselves*," says Mr. Hazlitt's note
authoritatively. Of course a noun ending in *s* is plural !
Not so fast. In spite of the dictionaries, *bays* was often
used in the singular.

> " Do plant a sprig of cypress, not of bays,"

says Robert Randolph in verses prefixed to his brother's
poems ; and Felltham in " Jonsonus Virbius,"

> " A greener bays shall crown Ben Jonson's name."

But we will cite Mr. Bayes himself : —

" And, where he took *it* up, resigns the *bays*."

" But we (defend us!) are divine,
 [Not] female, but madam born, and come
 From a right-honorable wombe." (p. 115.)

Here Mr. Hazlitt has ruined both sense and metre by
his unhappy " not." We should read " Female, but
madam-born," meaning clearly enough " we are women,
it is true, but of another race."

" In every hand [let] a cup be found
 That from all hearts a health may sound." (p. 121.)

Wrong again, and the inserted "let" ruinous to the measure. Is it possible that Mr. Hazlitt does not understand
so common an English construction as this ?

" First told thee into th' ayre, then to the ground." (p. 141.)

Mr. Hazlitt inserts the " to," which is not in the original,
from another version. Lovelace wrote " ayër." We
have noted two other cases (pp. 203 and 248) where he
makes the word a dissyllable. On the same page we
have " shewe's " changed to " shew " because Mr. Hazlitt
did not know it meant " show us " and not " shows." On
page 170, " their " is substituted for "her," which refers to Lucasta, and could refer to nothing else.

Mr. Hazlitt changes " quarrels *the* student Mercury "
to " quarrels *with*," not knowing that *quarrels* was once
used as a transitive verb. (p. 189.)

Wherever he chances to notice it, Mr. Hazlitt changes
the verb following two or more nouns connected by an
"and " from singular to plural. For instance : —

" You, sir, alone, fame, and all conquering rhyme
 File the set teeth," &c. (p. 224.)

for "files." Lovelace commonly writes so ; — on p. 181,
where it escaped Mr. Hazlitt's grammatical eye, we
find, —

" But broken faith, and th' cause of it,
 All damning gold, *was* damned to the pit."

Indeed, it was usual with writers of that day.   Milton in one of his sonnets has, —

"Thy worth and skill *exempts* thee from the throng," —

and Leigh Hunt, for the sake of the archaism, in one of his, " Patience and Gentleness *is* power."

Weariness, and not want of matter, compels us to desist from further examples of Mr. Hazlitt's emendations.   But we must also give a few specimens of his notes, and of the care with which he has corrected the punctuation.

In a note on "flutes of canary" (p. 76) too long to quote, Mr. Hazlitt, after citing the glossary of Nares (edition of 1859, by Wright and Halliwell, a very careless book, to speak mildly), in which *flute* is conjectured to mean *cask*, says that he is not satisfied, but adds, " I suspect that a flute *of canary* was so called from the cask having several vent-holes."   But flute means simply a tall glass.   Lassel, describing the glass-making at Murano, says, "For the High Dutch they have high glasses called *Flutes*, a full yard long."   So in Dryden's *Sir Martin Mar-all*, "bring two flute-*glasses* and some stools, ho !   We 'll have the ladies' health."   The origin of the word, though doubtful, is probably nearer to *flood* than *flute*.   But conceive of two gentlemen, members of one knows not how many learned societies, like Messrs. Wright and Halliwell, pretending to edit Nares, when they query a word which they could have found in any French or German dictionary !

On page 93 we have, —

" Hayle, holy cold! chaste temper, hayle! the fire
Raved o'er my purer thoughts I feel t' expire."

Mr. Hazlitt annotates thus : " *Rav'd* seems here to be equivalent to *reav'd* or *bereav'd*.   Perhaps the correct reading may be 'reav'd.'   See Worcester's *Dictionary*, art. RAYE, where Menage's supposition of affinity between *rave* and *bereave* is perhaps a little too slightingly treated."

The meaning of Lovelace was, "the fire *that* raved." But what Mr. Hazlitt would make with "reaved o'er my purer thoughts," we cannot conceive. On the whole, we think he must have written the note merely to make his surprising glossological suggestion. All that Worcester does for the etymology, by the way, is to cite Richardson, no safe guide.

"Where now one *so so* spatters, t'other: no!" (p. 112.)

The comma in this verse has, of course, no right there, but Mr. Hazlitt leaves the whole passage so corrupt that we cannot spend time in disinfecting it. We quote it only for the sake of his note on "*so so*." It is marvellous.

"An exclamation of approval when an actor made a hit. The corruption seems to be somewhat akin to the Italian, '*si, si*,' a corruption of '*sia, sia*.'"

That the editor of an English poet need not understand Italian we may grant, but that he should not know the meaning of a phrase so common in his own language as *so-so* is intolerable. Lovelace has been saying that a certain play might have gained applause under certain circumstances, but that everybody calls it *so-so*, — something very different from "an exclamation of approval," one should say. The phrase answers exactly to the Italian *così così*, while *sì* (not *si*) is derived from *sic*, and is analogous with the affirmative use of the German *so* and the Yankee *jes' so*.

"Oh, how he hast'ned death, burnt to be fryed!" (p. 141.)

The note on *fryed* is, —

"I. e. freed. *Free* and *freed* were sometimes pronounced like *fry* and *fryed;* for Lord North, in his *Forest of Varieties*, 1645, has these lines:—

> ' Birds that long have lived free,
>   Caught and cag'd, but pine and die.'

Here evidently *free* is intended to rhyme with *die*.''

"Evidently!" An instance of the unsafeness of rhyme as a guide to pronunciation. It was *die* that had the sound of *dee*, as everybody (but Mr. Hazlitt) knows. Lovelace himself rhymes *die* and *she* on p. 269. But what shall we say to our editor's not knowing that *fry* was used formerly where we should say *burn?* Lovers used to *fry* with love, whereas now they have got out of the frying-pan into the fire. In this case a martyr is represented as burning (i. e. longing) to be fried (i. e. burned).

"Her beams ne'er shed or change like th' hair of day." (p. 224.)

Mr. Hazlitt's note is, —

"*Hair* is here used in what has become quite an obsolete sense. The meaning is outward form, nature, or character. The word used to be by no means uncommon; but it is now, as was before remarked, out of fashion; and indeed I do not think that it is found even in any old writer used exactly in the way in which Lovelace has employed it."

We should think not, as Mr. Hazlitt understands it! Did he never hear of the golden hair of Apollo, — of the *intonsum Cynthium?* Don Quixote was a better scholar where he speaks of *las doradas hebras de sus hermosos cabellos.* But *hair* never meant what Mr. Hazlitt says it does, even when used as he supposes it to be here. It had nothing to do with "outward form, nature, or character," but had a meaning much nearer what we express by temperament, which its color was and is thought to indicate.

On p. 232 "*wild* ink" is explained to mean "*unrefined.*" It is a mere misprint for "*vild.*"

Page 237, Mr. Hazlitt, explaining an illusion of Lovelace to the "east and west" in speaking of George

Sandys, mentions Sandys's Oriental travels, but seems
not to know that he translated Ovid in Virginia.

Pages 251, 252 : —

> " And as that soldier conquest doubted not,
> Who but one splinter had of Castriot,
> But would assault ev'n death, so strongly charmed,
> And naked oppose rocks, with this bone armed."

Mr. Hazlitt reads *his* for *this* in the last verse, and his
note on " bone " is : —

> " And he found a new jawbone of an ass, and put forth
> his hand and took it, and slew a thousand men therewith.
> (Judges xv. 15.) "

Could the farce of " editing" go further ?   To make a
" splinter of Castriot " an ass's jawbone is a little too
bad.   We refer Mr. Hazlitt to " The Life of George Castriot, King of Epirus and Albania," &c., &c., (Edinburgh,
1753,) p. 32, for an explanation of this profound difficulty.   He will there find that the Turkish soldiers wore
relics of Scanderbeg as charms.

Perhaps Mr. Hazlitt's most astounding note is on the
word *pickear*.   (p. 203.)

> " So within shot she doth pickear,
> Now gall's [galls] the flank and now the rear."

" In the sense in which it is here used this word seems to
be peculiar to Lovelace. *To pickear*, or *pickeer*, means *to
skirmish.*"   And, pray, what other possible meaning can
it have here ?

Of his corrections of the press we will correct a few
samples.

Page 34, for " Love *nee're* his standard," read " *neere.*"
Page 82, for " fall *too*," read " fall *to* " (or, as we ought to
print such words, " fall-to ").   Page 83, for " star-made
firmament," read " star, made firmament."   Page 161,
for " To look their enemies *in* their hearse," read, both
for sense and metre, *into*.   Page 176, for " the gods *have*

15 *

kneeled," read *had*. Page 182, for " In beds they tumbled *off* their own," read *of*. Page 184, for " in mine one monument I lie," read *owne*. Page 212, for " Deucalion's *black*flung stone," read " backflung." Of the punctuation we shall give but one specimen, and that a fair average one : —

> " Naso to his Tibullus flung the wreath,
> He to Catullus thus did each bequeath.
> This glorious circle, to another round,
> At last the temples of a god it bound."

Our readers over ten years of age will easily correct this for themselves.

Time brings to obscure authors* an odd kind of reparation, an immortality, not of love and interest and admiration, but of curiosity merely. In proportion as their language was uncouth, provincial, or even barbarous, their value becomes the greater. A book of which only a single copy escaped its natural enemies, the pastry-cook and trunk-maker, may contain one word that makes daylight in some dark passage of a great author, and its name shall accordingly live forever in a note. Is not, then, a scholiastic athanasy better than none ? And if literary vanity survive death, or even worse, as Brunetto Latini's made him insensible for a moment to the rain of fire and the burning sand, the authors of such books as are not properly literature may still comfort themselves with a *non omnis moriar*, laying a mournful emphasis on the adjective, and feeling that they have not lived wholly in vain while they share with the dodo a fragmentary continuance on earth. To be sure, the immortality, such as it is, belongs less to themselves than to the famous men they help to illustrate. If they escape oblivion, it is by a back door, as it were, and they

---

* Early Popular Poetry. Edited by W. Carew Hazlitt.

survive only in fine print at the page's foot. At the
banquet of fame they sit below the salt. After all, perhaps, the next best thing to being famous or infamous
is to be utterly forgotten, for this also is to achieve a
kind of definite result by living. To hang on the perilous edge of immortality by the nails, liable at any moment to drop into the fathomless ooze of oblivion, is at
best a questionable beatitude. And yet sometimes the
merest barnacles that have attached themselves to the
stately keels of Dante or Shakespeare or Milton have
an interest of their own by letting us know in what remote waters those hardy navigators went a pearl-fishing.
Has not Mr. Dyce traced Shakespeare's "dusty death"
to Anthony Copley, and Milton's "back resounded
Death!" to Abraham Fraunce? Nay, is it not Bernard
de Ventadour's lark that sings forever in the diviner air
of Dante's Paradise?

> " Quan vey laudeta mover
> De joi sas alas contra'l rai,
> Que s'oblida e s laissa cazer
> Per la doussor qu 'al cor li 'n vai."

> " Qual lodoletta che in aere si spazia,
> Prima cantando, e poi tace contenta
> Dell' ultima dolcezza che la sazia."

We are not sure that Bernard's "Que s'oblida e s
laissa cazer" is not sweeter than Dante's "tace conten-
ta," but it was plainly the *doussor* that gave its cue to
the greater poet's memory, and he has improved on it
with that exquisite *ultima*, as his master Virgil sometimes did on Homer.

But authors whose interest for us is mainly biblio-
graphic belong rather in such collections as Mr. Alli-
bone's. As literature they are oppressive; as items of
literary history they find their place in that vast list
which records not only those named for promotion, but
also the killed, wounded, and missing in the Battle of

the Books. There our hearts are touched with something of the same vague pathos that dims the eye in
some deserted graveyard. The brief span of our earthly
immortalities is brought home to us as nowhere else.
What a necrology of notability! How many a contro-
versialist, terrible in his day, how many a rising genius
that somehow stuck on the horizon, how many a withering satirist, lies here shrunk all away to the tombstone
brevity of a name and date! Think of the aspirations,
the dreams, the hopes, the toil, the confidence (of himself and wife) in an impartial and generous posterity, —
and then read "Smith J. [ohn?] 1713–1784 (?). The
Vision of Immortality, an Epique Poem in twelve books,
1740, 4to. See *Lowndes.*" The time of his own death
less certain than that of his poem, (which we may fix
pretty safely in 1740,) and the only posterity that took
any interest in him the indefatigable compiler to whom
a name was valuable in proportion as it was obscure.
Well, to have even so much as your title-page read after
it has rounded the corner of its first century, and to
enjoy a posthumous public of one is better than nothing.
This is the true Valhalla of Mediocrity, the *Libro d'oro*
of the *onymi-anonymi,* of the never-named authors who
exist only in name. Parson Adams would be here had
he found a printer for his sermons, and Mr. Primrose,
if a copy existed of his tracts on monogamy. Papyror-
cetes junior will turn here with justifiable pride to the
name of his respectable progenitor. Here we are secure
of perpetuity at least, if of nothing better, and are
sons though we may not be heirs, of fame. Here is a
handy and inexpensive substitute for the waxen *imagines*
of the Roman patriciate, for those must have been in-
convenient to pack on a change of lodgings, liable to
melt in warm weather (even the elder Brutus himself
might soften in the dog-days) and not readily salable

unless to some *novus homo* willing to buy a set of ancestors ready-made, as some of our own enthusiasts in gene-
alogy are said to order a family-tree from the heraldic
nurseryman, skilled to imp a slip of Scroggins on a
stock of De Vere or Montmorenci. Fame, it should
seem, like electricity, is both positive and negative, and
if a writer must be Somebody to make himself of permanent interest to the world at large, he must not less be
Nobody to have his namelessness embalmed by M. Gué-
rard. The benignity of Providence is nowhere more
clearly to be seen than in its compensations. As there
is a large class of men madly desirous to decipher cunei-
form and other inscriptions, simply because of their il-
legibility, so there is another class driven by a like irresistible instinct to the reprinting of unreadable books.
Whether these have even a philologic value for us depends on the accuracy and learning bestowed upon them
by the editor.

For there is scarcely any rubbish-heap of literature out
of which something precious may not be raked by the
diligent explorer, and the late Mr. Dyce (since Gifford,
the best editor of our literature of the Tudor and Jaco-
bean periods) might well be called the Golden Dustman,
so many were the precious trifles sifted out by his intelligent industry. It would not be easy to name any
work more thoroughly done than his edition of Skelton.
He was not a philologist in the stricter sense, but no
man had such a commonplace-book as he, or knew so exactly the meaning with which words were used during
the period he did so much to illustrate. Elegant scholar
ship is not often, as in him, patient of drudgery and
conscientious in painstaking. Between such a man and
Mr. Carew Hazlitt the contrast is by no means agreeable.
The one was not more distinguished by modest accuracy
than the other is by the rash conceit of that half-knowl-

edge which is more mischievous in an editor than down-right ignorance. This language is strong because it is true, though we should not have felt called upon to use it but for the vulgar flippancy with which Mr. Hazlitt alludes depreciatingly to the labors of his predecessors, — to such men as Ritson, Utterson, Wright, and Sir Frederick Madden, his superiors in everything that goes to the making of a good editor. Most of them are now dead and nailed in their chests, and it is not for us to forget the great debt we owe to them, and others like them, who first opened paths for us through the tangled wilderness of our early literature. A modern editor, with his ready-made helps of glossary, annotation, and comment, should think rather of the difficulties than the defects of these pioneers.

How different is Mr. Hazlitt's spirit from that of the thorough and therefore modest scholar! In the Preface to his *Altenglische Sprachproben*, Mätzner says of an editor, *das Beste was er ist verdankt er Andern*, an accidental pentameter that might seem to have dropped out of *Nathan der Weise*. Mr. Hazlitt would profit much by getting some friend to translate for him the whole paragraph in which it occurs.

We see it announced that Mr. Hazlitt is to superintend a new edition of Warton's History of English Poetry, and are pained to think of the treatment that robust scholar and genial poet is likely to receive at the hands of an editor without taste, discrimination, or learning. Of his taste a single specimen may suffice. He tells us that "in an artistic and constructive point of view, the *Mylner of Abington* is superior to its predecessor," that predecessor being Chaucer's *Reve's Tale*, which, with his usual inaccuracy, he assigns to the *Miller!* Of his discrimination we have a sufficient test in the verses he has fathered upon Herrick in a late edition of the most graceful of our lyric poets. Perhaps discrimination is not, after all, the right word, for we have sometimes seen cause to doubt whether Mr. Hazlitt ever reads carefully the very documents he prints. For example, in the Biographical Notice prefixed to the Herrick he says (p. xvii) : "Mr. W. Perry Herrick has plausibly suggested that the payments made by Sir William to his nephew were simply on account of the fortune which belonged to Robert in right of his father, and which his uncle held in trust ; this was about £ 400 ; and I think from allusions in the letters printed elsewhere that this view may be the correct one." *May* be ! The poet says expressly, "I entreat you out of *my little possession* to deliver to this bearer the *customarye* £ 10, without which I cannot meate [?] my ioyrney." The words we have italicized are conclusive. By the way, Mr. Hazlitt's wise-looking query after "meate" is conclusive also as to his fitness for editorship. Did he never hear of the familiar phrase " to *meet* the expense "? If so trifling a misspelling can mystify him, what must be the condition of his mind in face of the more than Protean travesties which words underwent before they were uniformed by Johnson and Walker ? Mr. Hazlitt's mind, to be sure, like the wind Cecias, always finds its own fog. In another of Herrick's letters we find, "For what her monie can be effected (*sic*) when there is diuision 'twixt the hart and hand ?" " Her monie " of course means *harmonie*, and *effected* is therefore right. What Mr. Hazlitt may have meant by his " (*sic*) " it were idle to inquire.

We have already had occasion to examine some of Mr. Hazlitt's work, and we are sorry to say that in the four volumes before us we find no reason for changing our opinion of his utter disqualification for the duties of editorship. He seldom clears up a real difficulty (never,

we might say, with lights of his own), he frequently
creates a darkness where none was before, and the peculiar *bumptiousness* of his incapacity makes it particularly
offensive. We shall bring a few instances in proof of
what we assert, our only embarrassment being in the
superabundance of our material. In the Introduction to
the second volume of his collection, Mr. Hazlitt speaks
of "the utter want of common care on the part of previous editors of our old poetry." Such oversights as he
has remarked upon in his notes are commonly errors
of the press, a point on which Mr. Hazlitt, of all men,
should have been charitable, for his own volumes are
full of them. We call his attention to one such which
is rather amusing. In his "additional notes" we find
"line 77, *wylle*. Strike out the note upon this word ;
but the explanation is correct. *Be wroght* was a misprint, however, for *he wroght*." The error occurs in a
citation of three lines in which *lother* is still left for
tother. The original note affords us so good an example
of Mr. Hazlitt's style of editing as to be worth preserv-
ing. In the "Kyng and the Hermit" we read, —

> "He ne wyst w[h]ere that he was
> Ne out of the forest for to passe,
> And thus he rode all wylle."

And here is Mr. Hazlitt's annotation on the word
wylle : —

"*i. e.* evil. In a MS. of the *Tale of the Basyn*, supposed by Mr. Wright, who edited it in 1836, to be written in the Salopian dialect, are the following lines : —

> 'The lother hade litull thoght,
> Off husbandry cowth he noght,
> But alle his wyves *will* be wroght.' " (Vol. I. p. 16.)

It is plain that he supposed *will*, in this very simple passage, to mean *evil !* This he would seem to rectify, but
at the same time takes care to tell us that "the expla-

nation [of *wylle*] is correct." He is willing to give up one blunder, if only he may have one left to comfort himself withal! *Wylle* is simply a rhyming fetch for *wild*, and the passage means that the king rode at random. The use of *wild* with this meaning is still common in such phrases as "he struck wild." In "Havelok" we find it in the nearly related sense of *being at a loss, knowing not what to do :* —

> " To lincolne barfot he yede
> Hwan he kam ther he was ful *wil*,
> Ne hauede he no frend to gangen til."

All wylle, in short, means the kind of editing that is likely to be done by a gentleman who picks up his misinformation as he goes along. We would hint that a person must know *something* before he can use even a glossary with safety.

In the " King and the Barker," when the tanner finds out that it is the king whom he has been treating so familiarly, and falls upon his knees, Mr. Hazlitt prints,

> " He had no meynde of hes hode, nor cape, ne radell,"

and subjoins the following note : " Radell, or raddle, signifies a side of a cart; but here, apparently, stands for the cart itself. Ritson printed *ner adell*." Mr. Hazlitt's explanation of *raddle*, which he got from Halliwell, is incorrect. The word, as its derivation (from O. F. *rastel*) implies, means the side or end of a *hay*-cart, in which the uprights are set like the teeth of a rake. But what has a cart to do here ? There is perhaps a touch of what an editor of old doggerel would benignantly call humor, in the tanner's forgetfulness of his raiment, but the cart is as little to the purpose as one of Mr. Hazlitt's own notes. The tanner was on horseback, as the roads of the period required that he should be, and good old Ritson was plainly on the right track in his reading, though his text was muddled by a misprint.

w

As it was, he got *one* word right, and so far has the advantage of Mr. Hazlitt. The true reading is, of course, *ner a dell*, never a deal, not a whit. The very phrase occurs in another poem which Mr. Hazlitt has reprinted in his collection, —

> " For *never a dell*
> He wyll me love agayne." (Vol. III. p. 2.)

That *adell* was a misprint in Ritson is proved by the fact that the word does not appear in his glossary. If we were to bring Mr. Hazlitt to book for his misprints ! In the poem we have just quoted he gravely prints, —

> " Matter in dede,
> My sides did blede,"

for "mother, indede," "through ryght wysenes" for "though ryghtwisenes," "with man vnkynde" for "sith man vnkynde," "ye knowe a parte" for "ye knowe aperte," " here in " for "herein," all of which make nonsense, and all come within the first one hundred and fifty lines, and those of the shortest, mostly of four syllables each. Perhaps they rather prove ignorance than want of care. One blunder falling within the same limits we have reserved for special comment, because it affords a good example of Mr. Hazlitt's style of editing :—

> " Your herte souerayne
> Clouen in twayne
> By longes the blynde." (Vol. III. p. 7.)

Here the uninstructed reader would be as completely in the dark as to what *longes* meant as the editor plainly was himself. The old rhymer no doubt wrote Longis, meaning thereby Longinus, a personage familiar enough, one should think, to any reader of mediæval poetry. Mr. Hazlitt absolves himself for not having supplied a glossary by the plea that none is needed by the class of readers for whom his volumes are intended. But this will hardly seem a valid excuse for a gentleman who

often goes out of his way to explain in his notes such
simple matters as that " shape " means "form," and that
" Johan of the golden mouthe " means " St. Chrysostom,"
which, indeed, it does not, any more than Johannes Bap-
tista means St. Baptist.   We will supply Mr. Hazlitt
with an illustration of the passage from Bekker's *Fera-
bras*, the more willingly as it may direct his attention to
a shining example of how an old poem should be
edited : —

> " en la crotz vos pendero li fals Iuzieu truan,
> can Longis vos ferie de sa lansa trencan:
> el non avia vist en trastot son vivan;
> lo sanc li venc per l'asta entro al punh colan;
> e [el] toquet ne sos huelhs si vic el mantenan."

Mr. Hazlitt, to be sure (who prints *sang parlez* for *sanz
parler*) (Vol. I. p. 265), will not be able to form any notion of what these verses mean, but perhaps he will be
able to draw an inference from the capital L that *longes*
is a proper name.   The word *truan* at the end of the first
verse of our citation may also suggest to him that *truant*
is not quite so satisfactory an explanation of the word
trewāt as he seems to think.   (Vol. IV. p. 24, *note*.)   In
deference to Mr. Hazlitt's presumed familiarity with an
author sometimes quoted by him in his notes, we will
point him to another illustration : —

> " Ac ther cam forth a knyght,
> With a kene spere y-grounde
> Highte Longeus, as the lettre telleth,
> And longe hadde lore his sighte."
>
> *Piers Ploughman*, Wright, p. 374.

Mr. Hazlitt shows to peculiar advantage where old
French is in question.   Upon the word *Osyll* he favors
us with the following note : "The blackbird.   In East
Cornwall *ozell* is used to signify the windpipe, and thence
the bird may have had its name, as Mr. Couch has suggested to me."   (Vol. II. p. 25.)   Of course the black-

bird, alone among fowls, is distinguished by a windpipe!
The name is merely another form of O. F. *oisil*, and was
usurped naturally enough by one of the commonest
birds, just as *pajaro* (L. *passer*) in Spanish, by a similar
process in the opposite direction, came to mean bird in
general. On the very next page he speaks of "the Romance which is vulgarly entitled *Lybeaus Disconus*, i. e.
Le Beau Disconnu." If he had corrected *Disconus* to
Desconus, all had been well; but *Disconnu* neither is nor
ever was French at all. Where there is blundering to
be done, one stone often serves Mr. Hazlitt for two birds.
Ly beaus Disconus is perfectly correct old French, and
another form of the adjective (*bius*) perhaps explains the
sound we give to the first syllable of *beauty* and *Beau-
fort.* A barrister at law, as Mr. Hazlitt is, may not be
called on to know anything about old English or modern
French, but we might fairly expect him to have at least
a smattering of Law French! In volume fourth, page
129, a goodman trying his wife,

> " Bad her take the pot that sod ouer the fire
> And set it abooue vpon the astire."

Mr. Hazlitt's note upon *astire* is "hearth, i. q. *astre.*"
Knowing that the modern French was âtre, he too
rashly inferred a form which never existed except in
Italian. The old French word is *aistre* or *estre*, but Mr.
Hazlitt, as usual, prefers something that is neither old
French nor new. We do not pretend to know what
astire means, but a hearth that should be *abooue* the pot
seething over the fire would be unusual, to say the least,
in our semi-civilized country.

In the "Lyfe of Roberte the Deuill" (Vol. I. p. 232),
Mr. Hazlitt twice makes a knight *sentre* his lance, and
tells us in a note that the "Ed. 1798 has *fentered*," a
very easy misprint for the right word *feutered*. What
Mr. Hazlitt supposed to be the meaning of *sentre* he has

not vouchsafed to tell us. *Fautre* (sometimes *faltre* or *feutre*) means in old French the *rest* of a lance. Thus in the *Roman du Renart* (26517),

> " Et mist sa lance sor le *fautre*."

But it also meant a peculiar *kind* of rest. In Sir F. Madden's edition of *Gawayne* (to which Mr. Hazlitt refers occasionally) we read,

> " They *feutred* their lances, these knyghtes good ";

and in the same editor's " William and the Werwolf,"

> " With sper festened in *feuter*, him for to spille."

In a note on the latter passage Sir F. Madden says, " There seems no reason, however, why it [feuter] should not mean the rest attached to the armour." But Roquefort was certainly right in calling it a " garniture d'une selle pour tenir la lance." A spear fastened to the saddle gave more deadly weight to the blow. The *"him for to spille"* implies this. So in " Merlin " (E. E. Text Soc., p. 488) : " Than thei toke speres grete and rude, and putte hem in fewtre, and that is the grettest crewelte that oon may do, ffor turnement oweth to be with-oute felonye, and they meved to smyte hem as in mortall werre." The context shows that the *fewtre* turned sport into earnest. A citation in Raynouard's *Lexique Roman* (though wrongly explained by him) directed us to a passage which proves that this particular kind of rest for the lance was attached to the saddle, in order to render the blow heavier : —

> " Lances *à* [lege *as*] *arçons* afeutrées
> *Pour plus de dures colées rendre*."
> *Branche des Royaux Lignages*, 4514, 4515.

Mr. Hazlitt, as we have said, lets no occasion slip to insinuate the inaccuracy and carelessness of his predecessors. The long and useful career of Mr. Wright,

who, if he had given us nothing more than his excellent edition of "Piers Ploughman" and the volume of
"Ancient Vocabularies," would have deserved the gratitude of all lovers of our literature or students of our
language, does not save him from the severe justice of
Mr. Hazlitt, nor is the name of Warton too venerable to
be coupled with a derogatory innuendo. Mr. Wright
needs no plea in abatement from us, and a mischance of
Mr. Hazlitt's own has comically avenged Warton. The
word *prayer*, it seems, had somehow substituted itself
for *prayse* in a citation by Warton of the title of the
"Schole-House of Women."   Mr. Hazlitt thereupon
takes occasion to charge him with often "speaking at
random," and after suggesting that it might have been
the blunder of a copyist, adds, "or it is by no means
impossible that Warton himself, having been allowed
to inspect the production, was guilty of this oversight."
(Vol. IV. p. 98.)   Now, on the three hundred and eighteenth page of the same volume, Mr. Hazlitt has allowed
the following couplet to escape his conscientious attention : —

> "Next, that no gallant should not ought suppose
> That *prayers* and glory doth consist in cloathes."

Lege, nostro periculo, PRAYSE !   Were dear old Tom still
on earth, he might light his pipe cheerfully with any
one of Mr. Hazlitt's pages, secure that in so doing he
was consuming a brace of blunders at the least.   The
word *prayer* is an unlucky one for Mr. Hazlitt.   In the
"Knyght and his Wyfe" (Vol. II. p. 18) he prints : —

> "And sayd, Syre, I rede we make
> In this chapel oure prayers,
> That God us kepe both in ferrus."

Why did not Mr. Hazlitt, who explains so many things
that everybody knows, give us a note upon *in ferrus* ?
It would have matched his admirable elucidation of

waygose, which we shall notice presently. Is it not barely possible that the MS. may have read *prayere* and *in fere?* *Prayere* occurs two verses further on, and not as a rhyme.

Mr. Hazlitt even sets Sir Frederick Madden right on a question of Old English grammar, telling him superciliously that *can*, with an infinitive, in such phrases as *he can go*, is used not "to denote a *past* tense, but an *imperfect* tense." By *past* we suppose him to mean *perfect*. But even if an imperfect tense were not a past one, we can show by a passage in one of the poems in this very collection that *can*, in the phrases referred to, sometimes not only denotes a past but a perfect tense : —

> " And thorow that worde y felle in pryde;
> As the aungelle can of hevyn glyde,
> And with the tywnkling * of an eye
> God for-dud alle that maystrye
> And so hath he done for my gylte."

Now the angel here is Lucifer, and *can of hevyn glyde* means simply *fell from heaven*, not *was falling*. It is in the same tense as *for-dud* in the next line. The fall of the angels is surely a *fait accompli*. In the last line, by the way, Mr. Hazlitt changes " my for " to " for my," and wrongly, the *my* agreeing with *maystrye* understood. In modern English we should use *mine* in the same way. But Sir Frederick Madden can take care of himself.

We have less patience with Mr. Hazlitt's impertinence to Ritson, a man of ample reading and excellent taste in selection, and who, real scholar as he was, always drew from original sources. We have a *foible* for Ritson with his oddities of spelling, his acerb humor, his unconsciously depreciatory mister Tyrwhitts and mister Bryants, and his obstinate disbelief in Doctor Percy's

---

* The careless Ritson would have printed this *twynkling*.

folio manuscript. Above all, he was a most conscientious editor, and an accurate one so far as was possible with the lights of that day. Mr. Hazlitt has reprinted two poems, "The Squyr of Low Degre" and "The Knight of Curtesy," which had already been edited by Ritson. The former of these has passages that are unsurpassed in simple beauty by anything in our earlier poetry. The author of it was a good versifier, and Ritson, though he corrected some glaring errors, did not deal so trenchantly with verses manifestly lamed by the copyist as perhaps an editor should.* Mr. Hazlitt says of Ritson's text, that "it offers more than *an hundred* departures from the original," and of the "Knight of Courtesy," that "Ritson's text is by no means accurate." Now Mr. Hazlitt has adopted nearly all of Ritson's emendations, without giving the least hint of it. On the contrary, in some five or six instances, he gives the original reading in a foot-note with an "old ed. has" so and so, thus leaving the reader to infer that the corrections were his own. Where he has not followed Ritson, he has almost uniformly blundered, and that through sheer ignorance. For example, he prints,

"Alas! it tourned to *wroth her heyle*,"

where Ritson had substituted *wrotherheyle.* The measure shows that Ritson was right. *Wroth her heyle,* moreover, is nonsense. It should have been *wrother her heyle* at any rate, but the text is far too modern to admit of that archaic form. In the "Debate of the Body and the Soul" (Mätzner's A. E. Sprachproben, 103) we have,

* For example: —
"And in the arber was a tre
A fairer in the world might none be,"
should certainly read,
"None fairer in the world might be."

> " Why schope thou me to wrother-hele,"

and in "Dame Siris " (Ibid., 110),

> " To goder hele ever came thou hider."

Mr. Hazlitt prints,

> " For yf it may be found in thee
> That thou them [de] fame for enuyte."

The emendation [de] is Ritson's, and is probably right, though it would require, for the metre's sake, the elision of *that* at the beginning of the verse. But what is *enuyte?* Ritson reads *enmyte*, which is, of course, the true reading. Mr. Hazlitt prints (as usual either without apprehending or without regarding the sense),

> " With browes *bent* and eyes full mery,"

where Ritson has *brent*, and gives parallel passages in his note on the word. Mr. Hazlitt gives us

> " To here the bugles there yblow,
> With their *bugles* in that place,"

though Ritson had made the proper correction to *begles*. Mr. Hazlitt, with ludicrous *nonchalance*, allows the Squire to press into the throng

> " With a *bastard* large and longe,"

and that with the right word (*baslarde*) staring him in the face from Ritson's text. We wonder he did not give us an illustrative quotation from Falconbridge ! Both editors have allowed some gross errors to escape, such as " come *not* " for " come " (v. 425) ; "so leue *he* be " for " ye be " (v. 593) ; " vnto *her* chambre " for " vnto your " (v. 993) ; but in general Ritson's is the better and more intelligent text of the two. In the "Knight of Curtesy," Mr. Hazlitt has followed Ritson's text almost *literatim*. Indeed, it is demonstrable that he gave it to his printers as *copy* to set up from. The proof is this : Ritson has accented a few words ending in *tè*.

16

Generally he uses the grave accent, but now and then
the acute. Mr. Hazlitt's text follows all these variations
exactly. The main difference between the two is that
Ritson prints the first personal pronoun *i*, and Mr. Hazlitt, I. Ritson is probably right; for in the "Schole-
house of Women" (vv. 537, 538) where the text no
doubt was

> " i [i. e. *one*] deuil a woman to speak may constrain,
>   But all that in hel be cannot let it again,"

Mr. Hazlitt changes "i" to "A," and says in a note,
"Old ed. has *I*." That by his correction he should miss
the point was only natural; for he evidently conceives
that the *sense* of a passage does not in the least concern
an editor. An instance or two will suffice. In the
"Knyght and his Wyfe" (Vol. II. p. 17) we read,

> " The fynd tyl hure hade myche tene
>   As hit was a sterfull we seme! "

Mr. Hazlitt in a note explains *tene* to mean "trouble or
sorrow"; but if that were its meaning here, we should
read *made*, and not *hade*, which would give to the word
its other sense of *attention*. The last verse of the couplet Mr. Hazlitt seems to think perfectly intelligible as it
stands. We should not be surprised to learn that he
looked upon it as the one gem that gave lustre to a poem
otherwise of the dreariest. We fear we shall rob it of all
its charm for him by putting it into modern English : —

> " As it was after full well seen."

So in the "Smyth and his Dame" (Vol. III. p. 204)
we read,

> " It were a lytele maystry
>   To make a blynde man to se,"

instead of "*as* lytell." It might, indeed, be as easy to
perform the miracle on a blind man as on Mr. Hazlitt.
Again, in the same poem, a little further on,

> " For I tell the now trevely,
> Is none so wyse ne *to* sle,
> But ever *ye* may som what lere,"

which, of course, should be,

> " ne *so* sle
> But ever *he* may som what lere."

Worse than all, Mr. Hazlitt tells us (Vol. I. p. 158) that when they bury the great Khan, they lay his body in a tabernacle,

> " With sheld and spere and other wede
> With a whit mere to gyf him in ylke."

We will let Sir John Maundeville correct the last verse : " And they seyn that when he shale come into another World . . . . the mare schalle *gheven him mylk.*" Mr. Hazlitt gives us some wretched doggerel by "Piers of Fulham," and gives it swarming with blunders. We take at random a couple of specimens : —

> " And loveship goith ay to warke
> Where that presence is put a bake," (Vol. II. pp. 13, 14,)

where we should read " love's ship," " wrake," and " abake." Again, just below,

> " Ffor men haue seyn here to foryn,
> That love laughet when men be forsworn."

Love should be "Iove." Ovid is the obscure person alluded to in the " men here to foryn " :

> " Jupiter e cœlo perjuria ridet amantum."

We dare say Mr. Hazlitt, if he ever read the passage, took it for granted that " to foryn " meant *too foreign,* and gave it up in despair. But surely Shakespeare's

> " At lovers' perjuries,
> They say, Jove laughs,"

is not too foreign to have put him on the right scent.

Mr. Hazlitt is so particular in giving us *v* for *u* and *vice versa,* that such oversights are a little annoying.

Every man his own editor seems to be his theory of the way in which old poetry should be reprinted. On this plan, the more riddles you leave (or make) for the reader to solve, the more pleasure you give him. To correct the blunders in any book edited by Mr. Hazlitt would give the young student a pretty thorough training in archaic English. In this sense the volumes before us might be safely recommended to colleges and schools. When Mr. Hazlitt undertakes to correct, he is pretty sure to go wrong. For example, in " Doctour Doubble Ale " (Vol. III. p. 309) he amends thus : —

> " And sometyme mikle strife is
> Among the ale wyfes, [y-wis] ;

where the original is right as it stands. Just before, in the same poem, we have a parallel instance : —

> " And doctours dulpatis
> That falsely to them pratis,
> And bring them to the gates."

The original probably reads (or should read) *wyfis* and *gatis*. But it is too much to expect of Mr. Hazlitt that he should remember the very poems he is editing from one page to another, nay, as we shall presently show, that he should even read them. He will change *be* into *ben* where he should have let it alone (though his own volumes might have furnished him with such examples as " were go," " have se," " is do," and fifty more), but he will sternly retain *bene* where the rhyme requires *be*, and Ritson had so printed. In " Adam Bel " the word *pryme* occurs (Vol. II. p. 140), and he vouchsafes us the following note : " i. e. noon. It is commonly used by early writers in this sense. In the *Four* P. P., by John Heywood, circa 1540, the apothecary says

> ' If he taste this boxe nye aboute the pryme
> By the masse, he is in heven or even songe tyme.' "

Let our readers admire with us the easy "it is commonly used" of Mr. Hazlitt, as if he had store of other
examples in his note-book. He could an if he would !
But unhappily he borrowed this single quotation from
Nares, and, as usual, it throws no scintilla of light upon
the point in question, for his habit in annotation is to
find by means of a glossary some passage (or passages if
possible) in which the word to be explained occurs, and
then — why, then to give the word as an explanation of
itself. But in this instance, Mr. Hazlitt, by the time he
had reached the middle of his next volume (Vol. III.
p. 281) had wholly forgotten that *pryme* was "commonly
used by early writers" for *noon*, and in a note on the following passage,

> " I know not whates a clocke
>   But by the countre cocke,
>   The mone nor yet the pryme,
>   Vntyll the sonne do shyne,"

he informs us that it means "six o'clock in the morning " ! Here again this editor, who taxes Ritson with
want of care, prints *mone* for *none* in the very verse he
is annotating, and which we may therefore presume
that he had read. A man who did not know the moon
till the sun showed it him is a match even for Mr. Hazlitt himself. We wish it were as easy as he seems to
think it to settle exactly what *pryme* means when used
by our "early writers," but it is at least absolutely certain that it did not mean *noon*.

But Mr. Hazlitt, if these volumes are competent witnesses, knows nothing whatever about English, old or
new. In the "Mery Jest of Dane Hew" he finds the
following verses,

> " Dame he said what shall we now doo
>   Sir she said so mote go
>   The munk in a corner ye shall lay "

which we print purposely without punctuation.   Mr.
Hazlitt prints them thus,

> " Dame, he said, what shall we now doo?
>   Sir, she said, so mote [it] go.
>   The munk," &c.,

and gives us a note on the locution he has invented to
this effect, "? so might it be managed."   And the
Chancellor said, *I doubt!*   Mr. Hazlitt's query makes
such a singular exception to his more natural mood of
immediate inspiration that it is almost pathetic.   The
amended verse, as everybody (not confused by too great
familiarity with our " early writers ") knows, should
read,

> " Sir, she said, so might I go,"

and should be followed only by a comma, to show its
connection with the next.   The phrase " so mote I go,"
is as common as a weed in the works of the elder poets,
both French and English ; it occurs several times in Mr.
Hazlitt's own collection, and its other form, " so mote I
fare," which may also be found there, explains its meaning.   On the phrase *point-device* (Vol. III. p. 117) Mr.
Hazlitt has a positively incredible note, of which we
copy only a part : " This term, which is commonly used
in early poems " [mark once more his intimacy with our
earlier literature] " to signify extreme exactitude, originated in the points which were marked on the astrolabe,
as one of the means which the astrologers and dabblers
in the black art adopted to enable them (as they pretended) to read the fortunes of those by whom they were
consulted in the stars and planetary orbs.   The excessive precision which was held to be requisite in the
delineation of these points " [the delineation of a *point*
is good !] " &c. on the astrolabe, led to *point-device*, or
points-device (as it is sometimes found spelled), being
used as a proverbial expression for minute accuracy of

any kind." Then follows a quotation from Gower, in which an astrolabe is spoken of "with points and cercles merveilous," and the note proceeds thus : " Shakespeare makes use of a similar figure of speech in the *Tempest*, I. 2, where the following dialogue takes place between Prospero and Ariel : —

> *' Prosp.* Hast thou, spirit,
> Performed *to point* the tempest that I bade thee ?
> *Ar.* In every article.' "

Neither the proposed etymology nor the illustration requires any remark from us. We will only say that *point-device* is excellently explained and illustrated by Wedgwood.

We will give a few more examples out of many to show Mr. Hazlitt's utter unfitness for the task he has undertaken. In the " Kyng and the Hermyt " are the following verses,

> " A wyld wey, I hold, it were
> The wey to wend, I you swere,
> Bot ye the dey may se,"

meaning simply, " I think it would be a wild thing (in you) to go on your way unless you wait for daylight." Mr. Hazlitt punctuates and amends thus : —

> " A wyld wey I hold it were,
> The wey to wend, I you swere,
> Ye bot [by] the dey may se." (Vol. I. p. 19.)

The word *bot* seems a stumbling-block to Mr. Hazlitt. On page 54 of the same volume we have,

> " Herd i neuere bi no leuedi
> *Hote* hendinesse and curteysi."

The use of the word *by* as in this passage would seem familiar enough, and yet in the " Hye Way to the Spittel Hous " Mr. Hazlitt explains it as meaning *be*. Any boy knows that *without* sometimes means *unless* (Fielding uses it often in that sense), but Mr. Hazlitt seems unaware of the fact. In his first volume (p. 224) he gravely prints : —

> " They trowed verelye that she shoulde dye;
> *With that* our ladye wold her helpe and spede."

The semicolon after *dye* shows that this is not a misprint, but that the editor saw no connection between the first verse and the second. In the same volume (p. 133) we have the verse,

> " He was a grete tenement man, and ryche of londe and lede,"

and to *lede* Mr. Hazlitt appends this note : " *Lede,* in early English, is found in various significations, but here stands as the plural of *lad,* a servant." In what conceivable sense is it the plural of *lad?* And does *lad* necessarily mean a servant? The *Promptorium* has *ladde* glossed by *garcio,* but the meaning *servant,* as in the parallel cases of παις, *puer, garçon,* and *boy,* was a derivative one, and of later origin. The word means simply *man* (in the generic sense) and in the plural *people.* So in the " Squyr of Low Degre,"

> " I will forsake both land and *lede,*"

and in the " Smyth and his Dame,"

> " That hath both land and *lyth.*"

The word was *not* " used in various significations." Even so lately as " Flodden Ffeild " we find,

> " He was a noble *leed* of high degree."

Connected with *land* it was a commonplace in German as well as in English. So in the *Tristan* of Godfrey of Strasburg,

> „Er Bevalch sin lib t vnde sin lant
> An sines marscalkes hant.‟

Mr. Hazlitt is more nearly right than usual when he says that in the particular case cited above *lede* means *servants.* But were these of only one sex? Does he not know that even in the middle of the last century when an English nobleman spoke of "my people," he meant simply his domestics?

Encountering the familiar phrase *No do!* (Vol. IV. p. 64), Mr. Hazlitt changes it to *Not do!* He informs us that *Goddes are* (Vol. I. p. 197) means "God's heir"! He says (Vol II. p. 146): "*To borrow,* in the sense of *to take, to guard,* or *to protect,* is so common in early English that it is unnecessary to bring forward any illustration of its use in this way." But he relents, and presently gives us two from *Ralph Roister Doister,* each containing the phrase "Saint George to borrow!" That *borrow* means *take* no owner of books need be told, and Mr. Hazlitt has shown great skill in *borrowing* other people's illustrations for his notes, but the phrase he quotes has no such meaning as he gives it. Mr. Dyce in a note on Skelton explains it rightly, "St. George being my pledge or surety."

We gather a few more of these flowers of exposition and etymology : —

"The while thou sittest in chirche, thi bedys schalt thou bidde."
(Vol. I. p. 181.)

i. e. thou shalt offer thy prayers. Mr. Hazlitt's note on *bidde* is, "i. e. *bead.* So in *The Kyng and the Hermit,* line 111 : —

'That herd an hermyte there within
Unto the gate he gan to wyn
Bedying his prayer.'"

Precisely what Mr. Hazlitt understands by *beading* (or indeed by anything else) we shall not presume to divine, but we *should* like to hear him translate "if any man bidde the worshyp," which comes a few lines further on. Now let us turn to page 191 of the same volume. "Maydenys ben loneliche and no thing sekir." Mr. Hazlitt tells us in a note that "sekir or sicker" is a very common form of *secure,* and quotes in illustration

16 *   x

from the prose *Morte Arthure,* " A ! said Sir Launcelot,
comfort yourselfe, for it shall bee unto us as a great
honour, and much more then if we died in any other
places : for of death wee be *sicker*." Now in the text
the word means *safe,* and in the note it means *sure.*
Indeed *sure,* which is only a shorter form of *secure,* is its
ordinary meaning. " I mak sicker," said Kirkpatrick, a
not unfitting motto for certain editors, if they explained
it in their usual phonetic way.

In the " Frere and the Boye," when the old man has
given the boy a bow, he says : —

> " Shote therin, whan thou good thynke;
> For yf thou shote and wynke,
> The prycke thow shalte hytte."

Mr. Hazlitt's explanation of *wynke* is " to close one eye
in taking aim," and he quotes a passage from Gascoigne
in support of it. Whatever Gascoigne meant by the
word (which is very doubtful), it means nothing of the
kind here, and is another proof that Mr. Hazlitt does
not think it so important to understand what he reads
as St. Philip did. What the old man said was, " even
if you shut both your eyes, you can't help hitting the
mark." So in " Piers Ploughman " (Whitaker's text),

> " Wynkyng, as it were, wytterly ich saw hyt."

Again, for our editor's blunders are as endless as the
heads of an old-fashioned sermon, in the " Schole-House
of Women " (Vol. IV. p. 130), Mr. Hazlitt has a note on
the phrase " make it nice,"

> (" And yet alwaies they bible bable
> Of euery matter and make it nice,")

which reads thus : " To make it pleasant or *snug.* I do
not remember to have seen the word used in this sense
very frequently. But Gascoigne has it in a precisely
similar way : —

'The glosse of gorgeous Courtes by thee did please mine eye,
A stately sight me thought it was to see the braue go by,
To see their feathers flaunte, to make [marke!] their straunge deuise,
To lie along in ladies lappes, to lispe, and make it nice.' "

To *make it nice* means nothing more nor less than to *play the fool*, or rather, to *make a fool of yourself, faire le niais.* In old English the French *niais* and *nice*, from similarity of form and analogy of meaning, naturally fused together in the word *nice*, which, by an unusual luck, has been promoted from a derogatory to a respectful sense. Gascoigne's *lispe* might have put Mr. Hazlitt on his guard, if he ever considered the sense of what he quotes. But he never does, nor of what he edits either. For example, in the "Smyth and his Dame" we find the following note : "*Prowe*, or *proffe*, is not at all uncommon as a form of *profit*. In the 'Seven Names of a Prison,' a poem printed in *Reliquiæ Antiquæ*, we have, —

' Quintum nomen istius foveæ ita probatum,
A place of *proff* for man to know bothe frend and foo.' "

Now *proff* and *prow* are radically different words. *Proff* here means *proof*, and if Mr. Hazlitt had read the stanza which he quotes, he would have found (as in all the others of the same poem) the meaning repeated in Latin in the last line, *probacio amicorum.*

But we wish to leave our readers (if not Mr. Hazlitt) in good humor, and accordingly we have reserved two of his notes as *bonnes bouches.* In "Adam Bel," when the outlaws ask pardon of the king,

" They kneled downe without lettyng
And each helde vp his hande."

To this passage (tolerably plain to those not *too* familiar with "our early literature") Mr. Hazlitt appends this solemn note : '*To hold up the hand* was formerly a sign of respect or concurrence, or a mode of taking an oath ;

and thirdly as a signal for mercy.   In all these senses it
has been employed from the most ancient times ; nor is it
yet out of practice, as many savage nations still testify
their respect to a superior by holding their hand [either
their hands or *the hand*, Mr. Hazlitt !] over their head.
Touching the hat appears to be a vestige of the same
custom.   In the present passage the three outlaws may
be understood to kneel on approaching the throne, and
to hold up each a hand as a token that they desire to
ask the royal clemency or favour.   In the lines which are
subjoined it [what ?] implies a solemn assent to an oath :

> ' This swore the duke and all his men,
>   And all the lordes that with him lend,
>   And tharto to * held they up thaire hand.' "
>   Minot's Poems, ed. 1825, p. 9.

The admirable Tupper could not have done better than
this, even so far as the mere English of it is concerned.
Where all is so fine, we hesitate to declare a preference,
but, on the whole, must give in to the passage about
touching the hat, which is as good as " mobbled queen."
The Americans are still among the " savage nations "
who " imply a solemn assent to an oath " by holding
up the hand.   Mr. Hazlitt does not seem to know that
the question whether to kiss the book or hold up the
hand was once a serious one in English politics.

But Mr. Hazlitt can do better even than this !   Our
readers may be incredulous; but we shall proceed to
show that he can.   In the " Schole-House of Women,"
among much other equally delicate satire of the other
sex (if we may venture still to call them so), the satirist
undertakes to prove that woman was made, not of the
rib of a man, but of a dog : —

---

* The *to* is, we need not say, an addition of Mr. Hazlitt's.   What
faith can we put in the text of a man who so often copies even his
quotations inaccurately ?

" And yet the rib, as I suppose,
  That God did take out of the man
  A dog vp caught, and a way gose
  Eat it clene; so that as than
  The woork to finish that God began
  Could not be, as we haue said,
  Because the dog the rib conuaid.
     A remedy God found as yet;
  Out of the dog he took a rib."

Mr. Hazlitt has a long note on *way gose,* of which the first sentence shall suffice us : " The origin of the term way-goose is involved in some obscurity." We should think so, to be sure ! Let us modernize the spelling and grammar, and correct the punctuation, and then see how it looks : —

" A dog up caught and away goes,
    Eats it up."

We will ask Mr. Hazlitt to compare the text, as he prints it, with

"Into the hall he gose." (Vol. III. p. 67.)

We should have expected a note here on the " hall he-goose." Not to speak of the point of the joke, such as it is, a goose that could eat up a man's rib could only be matched by one that could swallow such a note, — or write it !

We have made but a small florilegium from Mr. Hazlitt's remarkable volumes. His editorial method seems to have been to print as the Lord would, till his eye was caught by some word he did not understand, and then to make the reader comfortable by a note showing that the editor is as much in the dark as he. We are profoundly thankful for the omission of a glossary. It would have been a nursery and seminary of blunder. To expose pretentious charlatanry is sometimes the unpleasant duty of a reviewer. It is a duty we never seek, and should not have assumed in this case but for the impertinence with which Mr. Hazlitt has treated dead and living scholars, the latchets of whose shoes he is not worthy to unloose, and to express their gratitude to whom is, or ought to be, a pleasure to all honest lovers of their mother-tongue. If he who has most to learn be the happiest man, Mr. Hazlitt is indeed to be envied; but we hope he will learn a great deal before he lays his prentice hands on Warton's "History of English Poetry," a classic in its own way. If he does not learn before, he will be likely to learn after, and in no agreeable fashion.

EMERSON THE LECTURER.

IT is a singular fact, that Mr. Emerson is the most steadily attractive lecturer in America. Into that somewhat cold-waterish region adventurers of the sensational kind come down now and then with a splash, to become disregarded King Logs before the next season. But Mr. Emerson always draws. A lecturer now for something like a third of a century, one of the pioneers of the lecturing system, the charm of his voice, his manner, and his matter has never lost its power over his earlier hearers, and continually winds new ones in its enchanting meshes. What they do not fully understand they take on trust, and listen, saying to themselves, as the old poet of Sir Philip Sidney, —

> " A sweet, attractive, kind of grace,
> A full assurance given by looks,
> Continual comfort in a face,
> The lineaments of gospel books."

We call it a singular fact, because we Yankees are thought to be fond of the spread-eagle style, and nothing can be more remote from that than his. We are reckoned a practical folk, who would rather hear about a new air-tight stove than about Plato ; yet our favorite teacher's practicality is not in the least of the Poor Richard variety. If he have any Buncombe constituency, it is that unrealized commonwealth of philosophers which Plotinus proposed to establish ; and if he were to make an almanac, his directions to farmers would

be something like this: "OCTOBER: *Indian Summer;*
now is the time to get in your early Vedas." What,
then, is his secret? Is it not that he out-Yankees us
all? that his range includes us all? that he is equally at
home with the potato-disease and original sin, with peg-
ging shoes and the Over-soul? that, as we try all trades,
so has he tried all cultures? and above all, that his
mysticism gives us a counterpoise to our super-practi-
cality?

There is no man living to whom, as a writer, so many
of us feel and thankfully acknowledge so great an indebtedness for ennobling impulses, — none whom so
many cannot abide. What does he mean? ask these
last. Where is his system? What is the use of it
all? What the deuse have we to do with Brahma?
I do not propose to write an essay on Emerson at this
time. I will only say that one may find grandeur
and consolation in a starlit night without caring to
ask what it means, save grandeur and consolation;
one may like Montaigne, as some ten generations before us have done, without thinking him so systematic
as some more eminently tedious (or shall we say tediously eminent?) authors; one may think roses as
good in their way as cabbages, though the latter would
make a better show in the witness-box, if cross-examined
as to their usefulness; and as for Brahma, why, he can
take care of himself, and won't bite us at any rate.

The bother with Mr. Emerson is, that, though he
writes in prose, he is essentially a poet. If you undertake to paraphrase what he says, and to reduce it to
words of one syllable for infant minds, you will make as
sad work of it as the good monk with his analysis of
Homer in the "Epistolæ Obscurorum Virorum." We
look upon him as one of the few men of genius whom
our age has produced, and there needs no better proof

or it than his masculine faculty of fecundating other
minds. Search for his eloquence in his books and you
will perchance miss it, but meanwhile you will find that
it has kindled all your thoughts. For choice and pith
of language he belongs to a better age than ours, and
might rub shoulders with Fuller and Browne, — though
he does use that abominable word *reliable.* His eye
for a fine, telling phrase that will carry true is like
that of a backwoodsman for a rifle ; and he will dredge
you up a choice word from the mud of Cotton Mather
himself. A diction at once so rich and so homely as
his I know not where to match in these days of writing by the page ; it is like homespun cloth-of-gold.
The many cannot miss his meaning, and only the few
can find it. It is the open secret of all true genius.
It is wholesome to angle in those profound pools, though
one be rewarded with nothing more than the leap of
a fish that flashes his freckled side in the sun and as
suddenly absconds in the dark and dreamy waters again.
There is keen excitement, though there be no ponderable
acquisition. If we carry nothing home in our baskets,
there is ample gain in dilated lungs and stimulated
blood. What does he mean, quotha ? He means inspiring hints, a divining-rod to your deeper nature.
No doubt, Emerson, like all original men, has his peculiar audience, and yet I know none that can hold a
promiscuous crowd in pleased attention so long as he.
As in all original men, there is something for every
palate. "Would you know," says Goethe, "the ripest
cherries ? Ask the boys and the blackbirds."

The announcement that such a pleasure as a new
course of lectures by him is coming, to people as old as
I am, is something like those forebodings of spring that
prepare us every year for a familiar novelty, none the
less novel, when it arrives, because it is familiar. We

know perfectly well what we are to expect from Mr. Emerson, and yet what he says always penetrates and stirs
us, as is apt to be the case with genius, in a very un-
looked-for fashion. Perhaps genius is one of the few
things which we gladly allow to repeat itself, — one of
the few that multiply rather than weaken the force of
their impression by iteration ? Perhaps some of us hear
more than the mere words, are moved by something
deeper than the thoughts ? If it be so, we are quite
right, for it is thirty years and more of "plain living
and high thinking" that speak to us in this altogether
unique lay-preacher. We have shared in the beneficence
of this varied culture, this fearless impartiality in criticism and speculation, this masculine sincerity, this sweetness of nature which rather stimulates than cloys, for a
generation long. If ever there was a standing testi-
monial to the cumulative power and value of Character,
(and we need it sadly in these days,) we have it in this
gracious and dignified presence. What an antiseptic
is a pure life ! At sixty-five (or two years beyond his
grand climacteric, as he would prefer to call it) he has
that privilege of soul which abolishes the calendar, and
presents him to us always the unwasted contemporary
of his own prime. I do not know if he seem old to his
younger hearers, but we who have known him so long
wonder at the tenacity with which he maintains himself
even in the outposts of youth. I suppose it is not the
Emerson of 1868 to whom we listen. For us the whole
life of the man is distilled in the clear drop of every
sentence, and behind each word we divine the force of a
noble character, the weight of a large capital of thinking and being. We do not go to hear what Emerson
says so much as to hear Emerson. Not that we perceive any falling-off in anything that ever was essential
to the charm of Mr. Emerson's peculiar style of thought

or phrase. The first lecture, to be sure, was more dis-
jointed even than common. It was as if, after vainly
trying to get his paragraphs into sequence and order, he
had at last tried the desperate expedient of *shuffling*
them. It was chaos come again, but it was a chaos full
of shooting-stars, a jumble of creative forces. The
second lecture, on "Criticism and Poetry," was quite up
to the level of old times, full of that power of strangely-
subtle association whose indirect approaches startle the
mind into almost painful attention, of those flashes of
mutual understanding between speaker and hearer that
are gone ere one can say it lightens. The vice of Emerson's criticism seems to be, that while no man is so
sensitive to what is poetical, few men are less sensible
than he of what makes a poem. He values the solid
meaning of thought above the subtler meaning of style.
He would prefer Donne, I suspect, to Spenser, and sometimes mistakes the queer for the original.

To be young is surely the best, if the most precarious,
gift of life; yet there are some of us who would hardly
consent to be young again, if it were at the cost of our
recollection of Mr. Emerson's first lectures during the
consulate of Van Buren. We used to walk in from the
country to the Masonic Temple (I think it was), through
the crisp winter night, and listen to that thrilling voice
of his, so charged with subtle meaning and subtle music,
as shipwrecked men on a raft to the hail of a ship that
came with unhoped-for food and rescue. Cynics might
say what they liked. Did our own imaginations trans-
figure dry remainder-biscuit into ambrosia? At any
rate, he brought us *life*, which, on the whole, is no bad
thing. Was it all transcendentalism? magic-lantern
pictures on mist? As you will. Those, then, were just
what we wanted. But it was not so. The delight and
the benefit were that he put us in communication with

a larger style of thought, sharpened our wits with a more pungent phrase, gave us ravishing glimpses of an ideal under the dry husk of our New England ; made us conscious of the supreme and everlasting originality of whatever bit of soul might be in any of us ; freed us, in short, from the stocks of prose in which we had sat so long that we had grown wellnigh contented in our cramps.   And who that saw the audience will ever forget it, where every one still capable of fire, or longing to renew in them the half-forgotten sense of it,. was gathered ?   Those faces, young and old, agleam with pale intellectual light, eager with pleased attention, flash upon me once more from the deep recesses of the years with an exquisite pathos.   Ah, beautiful young eyes, brimming with love and hope, wholly vanished now in that other world we call the Past, or peering doubtfully through the pensive gloaming of memory, your light impoverishes these cheaper days !   I hear again that rustle of sensation, as they turned to exchange glances over some pithier thought, some keener flash of that humor which always played about the horizon of his mind like heat-lightning, and it seems now like the sad whisper of the autumn leaves that are whirling around me.   But would my picture be complete if I forgot that ample and vegete countenance of Mr. R—— of W——, — how, from its regular post at the corner of the front bench, it turned in ruddy triumph to the profaner audience as if he were the inexplicably appointed fugleman of appreciation ?   I was reminded of him by those hearty cherubs in Titian's Assumption that look at you as who should say, " Did you ever see a Madonna like *that* ? Did you ever behold one hundred and fifty pounds of womanhood mount heavenward before like a rocket ? "

To some of us that long-past experience remains as the most marvellous and fruitful we have ever had.   Emerson

awakened us, saved us from the body of this death. It
is the sound of the trumpet that the young soul longs
for, careless what breath may fill it. Sidney heard it in
the ballad of "Chevy Chase," and we in Emerson. Nor
did it blow retreat, but called to us with assurance of
victory. Did they say he was disconnected? So were
the stars, that seemed larger to our eyes, still keen with
that excitement, as we walked homeward with prouder
stride over the creaking snow. And were *they* not knit
together by a higher logic than our mere sense could
master? Were we enthusiasts? I hope and believe we
were, and am thankful to the man who made us worth
something for once in our lives. If asked what was left?
what we carried home? we should not have been careful
for an answer. It would have been enough if we had
said that something beautiful had passed that way. Or
we might have asked in return what one brought away
from a symphony of Beethoven? Enough that he had
set that ferment of wholesome discontent at work in us.
There is one, at least, of those old hearers, so many of
whom are now in the fruition of that intellectual beauty
of which Emerson gave them both the desire and the
foretaste, who will always love to repeat : —

> " Che in la mente m'è fitta, ed or m'accuora
> La cara e buona immagine paterna
> Di voi, quando nel mondo ad ora ad ora
> M'insegnavaste come l'uom s'eterna."

I am unconsciously thinking, as I write, of the third
lecture of the present course, in which Mr. Emerson
gave some delightful reminiscences of the intellectual
influences in whose movement he had shared. It was
like hearing Goethe read some passages of the "Wahr-
heit aus seinem Leben." Not that there was not a little
Dichtung, too, here and there, as the lecturer built up
so lofty a pedestal under certain figures as to lift them

into a prominence of obscurity, and seem to masthead
them there. Everybody was asking his neighbor who
this or that recondite great man was, in the faint hope
that somebody might once have heard of him. There
are those who call Mr. Emerson cold. Let them revise
their judgment in presence of this loyalty of his that
can keep warm for half a century, that never forgets a
friendship, or fails to pay even a fancied obligation to
the uttermost farthing. This substantiation of shadows
was but incidental, and pleasantly characteristic of the
man to those who know and love him. The greater part
of the lecture was devoted to reminiscences of things
substantial in themselves. He spoke of Everett, fresh
from Greece and Germany; of Channing; of the translations of Margaret Fuller, Ripley, and Dwight; of the
Dial and Brook Farm. To what he said of the latter
an undertone of good-humored irony gave special zest.
But what every one of his hearers felt was that the protagonist in the drama was left out. The lecturer was
no Æneas to babble the *quorum magna pars fui*, and, as
one of his listeners, I cannot help wishing to say how
each of them was commenting the story as it went along,
and filling up the necessary gaps in it from his own private store of memories. His younger hearers could not
know how much they owed to the benign impersonality,
the quiet scorn of everything ignoble, the never-sated
hunger of self-culture, that were personified in the man
before them. But the older knew how much the country's intellectual emancipation was due to the stimulus
of his teaching and example, how constantly he had kept
burning the beacon of an ideal life above our lower
region of turmoil. To him more than to all other causes
together did the young martyrs of our civil war owe the
sustaining strength of thoughtful heroism that is so
touching in every record of their lives. Those who are

grateful to Mr. Emerson, as many of us are, for what they feel to be most valuable in their culture, or perhaps I should say their impulse, are grateful not so much for any direct teachings of his as for that inspiring lift which only genius can give, and without which all doctrine is chaff.

This was something like the *caret* which some of us older boys wished to fill up on the margin of the master's lecture. Few men have been so much to so many, and through so large a range of aptitudes and temperaments, and this simply because all of us value manhood beyond any or all other qualities of character. We may suspect in him, here and there, a certain thinness and vagueness of quality, but let the waters go over him as they list, this masculine fibre of his will keep its lively color and its toughness of texture. I have heard some great speakers and some accomplished orators, but never any that so moved and persuaded men as he. There is a kind of undertow in that rich baritone of his that sweeps our minds from their foothold into deeper waters with a drift we cannot and would not resist. And how artfully (for Emerson is a long-studied artist in these things) does the deliberate utterance, that seems waiting for the fit word, appear to admit us partners in the labor of thought and make us feel as if the glance of humor were a sudden suggestion, as if the perfect phrase lying written there on the desk were as unexpected to him as to us ! In that closely-filed speech of his at the Burns centenary dinner every word seemed to have just dropped down to him from the clouds. He looked far away over the heads of his hearers, with a vague kind of expectation, as into some private heaven of invention, and the winged period came at last obedient to his spell. " My dainty Ariel !" he seemed murmuring to himself as he cast down his eyes as if in deprecation of the frenzy of approval and caught another sentence from the Sibylline leaves that lay before him ambushed behind a dish of fruit and seen only by nearest neighbors. Every sentence brought down the house, as I never saw one brought down before, — and it is not so easy to hit Scotsmen with a sentiment that has no hint of native brogue in it. I watched, for it was an interesting study, how the quick sympathy ran flashing from face to face down the long tables, like an electric spark thrilling as it went, and then exploded in a thunder of plaudits. I watched till tables and faces vanished, for I, too, found myself caught up in the common enthusiasm, and my excited fancy set me under the *bema* listening to him who fulmined over Greece. I can never help applying to him what Ben Jonson said of Bacon : "There happened in my time one noble speaker, who was full of gravity in his speaking. His language was nobly censorious. No man ever spake more neatly, more pressly, more weightily, or suffered less emptiness, less idleness, in what he uttered. No member of his speech but consisted of his own graces. His hearers could not cough, or look aside from him, without loss. He commanded where he spoke." Those who heard him while their natures were yet plastic, and their mental nerves trembled under the slightest breath of divine air, will never cease to feel and say : —

> "Was never eye did see that face,
> Was never ear did hear that tongue,
> Was never mind did mind his grace,
> That ever thought the travail long;
> But eyes, and ears, and every thought,
> Were with his sweet perfections caught."

POPE.

—◆—

IN 1675 Edward Phillips, the elder of Milton's nephews, published his *Theatrum Poetarum*. In his Preface and elsewhere there can be little doubt that he reflected the æsthetic principles and literary judgments of his now illustrious uncle, who had died in obscurity the year before.* The great poet who gave to English blank verse the grandeur and compass of organ-music, and who in his minor poems kept alive the traditions of Fletcher and Shakespeare, died with no foretaste, and yet we may believe as confident as ever, of that " immortality of fame " which he tells his friend Diodati he was " meditating with the help of Heaven " in his youth. He who may have seen Shakespeare, who doubtless had seen Fletcher, and who perhaps personally knew Jonson,† lived to see that false school of writers whom he qualified as " good rhymists, but no poets," at once the idols and the victims of the taste they had corrupted. As he saw, not without scorn, how they found universal hearing, while he slowly won his audience fit though few, did he ever think of the hero of his own epic at the ear of Eve ? It is not impossible ; but however that may be, he sowed in his nephew's book the dragon's teeth of that long war which, after the lapse of a century and a

* This was Thomas Warton's opinion.

† Milton, a London boy, was in his eighth. seventeenth, and twenty-ninth years, respectively, when Shakespeare (1616), Fletcher (1625), and B. Jonson (1637) died.

half, was to end in the expulsion of the usurping dynasty and the restoration of the ancient and legitimate race whose claim rested on the grace of God. In the following passage surely the voice is Milton's, though the hand be that of Phillips : " Wit, ingenuity, and learning in verse, even elegancy itself, though that comes nearest, are one thing ; true native poetry is another, in which there is a certain air and spirit, which, perhaps, the most learned and judicious in other arts do not perfectly apprehend ; much less is it attainable by any art or study." The man who speaks of elegancy as coming nearest, certainly shared, if he was not repeating, the opinions of him who thirty years before had said that " decorum " (meaning a higher or organic unity) was " the grand masterpiece to observe " in poetry.*

It is upon this text of Phillips (as Chalmers has remarked) that Joseph Warton bases his classification of poets in the dedication to Young of the first volume of his essay on the Genius and Writings of Pope, published in 1756. That was the earliest public and official declaration of war against the reigning mode, though private hostilities and reprisals had been going on for some time. Addison's panegyric of Milton in the Spectator was a criticism, not the less damaging because indirect, of the superficial poetry then in vogue. His praise of the old ballads condemned by innuendo the artificial elaboration of the drawing-room pastoral by contrasting it with the simple sincerity of nature. Himself incapable of being natural except in prose, he had an instinct for the genuine virtues of poetry as sure as that of Gray. Thomson's " Winter " (1726) was a direct protest against the literature of Good Society, going as it did to prove that the noblest society was that of one's own mind heightened by the contemplation of outward

* In his Tractate on Education.

nature. What Thomson's poetical creed was may be
surely inferred from his having modelled his two principal poems on Milton and Spenser, ignoring rhyme
altogether in the "Seasons," and in the "Castle of
Indolence" rejecting the stiff mould of the couplet.
In 1744 came Akenside's "Pleasures of Imagination,"
whose very title, like a guide-post, points away from the
level highway of commonplace to mountain-paths and
less domestic prospects. The poem was stiff and unwilling, but in its loins lay the seed of nobler births, and
without it the "Lines written at Tintern Abbey" might
never have been. Three years later Collins printed his
little volume of Odes, advocating in theory and ex-
emplifying in practice the natural supremacy of the
imagination (though he called it by its older name of
fancy) as a test to distinguish poetry from verse-making.
The whole Romantic School, in its germ, no doubt, but
yet unmistakably foreshadowed, lies already in the
"Ode on the Superstitions of the Highlands." He
was the first to bring back into poetry something of the
antique fervor, and found again the long-lost secret of
being classically elegant without being pedantically cold.
A skilled lover of music,* he rose from the general
sing-song of his generation to a harmony that had been
silent since Milton, and in him, to use his own words,

"The force of energy is found,
And the sense rises on the wings of sound."

But beside his own direct services in the reformation
of our poetry, we owe him a still greater debt as the
inspirer of Gray, whose "Progress of Poesy," in reach,
variety, and loftiness of poise, overflies all other English lyrics like an eagle. In spite of the dulness of contemporary ears, preoccupied with the continuous hum

* Milton, Collins, and Gray, our three great masters of harmony
were all musicians.

of the popular hurdy-gurdy, it was the prevailing blast
of Gray's trumpet that more than anything else called
men back to the legitimate standard.* Another poet,
Dyer, whose "Fleece" was published in 1753, both in
the choice of his subject and his treatment of it gives
further proof of the tendency among the younger generation to revert to simpler and purer models. Plainly

* Wordsworth, who recognized forerunners in Thomson, Collins,
Dyer, and Burns, and who chimes in with the popular superstition
about Chatterton, is always somewhat niggardly in his appreciation
of Gray. Yet he owed him not a little. Without Gray's tune in his
ears, his own noblest Ode would have missed the varied modulation
which is one of its main charms. Where he forgets Gray, his verse
sinks to something like the measure of a jig. Perhaps the suggestion
of one of his own finest lines,

("The light that never was on land or sea,")

was due to Gray's

"Orient hues unborrowed of the sun."

I believe it has not been noticed that among the verses in Gray's
"Sonnet on the Death of West," which Wordsworth condemns as of
no value, the second —

"And reddening Phœbus lifts his golden fires" —

is one of Gray's happy reminiscences from a poet in some respects
greater than either of them: —

Jamque *rubrum* tremulis jubar *ignibus erigere alte*
Cum cœptat natura.

LUCRET., iv. 404, 405.

Gray's taste was a sensitive divining-rod of the sources whether of
pleasing or profound emotion in poetry. Though he prized pomp, he
did not undervalue simplicity of subject or treatment, if only the
witch Imagination had cast her spell there. Wordsworth loved solitude in his appreciations as well as in his daily life, and was the
readier to find merit in obscurity, because it gave him the pleasure of
being a first discoverer all by himself. Thus he addresses a sonnet to
John Dyer. But Gray was one of "the pure and powerful minds"
who had discovered Dyer during his lifetime, when the discovery of
poets is more difficult. In 1753 he writes to Walpole: "Mr. Dyer has
more poetry in his imagination than almost any of our number, but
rough and injudicious." Dyer has one fine verse, —

"On the dark level of adversity."

enough, Thomson had been his chief model, though there are also traces of a careful study of Milton.

Pope had died in 1744, at the height of his renown, the acknowledged monarch of letters, as supreme as Voltaire when the excitement and exposure of his coronation-ceremonies at Paris hastened his end a generation later. His fame, like Voltaire's, was European, and the style which he had carried to perfection was paramount throughout the cultivated world. The new edition of the "Dunciad," with the Fourth Book added, published the year before his death, though the substitution of Cibber for Theobald made the poem incoherent, had yet increased his reputation and confirmed the sway of the school whose recognized head he was, by the poignancy of its satire, the lucidity of its wit, and the resounding, if somewhat uniform march, of its numbers. He had been translated into other languages living and dead. Voltaire had long before pronounced him "the best poet of England, and at present of all the world." * It was the apotheosis of clearness, point, and technical skill, of the ease that comes of practice, not of the fulness of original power. And yet, as we have seen, while he was in the very plenitude of his power, there was already a widespread discontent, a feeling that what "comes nearest," as Phillips calls it, may yet be infinitely far from giving those profounder and incalculable satisfactions of which the soul is capable in poetry. A movement was gathering strength which prompted

> "The age to quit their clogs
> By the known rules of virtuous liberty."

Nor was it wholly confined to England. Symptoms of a similar reaction began to show themselves on the Conti-

---

* MS. letter of Voltaire, cited by Warburton in his edition of Pope, Vol. IV. p. 38, note. The date is 15th October, 1726. I do not find it in Voltaire's Correspondence.

nent, notably in the translation of Milton (1732) and the publication of the *Nibelungen Lied* (1757) by Bodmer, and the imitations of Thomson in France. Was it possible, then, that there was anything better than good sense, elegant diction, and the highest polish of style? Could there be an intellectual appetite which antithesis failed to satisfy? If the horse would only have faith enough in his green spectacles, surely the straw would acquire, not only the flavor, but the nutritious properties of fresh grass. The horse was foolish enough to starve, but the public is wiser. It is surprising how patiently it will go on, for generation after generation, transmuting dry stubble into verdure in this fashion.

The school which Boileau founded was critical and not creative. It was limited, not only in its essence, but by the capabilities of the French language and by the natural bent of the French mind, which finds a predominant satisfaction in phrases if elegantly turned, and can make a despotism, political or æsthetic, palatable with the pepper of epigram. The style of Louis XIV. did what his armies failed to do. It overran and subjugated Europe. It struck the literature of imagination with palsy, and it is droll enough to see Voltaire, after he had got some knowledge of Shakespeare, continually endeavoring to reassure himself about the poetry of the *grand siècle,* and all the time asking himself, "Why, in the name of all the gods at once, is this *not* the real thing?" He seems to have felt that there was a dreadful mistake somewhere, when poetry must be called upon to prove itself inspired, above all when it must demonstrate that it is interesting, all appearances to the contrary notwithstanding. Difficulty, according to Voltaire, is the tenth Muse; but how if there were difficulty in reading as well as writing? It was something, at any rate, which an increasing number of persons were perverse enough to feel in attempting

the productions of a pseudo-classicism, the classicism of
red heels and periwigs. Even poor old Dennis himself
had arrived at a kind of muddled notion that artifice was
not precisely art, that there were depths in human nature
which the most perfectly manufactured line of five feet
could not sound, and passionate elations that could not
be tuned to the lullaby seesaw of the couplet. The satisfactions of a conventional taste were very well in their
own way, but were they, after all, the highest of which
men were capable who had obscurely divined the Greeks,
and who had seen Hamlet, Lear, and Othello upon the
stage? Was not poetry, then, something which delivered
us from the dungeon of actual life, instead of basely
reconciling us with it?

A century earlier the school of the *cultists* had established a dominion, ephemeral, as it soon appeared, but
absolute while it lasted. Du Bartas, who may, perhaps,
as fairly as any, lay claim to its paternity,* had been
called divine, and similar honors had been paid in turn
to Gongora, Lilly, and Marini, who were in the strictest
sense contemporaneous. The infection of mere fashion
will hardly account satisfactorily for a vogue so sudden
and so widely extended. It may well be suspected that
there was some latent cause, something at work more
potent than the fascinating mannerism of any single author in the rapid and almost simultaneous diffusion of
this purely cutaneous eruption. It is not improbable
that, in the revival of letters, men whose native tongues
had not yet attained the precision and grace only to
be acquired by long literary usage, should have learned
from a study of the Latin poets to value the form above

---

* Its taste for verbal affectations is to be found in the *Roman de la
Rose*, and (yet more absurdly forced) in Gauthier de Coinsy; but in
Du Bartas the research of effect not seldom subjugates the thought as
well as the phrase.

the substance, and to seek in mere words a conjuring
property which belongs to them only when they catch
life and meaning from profound thought or powerful
emotion.   Yet this very devotion to expression at the
expense of everything else, though its excesses were fatal
to the innovators who preached and practised it, may
not have been without good results in refining language
and fitting it for the higher uses to which it was destined.   The *cultists* went down before the implacable
good sense of French criticism, but the defect of this
criticism was that it ignored imagination altogether, and
sent Nature about her business as an impertinent bag-
gage whose household loom competed unlawfully with
the machine-made fabrics, so exquisitely uniform in pattern, of the royal manufactories.   There is more than a
fanciful analogy between the style which Pope brought
into vogue and that which for a time bewitched all ears
in the latter half of the sixteenth century.   As the master had made it an axiom to avoid what was mean or
low, so the disciples endeavored to escape from what was
common.   This they contrived by the ready expedient
of the periphrasis.   They called everything something
else.   A boot with them was

> " The shining leather that encased the limb ";

coffee became

> " The fragrant juice of Mocha's berry brown ";

and they were as liberal of epithets as a royal christen-
ing of proper names.   Two in every verse, one to balance the other, was the smallest allowance.   Here are
four successive verses from " The Vanity of Human
Wishes " : —

> " The *encumbered* oar scarce leaves the *dreaded* coast
> Through *purple* billows and a *floating* host.
> The *bold* Bavarian in a *luckless* hour
> Tries the *dread* summits of *Cæsarian* power."

This fashion perished also by its own excess, but the criticism which laid at the door of the master all the faults of his pupils was unjust. It was defective, moreover, in overlooking how much of what we call natural is an artificial product, above all in forgetting that Pope had one of the prime qualities of a great poet in exactly answering the intellectual needs of the age in which he lived, and in reflecting its lineaments. He did in some not inadequate sense hold the mirror up to nature. His poetry is not a mountain-tarn, like that of Wordsworth; it is not in sympathy with the higher moods of the mind; yet it continues entertaining, in spite of all changes of mode. It was a mirror in a drawing-room, but it gave back a faithful image of society, powdered and rouged, to be sure, and intent on trifles, yet still as human in its own way as the heroes of Homer in theirs.

For the popularity of Pope, as for that of Marini and his sect, circumstances had prepared the way. English literature for half a century after the Restoration showed the marks both of a moral reaction and of an artistic vassalage to France. From the compulsory saintship and cropped hair of the Puritans men rushed or sneaked, as their temperaments dictated, to the opposite cant of sensuality and a wilderness of periwig. Charles II. had brought back with him from exile French manners, French morals, and above all French taste. Misfortune makes a shallow mind sceptical. It had made the king so; and this, at a time when court patronage was the main sinew of authorship, was fatal to the higher qualities of literature. That Charles should have preferred the stately decorums of the French school, and should have mistaken its polished mannerism for style, was natural enough. But there was something also in the texture of the average British mind which prepared it for this subjugation from the other side of the Channel.

17 *

No observer of men can have failed to notice the clumsy respect which the understanding pays to elegance of manner and *savoir-faire*, nor what an awkward sense of inferiority it feels in the presence of an accomplished worldliness. The code of society is stronger with most persons than that of Sinai, and many a man who would not scruple to thrust his fingers in his neighbor's pocket would forego green peas rather than use his knife as a shovel. The submission with which the greater number surrender their natural likings for the acquired taste of what for the moment is called the World is a highly curious phenomenon, and, however destructive of originality, is the main safeguard of society and nurse of civility. Any one who has witnessed the torments of an honest citizen in a foreign gallery before some hideous martyrdom which he feels it his duty to admire, though it be hateful to him as nightmare, may well doubt whether the gridiron of the saint were hotter than that of the sinner. It is only a great mind or a strong character that knows how to respect its own provincialism and can dare to be in fashion with itself. The bewildered clown with his " Am I Giles ? or am I not ? " was but a type of the average man who finds himself uniformed, drilled, and keeping step, whether he will or no, with the company into which destiny or chance has drafted him, and which is marching him inexorably away from everything that made him comfortable.

The insularity of England, while it fostered pride and reserve, entailed also that sensitiveness to ridicule which haunts pride like an evil genius. " The English," says Barclay, writing half a century before the Restoration, "have for the most part grave minds and withdrawn, as it were, into themselves for counsel; they wonderfully admire themselves and the manners, genius, and spirit of their own nation. In salutation or in

writing they endure not (unless haply imbued with foreign manners) to descend to those words of imaginary
servitude which the refinement (*blandities*) of ages hath
invented." * Yet their fondness of foreign fashions had
long been the butt of native satirists. Every one re-
members Portia's merry picture of the English lord :
" How oddly he is suited ! I think he bought his doub-
let in Italy, his round hose in France, his bonnet in
Germany, and his behavior everywhere." But while
she laughs at his bungling efforts to make himself a cos-
mopolite in externals, she hints at the persistency of
his inward Anglicism : " He hath neither Latin, French,
nor Italian." In matters of taste the Anglo-Saxon mind
seems always to have felt a painful distrust of itself,
which it betrays either in an affectation of burly contempt or in a pretence of admiration equally insincere.
The young lords who were to make the future court of
Charles II. no doubt found in Paris an elegance beside
which the homely bluntness of native manners seemed
rustic and underbred. They frequented a theatre where
propriety was absolute upon the stage, though license
had its full swing behind the scenes. They brought
home with them to England debauched morals and
that urbane discipline of manners which is so agreeable a substitute for discipline of mind. The word
" genteel " came back with them, an outward symptom
of the inward change. In the last generation, the men
whose great aim was success in the Other World had
wrought a political revolution ; now, those whose ideal
was prosperity in This World were to have their turn
and to accomplish with their lighter weapons as great a
change. Before the end of the seventeenth century
John Bull was pretty well persuaded, in a bewildered
kind of way, that he had been vulgar, and especially

* *Barclaii Satyricon*, p. 382. Barclay had lived in France.

that his efforts in literature showed marks of native vig-
or, indeed, but of a vigor clownish and uncouth. He
began to be ashamed of the provincialism which had
given strength, if also something of limitation, to his
character.

Waller, who spent a whole summer in polishing the
life out of ten lines to be written in the Tasso of the
Duchess of York, expresses the prevailing belief as regarded poetry in the prologue to his "improvement" of
the "Maid's Tragedy" of Beaumont and Fletcher. He
made the play *reasonable*, as it was called, and there is
a pleasant satire in the fact that it was refused a license
because there was an immoral king in it. On the throne,
to be sure, — but on the stage ! Forbid it, decency !

> " Above our neighbors' our conceptions are,
> But faultless writing is the effect of care ;
> Our lines reformed, and not composed in haste,
> Polished like marble, would like marble last.
>
> . . . . .
>
> Were we but less indulgent to our fau'ts,
> And patience had to cultivate our thoughts,
> Our Muse would flourish, and a nobler rage
> Would honor this than did the Grecian stage."

It is a curious comment on these verses in favor of careful writing, that Waller should have failed even to express his own meaning either clearly or with propriety.
He talks of "cultivating our thoughts," when he means
"pruning our style" ; he confounds the Muse with the
laurel, or at any rate makes her a plant, and then goes
on with perfect equanimity to tell us that a nobler
"rage" (that is, madness) than that of Greece would
follow the horticultural devices he recommends. It
never seems to have occurred to Waller that it is the
substance of what you polish, and not the polish itself,
that insures duration. Dryden, in his rough-and-ready
way, has hinted at this in his verses to Congreve on the

"Double Dealer." He begins by stating the received
theory about the improvement of English literature under the new *régime*, but the thin ice of sophistry over
which Waller had glided smoothly gives way under his
greater weight, and he finds himself in deep water ere
he is aware.

> "Well, then, the promised hour has come at last,
> The present age in wit obscures the past;
> Strong were our sires, and as they fought they writ,
> Conquering with force of arm * and dint of wit.
> Theirs was the giant race before the Flood;
> And thus when Charles returned our Empire stood;
> Like Janus he the stubborn soil manured,
> With rules of husbandry the rankness cured,
> Tamed us to manners when the stage was rude,
> And boisterous English wit with art endued;
> Our age was cultivated thus at length,
> But what we gained in skill we lost in strength;
> Our builders were with want of genius curst,
> The second temple was not like the first."

There would seem to be a manifest reminiscence of
Waller's verse in the half-scornful emphasis which Dryden lays on " cultivated." Perhaps he was at first led to
give greater weight to correctness and to the restraint
of arbitrary rules from a consciousness that he had a
tendency to hyperbole and extravagance. But he afterwards became convinced that the heightening of discourse by passion was a very different thing from the
exaggeration which heaps phrase on phrase, and that
genius, like beauty, can always plead its privilege. Dryden, by his powerful example, by the charm of his verse
which combines vigor and fluency in a measure perhaps
never reached by any other of our poets, and above all
because it is never long before the sunshine of his cheerful good sense breaks through the clouds of rhetoric,

---

* Usually printed *arms*, but Dryden certainly wrote *arm*, to corre-
spond with *dint*, which he used in its old meaning of a downright
blow.

and gilds the clipped hedges over which his thought clambers like an unpruned vine, — Dryden, one of the most truly English of English authors, did more than all others combined to bring about the triumphs of French standards in taste and French principles in criticism. But he was always like a deserter who cannot feel happy in the victories of the alien arms, and who would go back if he could to the camp where he naturally belonged. Between 1660 and 1700 more French words, I believe, were directly transplanted into our language than in the century and a half since. What was of more consequence, French ideas came with them, shaping the form, and through that modifying the spirit, of our literature.

Voltaire, though he came later, was steeped in the theories of art which had been inherited as traditions of classicism from the preceding generation. He had lived in England, and, I have no doubt, gives us a very good notion of the tone which was prevalent there in his time, an English version of the criticism imported from France. He tells us that Mr. Addison was the first Englishman who had written a *reasonable* tragedy. And in spite of the growling of poor old Dennis, whose sandy pedantry was not without an oasis of refreshing sound judgment here and there, this was the opinion of most persons at that day, except, it may be suspected, the judicious and modest Mr. Addison himself. Voltaire says of the English tragedians, — and it will be noticed that he is only putting, in another way, the opinion of Dryden, — " Their productions, almost all barbarous, without polish, order, or probability, have astonishing gleams in the midst of their night ; . . . . it seems sometimes that nature is not made in England as it is elsewhere." *Eh bien,* the inference is that we must try and make it so ! The world must be uniform in order to be comfortable, and what fashion so becoming as the one we have invented in Paris ? It is not a little amusing that when Voltaire played master of ceremonies to introduce the *bizarre* Shakespeare among his countrymen, that other kind of nature made a profounder impression on them than quite pleased him. So he turned about presently and called his whilome *protége* a buffoon.

The condition of the English mind at the close of the seventeenth century was such as to make it particularly sensitive to the magnetism which streamed to it from Paris. The loyalty of everybody both in politics and religion had been put out of joint. A generation of materialists, by the natural rebound which inevitably follows over-tension, was to balance the ultra-spiritualism of the Puritans. As always when a political revolution has been wrought by moral agencies, the plunder had fallen mainly to the share of the greedy, selfish, and unscrupulous, whose disgusting cant had given a taint of hypocrisy to piety itself. Religion, from a burning conviction of the soul, had grown to be with both parties a political badge, as little typical of the inward man as the scallop of a pilgrim. Sincerity is impossible, unless it pervade the whole being, and the pretence of it saps the very foundation of character. There seems to have been an universal scepticism, and in its worst form, that is, with an outward conformity in the interest of decorum and order. There was an unbelief that did not believe even in itself.

The difference between the leading minds of the former age and that which was supplanting it went to the very roots of the soul. Milton was willing to peril the success of his crowning work by making the poetry of it a stalking-horse for his theological convictions. What was that Fame

> " Which the clear spirit doth raise
> To scorn delights and live laborious days,"

to the crown of a good preacher who sets

> " The hearts of men on fire
> To scorn the sordid world and unto heaven aspire " ?

Dean Swift, who aspired to the mitre, could write a book whose moral, if it had any, was that one religion was as good as another, since all were political devices, and accepted a cure of souls when it was more than doubtful whether he believed that his fellow-creatures had any souls to be saved, or, if they had, whether they were worth saving. The answer which Pulci's Margutte makes to Morgante, when asked if he believed in Christ or Mahomet, would have expressed well enough the creed of the majority of that generation : —

> " To tell thee truly,
> My faith in black 's no greater than in azure,
> But I believe in capons, roast-meat, bouilli,
> And in good wine my faith 's beyond all measure." *

It was a carnival of intellect without faith, when men could be Protestant or Catholic, both at once, or by turns, or neither, as suited their interest, when they could swear one allegiance and keep on safe terms with the other, when prime ministers and commanders-in-chief could be intelligencers of the Pretender, nay, when even Algernon Sidney himself could be a pensioner of France. What morality there was, was the morality of appearances, of the side that is turned toward men and not toward God. The very shamelessness of Congreve is refreshing in that age of sham.

It was impossible that anything truly great, that is, great on the moral and emotional as well as the intellectual side, should be produced by such a generation. But something intellectually great could be and was.

* Morgante, xviii. 115.

The French mind, always stronger in perceptive and analytic than in imaginative qualities, loving precision, grace, and finesse, prone to attribute an almost magical power to the scientific regulation whether of politics or religion, had brought wit and fancy and the elegant arts of society to as great perfection as was possible by the *a priori* method. Its ideal in literature was to conjure passion within the magic circle of courtliness, or to combine the appearance of careless ease and gayety of thought with intellectual exactness of statement. The eternal watchfulness of a wit that never slept had made it distrustful of the natural emotions and the unconventional expression of them, and its first question about a sentiment was, Will it be *safe?* about a phrase, Will it pass with the Academy? The effect of its example on English literature would appear chiefly in neatness and facility of turn, in point and epigrammatic compactness of phrase, and these in conveying conventional sentiments and emotions, in appealing to good society rather than to human nature. Its influence would be greatest where its success had been most marked, in what was called moral poetry, whose chosen province was manners, and in which satire, with its avenging scourge, took the place of that profounder art whose office it was to purify, not the manners, but the source of them in the soul, by pity and terror. The mistake of the whole school of French criticism, it seems to me, lay in its tendency to confound what was common with what was vulgar, in a too exclusive deference to authority at the expense of all free movement of the mind.

There are certain defects of taste which correct themselves by their own extravagance. Language, I suspect, is more apt to be reformed by the charm of some master of it, like Milton, than by any amount of precept. The influence of second-rate writers for evil is at best ephem-

z

eral, for true style, the joint result of culture and natural aptitude, is always in fashion, as fine manners always are, in whatever clothes. Perhaps some reform was needed when Quarles, who had no mean gift of poesy, could write,

> "My passion has no April in her eyes:
> I cannot spend in mists; I cannot mizzle;
> My fluent brains are too severe to drizzle
> Slight drops." *

Good taste is an excellent thing when it confines itself to its own rightful province of the proprieties, but when it attempts to correct those profound instincts out of whose judgments the higher principles of æsthetics have been formulated, its success is a disaster. During the era when the French theory of poetry was supreme, we notice a decline from imagination to fancy, from passion to wit, from metaphor, which fuses image and thought in one, to simile, which sets one beside the other, from the supreme code of the natural sympathies to the parochial by-laws of etiquette. The imagination instinctively Platonizes, and it is the essence of poetry that it should be unconventional, that the soul of it should subordinate the outward parts ; while the artificial method proceeds from a principle the reverse of this, making the spirit lackey the form.

Waller preaches up this new doctrine in the epilogue to the "Maid's Tragedy" : —

> "Nor is 't less strange such mighty wits as those
> Should use a style in tragedy like prose;
> Well-sounding verse, where princes tread the stage,
> Should speak their virtue and describe their rage."

---

* Elegie on Doctor Wilson. But if Quarles had been led astray by the vices of Donne's manner, he had good company in Herbert and Vaughan. In common with them, too, he had that luck of simpleness which is even more delightful than wit. In the same poem he says, —

> "Go, glorious soul, and lay thy temples down
> In Abram's bosom, *in the sacred down*
> *Of soft eternity.*"

That it should be beneath the dignity of princes to speak in anything but rhyme can only be paralleled by Mr. Puff's law that a heroine can go decorously mad only in white satin. Waller, I suppose, though with so loose a thinker one cannot be positive, uses "describe" in its Latin sense of limitation. Fancy Othello or Lear confined to this go-cart! Phillips touches the true point when he says, "And the truth is, the use of measure alone, without any rime at all, would give more scope and liberty both to style and fancy than can possibly be observed in rime." * But let us test Waller's method by an example or two. His monarch made *reasonable*, thus discourses : —

> " Courage our greatest failings does supply,
> And makes all good, or handsomely we die.
> Life is a thing of common use; by heaven
> As well to insects as to monarchs given;
> But for the crown, 't is a more sacred thing;
> I 'll dying lose it, or I 'll live a king.
> Come, Diphilus, we must together walk
> And of a matter of importance talk."   [*Exeunt.*

Blank verse, where the sentiment is trivial as here, merely removes prose to a proper ideal distance, where it is in keeping with more impassioned parts, but commonplace set to this rocking-horse jog irritates the nerves. There is nothing here to remind us of the older tragic style but the *exeunt* at the close. Its pithy conciseness and the relief which it brings us from his majesty's prosing give it an almost poetical savor. Aspatia's reflections upon suicide (or "suppressing our breath," as she calls it), in the same play, will make few readers regret that Shakespeare was left to his own unassisted barbarism when he wrote Hamlet's soliloquy on the same topic : —

> " 'T was in compassion of our woe
> That nature first made poisons grow,

* Preface to the *Theatrum.*

> For hopeless wretches such as I
> Kindly providing means to die:
> As mothers do their children keep,
> So Nature feeds and makes us sleep.
> The indisposed she does invite
> To go to bed before 't is night."

Correctness in this case is but a synonyme of monotony, and words are chosen for the number of their syllables, for their rubbishy value to fill-in, instead of being forced upon the poet by the meaning which occupies the mind. Language becomes useful for its diluting properties, rather than as the medium by means of which the thought or fancy precipitate themselves in crystals upon a connecting thread of purpose. Let us read a few verses from Beaumont and Fletcher, that we may feel fully the difference between the rude and the reformed styles. This also shall be a speech of Aspatia's. Antiphila, one of her maidens, is working the story of Theseus and Ariadne in tapestry, for the older masters loved a picturesque background and knew the value of fanciful accessaries. Aspatia thinks the face of Ariadne not sad enough : —

> "Do it by me,
> Do it again by me, the lost Aspatia,
> And you shall find all true but the wild island.
> Suppose I stand upon the seabeach now,
> Mine arms thus, and my hair blown with the wind,
> Wild as that desert; and let all about me
> Be teachers of my story. Do my face
> (If ever thou hadst feeling of a sorrow)
> Thus, thus, Antiphila; strive to make me look
> Like sorrow's monument; and the trees about me
> Let them be dry and leafless; let the rocks
> Groan with continual surges; and behind me
> Make all a desolation."

What instinctive felicity of versification! what sobbing breaks and passionate repetitions are here!

We see what the direction of the new tendency was, but it would be an inadequate or a dishonest criticism that should hold Pope responsible for the narrow compass of the instrument which was his legacy from his immediate predecessors, any more than for the wearisome thrumming-over of his tune by those who came after him and who had caught his technical skill without his genius. The question properly stated is, How much was it possible to make of the material supplied by the age in which he lived? and how much did he make of it? Thus far, among the great English poets who preceded him, we have seen actual life represented by Chaucer, imaginative life by Spenser, ideal life by Shakespeare, the interior life by Milton. But as everything aspires to a rhythmical utterance of itself, so conventional life, itself a new phenomenon, was waiting for its poet. It found or made a most fitting one in Pope. He stands for exactness of intellectual expression, for perfect propriety of phrase (I speak of him at his best), and is a striking instance how much success and permanence of reputation depend on conscientious finish as well as on native endowment. Butler asks, —

> " Then why should those who pick and choose
> The best of all the best compose,
> And join it by Mosaic art,
> In graceful order, part to part,
> To make the whole in beauty suit,
> Not merit as complete repute
> As those who, with less art and pain,
> Can do it with their native brain? "

Butler knew very well that precisely what stamps a man as an artist is this power of finding out what *is* " the best of all the best."

I confess that I come to the treatment of Pope with diffidence. I was brought up in the old superstition that he was the greatest poet that ever lived; and when I came to find that I had instincts of my own, and my mind was brought in contact with the apostles of a more esoteric doctrine of poetry, I felt that ardent desire for smashing the idols I had been brought up to worship, without any regard to their artistic beauty, which characterizes youthful zeal. What was it to me that Pope was called a master of style? I felt, as Addison says in his Freeholder when answering an argument in favor of the Pretender because he could speak English and George I. could not, "that I did not wish to be tyrannized over in the best English that ever was spoken." The young demand thoughts that find an echo in their real and not their acquired nature, and care very little about the dress they are put in. It is later that we learn to like the conventional, as we do olives. There was a time when I could not read Pope, but disliked him on principle as old Roger Ascham seems to have felt about Italy when he says, "I was once in Italy myself, but I thank God my abode there was only nine days."

But Pope fills a very important place in the history of English poetry, and must be studied by every one who would come to a clear knowledge of it. I have since read over every line that Pope ever wrote, and every letter written by or to him, and that more than once. If I have not come to the conclusion that he is the greatest of poets, I believe that I am at least in a condition to allow him every merit that is fairly his. I have said that Pope as a literary man represents precision and grace of expression ; but as a poet he represents something more, — nothing less, namely, than one of those eternal controversies of taste which will last as long as the imagination and understanding divide men between them. It is not a matter to be settled by any amount of argument or demonstration. There are born Popists or Wordsworthians, Lockists or Kantists, and there is nothing more to be said of the matter.

Wordsworth was not in a condition to do Pope justice.

A man brought up in sublime mountain solitudes, and whose nature was a solitude more vast than they, walking an earth which quivered with the throe of the French Revolution, the child of an era of profound mental and moral movement, it could not be expected that he should be in sympathy with the poet of artificial life. Moreover, he was the apostle of imagination, and came at a time when the school which Pope founded had degenerated into a mob of mannerists who wrote with ease, and who with their congenial critics united at once to decry poetry which brought in the dangerous innovation of having a soul in it.

But however it may be with poets, it is very certain that a reader is happiest whose mind is broad enough to enjoy the natural school for its nature, and the artificial for its artificiality, provided they be only good of their kind. At any rate, we must allow that the man who can produce one perfect work is either a great genius or a very lucky one; and so far as we who read are concerned, it is of secondary importance which. And Pope has done this in the "Rape of the Lock." For wit, fancy, invention, and keeping, it has never been surpassed. I do not say there is in it poetry of the highest order, or that Pope is a poet whom any one would choose as the companion of his best hours. There is no inspiration in it, no trumpet-call, but for pure entertainment it is unmatched. There are two kinds of genius. The first and highest may be said to speak out of the eternal to the present, and must compel its age to understand *it;* the second understands its age, and tells it what it wishes to be told. Let us find strength and inspiration in the one, amusement and instruction in the other, and be honestly thankful for both.

The very earliest of Pope's productions give indications of that sense and discretion, as well as wit, which after-

ward so eminently distinguished him. The facility of
expression is remarkable, and we find also that perfect
balance of metre, which he afterward carried so far as to
be wearisome. His pastorals were written in his sixteenth year, and their publication immediately brought
him into notice. The following four verses from his
first pastoral are quite characteristic in their antithetic
balance : —

> " You that, too wise for pride, too good for power,
>   Enjoy the glory to be great no more,
>   And carrying with you all the world can boast,
>   To all the world illustriously are lost ! "

The sentiment is affected, and reminds one of that future
period of Pope's Correspondence with his Friends, when
Swift, his heart corroding with disappointed ambition at
Dublin, Bolingbroke raising delusive turnips at his farm,
and Pope pretending not to feel the lampoons which
imbittered his life, played together the solemn farce of
affecting indifference to the world by which it would
have agonized them to be forgotten, and wrote letters
addressed to each other, but really intended for that
posterity whose opinion they assumed to despise.

In these pastorals there is an entire want of nature.
For example in that on the death of Mrs. Tempest : —

> " Her fate is whispered by the gentle breeze
>   And told in sighs to all the trembling trees ;
>   The trembling trees, in every plain and wood,
>   Her fate remurmur to the silver flood :
>   The silver flood, so lately calm, appears
>   Swelled with new passion, and o'erflows with tears ;
>   The winds and trees and floods her death deplore
>   Daphne, our grief ! our glory now no more ! "

All this is as perfectly professional as the mourning
of an undertaker. Still worse, Pope materializes and
makes too palpably objective that sympathy which our
grief forces upon outward nature. Milton, before making the echoes mourn for Lycidas, puts our feelings in

tune, as it were, and hints at his own imagination as the source of this emotion in inanimate things, —

> "But, O the heavy change now thou art gone!"

In "Windsor Forest" we find the same thing again :—

> "Here his first lays majestic Denham sung,
> There the last numbers flowed from Cowley's tongue;
> O early lost, what tears the river shed
> When the sad pomp along his banks was led!
> His drooping swans on every note expire,
> And on his willows hung each muse's lyre!"

In the same poem he indulges the absurd conceit that,

> "Beasts urged by us, their fellow-beasts pursue,
> And learn of man each other to undo";

and in the succeeding verses gives some striking instances of that artificial diction, so inappropriate to poems descriptive of natural objects and ordinary life, which brought verse-making to such a depth of absurdity in the course of the century.

> "With slaughtering guns, the unwearied fowler roves
> Where frosts have whitened all the naked groves;
> Where doves in flocks the leafless trees o'ershade,
> And lonely woodcocks haunt the watery glade;
> He lifts the tube and levels with his eye,
> Straight a short thunder breaks the frozen sky:
> Oft as in airy rings they skim the heath,
> The clamorous lapwings feel the leaden death;
> Oft as the mounting larks their notes prepare,
> They fall and leave their little lives in air."

Now one would imagine that the *tube* of the fowler was a telescope instead of a gun. And think of the larks preparing their notes like a country choir! Yet even here there are admirable lines, —

> "Oft as in airy rings they skim the heath,"
> "They fall and leave their little lives in air,"

for example.

In Pope's next poem, the "Essay on Criticism," the

18

wit and poet become apparent. It is full of clear thoughts, compactly expressed. In this poem, written when Pope was only twenty-one, occur some of those lines which have become proverbial ; such as

> "A little learning is a dangerous thing";
>
> "For fools rush in where angels fear to tread ";
>
> "True wit is Nature to advantage dressed,
> What oft was thought, but ne'er so well expressed."
>
> "For each ill author is as bad a friend."

In all of these we notice that terseness in which (regard being had to his especial range of thought) Pope has never been equalled. One cannot help being struck also with the singular *discretion* which the poem gives evidence of. I do not know where to look for another author in whom it appeared so early, and, considering the vivacity of his mind and the constantly besetting temptation of his wit, it is still more wonderful. In his boyish correspondence with poor old Wycherley, one would suppose him to be the man and Wycherley the youth. Pope's understanding was no less vigorous (when not the dupe of his nerves) than his fancy was lightsome and sprightly.

I come now to what in itself would be enough to have immortalized him as a poet, the "Rape of the Lock," in which, indeed, he appears more purely as poet than in any other of his productions. Elsewhere he has shown more force, more wit, more reach of thought, but nowhere such a truly artistic combination of elegance and fancy. His genius has here found its true direction, and the very same artificiality, which in his pastorals was unpleasing, heightens the effect, and adds to the general keeping. As truly as Shakespeare is the poet of man, as God made him, dealing with great passions and innate motives, so truly is Pope the poet of society, the delineator of manners, the exposer of those motives which may be called *acquired*, whose spring is in institutions and habits of purely worldly origin.

The "Rape of the Lock" was written in Pope's twenty-fourth year, and the machinery of the Sylphs was added at the suggestion of Dr. Garth, — a circumstance for which we can feel a more unmixed gratitude to him than for writing the "Dispensary." The idea was taken from that entertaining book " The Count de Gabalis," in which Fouquè afterward found the hint for his "Undine"; but the little sprites as they appear in the poem are purely the creation of Pope's fancy.

The theory of the poem is excellent. The heroic is out of the question in fine society. It is perfectly true that almost every door we pass in the street closes upon its private tragedy, but the moment a *great* passion enters a man he passes at once out of the artificial into the human. So long as he continues artificial, the sublime is a conscious absurdity to him. The mock-heroic then is the only way in which the petty actions and sufferings of the fine world can be epically treated, and the contrast continually suggested with subjects of larger scope and more dignified treatment, makes no small part of the pleasure and sharpens the point of the wit. The invocation is admirable : —

> " Say, what strange motive, Goddess, could compel,
> A well-bred lord to assault a gentle belle?
> O say what stranger cause, yet unexplored,
> Could make a gentle belle reject a lord?"

The keynote of the poem is here struck, and we are able to put ourselves in tune with it. It is not a parody of the heroic style, but only a setting it in satirical juxtaposition with cares and events and modes of thought with which it is in comical antipathy, and while *it* is not degraded, *they* are shown in their triviality. The "clouded cane," as compared with the Homeric spear, indicates the difference of scale, the lower plane of emotions and passions. The opening of the action, too, is equally good : —

> " Sol through white curtains shot a timorous ray,
> And oped those eyes that must eclipse the day,
> Now lapdogs give themselves the rousing shake,
> And sleepless lovers just at twelve awake;
> Thrice rung the bell, the slipper knocked the ground,
> And the pressed watch returned a silver sound."

The mythology of the Sylphs is full of the most fanciful wit; indeed, wit infused with fancy is Pope's peculiar merit. The Sylph is addressing Belinda : —

> " Know, then, unnumbered spirits round thee fly,
> The light militia of the lower sky;
> These, though unseen, are ever on the wing,
> Hang o'er the box and hover round the ring.
> As now your own our beings were of old,
> And once enclosed in woman's beauteous mould;
> Think not, when woman's transient breath is fled,
> That all her vanities at once are dead;
> Succeeding vanities she still regards,
> And, though she plays no more, o'erlooks the cards.
> For when the fair in all their pride expire,
> To their first elements their souls retire;
> The sprites of fiery termagants in flame
> Mount up and take a salamander's name;
> Soft yielding nymphs to water glide away
> And sip, with nymphs, their elemental tea;
> The graver prude sinks downward to a gnome,
> In search of mischief still on earth to roam;
> The light coquettes in sylphs aloft repair
> And sport and flutter in the fields of air."

And the contrivance by which Belinda is awakened is also perfectly in keeping with all the rest of the machinery : —

> " He said: when Shock, who thought she slept too long,
> Leaped up and waked his mistress with his tongue;
> 'T was then, Belinda, if report say true,
> Thy eyes first opened on a *billet-doux*."

Throughout this poem the satiric wit of Pope peeps out
in the pleasantest little smiling ways, as where, in describing the toilet-table, he says : —

> " Here files of pins extend their shining rows,
> Puffs, powders, patches, Bibles, *billet-doux*."

Or when, after the fatal lock has been severed,

> " Then flashed the living lightning from her eyes,
> And screams of horror rend the affrighted skies,
> Not louder shrieks to pitying Heaven are cast
> When husbands or when lapdogs breathe their last;
> Or when rich china-vessels, fallen from high,
> In glittering dust and painted fragments lie! "

And so, when the conflict begins : —

> " Now Jove suspends his golden scales in air;
> Weighs the men's wits against the ladies' hair;
> The doubtful beam long nods from side to side;
> At length the wits mount up, the hairs subside."

But more than the wit and fancy, I think, the perfect
keeping of the poem deserves admiration. Except a
touch of grossness, here and there, there is the most
pleasing harmony in all the conceptions and images.
The punishments which he assigns to the sylphs who
neglect their duty are charmingly appropriate and ingenious : —

> " Whatever spirit, careless of his charge,
> His post neglects, or leaves the fair at large,
> Shall feel sharp vengeance soon o'ertake his sins;
> Be stopped in vials or transfixed with pins,
> Or plunged in lakes of bitter washes lie,
> Or wedged whole ages in a bodkin's eye;
> Gums and pomatums shall his flight restrain,
> While clogged he beats his silver wings in vain;
> Or alum styptics with contracting power,
> Shrink his thin essence like a rivelled flower;
> Or as Ixion fixed the wretch shall feel
> The giddy motion of the whirling wheel,
> In fumes of burning chocolate shall glow,
> And tremble at the sea that froths below! "

The speech of Thalestris, too, with its droll climax, is equally good : —

> " Methinks already I your tears survey,
> Already hear the horrid things they say,
> Already see you a degraded toast,
> And all your honor in a whisper lost!
> How shall I then your helpless fame defend?
> 'T will then be infamy to seem your friend!
> And shall this prize, the inestimable prize,
> Exposed through crystal to the gazing eyes,
> And heightened by the diamond's circling rays,
> On that rapacious hand forever blaze?
> Sooner shall grass in Hydepark Circus grow,
> And wits take lodging in the sound of Bow,
> Sooner let earth, air, sea, in chaos fall,
> Men, monkeys, lapdogs, parrots, perish all ! "

So also Belinda's account of the morning omens : —

> " 'T was this the morning omens seemed to tell;
> Thrice from my trembling hand the patch-box fell;
> The tottering china shook without a wind;
> Nay, Poll sat mute, and Shock was most unkind."

The idea of the goddess of Spleen, and of her palace, where

> " The dreaded East is all the wind that blows,"

was a very happy one. In short, the whole poem more truly deserves the name of a creation than anything Pope ever wrote. The action is confined to a world of his own, the supernatural agency is wholly of his own contrivance, and nothing is allowed to overstep the limitations of the subject. It ranks by itself as one of the purest works of human fancy; whether that fancy be strictly poetical or not is another matter. If we compare it with the " Midsummer-night's Dream," an uncomfortable doubt is suggested. The perfection of form in the " Rape of the Lock " is to me conclusive evidence that in it the natural genius of Pope found fuller and freer expression than in any other of his poems. The others are aggregates of brilliant passages rather than harmonious wholes.

> Let us (since life can little more supply
> Than just to look about us and to die)
> Expatiate free o'er all this scene of man,
> A mighty maze,— but not without a plan ";

To expatiate *o'er* a mighty maze is rather loose writing
but the last verse, as it stood in the original editions,
was,

> " A mighty maze of walks without a plan ";

and perhaps this came nearer Pope's real opinion than
the verse he substituted for it. Warburton is careful
not to mention *this* variation in his notes. The poem is
everywhere as remarkable for its confusion of logic as it
often is for ease of verse and grace of expression. An
instance of both occurs in a passage frequently quoted : —

> " Heaven from all creatures hides the book of fate;
> All but the page prescribed, their present state;
> From brutes what men, from men what spirits know,
> Or who would suffer being here below?
> The lamb thy riot dooms to bleed to-day,
> Had he thy reason, would he skip and play?
> Pleased to the last, he crops the flowery food,
> And licks the hand just raised to shed his blood.
> O, blindness to the future kindly given
> That each may fill the circle meant by heaven!
> Who sees with equal eye, as God of all,
> A hero perish or a sparrow fall,
> Atoms or systems into ruin hurled,
> And now a bubble burst, and now a world! "

Now, if "heaven from all creatures hides the book of
fate," why should not the lamb " skip and play," if he
had the reason of man? Why, because he would then
be able to read the book of fate. But if man himself
cannot, why, then, could the lamb with the reason of
man? For, if the lamb had the reason of man, the
book of fate would still be hidden, so far as himself was
concerned. If the inferences we can draw from appearances are equivalent to a knowledge of destiny, the
knowing enough to take an umbrella in cloudy weather

18*   ▲▲

might be called so. There is a manifest confusion between what we know about ourselves and about other people ; the whole point of the passage being that we are always mercifully blinded to *our own* future, however much reason we may possess. There is also inaccuracy as well as inelegance in saying,

> " Heaven,
> *Who* sees with equal eye, as God of all,
> A hero perish or a sparrow fall."

To the last verse Warburton, desirous of reconciling his author with Scripture, appends a note referring to Matthew x. 29 : "Are not two sparrows sold for one farthing? and one of them shall not fall to the ground without your Father." It would not have been safe to have referred to the thirty-first verse : "Fear ye not, therefore, *ye are of more value* than many sparrows."

To my feeling, one of the most beautiful passages in the whole poem is that familiar one : —

> " Lo, the poor Indian whose untutored mind
> Sees God in clouds, or hears him in the wind,
> His soul proud science never taught to stray
> Far as the solar walk or milky way:
> Yet simple Nature to his hope has given
> Behind the cloud-topt hill a humbler heaven;
> Some safer world in depth of woods embraced,
> Some happier island in the watery waste,
> Where slaves once more their native land behold,
> No fiends torment, no Christians thirst for gold.
> To *be* contents his natural desire,
> He asks no angel's wing, no seraph's fire,
> But thinks, admitted to that equal sky,
> His faithful dog shall bear him company."

But this comes in as a corollary to what went just before : —

> " Hope springs eternal in the human breast,
> Man never is but always to be blest;
> The soul, uneasy, and confined from home,
> Rests and expatiates in a life to come."

Then follows immediately the passage about the poor Indian, who, after all, it seems, is contented with merely *being,* and whose soul, therefore, is an exception to the general rule. And what have the "solar walk" (as he calls it) and "milky way" to do with the affair? Does our hope of heaven depend on our knowledge of astronomy? Or does he mean that science and faith are necessarily hostile? And, after being told that it is the "untutored mind" of the savage which "sees God in clouds and hears him in the wind," we are rather surprised to find that the lesson the poet intends to teach is that

"All are but parts of one stupendous whole,
  Whose body Nature is, and God the soul.
  That, changed through all, and yet in all the same,
  Great in the earth, as in the ethereal frame,
  Warms in the sun, refreshes in the breeze,
  Glows in the stars, and blossoms in the trees."

So that we are no better off than the untutored Indian, after the poet has tutored us. Dr. Warburton makes a rather lame attempt to ward off the charge of Spinozism from this last passage. He would have found it harder to show that the acknowledgment of any divine revelation would not overturn the greater part of its teachings. If Pope intended by his poem all that the bishop takes for granted in his commentary, we must deny him what is usually claimed as his first merit,— clearness. If he did *not,* we grant him clearness as a writer at the expense of sincerity as a man. Perhaps a more charitable solution of the difficulty would be, that Pope's precision of thought was no match for the fluency of his verse.

Lord Byron goes so far as to say, in speaking of Pope, that he who executes the best, no matter what his department, will rank the highest. I think there are enough indications in these letters of Byron's, however, that they were written rather more against Wordsworth than for Pope. The rule he lays down would make Voltaire a greater poet, in some respects, than Shakespeare. Byron cites Petrarch as an example ; yet if Petrarch had put nothing more into his sonnets than *execution*, there are plenty of Italian sonneteers who would be his match. But, in point of fact, the department chooses the man and not the man the department, and it has a great deal to do with our estimate of him. Is the department of Milton no higher than that of Butler ? Byron took especial care not to write in the style he commended. But I think Pope has received quite as much credit in respect even of execution as he deserves. Surely execution is not confined to versification alone. What can be worse than this ?

> " At length Erasmus, that great, injured name,
> (The glory of the priesthood and the shame,)
> Stemmed the wild torrent of a barbarous age,
> And drove those holy vandals off the stage."

It would have been hard for Pope to have found a prettier piece of confusion in any of the small authors he laughed at than this image of a great, injured name stemming a torrent and driving vandals off the stage. And in the following verses the image is helplessly confused : —

> "Kind self-conceit to some her glass applies,
> Which no one looks in with another's eyes,
> But, as the flatterer or dependant paint,
> Beholds himself a patriot, chief, or saint."

The use of the word " applies " is perfectly un-English ; and it seems that people who look in this remarkable glass see their pictures and not their reflections. Often, also, when Pope attempts the sublime, his epithets become curiously unpoetical, as where he says, in the Dunciad,

> " As, one by one, at dread Medea's strain,
> The sickening stars fade off *the ethereal plain*."

And not seldom he is satisfied with the music of the verse without much regard to fitness of imagery ; in the " Essay on Man," for example : —

> " Passions, like elements, though born to fight,
> Yet, mixed and softened, in his work unite;
> These 't is enough to temper and employ;
> But what composes man can man destroy?
> Suffice that Reason keep to Nature's road,
> Subject, compound them, follow her and God.
> Love, Hope, and Joy, fair Pleasure's smiling train,
> Hate, Fear, and Grief, the family of Pain,
> These, mixed with Art, and to due bounds confined,
> Make and maintain the balance of the mind."

Here reason is represented as an apothecary compounding pills of " pleasure's smiling train " and the " family of pain." And in the Moral Essays,

> " Know God and Nature only are the same;
> In man the judgment shoots at flying game,
> A bird of passage, gone as soon as found,
> Now in the moon, perhaps, now under ground."

The "judgment shooting at flying game " is an odd image enough ; but I think a bird of passage, now in the moon and now under ground, could be found nowhere — out of Goldsmith's Natural History, perhaps. An epigrammatic expression will also tempt him into saying something without basis in truth, as where he ranks together " Macedonia's madman and the Swede," and says that neither of them "looked forward farther than his nose," a slang phrase which may apply well enough to Charles XII., but certainly not to the pupil of Aristotle, who showed himself capable of a large political forethought. So, too, the rhyme, if correct, is a sufficient apology for want of propriety in phrase, as where he makes " Socrates *bleed*."

But it is in his Moral Essays and parts of his Satires that Pope deserves the praise which he himself desired : —

> " Happily to steer
> From grave to gay, from lively to severe,
> Correct with spirit, eloquent with ease,
> Intent to reason, or polite to please."

Here Pope must be allowed to have established a style
of his own, in which he is without a rival. One can
open upon wit and epigram at any page.

> " Behold, if Fortune or a mistress frowns,
> Some plunge in business, other shave their crowns;
> To ease the soul of one oppressive weight,
> This quits an empire, that embroils a state;
> The same adust complexion has impelled,
> Charles to the convent, Philip to the field."

Indeed, I think one gets a little tired of the invariable
this set off by the inevitable *that*, and wishes antithesis
would let him have a little quiet now and then. In the
first couplet, too, the conditional "frown" would have
been more elegant. But taken as detached passages,
how admirably the different characters are drawn, so
admirably that half the verses have become proverbial.
This of Addison will bear reading again : —

> " Peace to all such: but were there one whose fires
> True genius kindles and fair fame inspires;
> Blest with each talent and each art to please,
> And born to write, converse, and live with ease;
> Should such a man, too fond to rule alone,
> Bear like the Turk no brother near the throne,
> View him with scornful yet with jealous eyes,
> And hate for arts that caused himself to rise,
> Damn with faint praise, assent with civil leer,
> And, without sneering, teach the rest to sneer;
> Willing to wound and yet afraid to strike,
> Just hint a fault and hesitate dislike,
> Alike reserved to blame or to commend,
> A timorous foe and a suspicious friend;
> Dreading e'en fools, by flatterers besieged,
> And *so* obliging that he ne'er obliged;
> Like Cato give his little Senate laws,
> And sit attentive to his own applause,
> While wits and templars every sentence raise,
> And wonder with a foolish face of praise; —

were mostly addressed to the public, perhaps even to posterity. But letters, however carefully drilled to be circumspect, are sure to blab, and those of Pope leave in the reader's mind an unpleasant feeling of circumspection, — of an attempt to look as an eminent literary character should rather than as the man really was. They have the unnatural constraint of a man in full dress sitting for his portrait and endeavoring to look his best. We never catch him, if he can help it, at unawares. Among all Pope's correspondents, Swift shows in the most dignified and, one is tempted to say, the most amiable light. It is creditable to the Dean that the letters which Pope addressed to him are by far the most simple and straightforward of any that he wrote. No sham could encounter those terrible eyes in Dublin without wincing. I think, on the whole, that a revision of judgment would substitute " discomforting consciousness of the public " for " insincerity " in judging Pope's character by his letters. He could not shake off the habits of the author, and never, or almost never, in prose, acquired that knack of seeming carelessness that makes Walpole's elaborate compositions such agreeable reading. Pope would seem to have kept a commonplace-book of phrases proper to this or that occasion; and he transfers a compliment, a fine moral sentiment, nay, even sometimes a burst of passionate ardor, from one correspondent to another, with the most cold-blooded impartiality. Were it not for this curious economy of his, no one could read his letters to Lady Wortley Montague without a conviction that they were written by a lover. Indeed, I think nothing short of the *spretæ injuria formæ* will account for (though it will not excuse) the savage vindictiveness he felt and showed towards her. It may be suspected also that the bitterness of caste added gall to his resentment. His enemy wore

that impenetrable armor of superior rank which rendered her indifference to his shafts the more provoking
that it was unaffected. Even for us his satire loses its
sting when we reflect that it is not in human nature for a
woman to have had two such utterly irreconcilable characters as those of Lady Mary before and after her quarrel
with the poet. In any view of Pope's conduct in this
affair, there is an ill savor in his attempting to degrade
a woman whom he had once made sacred with his love.
Spenser touches the right chord when he says of the
Rosalind who had rejected him,

> " Not, then, to her, that scornéd thing so base,
> But to myself the blame, that lookt so high;
> Yet so much grace let her vouchsafe to grant
> To simple swain, sith her I may not love,
> Yet that I may her honor paravant
> And praise her worth, though far my wit above;
> Such grace shall be some guerdon of the grief
> And long affliction which I have endured."

In his correspondence with Aaron Hill, Pope, pushed
to the wall, appears positively mean. He vainly endeavors to show that his personalities had all been written in the interests of literature and morality, and from
no selfish motive. But it is hard to believe that Theobald would have been deemed worthy of his disgustful
pre-eminence but for the manifest superiority of his
edition of Shakespeare, or that Addison would have
been so adroitly disfigured unless through wounded self-
love. It is easy to conceive the resentful shame which
Pope must have felt when Addison so almost contemptuously disavowed all complicity in his volunteer defence
of *Cato* in a brutal assault on Dennis. Pope had done
a mean thing to propitiate a man whose critical judgment he dreaded ; and the great man, instead of thanking him, had resented his interference as impertinent.
In the whole portrait of Atticus one cannot help feeling

that Pope's satire is not founded on knowledge, but rather on what his own sensitive suspicion divined of the opinions of one whose expressed preferences in poetry implied a condemnation of the very grounds of the satirist's own popularity. We shall not so easily give up the purest and most dignified figure of that somewhat vulgar generation, who ranks with Sidney and Spenser, as one of the few perfect gentlemen in our literary annals. A man who could command the unswerving loyalty of honest and impulsive Dick Steele could not have been a coward or a backbiter. The only justification alleged by Pope was of the flimsiest kind, namely, that Addison regretted the introduction of the sylphs in the second edition of the " Rape of the Lock," saying that the poem was *merum sal* before. Let any one ask himself how he likes an author's emendations of any poem to which his ear had adapted itself in its former shape, and he will hardly think it needful to charge Addison with any mean motive for his conservatism in this matter. One or two of Pope's letters are so good as to make us regret that he did not oftener don the dressing-gown and slippers in his correspondence. One in particular, to Lord Burlington, describing a journey on horseback to Oxford with Lintot the bookseller, is full of a lightsome humor worthy of Cowper, almost worthy of Gray.

Joseph Warton, in summing up at the end of his essay on the genius and writings of Pope, says that the largest part of his works " is of the *didactic, moral,* and *satiric ;* and, consequently, not of the most *poetic* species of *poetry ;* whence it is manifest that *good sense* and *judgment* were his characteristical excellences rather than *fancy* and *invention.*" It is plain that in any strict definition there can be only one kind of poetry, and that what Warton really meant to say was that Pope

was not a poet at all. This, I think, is shown by what
Johnson says in his " Life of Pope," though he does not
name Warton. The dispute on this point went on with
occasional lulls for more than a half-century after Warton's death. It was renewed with peculiar acrimony
when the Rev. W. L. Bowles diffused and confused Warton's critical opinions in his own peculiarly helpless way
in editing a new edition of Pope in 1806. Bowles entirely mistook the functions of an editor, and maladroitly
entangled his judgment of the poetry with his estimate
of the author's character.* Thirteen years later, Campbell, in his " Specimens," controverted Mr. Bowles's estimate of Pope's character and position, both as man and
poet. Mr. Bowles replied in a letter to Campbell on
what he called " the invariable principles of poetry."
This letter was in turn somewhat sharply criticised by
Gilchrist in the Quarterly Review. Mr. Bowles made an
angry and unmannerly retort, among other things charg-
ing Gilchrist with the crime of being a tradesman's son,
whereupon the affair became what they call on the
frontier a free fight, in which Gilchrist, Roscoe, the elder
Disraeli, and Byron took part with equal relish, though
with various fortune. The last shot, in what had grown
into a thirty years' war, between the partisans of what
was called the Old School of poetry and those of the
New, was fired by Bowles in 1826. Bowles, in losing
his temper, lost also what little logic he had, and though,
in a vague way, æsthetically right, contrived always to
be argumentatively wrong. Anger made worse confusion in a brain never very clear, and he had neither the

* Bowles's Sonnets, wellnigh forgotten now, did more than his con-
troversial writings for the cause he advocated. Their influence upon
the coming generation was great (greater than we can well account
for) and beneficial. Coleridge tells us that he made forty copies of
them while at Christ's Hospital. Wordsworth's prefaces first made
imagination the true test of poetry, in its more modern sense. But
they drew little notice till later.

scholarship nor the critical faculty for a vigorous exposition of his own thesis. Never was wilder hitting than his, and he laid himself open to dreadful punishment, especially from Byron, whose two letters are masterpieces of polemic prose. Bowles most happily exemplified in his own pamphlets what was really the turning-point of the whole controversy (though all the combatants more or less lost sight of it or never saw it), namely, that without clearness and terseness there could be no good writing, whether in prose or verse ; in other words that, while precision of phrase presupposes lucidity of thought, yet good writing is an art as well as a gift. Byron alone saw clearly that here was the true knot of the question, though, as his object was mainly mischief, he was not careful to loosen it. The sincerity of Byron's admiration of Pope has been, it seems to me, too hastily doubted. What he admired in him was that patience in careful finish which he felt to be wanting in himself and in most of his contemporaries. Pope's assailants went so far as to make a defect of what, rightly considered, was a distinguished merit, though the amount of it was exaggerated. The weak point in the case was that his nicety concerned itself wholly about the phrase, leaving the thought to be as faulty as it would, and that it seldom extended beyond the couplet, often not beyond a single verse. His serious poetry, therefore, at its best, is a succession of loosely strung epigrams, and no poet more often than he makes the second line of the couplet a mere trainbearer to the first. His more ambitious works may be defined as careless thinking carefully versified. Lessing was one of the first to see this, and accordingly he tells us that "his great, I will not say greatest, merit lay in what we call the mechanic of poetry." * Lessing,

* Briefe die neueste Litteratur betreffend, 1759, II. Brief. See also his more elaborate criticism of the " Essay on Man " (Pope ein Metaphysiker), 1755.

with his usual insight, parenthetically qualifies his statement ; for where Pope, as in the " Rape of the Lock," found a subject exactly level with his genius, he was able to make what, taken for all in all, is the most perfect poem in the language.

It will hardly be questioned that the man who writes what is still piquant and rememberable, a century and a quarter after his death, was a man of genius. But there are two modes of uttering such things as cleave to the memory of mankind. They may be said or sung. I do not think that Pope's verse anywhere sings, but it should seem that the abiding presence of fancy in his best work forbids his exclusion from the rank of poet. The atmosphere in which he habitually dwelt was an essentially prosaic one, the language habitual to him was that of conversation and society, so that he lacked the help of that fresher dialect which seems like inspiration in the elder poets. His range of associations was of that narrow kind which is always vulgar, whether it be found in the village or the court. Certainly he has not the force and majesty of Dryden in his better moods, but he has a grace, a finesse, an art of being pungent, a sensitiveness to impressions, that would incline us to rank him with Voltaire (whom in many ways he so much resembles), as an author with whom the gift of writing was primary, and that of verse secondary. No other poet that I remember ever wrote prose which is so purely prose as his ; and yet, in any impartial criticism, the " Rape of the Lock " sets him even as a poet far above many men more largely endowed with poetic feeling and insight than he.

A great deal must be allowed to Pope for the age in which he lived, and not a little, I think, for the influence of Swift. In his own province he still stands unapproachably alone. If to be the greatest satirist of individual men, rather than of human nature, if to be the highest expression which the life of the court and the ball-room has ever found in verse, if to have added more phrases to our language than any other but Shakespeare, if to have charmed four generations make a man a great poet, — then he is one. He was the chief founder of an artificial style of writing, which in his hands was living and powerful, because he used it to express artificial modes of thinking and an artificial state of society. Measured by any high standard of imagination, he will be found wanting; tried by any test of wit, he is unrivalled.

THE END.

REBECCA ROSS

DREAMS

LIE

BENEATH

Quill Tree Books
An Imprint of HarperCollinsPublishers

Quill Tree Books is an imprint of HarperCollins Publishers.

Dreams Lie Beneath
Copyright © 2021 by Rebecca Ross LLC
Map illustration © 2021 by Virginia Allyn
All rights reserved. Manufactured in Lithuania. No part of this book may be
used or reproduced in any manner whatsoever without written permission
except in the case of brief quotations embodied in critical articles and reviews.
For information address HarperCollins Children's Books, a division of
HarperCollins Publishers, 195 Broadway, New York, NY 10007.
www.epicreads.com

Library of Congress Control Number: 2021936685
ISBN 978-0-06-301594-4 (pbk)

Typography by Molly Fehr
22 23 24 25 26   SB   10 9 8 7 6 5 4 3 2 1
❖
First paperback edition, 2022

To my parents, who first taught me how to dream

THE REALM

THE
SEREN DUCHY

THE FORTRESS
IN THE CLOUDS

ULLA ◆

THE
MOUNTAIN DOORS

STARLING RIVER

HERESWITH
◆

N

THE
BARDYLLIS DUCHY

W   E

S

OF AZENOR

THE WYNTROUGH DUCHY

MARKSWORTH

CATRINE RIVER

ENDELLION

THE MERROW SEA

AMARYS

THE BOOK OF NIGHTMARES

PART 1

Magic of Old

1

September's new moon waited for the sun to set, and I found myself trapped in Mazarine's library, drawing her twelfth portrait by candlelight. For as long as I had known her, she had never left her house during the day, and she kept her curtains closed while the sun reigned. She liked to summon me every few months for various things, the foremost to commit her face to paper with my charcoal stick as if she forgot what she looked like, the second to read to her from one of her leather-bound books. I was eager to do both because she paid me well, and I liked the stories I could sometimes coax from her. Stories that came from the mountains. Stories that were nearly forgotten, turning into dust.

"Do I look the same as I did the last time you drew me?" she asked from where she sat in a chair, its armrests carved as roaring lions. She was wearing her usual raiment: an elegant velvet gown the shade of blood with a diamond necklace anchored at her neck.

The stone caught the firelight every time she breathed, winking with secrets.

"You look unchanged," I replied, thinking that I'd drawn her only three months ago, and I continued with my sketch of her.

She was proud, even with her multitude of wrinkles and her age spots and her strange beady eyes. I liked her confidence, and I drew it in the tilt of her chin, the hint of her knowing smile, and the waves of her long quicksilver hair. I wondered how old she was, but I didn't dare ask.

Sometimes I feared her, although I couldn't explain why. She was ancient. I had rarely seen her move from the furniture scattered about this gilded, shadowed room. And yet something pulsed from her. Something I couldn't identify but all the same cautioned me to keep my eyes open in her presence.

"Your father does not like when I summon you here," she drawled in a smoky voice. "He does not like you alone with me, does he?"

Her words unsettled me, but I concealed my feelings. The dimness of the room was like a cloak, and while it seemed impossible to draw a portrait in such poor light, I did it well.

"My father simply needs me home on time today," I said, and she knew what I implied.

"Ah, a new moon awaits you tonight," said Mazarine. "Tell me, Clementine . . . have you read one of my nightmares recorded in your father's book?"

I had not, because there were no recordings of her nightmares in the book my father filled and guarded. I didn't want to confess such to her, for fear it might upset her.

And so I lied.

"My father doesn't let me read all his recordings. I'm only an apprentice, Ms. Thimble."

"Ah," she said, drinking from a sparkling glass of wine. "You are an apprentice, but you wage war beside him on new moon nights. And you are just as strong and skilled as him. I have watched you fight in the streets on the darkest nights. You will surpass him, Clementine. Your magic shines brighter than his."

I finished with her portrait at last. Partly because her words fed a hungry spirit within me that I strove to keep hidden.

"Your portrait is done." I set down my charcoal, wiped my fingers on my skirt, and walked the paper to her. She studied it by the candlelight that burned from iron stands around her, wax dripping like stalactites.

She was quiet for a long moment. A bead of perspiration began to trace my back, and I felt anxious until she grinned, her yellow teeth gleaming in the firelight.

"Yes, I am unchanged. What a relief." She laughed, but the sound was far from reassuring.

My blood hummed with warning.

I gathered my supplies, tucking them into my leather satchel, eager to be gone. I couldn't judge the time of day, since Mazarine had the curtains drawn, but I sensed that afternoon was waning.

I needed to get home.

"A magician and an artist," Mazarine mused, admiring my sketch of her. "An artist and a magician. Which one do you desire to be more? Or perhaps you dream of learning *deviah* magic and combining the two. I would indeed like to see an enchanted drawing of yours someday, Clementine."

I hefted the satchel strap onto my shoulder, standing halfway between her chair and the double doors. I didn't want to say that she was right, but she had an uncanny sense of reading people. She had also watched me grow up in this town.

Since I was eight, my father had instructed me in *avertana* magic, a defensive magic that lent its strength to spars and duels. We often faced spells bent by malicious intent, which made for dangerous and unpredictable situations, such as the new moon nights. And I liked *avertana* more for those things, but I also had started thinking of the other two studies of magic, *metamara* and *deviah*—but *deviah* in particular. To take one's skill and create an enchanted object was no simple feat, and I had read of magicians who had devoted decades of their lives to reach such achievement.

I needed more time. More time to hone my craft of art before I tried to layer magic within it. I had taught myself how to draw and had gradually become proficient with charcoal, as art supplies were hard to come by in this rustic town, but I knew my experience was lacking, and there were many other branches of art, waiting for me to explore.

"Perhaps one day," I replied.

"Hmm" was all Mazarine said.

She at last rose from her chair with a slight grunt, as if her bones ached. I always forgot how tall she was, and I waited while she crossed to the other side of the room, where a bureau sat in a darkened corner. I listened to her open the drawers; I listened to the chime of coins as she gathered them in her hand.

"You claim I am unchanged," she said, coming to meet me where I stood. "And yet you are not, Clementine. Your skill is improving, in magic as well as art." And she extended her fist—knuckles like hills, veins like rivers beneath her papery skin, fingers full of coins.

I turned up my palm, and she paid me double. More than she had ever bestowed upon me before.

"This is very generous, Ms. Thimble."

"Your father and that housekeeper of his who looks after you may not like me. But you are the only one in this town who does not fear me. And I reward such valor."

I held her gaze, hoping my wariness wasn't shining like ice within me.

"Let me walk you out," Mazarine said with a sweep of her arm. "The day grows old, and you must prepare for tonight."

But she didn't move, and I sensed she wanted me to precede her. I led the way to the double doors, and she remained two steps behind me. We passed a mirror hanging on the wall, which I had never noticed before. Its frame was golden and elaborate, fashioned as vines and oak leaves. I saw my reflection—a girl with a smudge of charcoal on her chin and thick copper hair that refused to be tamed by a braid. My gaze began to shift to the doors when I caught a glimpse of what walked behind me.

Not Mazarine. Not the elderly woman I had drawn multiple times.

She was something else, tall and broad shouldered, her face creased and jagged like rocks, with a long nose that hovered over a thin, crooked mouth. Her skin was pale and her hair was still silver, but it was long and wiry, and threaded with leaves and sticks and thorny vines, as if she had risen from a forest. Two horns crowned her head, small and pointed, gleaming like bone.

Her eyes, large and dark and glittering with glee, met mine in the mirror for a fleeting moment, and I knew that I had just beheld her true nature. She knew it, too, and yet I didn't react. I told myself to walk no faster, to breathe no deeper. To remain calm and poised. I swallowed the urge to bolt and I paused at the doors, to give her time to open them for me.

"You can find your way out from here?" she asked.

I smiled. My face felt strange, and I imagined I was grimacing. "Of course." Once more, she appeared as the elderly woman that I had always known. But her eyes . . . I saw a trace of the wild being that she truly was, flaring like embers.

"Good. Until next time, Clementine."

I slipped past her and made my way down the curling stairwell, my boots clicking on the marble in a measured pace, because I knew she was listening.

Her butler—an old, craggy man dressed in livery of a lord long dead—was sitting in a chair by the front door, snoring. I tried to sneak past him, but he startled and stood, fumbling for the door handle.

"A good day to you, Miss Clem," he said in a raspy voice. "And may you be victorious in battle tonight, with the new moon."

"Thank you, Mr. Wetherbee."

While his eyes were gentle and haunted by cataracts, the sort of eyes a grandfather might have, I couldn't help but wonder what reflection he cast in a mirror: if he was the old human man he appeared to be, or if he was something quite different.

I passed over the threshold, descending the steps to the gravel path that led to the road. Triangles of shrubs grew in perfect symmetry, and when I reached the iron gate, I dared to glance back at the house.

It was a grand manor, built of red brick and three stories high, with square windows that glistened like teeth. The first magician of Hereswith had dwelled here, and then her successor. This had always been the domain of the town magician, and one would think magic still lingered in the walls and had seeped into the floors. And yet Mazarine had lived here for many years, according to the town records, and she was no magician.

She was not even human.

I wondered how she had accomplished such a feat, hiding her true face. Fooling us all.

I hesitated, as if to turn my back on the mansion was foolish. But at last, I pivoted away from the gate and began the brisk walk home.

Hereswith was not a vast town. My father and I could walk the entirety of it in the span of an hour. It was quaint, if one forgot the curse of the adjacent mountains. Cottages were snug, two storied, and built of stone and cob, capped with thatched roofs. Some had little gardens with ivy that attempted to eat the house; others had brightly painted front doors and mullioned windows blown from an erstwhile era. And then there was Mazarine's mansion, which felt overwhelmingly out of place with its grandness, but still lent character to the town.

To me, Hereswith was home, beloved, even as it seemed to languish beneath summer's final days. By late afternoon, when the sun began to set, the shadows from the Seren Mountains would reach us, and the breeze would smell of cold grass and smoldering wood and damp stone. Like old magic.

I never wanted to leave this place.

With each step I took from Mazarine's demesne, the more my doubt began to simmer. By appearances, Hereswith felt idyllic and charming. But I began to wonder if the town was hiding something beneath its exterior.

I learned a vital lesson from Mazarine that day. One that made me vow that I would never trust appearances alone.

2

"What is Mazarine?" I asked Imonie the moment I returned home. She was exactly where I knew she would be—in the kitchen, preparing dinner. My father and I always ate well on new moon nights, just before the streets turned deadly. If it wasn't for Imonie, the two of us would have been shriveled-up magicians with threadbare clothes and wounds that never healed properly.

She stood at the counter, peeling a mountain of potatoes. She was like a grandmother to me, although she was too young to be such a thing. She had never confessed her age, but I guessed she was in her early fifties. She was tall and trim and had threads of silver in her corn-silk hair, and while she rarely smiled, a few wrinkles touched the corners of her eyes.

"What do you mean?" Imonie asked, her attention devoted to her task. "Mazarine is a grumpy old woman."

"No, she's not."

It must have been the tone in my voice.

Imonie stopped her peeling and met my gaze. "Did she threaten you, Clem?"

"No," I said, despite the fact that there *had* been a moment when I'd felt afraid of her. When her gaze had met mine in the mirror.

"I've told you for years now to stay away from her."

"She's lonely and she pays me well. She also feeds me stories from the mountains." I intently watched Imonie's face, and I noticed how her brow furrowed. She longed to return to her ancestors' home in the Seren Mountains.

"I could tell you the same stories," Imonie said, and resumed her paring, viciously.

"Then why don't you?"

"Because they fill me with sorrow, Clem."

I fell quiet, feeling a twinge of regret. But in that silence, I thought of the mountain story she had told me often when I had begged her as a girl.

The realm of Azenor had not always been beset with tangible nightmares, although it was difficult to imagine such a world. It was all I had ever known, but Imonie had told me the legend that had started it all: Once, the mountains held a prosperous duchy. Magic itself had been first born in the summits, where the clouds touched the earth. But when the Duke of Seren was assassinated by his closest friends, the mountain province had sundered. Well versed in magic, the duke had cast a curse as he lay dying. No death and no dreams for those in his court who had been touched by the betrayal. They would live endlessly, watching as those they loved grew old and perished without them. And without dreams . . . their own hearts would become dry and brittle.

One does not realize how powerful a dream is, in the sleeping world as well as the waking one, until it has been stolen from them.

The duke had died on a new moon, and that was when the mountains began to spin nightmares into reality, all across the other two duchies of Azenor—the valleys and forests and meadows of Bardyllis and Wyntrough. No one could escape it, and so magicians had risen to answer the danger, perfecting the *avertana* branch of magic and becoming wardens of intricately mapped territories. Like my father.

Imonie hefted a sigh, as if she knew the exact story I was imagining. It seemed fitting for a new moon day, though. And she set down her potato and knife, leaning on the counter to fix a firm gaze on me.

"I can smell her from the road when I pass that ugly manor," she said. "Moss and stone and cold winter nights."

I waited for Imonie to continue, eager to know the truth. Eager to know who I had been drawing over and over for months now.

But then Imonie smirked and asked, "What do you think Mazarine is, Clem?"

"I think she's a troll from the mountains."

"You're probably right, although I haven't gotten close enough to her to see for myself."

"Is she cursed?"

"Cursed? I think whatever guise she dons is one of her own making, how she wants to be perceived. For while Hereswith has warmly welcomed those such as me from the mountain duchy . . . do you think the mortals here would be delighted to know a troll dwelled among you?"

"Most people would be afraid of her," I confessed. "Although it seems people already are."

"And perhaps she likes the fear," Imonie said. "Just enough to keep people and their suspicions away. So she can live peacefully here." Her eyes narrowed at me. "And how did you come to know her true nature?"

"I caught her reflection in a mirror," I answered, and remembered seeing her two steps behind, crouching toward me with her bloodied teeth and fierce, dark eyes. Would she have harmed me? I wanted to believe that she wouldn't.

I began to consider a spell I might craft to protect myself, sharpen my senses when I was in her presence.

"A foolish blunder on her part, then," said Imonie.

"Actually, I think she planned it," I countered, tracing the bow of my lips. "She wanted me to see who she truly is."

"Why?"

I realized I still had charcoal on my fingertips, that I must have smudged a mustache on my face. My hand drifted away to hold the strap of my satchel.

"I think she wants me to draw her true self."

"Of course she does!" Imonie grumbled, returning to her task. "Trolls are insufferably vain."

"Is something burning?" I asked, sniffing the air.

Imonie went rigid, and then rushed to the oven. A thin plume of smoke rose when she cracked the oven door. "You've made me burn the galettes!"

"They look fine," I reassured her as she took a mitt and retrieved them from the oven.

"Clementine?" my father called from upstairs.

Both Imonie and I froze. When she looked at me, I saw the worry in her expression.

"Is he still sick?" I whispered.

"His fever has yet to break," Imonie said. "Best you go up and see what he needs. Here, take him this cup of tea. Make sure he drinks it."

She took the kettle from the stove and poured a cup of a pungent-smelling brew that made my nose crinkle. But I took it as she ordered, nearly burning my hand on the mug. I didn't realize it, not until I was on my way to the stairs. I set my art satchel down and glanced at the table and saw only one place was set with the fine china. My place. Imonie had not set a dinner plate at my father's chair, which meant she believed he was too ill to face the new moon.

I had never encountered a new moon night on my own. He and I were always together in the streets, fighting as one.

Dismayed, I climbed the stairs and stepped into his bedroom.

My father was sitting up in his bed, leaning against the headboard, waiting for me. He seemed to get sick every year, right around this time. When summer surrendered to autumn, my father inevitably fell prey to a fever and a cough, blaming it on a final bloom of some vengeful valley weed. And while he always recovered within a few days, I still didn't know what to do with him when he was like this.

"Papa?" I tried to hand him the tea mug, but he motioned for me to set it on the bedside table. "Did you need something?"

"I received word of a nightmare this morning," he said.

"Whose?"

"Spruce Fielding's youngest daughter."

"Elle?"

"The very one. She had a nightmare last night. According to Spruce . . . it frightened her so badly that she hasn't spoken a word today."

I quirked my mouth to the side, my heart aching with this news. Children's nightmares were always the worst. They were the recordings that kept me up at night when I read them. They were the dreams I dreaded to see stalking the streets on new moon nights.

"And you need me to go and record it," I surmised, and a quiet thrill went through me. I had never been the one to divine a nightmare, or to record it in my father's book. I accompanied him most of the time, and I observed, and I read his recordings afterward so I could prepare for the new moon. But never on my own.

"Yes, Clem," Papa said, and I could not discern if he was proud or nervous. "Don't use the divining spell unless you absolutely *must*. And if you must, please use my spell, word for word."

I nodded and felt his gaze as I moved about his cluttered bedchamber, gathering supplies for the visitation.

"I will, Papa." I opened his cupboard, where a hoard of tiny blue vials waited within, gleaming in the light. Remedies. I selected two, the corked glass the size of my pinkie. The dark brew sloshed within them as I hesitated, thought better of it, and grabbed three more vials, slipping them into the deep pocket of my charcoal-streaked skirt.

"Divining," my father continued, as if he was about to impart a lecture. I inwardly braced myself. "Particularly done with . . . oh, how do I say this, with *precarious* intent, can open a door that you might not know how to close."

As if to prove a point, I shut the cupboard door, more forceful than necessary. I could hear the vials rattling in protest, and I met Papa's gaze, swallowing an impatient response. Sometimes he acted like I had no inkling how to cast a charm or divine a nightmare. This was a lesson I had heard countless times from him, before magic had even sparked at my fingertips.

"I haven't done anything precarious in *months*, Papa."

And by precarious, I meant *spontaneous*, when magic came to me in the moment. The sort of magic he was afraid of. That was why he was diligent in studying the nightmares, so he could prepare potential spells. His memory was immense and deep, and while I admired him for it . . . my strongest magic was forged from intuition.

I felt him watching me, thoughts churning. He was stern and imposing, even as he perspired from a fever, bedridden. I favored him in appearance, far more than I did my mother. My father and I were both tall and willow thin, with square jaws and large brown eyes and wiry auburn hair, lustrous as copper when it met the light. A stranger could tell we were kin from a mile away. But that was where our similarities ended. Our souls were two different points on a compass; the intent behind our magic flowed in opposite currents. He was cautious, reserved. Traditional. And I wasn't.

I knew what he saw in me. I was young and reckless. His one and only daughter, who favored the wilder, natural study of magic. My ideas and spells scared him sometimes, although he would never say such a thing aloud. Because without me, Papa would never take a risk.

"Pack what you need for the divination," he said.

Relieved that he believed me capable, I walked to his desk. A detailed map of Hereswith was spread over the wood, river rocks pinning down the four corners. It was a map I had memorized with its crooked, winding streets. Above the desk, shelves lined the wall, burdened with leather-bound spell books, stacks of paper, jars brimming with crushed flowers and salt crystals and swan quills, ornate ink pots, cast-iron spoons with jewels embedded in the handles, silver bowls nestled into each other, a potted fern whose wilting leaves dangled like unrequited love.

I gathered what I needed: a bowl that shone like a full moon, pink salt, dried gardenias, a spoon with an emerald chip, a pitcher full of water, a swan quill, a silver inkwell that was crafted as an octopus, its tentacles holding a vial of walnut ink. I charmed them all beneath my breath with a shrinking cantrip—a spell my mother had taught me—until the objects could sit cradled in my palm, and I slipped them into my pocket, where the remedies waited. The objects clinked like musical notes when they met, weightless as air.

My father made a noise of disapproval. Of course, he wasn't fond of any sort of *metamara* magic, which transformed and influenced objects.

"Why don't you pack a bag?" He indicated his worn leather satchel, sitting on the floor beside his writing chair, like a sad dog awaiting a walk.

"My pockets will do fine." My leather satchel was for my art supplies alone, and I didn't want it mixing with magical ones yet. "Now, then. Where is the book?"

"There will be absolutely *no* enchanting the book to make it fit in your pocket, Clementine."

"Very well. I'll carry it in my arms, like a good *avertana*."

Papa wasn't amused. But he relented, feeling the urgent pull of the afternoon, the slant of sunlight as it began to shift across the floor. I wouldn't have much time to fetch the nightmare. So he uttered a spell in his storytelling voice, smooth and polished like sanded oak. And the book of nightmares materialized. It had been sitting on the map of Hereswith, in the center of my father's desk, charmed invisible.

Clever, I thought. All these years, I had believed my father had simply hidden the prized ledger in a secret nook.

I took it reverently, surprised by how heavy it was. Seven magicians had kept detailed dream recordings before Papa had come to Hereswith, and I had always hoped to become the ninth magician, after my father retired. But I felt the weight of those inked dreams of people now dead and buried. I felt them as if I had embraced a millstone.

I met Papa's gaze, and he saw my shock. I hadn't realized it until now. The weight he carried as the town's magician. And suddenly . . . I didn't know if I was strong enough to bear it.

"Come here, daughter," he whispered.

I crossed the room, the book heavy in my arms, and sat on the edge of his bed. I could feel the feverish heat rolling off him in waves, and it made me worry.

"I've taught you all that I know," he said. "You'll do just fine recording this dream, as long as you stick to the rules and predetermined spells." He paused to study me with squinted eyes. "You know, it's not a bad thing to be fearful every now and then. The fear reminds you of limits, of what lines you should not cross. Of the doors you shouldn't open."

"Hmm."

"And what does that sound mean?"

I smiled. My dimples I had stolen from my mother, and I knew my father softened at the sight. "It means I hear you, Papa."

"Hear but do not heed?" he countered, but he was teasing. "Regardless, it's time for you to do a visitation on your own. Go to the Fieldings and come directly home. If you're not back before dusk, I will come searching for you. And we both don't want that."

"I will return with time to spare," I said, rising from the bed. "And if you're not feeling well by nightfall, then I can—"

"I will be more than fine when the new moon rises," Papa growled. "Tell Imonie to set me a place at the dinner table. We'll eat before we go, as we always do."

There was no sense in arguing with him, no sense in telling him that he might be more of a burden, that his fever would make him and his enchantments weak and frail.

"Drink your tea," I told him, and slipped from his bedroom.

I descended the curling stairwell of the cottage, scaring Dwindle, my old calico cat, on the way down.

"Did I hear your father say to set him a place at the table?" Imonie asked, her back angled to me as she tended to meat sizzling in a skillet.

I often forgot how sharp her hearing was. She could hear through walls, it seemed.

"You did, and I don't think he'll listen to reason." I stopped at the counter, where the pan of almost-burned cherry galettes was cooling. "And you should stop eavesdropping, by the way. One day you'll hear something you wish you hadn't."

"We'll see about that," Imonie said with a snort, seeming to answer both dilemmas—my father's stubbornness and her keen hearing. She glanced up at me, a rare smile warming her solemn face. "Now, are you going to help me fry this venison, or are you going to tend to that nightmare?"

"Ugh, I'm off, of course." I pushed away from the counter but swiped two cherry galettes.

"Clementine!" Imonie cried, but she wasn't surprised as I grinned and shoved one of the pastries in my mouth, bolting out the front door.

I lingered by the withering jasmine at the front gate, long enough to tuck the remaining pastry in my pocket and look up, to where the clouds were streaked like ribs across the sky, exposing a burning heart of sun.

What a strange day.

I glanced at the book of nightmares in my arms. It was a tome, the sort that could hold back an ironclad door. I had read only portions of it, and some accounts had made me laugh at their absurdity, while others had actually made me fall asleep, only to wake hours later with my cheek pressed against the caramel-tinged pages. But there were some recordings that made me shiver, dreams influenced by the mountains. They had sparked such fear in my bones that I hadn't slept for a week after reading them, although none of these nightmares belonged to me.

No. I studied nightmares, and I confronted them every new moon in the streets of Hereswith, when the magic flowed freely from the mountain fortress and dreams were cursed to material-ize. But I didn't know what it was like to experience a nightmare. What it felt like to wake frightened from something that felt hauntingly real.

As a magician, I chose to never dream.

3

I walked through town, holding the book of nightmares on my hip like it was a child, smiling and waving to the people I passed. All who I knew well, by name and by dream alike. I hurried when I reached the market, the heart of Hereswith, where both gossip and activity thrived. I didn't have time to be ensnared by either one, and I followed the eastern road to the lower edge of town, where the cottages became more distant from each other, melting into verdant patches of farms marked by low stone walls.

I smelled the Fieldings' sheep before I reached their gate. A black-and-white collie barked as I approached the front door, which sat ajar. I hesitated on the stoop; I could hear a faint argument, just within the cottage. . . .

"We can't afford it, Jane. Our daughters need bread more than they need dreamless sleep."

"Look at her, Spruce. Will you do nothing? She won't even speak!"

"The girls have brought this on themselves. I've said this time and time again, and those cards need to be—"

"Those were my *grandfather's* cards!"

Spruce sighed. "I've summoned the magician. If you won't see the cards burned . . . what more do you want me to do, woman?"

I didn't like Spruce Fielding's tone. I knocked on the door, and it creaked open farther, exposing the central room of the cottage. Jane Fielding, a woman whose blond hair was lank and streaked with gray, sat on a threadbare couch with a bundle of blankets—which was probably her youngest daughter—cradled on her lap. Spruce, a ruddy-faced man with a thick brown beard who was so tall he had to stoop to avoid banging his head on the timber beams, was pacing until he saw me.

"Miss Clem!" he said, surprised as he moved to greet me. "Thank you for coming. We were expecting—"

"My father," I concluded. "Yes, I know. But he's in bed fighting a fever. I've come in his stead."

"Oh, I'm sorry to hear that," Spruce said, removing his cap to twist it in his hands.

"Sorry that I'm here, or that my father is ill?" I jested, hoping to lighten the mood as well as the dread the Fieldings were expressing upon the realization that *I*, and not my esteemed father, had come to divine the nightmare.

Spruce was speechless. Sometimes the men of Hereswith didn't know how to take my wit. I stepped into the room, my eyes adjusting to the dim interior light.

All five of the Fielding daughters were present. Two were in the loft, peering down at me like roosted birds, and the other three were on the main level. The eldest was chopping carrots in the kitchen; the second-eldest, by the hearth, was trying to make a quilt out of scraps; and the youngest, the one whose dream I had come to glean, was indeed wrapped in her mother's arms. All the girls' names began with an *E*, to my distress. I could never keep any of them straight—Enya, Esther, Elizabeth, Edith—save for little Elle, who had a palindrome name, something I had always wanted.

Elle, who was around seven and far too thin and small for her age, blinked at me from the edge of her blanket.

"Hello, Elle," I greeted her. "May I come sit next to you?"

The little girl gave a curt nod, and I sat beside her and her mother on the lumpy couch, easing the book of nightmares down to rest on my thighs. I detested having an audience, how both parents watched me with wide, dubious eyes, and how the sisters froze like statues, soaking in my every move. Even the collie, who had snuck into the house, sat in a patch of sun, one blue eye and one brown eye pinned on me.

I hated resorting to stagecraft. The sort of magic my mother reveled in. The art of enchanted performance that provoked emotions in observers, whether it was horror, delight, or wonder.

But this was a moment for stagecraft if there ever was one. I could feel it call to me as the tension and worry began to overpower the room. And I was thankful for those early years, for my oldest memories. Memories I refrained from rousing too often, for fear they would crack me. A time long ago, when my parents had still been together in the city. All those evenings I had sat on my father's lap in the theater, watching Mama perform magic on the stage.

"I have something for you, Elle."

The little girl said nothing, only watched me with large, frightened eyes.

I held up my palms, to prove they were empty, before cupping my hands together. I silently called forth the cherry galette from my pocket, lifting one of my hands up in the air to reveal the pastry.

Jane Fielding gasped in delight—stagecraft *did* have its perks—and the wonder captured her youngest daughter. The blanket lowered a fraction, then a little more, until Elle's arms were free. She smiled and accepted the galette, and I suddenly wished I had brought more, to feed the four longing stares of the older girls.

The silence was awkward as Elle began to munch on the pastry. I decided this was a good time to prepare for the divination.

"Mr. Fielding? Do you mind bringing one of your kitchen chairs over here? I need to use it as a makeshift table."

He quickly obliged, shooing his daughter Elizabeth, who had been sewing by the hearth, out of the way.

Elizabeth left her scattering of quilt and stood near me. That was when I noticed one of the cards on the floor, nearly hidden beneath a square of fabric. Its illustration caught the light, even as the card itself was tattered. I discreetly studied it, unable to quell my interest as an artist.

The painting depicted a svelte man with a shock of long white hair, dressed in colorful, ornate raiment. A top hat sat on his head, spilling a shadow across his face. Only his crooked smile and his eyes could be discerned, glinting like two emeralds. His title was hand-lettered beneath his feet. *The Master of Coin.*

I wanted to reach for the card. I wanted to hold it and study its illustration, to learn from whoever had painted it, long ago. A story caught in time on paper.

And then I remembered myself. I was visiting as a magician, not a pining artist. But I now understood the conversation I had overheard on the stoop. The Fielding girls must have played a round of Seven Wraiths, and little Elle must have lost, ending up with one of the seven illustrated cards in her hand. While I had never played this game, as my father and Imonie both detested and forbade it, I knew there was great enchantment within its rules. To lose with one of the seven wraiths in your possession meant you would experience a nightmare the next time you lay down to sleep.

I withdrew my attention from the card and prepared for the divination. I called forth the trinkets from my pocket, speaking the reverse spell. They returned to their normal sizes without qualm: the silver bowl, which I filled with water from my pitcher, and the jars of salt and gardenia, the octopus inkstand and quill and the iron spoon with the emerald chip.

"Did you have to go to school to learn how to cast magic, Miss Clem?" Elizabeth asked.

"No. My father taught me most of what I know," I replied. "My mother also taught me a few spells."

Elle had finished devouring her galette. I took my time opening the book of nightmares, leafing through the fragile pages until I found the latest entry, which Papa had penned four days ago. One of Lucy Norrin's nightmares, which I often found to be ridiculous on the spectrum of dreams.

"Do you want to tell me your dream, Elle?" I asked.

Elle shook her head, her curls bobbing.

"She hasn't spoken one word today," Spruce said, hovering. "I've tried to get her to describe it, but it was that game . . . that bloody game!" He pointed upward, to the two daughters in the loft. "You should have known better than to let your little sister play."

"Mr. Fielding," I said coldly, drawing his attention. "It's paramount that the dreamer be calm when I cast a divination. If you can't be quiet, I'll have to ask you to step outside."

He was thunderstruck that I had spoken to him in such a way, but he swallowed his retort and silently stewed.

I smiled at Elle. "Then I must cast a spell, so I can see your dream. Is that okay, Elle?"

Elle clung to her mother, fearful.

"You won't have to see it again, Elle. Only I will. Okay?"

The child buried her face into Jane's chest, and Jane sighed. "Please do, Miss Clem. I know the evening is coming, and we mustn't keep you here much longer."

But I waited for Elle to glance at me again, more curious than afraid now.

I poured a few crystals of salt in one palm. Next, I gathered some dried gardenia petals in my other hand, extending my palms out to Elle.

"Which one do you like more?" I asked, coaxing the opposing fragrances to rise.

Elle studied them both but pointed to the clean rainstorm fragrance of the salt.

A girl after my own heart, I thought as I dropped the crystals into the bowl of water, returning the flowers to their jar. I took my spoon and began to hum my father's divination spell, stirring the water until the salt had dissolved and the emerald in the handle cast a green pallor on the surface.

The nightmare still lingered in the cottage.

As soon as I found the dream's door, etched in shadows in the center of the room, the Fielding family froze, as if I had stopped time. I knew they were experiencing the opposite from their vantage point; they were waiting with suspended breath, watching a glazed-eyed, entranced version of myself as I inwardly located the lurking threshold of the dream.

Focusing on the door, I rose and opened it.

I stepped into Elle's dream.

Elle is in the market of Hereswith, accompanied by two of her sisters and her father. Things feel normal but the light is gray, and distress ripples at the edges of the dream, like the pounding of a distant drum. The mountains are dark shadows in the distance, but fires burn along their slopes, marking the fortress in the clouds. Night falls, sudden and nonsensical, and the crowd in the market vanishes in a blink. Elle is alone, searching for her father, her sisters. A cold mountain wind blows, rattling shop signs and scattering loose papers on the street as Elle runs from door to door, knocking, begging to be let in. They are

all locked, the windows darkened, shuttered. And then comes a dif-
ferent noise. One that pierces Elle's heart with fear.

Heavy footsteps. They meet the cobblestones slowly, deliberately,
clinking like strange music.

At once, Elle's thoughts race.

Hide, hide. Whatever it is, don't let it find you. Hide . . .

She runs through the streets but there is nowhere to hide, and the
heavy footsteps faithfully follow her. They grow louder—closing the
distance between them—and Elle whimpers as she tumbles back into
the market green. She crawls toward a wagon and cowers beneath its
bed, crying, although no matter how hard she tries to scream for her
father, no sound emerges from her mouth.

She finally sees a glimpse of the one who is hounding her, whose
tread makes that strange music.

A knight is walking to her, as if he knows exactly where she hides.
She sees him from the knees down as he approaches the wagon in those
measured, heavy steps. His armored legs and feet gleam silver in the
darkness. Plated steel and rusted with blood.

He unsheathes a sword, but he lets the tip of it drag along the
cobblestones at his side, as if he wants to hear the tempered steel screech
and spark against the rock.

He comes to a stop, directly before the wagon. Elle trembles, stares
at his steel boots, the edge of his sword. And then she hears the creak of
his armor as he begins to bend, to crouch, reaching for her . . .

I jolted.

The dream had broken, spitting me back into reality, and I
drew in a deep breath.

I was sitting in the Fieldings' cottage. The afternoon was warm, the light golden as the family gazed at me, and yet I felt the chill of Elle's nightmare. I could still hear the echo of those strange, armored feet that had followed her. The ring of the sword dragging on the stones.

Who was he? I wondered, glancing at Elle.

But I couldn't ask the girl. Not now, with the dream lingering like smoke in the air, choking us both with fear.

I took up my quill and ink and recorded the nightmare swiftly in the book. My hand trembled; my penmanship was slanted and riddled with blots. Papa would no doubt notice later when he read it and asked me why this nightmare bothered me so badly.

"Well?" Spruce Fielding prodded when I had finished the recording, shutting the tome.

I looked up. "Well what?"

"What was the dream? Why won't she speak? Was it truly so frightening?"

I didn't reply. I began to gather my things, shrinking them back into my pocket until I remembered the remedies. I had brought five, and I withdrew the glass vials as I stood from the couch.

A swallowed remedy kept dreams at bay for an entire day. The good ones as well as the frightening ones. If drunk before bed, a person would experience a tranquil sleep. An inner fog, culled of dreams. Like my sleep, every single night.

I handed the first one to Elle. Then I moved to Elizabeth and gave her a vial. Next, the oldest sister in the kitchen. And lastly, I enchanted the remaining two remedies to float up to the loft, where the roosted sisters continued to observe. They reached out in awe when the vials hovered before them.

"I didn't ask for any remedies," Spruce said, wringing his hat again. "I can't pay for them. Why did you—"

"I know you didn't ask for them," I cut him off, weary. I smiled one last time at Elle and Jane Fielding before turning to leave. "I give them to your daughters freely, but I would like a word with you, sir."

Spruce followed me outside into the yard. The sun had already set behind the mountains and the shadows were long and cool. Dusk was coming, and I felt the urge to get home as quickly as I could.

"I know what you're going to say, Miss Clem," he said.

I arched a brow. "Oh? And what is that, Mr. Fielding?"

He raked his hands through his thin hair. "My daughters shouldn't be playing Seven Wraiths. I know your father disapproves of the game. I know it makes his work *that* much harder, with nightmares sprouting up like weeds, thanks to the cards being dealt. But I can't keep my daughters from playing it. They're of Seren ancestry; both my and Jane's families hail from the mountains. And so my daughters will continue to play the game, even with the threat of nightmares, just as Jane and I once did. Because we long for home, even as it lies in ruins, doomed. Even as we have never seen it with our own eyes. Only in dreams do we behold it."

Silent, I listened to his every word. I knew the Fieldings were of mountain descent, just as Imonie was. I knew they would not be able to return to the home of their ancestors until the new moon curse was ended. But I didn't think such a spell could be broken by playing a game of enchanted cards, which had ironically been inspired by the same curse. In particular, by the seven members of the mountain court who had each played a hand in the Duke of Seren's assassination.

"It's not my place to tell you whether or not your daughters should play the game," I said. "All I wanted to do is to remind you that the new moon comes tonight. Ensure your shutters are bolted, your doors are locked, your family and livestock are all safe inside tonight, Mr. Fielding."

"As I do every new moon, Miss Clem," he said, somewhat indignant. But then he seemed to realize what I was implying, because his scowl and voice mellowed. "You don't think . . . that my little Elle's nightmare will manifest tonight?"

I didn't know. But it inspired a tremor in me when I imagined coming face-to-face with the armored knight who reeked of violence, who had threatened a little girl. I had to confess that Elle's nightmare had felt alarmingly tangible. It had fooled me for a span of terrifying moments, when I had been her, believing everything was real and unfolding, as if I could have reached out and touched the cold glint of the knight's bloodied armor. And perhaps it was only due to my inexperience with divination, and perhaps it was only due to the fact that this nightmare had been spawned by a sinister card game. But it felt heavier than the others I had encountered.

I glanced at the mountains. If the new moon chose to spin Elle's nightmare when the stars began to burn . . . the knight wouldn't be a wisp in a dream. He would be flesh and blood encased in steel, and his sword would be ready to cut.

I wanted to know who he was, what he wanted. If he was inspired by someone.

I bade Spruce Fielding farewell and began to walk home, my gaze on the sunset. But I feared I wouldn't be able to find the answers I sought. Not until I challenged the knight in the streets of Hereswith.

4

"**M**iss Clem!"

I was just coming upon the market, which had become vacant as shops closed early for the evening, when I was intercepted by a frantic Lilac Westin, the revered baker in Hereswith. Flour dusted her face as she all but collided with me.

"Miss Clem, there are two men in the market!"

I blinked, wondering what this had to do with me. Whether she was attempting to play matchmaker, which she had woefully done with me in the past.

"Are men forbidden from the market these days, Miss Westin?"

"If only they could be," the baker countered, but then pondered on such a possibility, and her face creased with a frown. "Although my business would surely suffer for it. But no, there are two men—*strangers*—lurking about town, asking about your father."

"My father?" I echoed. "Why would they be asking after him?"

Lilac hesitated, and I saw the panic in her expression. Quickly, I moved around the baker and made for the market on quiet tread, hiding behind a stack of empty wire cages at the trader's stall. Lilac rushed behind me, and we stood in the shadows and watched the two men drift aimlessly about the market.

They were not what I expected. I had envisioned dignitaries sent by the Duke of Bardyllis to collect the town's dream tax, milling about with rings on every finger. Or perhaps delegates from the Luminous Society, visiting to ensure my father was adhering to all magical laws. Or perhaps descendants of the fallen mountain duchy, such as Imonie and the Fieldings, searching for a safe place to settle. But these two men were dressed in dark clothes, finely tailored, with silk-lined cloaks and rapiers belted at their sides. They were too young to be ranked members of the duke's court, too inexperienced to be delegates. Nor did they appear to be seeking sanctuary. But they boasted the air of ones who thought they were important, their posture stiff and proper.

They walked past a burning streetlamp, and I finally saw it. The men cast no shadows, and I sensed the illumination within them.

They were magicians.

"How long have they been in Hereswith?" I asked.

"For an hour now," Lilac said. "They've gone from shop to shop, asking where to find your father. None of us will tell them. And Mr. Jeffries—*bless* him—agreed to put their horses in his stable but closed the inn early, refusing to give them admittance, so they've been wandering, seeking hospitality and answers."

I continued to watch the magicians. One was blond, his hair trimmed short, his face coldly handsome as he knocked on the Brambles's door. The other magician had dark hair bound with a ribbon, and his face was trapped in a scowl, as if he had smelled something foul. They looked related, one like day, the other like night. Brothers, most likely.

And they could not be here for anything good.

They were uninvited, trespassing on my father's territory.

"I bet they're vultures," I murmured, thinking of all the magicians who visited Hereswith to glean information about the doomed fortress in the clouds. *Vultures* was the word we used for such people, because they only wanted stories from us before traveling to the mountain doors—the sole passage to the summit, where Seren's abandoned stronghold waited for someone to arrive and break the curse. One could reach the fortress if they could merely open the mountain doors, which sounded quite simple until one realized the doors were enchanted and impossible to open since the curse first fell a hundred years ago. But it didn't deter ambitious magicians from trying, and using us along the way.

"Miss Clem," Lilac whispered. "If they're vultures . . . why are they asking for your father?"

Her question gave me pause. She was right; when vultures arrived, they wanted to speak to mountain descendants, not the town warden. My voice wavered when I said, "Then they must be here to challenge my father for Hereswith."

It had been a good while since such an event had occurred. So long, in fact, that I had almost forgotten it always hung as a possibility.

I was ten years old the first time it happened. Two older magicians had come to town on the heels of the southern wind, just before the new moon, and had challenged my father for the right to guard Hereswith from nightmares. A year after that, another set of them had arrived, keen to win the town that thrived in the foothills of the infamous mountains. In both instances, the magicians *at least* had the courtesy to write to my father a fortnight in advance, informing him of their intentions. And while it didn't seem fair, the newcomers could lawfully win the title to become warden of the town and displace my father, but only if they defeated the nightmare before Papa did.

He had vanquished the challengers in both instances. But my father was ill tonight. I would most likely face the new moon on my own, and I had never encountered competition when it came to a nightmare's defeat.

"Are you going to speak with them, Miss Clem?"

I glanced at the baker, who had crossed her arms and was glaring in the direction of the men. "No, I'm not," I said, relieved the Brambles had refused to open the door to them.

"Then I will." Before I could ask what she planned to say to them, Lilac marched out into the market and drew their attention with a sharp whistle.

I remained lurking in the stall, and while I couldn't hear what the baker said, I saw her point to the northern street. Point to where Mazarine's mansion sat visible on the hill, catching the last hue of the sunset.

I watched, mouth ajar in horror, as the magicians nodded and began to take the northern road, up to the troll's mansion. I had every intention to go directly home and avoid crossing paths with them. I had every intention to mind my own business and leave the strangers to their fate.

In fact, I made it halfway home before I stopped at the cross-roads.

But I turned north and took a side street, rushing over the cobbles, cutting through a neighbor's garden, jumping a low rock fence, to catch the men before they became Mazarine's next unex-pected meal. If I hadn't known what she truly was, I wouldn't have chased after them. Or so I told myself as I hurried to meet them on the road. They were almost at her gate. And I had a moment of hesitation, a moment of doubt. . . .

"The magician you seek doesn't live here," I announced.

My voice startled them.

The blond actually made a noise and jumped, to my immense satisfaction, but the dark-headed one only widened his eyes at the sight of me emerging from the dusk.

"Of course the magician lives here," the blond said with a sweep of his hand. He glanced back to the manor. "This is the finest house in town."

"The magician doesn't live here," I said again, sharper. "And I must say it's a terrible night to arrive, gentlemen."

The dark-headed one studied me with hooded eyes. I sensed

he was not at all impressed until his gaze drifted to the book of nightmares I held. He saw the flame within me, then, although the dusk made it difficult to measure my lack of shadow. But he said nothing, only brought his gaze back to mine.

The blond, however, was belligerent. His pride was bruised from being turned away and snubbed by every single resident of Hereswith. "We know which night we arrive, miss. And *you* are not the town magician."

He meant it as an insult. I only smiled.

"Indeed not. That would be my father."

The magicians exchanged a careful glance.

"Then you must be Clementine Madigan," said the dark-headed one.

I had to swallow the shock of that—to hear my name flow from a strange magician's mouth. I hoped that I didn't flinch, that my smile didn't falter. "I am. And you're both lucky that I've chosen to aid you this night, despite the fact that you've arrived *unannounced*. Come, you can sup with my father and me, and we'll put you up for the night, since the new moon is rising and you need to be off the streets."

I turned and began to walk home, listening as the magicians scrambled to follow me.

Imonie heard us coming, long before I even laid a hand on our gate. She heard me and the tread of unfamiliar boots in my wake, and she threw open the door with a murderous look on her face.

"You're late, Clementine."

I came to a stop on the stoop, narrowing my eyes at her. "Yes, well, I ran into these two magicians on the street."

She scrutinized them over my shoulder. A long, uncomfortable moment passed. "I see that." She brought her eyes back to mine and said, "Go and tell your father we have company."

I did just as she bade, and found my father still in bed, flushed from fever.

"Who did you bring home?" he croaked at me.

I stood in the center of his chamber and stared at him, realizing he was worse than before.

Dread unfurled within me, and I set the book of nightmares back on his desk.

"I found two magicians wandering the town, seeking you. I brought them here, so they're off the streets tonight."

"You *what?*" He was suddenly ripping the quilts away, stumbling to his feet. I reached out to steady him, because he looked like he was a breath from fainting, his eyes unfocused until they found me. "Who are they?"

"I don't know their names yet."

"Are they from the Luminous Society?"

"No, they're not."

Papa stared at me, but he was not seeing me. His gaze was very distant, and he was suddenly shaking.

"You need to lie down . . ." I tried to direct him back to bed, but he broke from my grip, lumbering to his wardrobe and drawing out fresh clothes. A long-sleeved linen shirt, a green waistcoat with golden embroidery, a white cravat, a black jacket . . .

"Papa."

"Go and change, Clementine, and then return to me here," he

said, pausing to lean on the wardrobe. "We both must look our best tonight."

He must sense it, then. He was being challenged by upstarts for his town, for our home.

I left his chamber and shut the door, tarrying in the upper hallway, listening. Imonie was setting two more places at the table; she set the china down with clinking intensity. The magicians were quiet, but I heard them walking in the room beneath me, the floor protesting their elegant steps.

I slipped into my bedroom.

A few candelabras were lit, casting uneven shadows on the walls. My window was closed and shuttered tonight, because of the new moon. The desk before it was messy, crowded with my journals of spells and illustrations, a tray of pastels and charcoal and half-drawn imaginings. Imonie had already laid out clothes: my favorite black-and-white striped skirt with pockets, my weapon belt, a stark white chemise with billowy sleeves, a velvet bodice that laced up the front.

But I chose not to wear any of it. I poured lavender-steeped water into my basin and washed my face and arms. And then I went to my wardrobe and found the dress I wanted. A long-sleeved gown made of black velvet. I had only worn it once before, to a winter solstice party that my father didn't attend, and the looks I had drawn made me so self-conscious that I decided I wouldn't wear it again.

But this night seemed to call for it.

I undressed, remembered I still had tiny trinkets in my pockets, and returned them to their proper size. I drew the black dress on, pulling the golden ribbon at the bodice tight.

I brushed my hair but left it down, and I fastened my leather weapon belt to my waist. Two small daggers gleamed at my hips as I walked back to Papa's room. The belt had been his gift to me on my fifteenth birthday two years ago, when he had at last allowed me to join him in fighting on the new moons. In my mind, it marked my coming of age.

He was sitting in his chair this time, dressed in his finest and out of breath from the effort. This was truly going to be a disastrous night, I thought, and watched him frown at my choice of clothes.

"Where did *that* come from?" he asked.

"It's one of Mama's old dresses," I said. "She sent it to me last year."

His frown deepened, but then he coughed, and it seemed he forgot about the gown. I poured him a cup of water, which he drained, and then he stood and motioned for me to come closer.

"How are your stores, Clem?"

I knew he was asking about my reserved magic, the amount I had available to burn. Magicians could fuel their spells in one of three ways: body, mind, or heart. Depending on what energy force the magicians preferred to cast with, we needed things like food, drink, sleep, good company, books, art, music, and solitude to refill, or risked burning ourselves into oblivion.

I often cast with my mind and my body, and while the dream divination had drained a portion of my reserves, I measured myself and found that I still had plenty to give.

"My stores are good."

"Then I need you to glamour me."

"*Glamour* you? This fever must truly be making you senseless."

"Yes, just a little. To hide that I'm ill."

He waited for me to do something. I merely gaped up at him.

"Papa . . . I don't think—"

"This *is* a good idea," he said, reading my mind. "Please, daughter. This night is important, and I must make an appearance with the arrival of these . . . visitors."

"But I don't think you should fight tonight," I said. "You're far too sick for it."

"We'll see. Perhaps I'll feel better after dinner."

Unlikely. But he was right; these magicians had come all the way to Hereswith to see him, and he looked terrible.

I drew in a deep breath and worked a gentle charm over him. Another spell of my mother's. One that brushed away his paleness, the perspiration on his brow, his glazed eyes, the lankness of his hair, the uneven tilt of his shoulders. But the glamour wavered, and I saw a much different version of him. There was no gray at his temples, no hollowed cheekbones, no furrows in his skin. It was like catching a glimpse of him from the past when he had been younger, before I had been born, and it rattled me a moment. As soon as it came, the vision was gone, and I thought it must have been influenced by my glamour. He now looked vibrant and hale, just as I knew him to be, and I exhaled a soft sigh.

My father rushed his palms over the front of his jacket, which was already pristine under Imonie's care. He was nervous, I realized, and I reached out to take his hand. The fever still burned beneath his skin. I felt a stab of fear for him.

"Whatever the reason they've come," I began, "I'm sure it's not as terrible as we both imagine."

He only smiled at me, tucking my hand into the crook of his elbow.

Together, we descended.

5

The blond magician was beside the hearth, where the shelves overflowed with books. The dark-headed one was standing on the threshold of the solarium, gazing into the small glass chamber, where Papa and I grew an array of plants. The magicians reeked of curiosity and judgment, as if our provincial lives were something they would later spin into a joke they told at court, and I stiffened the moment they both turned toward my father and me.

Imonie had already taken their cloaks, and I could see they were dressed in the latest fashion: cream cravats, waistcoats embroidered with moon phases and stars, black jackets with coat-tails, trousers with silver trim running up the sides, knee-high boots that only carried a hint of dust from the road, and belts with rapiers sheathed at their sides.

I sensed their weapons were not intended to keep them safe on their travels.

"Mr. Ambrose Madigan," the blond greeted Papa with a sharp smile. "It's an honor to meet you. Allow me to introduce us. I'm Lennox Vesper, and this is my brother, Phelan."

"You're the Countess of Amarys's sons," my father said, and while he sounded polite, I heard the cold shift in his voice. "You're also a long way from home and the luxuries of your court. What brings you to the border?"

Lennox was still smiling, but it was stretched far too wide, and he reminded me of a puppet in a child's nightmare. "We've come to see Hereswith. To go as far as we can before stepping into the mountain duchy."

"The mountain duchy is no more," Papa said. "And Hereswith would have been better prepared if we had known of your visit."

"Yes, well, it was a sudden change in plans," said Lennox, and he glanced at his brother. Phelan was silent, but his eyes were on me, dark and inscrutable. On the gleam of weapons I wore at my hips.

"Come, then," my father said, indicating the table, where Imonie had just finished setting down dinner platters. "Eat with us tonight. Refresh yourselves. You must indeed be weary from a long journey."

"And we thank you for your generous hospitality, Mr. Madigan," Lennox said, and unbuckled his belt, leaving his rapier by the door.

Phelan followed suit, but I was not about to shed my weapons, even if it went against all manners to partake in a meal armed. The four of us arrived at the table, and an awkward moment passed.

The guests were to take their seats first, to lower themselves in gratitude, but the magicians were not sitting.

No, Phelan was staring at the meal that was spread between us, and Lennox was staring at me.

"Forgive me for asking, Miss Clementine," Lennox drawled. "But do you always take part in a meal with weapons on your belt?"

"It depends on the night," I replied. "And the company."

Lennox laughed, a garish sound that instantly set me on edge. Like Mazarine's laughter had. I felt my hands gripping the back of my chair, my knuckles draining white, and I wished I had let them knock on her door.

Phelan finally broke the tension. He drew back his chair, sitting with an elegance that was reminiscent of a waltz. My father and I waited for his brother to also relent, and then we were gathered at the table, ready to eat.

My stomach was wound in a knot, but I put a proper amount of food on my plate. Venison with currant jelly, rosemary potatoes, glazed carrots and beets, boiled eggs, and a cold salad of fruit and toasted nuts.

Imonie was pouring ginger beer in our glasses when Lennox sniffed his napkin, studied the water stains on his fork, and then cleared his throat.

"Do you mind if I cast a cantrip, Mr. Madigan?"

My father sounded wary. "What sort of spell is necessary during dinner?"

"To see what ingredients are in the food. I have a delicate disposition."

I snorted, only to draw everyone's attention. I raised my glass to them and drank, to hide the curl of my lips.

"Just eat the food, Lee," Phelan murmured with a twinge of mortification.

"You should cast too, you know," Lennox whispered in return, and that was when I realized *why* the magician wanted to sift through the food. He thought we had poisoned it, which was irrational, since my father and I were also eating from the same platters.

Papa came to a similar conclusion. "If you fear an upset stomach, don't worry. We have plenty of herbs to calm it. If you fear poison . . . then let me reassure you, Mr. Lennox. It's bad fortune to harm a guest under one's roof, and I don't intend on bringing terrible luck upon my household."

"What a reassurance," Lennox said, and he continued with his cantrip, searching the food on his plate and the ginger beer in his cup.

Imonie stood beside the china cabinet and watched with a flat expression. But her eyes shone like obsidian.

I forced myself to eat. I was sitting across from Phelan, and I noticed how he cut his meat into proper bites, how he handled his fork and knife. I made a point to be his opposite. My cutlery screeched against my plate, provoking winces from the men, and I put a hunk of meat in my mouth, my fork upside down.

Phelan watched in shock, as if he couldn't believe my manners. Lennox looked disgusted.

I smiled as I chewed, close lipped and full of terrible thoughts.

My father cleared his throat. "May I ask how long the two of you plan to stay in Hereswith?"

"It could be a short visit," Lennox said, dragging his disbelieving gaze from me. "But then again, we might decide to stay for a while."

"Could you please provide me with the date you'll be departing, then?" Papa continued, and from the corner of my eye, I saw his hand was trembling as he speared a potato with his fork.

"We have no definite date as of yet." Lennox sounded smug. "But as it is the new moon . . . I was wondering what sort of nightmares haunt your town, Mr. Madigan. Are they indeed vicious, since you dwell so near the mountains and the accursed Seren Duchy? What sort of terrors stalk the streets on the darkest of nights?"

My father was silent. But he stared across the table at Lennox Vesper, and I felt the chill in the air. A chill that expressed how angry my father was, even as he secretly smoldered with a fever beneath the glamour.

"The nightmares are mine to keep, Mr. Lennox," Papa said. "I'm the warden of Hereswith. These streets are mine to guard, these people mine to honor and protect. Despite your education and polished upbringing, you seem to have forgotten the most basic of laws and respect when it comes to the magic of dreams and guardianship."

Lennox chuckled, reaching for his ginger beer. "I've not forgotten at all, Mr. Madigan. My memory is rather sharp, and I do nothing without thought."

"Then let's not dance around the bear," I said, impatient. "What do you want?"

Lennox glanced at me, fair brow arched. "I believe that is something I need to discuss with your father, since he is the magician of Hereswith."

Despite my confidence, I felt my cheeks flush from the way he made me sound of little consequence. As if I were no one and nothing important.

For one brief, terrifying moment, I imagined Lennox had come to ask my father for a partnership. To have the opportunity to be warden of Hereswith alongside Papa. To uproot and replace me. I knew from my brief upbringing in the capital that nearly all warden magicians took partners, because the collection of dreams was a cumbersome task and nightmares had the capability of being anything. It was always best to have someone guarding your back on the new moon, to grant you aid if a violent dream unfolded.

"My daughter is my partner and has vast knowledge of magic," my father replied, as if he shared the same worry. My posture softened, relieved. Although I was not his partner *yet*. Only his apprentice. "Whatever you have to say to me can also be said to her."

"Yes, of course, Mr. Madigan," said Lennox with a forced smile and a graceful motion of his hand. "I suppose there is no sense in delaying, since night has fallen." But he glanced at his brother, as if seeking reassurance. Phelan was silent, staring into his goblet. He eventually lifted his eyes and nodded, and my dread rose, threatening to drown me.

Lennox stood.

He set his gaze on my father, and it seemed like the firelight dimmed and the shadows deepened around us. He withdrew a red silk handkerchief from the inner pocket of his jacket and dropped it onto the table. I watched the fabric flutter down, resting on the wood like a patch of blood.

"*Sever occisio loredania*. I have come to challenge you, Mr. Madigan. I have come on this new moon in the month of September to win the right of guardianship and the title of warden for Hereswith."

Lennox's announcement rang in the chamber, reverberating off the walls and the windows and the roof of my childhood, sundering my peace. The challenge teemed about us, shimmered in the air like rain in sun. I breathed it in, felt the incantation lock about my heart like an iron cage.

Sever occisio loredania.

My father and I sat frozen, staring up at the young magician. Lennox waited, shifting his weight as the heavy silence continued.

"Did you hear me, Mr. Madigan? I said I challenge you—"

My father rose. The chair nearly overturned in his haste, and my heart was pounding, my hands shaking as I also stood. Papa had not won the wardenship of Hereswith; it had been passed down to him when the previous magician had retired, nine years ago. He had never stood in the place of Lennox Vesper. He had never stolen territory from another magician.

"I heard you, Mr. Lennox," said Papa, and his voice was hoarse, his distress making my glamour waver on him for a breath. "I accept your challenge. You have an hour to make it to the market green of Hereswith, where Clementine and I will meet you for the challenge of the new moon."

Lennox bowed. He left his red handkerchief on the table as a mark of contract, and retrieved his cloak and weapon, Phelan following him. I held my breath as I watched them depart. Even Imonie seemed unable to breathe as she stood in the kitchen, staring at the table, the dinner half eaten on the plates.

The cottage was quiet again. A quiet that wanted to crush my heart.

I turned to look at Papa, my glamour melting away from him. It should have held for at least another hour, but my magic turned brittle in that moment.

"Here, Papa. Sit."

He allowed me to ease him back into the chair, and he sat with a groan.

"Imonie?" I glanced at her. "Some warm wine with clove and honey for Papa?"

She began to move to the wine cupboard until my father spoke.

"No," he said. We never drank before battle because it dulled the senses, and I knelt at Papa's side, my thoughts whirling.

"You're too ill to accept this challenge, Papa. Let me answer it for you."

"I've no choice, Clem. And I won't let you face them alone." He looked at me, his eyes bloodshot. "I've no choice," he repeated in a whisper, and rubbed his brow. We didn't have much time, and I cracked my knuckles, anxious until Papa took my hand.

"We have the advantage," he said, and Imonie rushed to make him a warm cup of tea since he would not take the wine. "We know the nightmares that might appear tonight. The magicians of Amarys don't."

"Yes, but . . ."

"We'll treat this night no differently, daughter," my father said. "Let me rest for half an hour and then we'll go." He leaned his head back against the chair and closed his eyes.

Imonie set the cup of steaming tea down on the table. She looked at my father before she pinned her gaze on me.

"This is your night, Clementine," Imonie said. "Your father will accompany you, but you'll have to be his strength. You'll have to defeat this dream before that upstart does. Be patient. Be shrewd."

I nodded. She spoke those four words to me—*be patient, be shrewd*—every new moon, just before I went to battle. I think she worried about a nightmare getting the best of me; I had a tendency to rush through things, although I had never been badly wounded before.

My courage wavered, but only for a moment.

I met Imonie's stare and offered her a tilt of a smile.

"Any other words of advice, Imonie?"

She snorted, but it was impossible to decipher what she was thinking.

"Don't underestimate these magicians. Particularly the quiet one. He was watching you very closely tonight."

I remembered the way Phelan had regarded me, the way he had spoken my name.

And all I could think was, *I should have let the troll devour them both.*

6

The night was cool and quiet as my father and I walked to the market. Every door was bolted, every shutter closed. It never ceased to surprise me how different Hereswith felt on new moon nights. Desolate and achingly silent, menace chilling the air like fog. It felt abandoned.

I dwelled on the legend of Seren's fall, like I did every new moon, my gaze drawn to the dark shadow of the mountains. The fortress in the clouds had been abandoned when the curse had been set a century ago, and yet I wondered what phantoms walked those mountain passages. What joy and light and friendship had once crowned the summit, before the duke's assassination. Before everything fell apart.

Some legends claimed the duke had been a cruel man, passing harsh judgments on his people. His sadism had been the reason why the seven members of his court were driven to kill him. But other stories depicted him as a gentle ruler, claiming his court plotted his demise because of their own desire to rule.

I wondered which one was true as I slowed my pace to keep in stride with Papa. His breaths were labored, his steps arduous. We were almost to the market; the constellations teemed above us, like sugar spilled across black velvet, and I drew in a deep breath.

"You never told me about Elle Fielding," he whispered.

Fetching Elle's nightmare already felt like a week ago. "I had to divine the dream. It was . . . unusual."

"How so?" Papa came to a stop and turned to face me.

"The setting was here, in the streets and market. She was being pursued by a knight."

"By night?" He indicated the celestial sky above us.

"No, a *knight*. An armored person of prowess." I paused, remembering the heavy cadence of his feet as he walked, the rust and blood on his steel. The sparks of his sword. "He was a threat, but I couldn't see his face. I couldn't discern what he wanted . . . but it was very sinister."

The silence roared between us. I glanced up to see a flicker of fear in Papa's face.

"What did the armor look like?" he asked sharply. "Was there anything strange about it?"

I tried to describe it, but I had only been afforded a glimpse of his legs.

"And what weapon did he carry?"

"A sword," I replied, frowning. "Have you seen this knight in a dream before?" I asked, which was a foolish question, as I had read all my father's nightmare recordings. Every single one. Unless he had some entries hidden from me. And I inevitably recalled Mazarine's words, spoken earlier that day. *Tell me, Clementine . . . have you read one of my nightmares recorded in your father's book?*

I had never read an entry of Mazarine's, which meant she either drank remedies and kept dreams at bay, like me, or she did dream and my father had broken a sacred law of wardenship by refusing to record her nightmares. I wondered why Papa would do such a thing—willingly omitting a nightmare from the ledger—and yet I couldn't find a good enough answer.

The possibility made me tense, and I stared up at my father, measuring his expression by starlight.

"No, I haven't seen a knight like this before in a dream. Come, daughter. The sons of Amarys are waiting. It's time to send them home." My father's swift dismissal only fueled my sudden reservations.

"You don't like their family?" I asked, remembering the ice in his voice when he had heard the brothers' names.

"Their mother is an old acquaintance of mine." That was all my father would say, and I was too hesitant to pry for a better answer.

Lennox and Phelan Vesper were waiting for us in the center of the market.

They stood like statues as Papa and I approached. They stood like they belonged here, like they had grown roots in Hereswith, and I inwardly despised them for it. Papa and I came to a stop a good distance from them, a safe stretch of grass between us.

"Are you certain you know what you're doing, Mr. Lennox?" my father called to him. "There is still a chance to recant your challenge and suffer no humiliation from it."

Lennox grinned that terrible puppet's smile. "I know what I do, Mr. Madigan. And there will be no humiliation on my part."

His confidence was unnerving, but I thought I saw Phelan roll his eyes, as if annoyed with his brother's theatrics. I watched the quiet brother closely, limned in starlight, seeking a weak point in his spirit.

Phelan looked at my father and said, "We don't want any bad blood between us, Mr. Madigan. Nor do we want there to be any unnecessary injuries tonight."

He is noble of heart, I thought. *Or considers himself to be.* Which almost made me laugh, because there was nothing honorable in arriving to another magician's territory unannounced and seeking to steal it.

"Do you want me to surrender without a fight, then, Mr. Phelan?" Papa countered, his voice edged with ire. "Do you want me to surrender this town and its inhabitants after I've given years of my life protecting it? Is that how wardenship works in the city you hail from?"

Phelan had the decency to appear briefly shamed.

"Of course not, Mr. Madigan," Lennox rushed to say. "And besides, you are here with your daughter, and we are ready to play out the challenge. Whoever defeats the nightmare will win the right to Hereswith."

"Win the right," Papa murmured, and I knew the words galled him, because they certainly irritated me. "Very well, then, Mr. Lennox. When the clock strikes nine, the new moon is announced, and your challenge will begin."

All of us glanced at the market clock, whose face was illuminated by lanternlight. Three minutes remained, and they dragged by like years.

I fought the temptation to pace, to fidget. I made myself stand like stone, just as the two upstarts did, and waited for the clock to strike nine.

Finally, the chime sounded.

And the mountain wind blew through the streets, sweet and dark and full of magic.

Lennox frowned as he glanced about the market, waiting for the nightmare to materialize. Sometimes the dreams were born quickly, as if they were ripe and bursting, eager for the mortal world. Sometimes the dreams arrived gradually, shade by shade, like an artist painting a canvas. Sometimes they were easy to defeat, and Papa and I would be home within the hour with only a few rips in our garments. Sometimes they lasted until dawn, stubborn and vicious and crafty.

As I waited to see whose nightmare greeted me that night, I noticed Lennox and Phelan were rigid, and I knew this victory was ours. Papa was right; we had the advantage. We possessed the knowledge, the experience. I knew every nook and cranny of the streets of Hereswith, every garden, the slant of every roof.

This town was my home, and I would defend it.

I noticed the rain before the men did. Before Papa, even. A drop fell in my hair, then on the back of my hand, the moisture gleaming like a jewel on my skin. I resisted the urge to look up at the sky, because I didn't want to tip off the magicians, but I took hold of Papa's arm and began to guide him away from the market.

"Papa, let's go," I whispered.

Lennox's eyes bugged at the sight of us retreating. I sensed he was tempted to follow us, to mimic everything we did, but Phelan had the same idea as me. He drew Lennox to the protection of one of the market stalls, and they melted into the shadows.

It was wonderful to no longer have to look at them. It was also unsettling, because now I wasn't sure where they were or what they were doing. But I inwardly shook myself alert, giving my focus to the nightmare that was coming to life.

Papa and I stood in the eastern street beneath a hanging shop sign as the rain began to fall thick and hard, drenching us within moments.

"Do you recognize this dream, Clem?" Papa asked me, bending close to my ear so I could hear him over the melody of the rain.

"I'm not sure." But I had an inkling. I looked down to the cobblestoned street, where puddles were beginning to deepen, iridescent.

And I knew it, then.

This was Archie Kipp's dream. A little boy who had almost drowned earlier that summer and now was terrified of water. A child's nightmare, and they were always the hardest ones to champion.

Papa recognized the dream when the puddles became ankle deep within a moment. "We need a boat," he murmured.

I nodded but waited, holding my magic on the tip of my tongue, where it crackled like salt as Papa strove to build us a boat. The water was rising quickly now. It was almost to my knees, and I felt my first true pang of trepidation.

"Papa?" He was taking too long. His magic was weak and dim, beating like a faint pulse. I saw that he was attempting to build something infallible, a small boat of tin and wood, and while I admired his sense of grandness, I knew the flood would rise swiftly. And once it did, the serpents would also arrive, slithering in the water.

"Let me," I said. Papa glanced my way, and I saw how he trembled with exhaustion. The waters were mid-thigh now, and I didn't want to drown tonight.

My father reluctantly nodded and I felt the shift of power flow from him to me. This battle was not ours anymore; it was mine.

I called to the stray pieces of nature around us—stalks of hay, threads of grass, feathers from nests, lichens from roofs, smoke from chimneys. I sensed I needed more, so I reached farther with my magic and gathered the distant sound of an argument leaking from a threshold, the wail of a baby, the song of a mother, the sting from a skinned knee. I wove everything together and I made a small boat, rough-hewn and narrow but sturdy.

It bobbed on the water as Papa lifted me up and set me within its frame. I helped him next, and the boat nearly tipped as he hefted himself up and over with a groan. But we were safe from the flood. I quickly created a paddle from a few floating sticks, propelling us along the streets that had transformed into canals. The water was deep, lapping at second-story windows, and I wondered how much deeper it would become. Would it continue to rise until it reached the mountaintops, until it reached the stars?

"Look for the key, Clem," my father said.

I didn't need his reminder, but I held my retort. Every nightmare had a "key" that could appear in a number of forms and be physically claimed. It was the way to break a dream swiftly. If the dreamer could recognize and claim the key while the nightmare was ensnaring them, then they would wake. It was a similar experience on the new moon. I needed to find the weak point of the dream, locate the key in whatever form it took tonight, and wield it before the Vesper brothers.

"First the flood, then the serpents," I reminded him, because the key to the dream would not appear until all the elements of the nightmare manifested. And so I navigated the boat and wiped rain from my eyes and waited for the snakes to arrive, my body tense as a coil, ready to spring into action.

My boat hit resistance. Frowning, I tried to paddle with deeper strokes, but the boat was hung up on something in the water.

"Can you see what's impeding us?" I asked Papa, since he was sitting at the bow.

He carefully shifted to peer over the edge. "Lily pads."

I sighed. Of course, I had forgotten about that one element of the nightmare. Archie was afraid of drowning, afraid of snakes in the water, and afraid of lily pads.

I quickly began to paddle us backward, and I could see the thick knot of lily pads on the water as we retreated. They seemed innocent, perched on the surface with their green leaves and blossoms, but I knew better than to trust them on the new moon.

I rowed to another street, my eyes constantly searching the water, awaiting the serpents. I imagined I saw something slithering through the depths, but it was difficult to tell for certain. The rain eased, the flood line coming to rest right at the eaves of roofs, and the lily pads were multiplying. I bumped into another nest of them and had to reroute yet again, and my shoulders were beginning to smolder from the effort; my hands were pruned.

I had nearly forgotten about the Vesper brothers until I caught a glimpse of them farther up the street, paddling in their own boat. They rounded a corner, slipping away from sight, and I had a strange urge to follow them.

"Don't lose focus, Clem," Papa said, and I had to swallow another quip.

My attention was drawn to the water beneath me, where a small golden light trembled beneath the surface. I leaned closer, the boat rocking, and realized it was a coin drifting through the water, as if someone had cast a wish into a pool.

"Do you see that?" I cried, and rose with haste, handing the paddle to my father.

"Clem, *wait—*"

But the coin was the key, I thought urgently, and it was about to fade away. I jumped overboard and let the water close over my head as I swam after that tantalizing gleam of gold. It led me through the streets, and I had to surface twice to gulp in fresh air. My father was close behind me, paddling the boat in my wake, and I descended into the water again, chasing the key.

I'm not sure what happened first. The water around me turned bitterly cold and I lost sight of my quarry. Pausing, I treaded in place and felt the corresponding tug in my lungs. I needed air, and I rushed to swim up to the surface. Only I couldn't find it. I was suddenly entangled with lily pads. I couldn't break through them; I couldn't reach the surface. In my panic, I couldn't recall a single convoluted spell for breathing underwater.

I fought and pushed and kicked. The more I resisted, the more I became entangled. My lungs burned; I was overwhelmed, fading in my own skin. Something slid past my leg. One of the serpents. My heart leapt in fear.

I'm about to drown. . . .

I quit trying to breach the surface and grappled for one of the daggers hooked to my belt. *Be calm*, I commanded myself as I methodically hacked at the lilies, hacked at the serpents that were gathering and weaving a net around me with their thin, long bodies.

I was nearing the surface, and I saw the shadow of a boat nearby, waiting for me. *Papa*. I kept my focus on it and broke the surface with a desperate gasp of air. My eyes stung, and I clambered for the boat, hefting myself up into its safety. Sprawled within its hull, I spluttered and coughed. I was trembling, and my head was throbbing, but a sharp sting on my left calf snagged my attention.

I drew up my dress to my knees, exposing a serpent latched to my leg, its fangs buried in my skin. It didn't feel real, even as my eyes smarted from the intense pain, and I merely gaped at it a moment, struggling to remember where I was, what was unfolding around me, my mind foggy from the lack of air.

A blaze of light shot like an arrow, striking the serpent dead. Its writhing body instantly went limp, but its fangs were still caught in my leg, and a hand I didn't recognize carefully unhinged the serpent and tossed it overboard.

My gaze rose.

Phelan Vesper.

I had climbed into *Phelan Vesper's* boat.

For a moment, all I could do was pant and stare at him in numb shock. I coughed again, my lungs burning vividly. I wiped my face and pushed my dress back down, hiding my legs and the blood that was trickling out of the fang marks.

"Are you all right?" he asked.

"I'm fine," I wheezed.

I closed my eyes and leaned back in his boat until I felt steady again. A foolish thing, as I shouldn't trust him. Particularly since I had no idea where his brother was.

I listened to the sound of his paddle dipping into the water as he rowed us away from the lily pads. I could have lain there, limbs melted like wax, for hours, but I forced myself to sit up and take in my surroundings.

I saw Papa farther down the street, the lilies blocking him from reaching me. But our gazes crossed, and he hurried to angle his boat into a side street. I knew what he wanted me to do.

The roofs around us bloomed like mushrooms from the water, and when Phelan rowed us close to one, I leaned toward him. My graceful motion had him instantly wary, and he stopped paddling, his eyes glinting with a dark warning to maintain my distance.

I ignored it, and I dared to touch his face, a fleeting caress that seemed to enchant him into stone.

"Thank you," I breathed. My hand slipped from his cheek and promptly shot a hole in the boat with a beam of magic. He startled as the water began to surge around our ankles.

I leapt to the nearest roof, struggling to find purchase in the thatch. I scrambled up to the apex of the roof and glanced back to see Phelan furiously trying to mend his boat, in vain. It was a moment from being completely submerged, and he glared at me.

"Your gratitude is noted, Miss Madigan," he said, and jumped onto the same roof as me.

I gave him a mock curtsy before I hurried down the other side, where Papa sat waiting for me. I settled into our boat and whispered, "Hurry, Papa."

My father paddled us away, and I glanced over my shoulder to see Phelan standing on the thatched roof, stranded. But I felt the bite of his gaze until we turned onto a different canal and he was finally lost from my sight.

Shuddering, I sat back and took a fortifying breath.

"I told you to *wait*, Clementine," my father growled.

"I know, and I'm sorry," I said, my attention straying to the challenge. "Have you seen Lennox?"

"He's in the water."

I looked over the edge of the boat, where serpents slithered just beneath the surface, and I saw the gleam of the key again. Drifting and taunting me to pursue it. A splash sounded behind me, and I turned to see Lennox cresting the water, slipping back into its domain, effortless as a fish. He swam alarmingly fast; he must have enchanted himself.

I stood in the boat as he passed by us, so swiftly not even the serpents could entangle him.

"Don't forget there's a cost to every charm, Clem," my father said, reading the anguish in my eyes.

"Yes, and we're about to lose this town, Papa." I watched as Lennox rose from the water again, to breathe before diving back beneath the surface. I remembered how it felt to nearly drown, how the water tried to sneak into me and weigh me down, and yet I couldn't bear to face this defeat. To have my home stolen from me by a magician like him.

I inhaled and spoke a long, twisted charm. Wild and spontaneous magic that lurked in my bones. I called upon the last of my reserves and watched the sadness overcome my father's face as gills blossomed in my neck and I struggled to breathe in the air, gasping.

I tumbled back into the water and filled myself with it, my gills flexing in relief. I found my second dagger on my belt and I took it in my hand, swimming and cutting through the serpents. I discovered that if I swam deep, where the cobblestones lurked like a riverbed, the snakes would not bother me, and so this was my path. It was dark and cold and quiet, but I could see the golden shine of the key up ahead. Lennox hovered near the surface, struggling with a patch of lily pads. He had charmed his feet into fins; that was why he was able to swim with such agility.

I neared the key, and my heart lifted as I anticipated ending this challenge. It had at last found its resting place on the street. I swam slow but steady, drawing in water, letting it wash through me, my hair streaming like a fiery pennant. I realized upon closer examination the key was a golden rock the size of my palm, wedged into the cobblestones, and I saw Lennox cut himself loose far above me. He noticed my presence then, and began a furious descent. I quickened my strokes, but my left leg was aching, the serpent's venom affecting how strongly I could kick.

I was reaching for the lambent stone when Lennox's fingers closed about it. He tugged, but the rock held fast, and he frantically worked to uproot it with his dagger. I knew his air was wearing thin—his face was mottled and I wondered if he was about to drown himself, all for pride. I wondered if I should interfere—if I should stab him—and the mere idea drummed an ache in my stomach.

So I waited. Waited for his lack of air to force him back to the surface, for him to abandon the key.

But his dagger found the root of the stone, and he worked it free from the ground. Instantly, the nightmare broke, and the flood began to drain into the hole the rock had left behind in the ground. I felt the water swirl around me, the pressure ease in my ears, my gills flutter in desperation. The serpents turned into silt, the lily pads into pollen.

It was over. I was vanquished.

And through the eddy of draining water, Lennox grinned at me.

7

"You dear, foolish, reckless girl," Imonie said to me, but there were tears in her eyes as she eased my head back beneath the water. I was sitting in the tub, my left leg hanging over the side so she could tend to the serpent bite. But my gills had yet to fade, and I couldn't breathe air. I was confined to the bath, where my gills would allow me a minute or two above the surface before they screamed for water.

There's a cost to every charm.

My father's words haunted me. Perhaps my gills would never fade. Perhaps I would be doomed to live the remainder of my life in a tub or a lake. I sank into the water and breathed it in, suddenly thankful that it muffled the sounds of the world. Sounds of Lennox speaking to Papa just beyond the closed door. Sounds of townspeople ringing the bell, distressed to hear that there was a new warden in Hereswith. Sounds of Imonie simultaneously scolding and praising me as she cried.

I had lost the town. Our home. And the guilt weighed heavily in my chest.

I remained beneath the surface, my heart broken. I felt as if I had been turned inside out of my own body, like I had been split open and I didn't know how to hold myself together. I was uncertain if it was due to the shock I was feeling, to acknowledge I had been defeated by Lennox, or if it was a side effect of my rash enchantment.

I knew a few fundamentals of *metamara* magic, which studied the transformations and adaptations of nature and objects. I knew enough to get me in trouble, and it made me think of my mother. Of what she would say to me if she saw me in this moment, half girl, half water creature.

Imonie's hands were gentle as she drew the poison from my wound with a salve, and when her ministrations were done, she left me alone. I remained in the water for another hour, until I felt the painful shift in my body. My gills closed, forcing me to sit up, to return to the air.

I coughed up the last bit of water. My skin was pruned as I carefully climbed out of the tub and dried off. I pulled the cork and watched the water swirl and drain, swirl and drain until the tub was empty.

I had hesitated. That was why I'd lost. I should have stabbed him. I shouldn't have waited for his air to run out, allowing him the chance to win. There was no one to blame but myself, and I longed to turn back time, to change my actions.

The mirror hanging above the washbasin drew my gaze, and I stood before it, as if I had forgotten my own face.

The gills had left behind scars in my neck. Three thin slashes on each side just beneath my jaw, catching the light like iridescent scales. I gently touched the scars, surprised by their tenderness. They would remind me of my loss, of my foolishness, and yet I didn't feel the urge to hide them.

I stepped into the dining room. Lennox was sitting at the table, papers spread out before him, spectacles perched on his nose. My father sat across from him, bleary eyed and still running a fever, drawing up the contract for the new warden. Phelan stood before the bookshelves, reading the illuminated spines and holding a cup of tea. Imonie was bustling in the kitchen, cooking away her distress. All four of them stopped their tasks and looked at me. I stood on the rug in a slant of morning sunlight, my black dress still wet from my long submersion, my hair a snarled, copper mess around my shoulders.

"Well met, Miss Clementine," Lennox said in a cheerful voice, holding up his glass of mulberry wine. "I must say you were a worthy opponent."

I said nothing, staring at him until his smirk eased and he returned his focus to the papers.

My father's gaze lingered on me the longest—he was noticing my new scars, how they gleamed every time I breathed—and he sighed as he resumed writing the document, his quill scratching over the paper. I walked past Phelan to the kitchen counter, where the teapot was still warm, and poured myself a cup. Imonie set down a pitcher of cream and the honeypot, as she knew my preferences, and I put far too much into my tea, stirring it around and around, my thoughts far away.

"How is your wound?"

I turned, startled to see Phelan was standing close to me. Imonie made a sound of dislike, but the magician didn't notice.

"I would say it's in the same condition as your boat, Mr. Vesper," I replied, and took a loud sip of tea, just to irritate him.

"Then it must be in shambles."

"An adequate word to describe it." I knew he was asking after my leg, but I spoke of the wound in my spirit.

He didn't glance away from me as I expected—it was rude to stare too long at someone in court, where he no doubt had grown up as a countess's son—and I wondered what he saw in me. I dropped my gaze first, unable to hold his uncanny stare.

"And when can we expect you to vacate this cottage, Mr. Madigan?" Lennox was saying.

"We'll be gone tomorrow," my father replied without hesitation.

I set my teacup down on the counter with a hard clunk. *Tomorrow?* The disbelief swelled within me, and I bit the inside of my cheek to hold back the torrent of words I wanted to spew.

"Excellent!" Lennox said. "I do believe this cottage will suit me very well, although there is that rather nice house on the hill. . . ."

"Yes, that's Mazarine Thimble's mansion." Papa's voice cracked with exhaustion. "It's her property and will most likely remain that way."

"Of course." Lennox's gaze drifted to the kitchen, where Imonie was banging pots in her fury. "And the housekeeper? Will she remain behind?"

"No," my father replied swiftly. "Imonie will be going with us.

If you want a cook or a housekeeper, you will have to find one on your own."

Imonie pretended she had not heard as she began to knead dough, but I felt the indignation for her. That this upstart would assume she would stay and work for him.

"And what of the dream tax?" Lennox asked. "How much does the town pay you for your services?"

"They pay us what they can, Mr. Lennox," I said, unable to remain silent a moment longer. "Sometimes with bread, sometimes with coin, sometimes nothing at all if their crop or craft has suffered a bad year."

"Nothing at all!" Incredulous, Lennox looked at my father, as if he was fervently hoping I was jesting. "And you still guard them from their nightmares, despite the fact they cannot even pay you a penny in gratitude?"

"We do," I said.

"Then how do you pay your dream tax to the duke?" Lennox asked, glancing between my father and me. "You *do* pay it, I hope?"

My father nodded. He looked tired, so weary. My heart ached.

"We pay what the duke requires," I said. And I thought of Mazarine and her trickle of coins, which had kept us afloat more times than I could count. "But this is a rural town, Mr. Lennox. This is not the pampered city life you know and are accustomed to. All of us work and pull our weight. Sometimes, a person cannot pay in coin, but we still record their nightmares and we still protect them. Now that you've been informed, you'll have to figure out a way to ensure the duke gets his taxes on time. And if you can't . . . then perhaps your mother can pay them for you."

"Mr. Madigan," Phelan said in a desperate tone, purposefully interrupting Lennox and me, sensing that we were about to strike up another duel. "Please don't feel as if you and Clementine and Imonie must rush away. You're welcome to stay here as long as you need."

"We'll be gone tomorrow," my father reiterated, and he set his glassy-eyed stare on me. "It would be a good idea to begin packing, Clem."

But where are we going to go?

I left my tea on the counter and ascended the stairs. Dwindle was curled up on my bed, purring, and I sat beside her, my hand stroking her calico fur.

Eventually, my damp gown drove me to the wardrobe. I shed the black silk and changed into a simple blue gown. I set to work packing my things, only to realize I had far too many books. I needed to give some of them away, and I began to make piles.

I was halfway through my endeavor when Papa stepped into the chamber, instantly casting a protective charm on the walls, the window, and the door. To keep our voices from being overheard.

"Make sure you pack everything, Clementine," he said. "Leave no trace of yourself behind in this house. No hair ribbon, no letters, no drawings. Not even an old pair of shoes."

I gaped up at my father. "You're worried. . . ."

"I'm not worried," he insisted. But I knew when he lied. His nostrils tended to flare when he spoke falsely. "But nor do I want to give anyone the chance to track where we go, or even summon us, if they were so bold to do so."

I tried to imagine Lennox taking an old ribbon of mine months from now and using it to cast the spell of summoning. It was a dangerous enchantment, one that would draw me into his presence whether I wanted to answer him or not. And I almost laughed at the absurdity until my father's scowl deepened.

"You need to take this seriously, Clem."

"I *am* taking this seriously!" I snapped, and indicated the scars on my neck. "I never wanted to leave this place. Our *home*, Papa!"

He flinched, as if I had struck him. At once, my temper faded.

"It's a great misfortune, and I'm sorry, daughter. I'm sorry I was not strong enough to help you last night."

I glanced away, unable to bear the sorrow in his eyes. My guilt flared again. If I had been craftier, bolder . . . I wouldn't have lost. "Where are we going?"

"I'm still considering our options. The most important thing at the moment is that you pack everything."

"I was planning to give some of my books away to the town girls. Could I still do that?"

His eyes flickered to the piles of books I had made on the floor. I read his mind: books were heavy and cumbersome to move with, even if one enchanted them into tiny charms.

"That would be fine," he replied. "So long as you erase your name on the cover and any notes you may have written in the margins and ensure none of your bookmarks are in the pages."

I nodded and watched him leave. And while I wanted to act

as if I was not rattled by his worry, I was. My hands shook as I went through the books I planned to donate, uttering a charm to vanish my handwriting. Because—*of course*—I was the sort of person who marked every book I owned. And as Papa knew well, I made my own bookmarks. I ended up recovering three of them, lost in the leaves of thick novels. By the end of my scouring, there were eleven volumes that I wanted to give to the Fielding girls.

I gathered the books into my arms and decided I would deliver them now.

The main level of the cottage was quiet. The Vesper brothers were gone, to my immense relief, and my father was in his own bedchamber, packing. Imonie was at the china cabinet, wrapping the porcelain in newspaper, but she didn't stop me when I slipped out the door into the warmth of late morning.

The last thing I desired was to be seen and stopped on the streets. I cast a simple *avertana* charm, one that would make me unnoticeable. And I walked the streets of Hereswith. Everyone was speaking of my father's displacement, because rumors traveled like wildfire here, and everyone had seen the Vesper brothers wandering about the evening before.

Most of the talk was hinged on disbelief and devastation, for my father was sincerely loved in this town. But there were a few conversations I heard, words that were hopeful for the new warden. My father was getting old, anyway. It was good to change magicians every now and then.

I reached the Fieldings' cottage.

With a deep sigh, I loosened my charm so I could be noticed

again, and was approaching the door, preparing to knock, when a sweet voice called my name from above.

"Miss Clem!"

I glanced up at the apple tree that flourished in the front yard. Elle was perched in its branches, harvesting the fruit, and I walked to stand among the roots, gazing up at her.

"Have you come to see my papa?" the girl asked as she began to descend the tree.

"No," I replied. "I've actually come to see you and your sisters."

"Me?" She dropped to the grass and set her basket of apples down. "What for?"

I extended the stack of books to her, watching as her eyes turned alight. "I fear that I'm leaving Hereswith, but I wanted to give these to you and your sisters before I departed. They were some of my favorite books when I was your age."

Her mouth hung agape as she took my books. I didn't realize I had accidentally put one of my art portfolios in the stack until she opened it and leaves of my most recent illustrations began to flutter, threatening to fly away on the wind.

"Oh!" I said, and reached for it. "Sorry. These need to stay with me."

Elle handed me the portfolio and I held it close to my chest as she continued to admire the books.

"Thank you, Miss Clem," she said in a reverent tone. As she hurried inside to share the news with her sisters, Spruce Fielding appeared on the threshold.

"I'm afraid we cannot pay you for the books."

"I don't want payment," I replied. "I give them freely to your daughters."

When Spruce merely stood there, blank with surprise, I bade him good day. I was striding to the gate when he hurried after me.

"Miss Clem! Wait a moment, please."

I tarried, wiping a smudge of charcoal from the cover of the portfolio. "Yes, Mr. Fielding?"

"We're very sorry to hear what happened last night," he said, and removed his cap, wringing it in his hands. "Your father is an excellent warden, someone we trusted. And we're sad to see both of you go."

"Thank you, Mr. Fielding."

"Must you leave? You can continue to reside here," he said. "In fact, we could build you a cottage on my lands, if you like."

This caught me by surprise. It only made my tears surge, and I at last realized why my father and I couldn't stay in Hereswith, why Papa wanted to leave so swiftly. "That's very kind of you, Mr. Fielding. But my father and I feel it's best to leave at once, so Mr. Vesper can begin to settle in and get to know all of you."

Spruce nodded, but he didn't look convinced. "I understand. But if you do change your mind . . . you and your father and Imonie will always have a home here."

The emotion welled in my throat. I smiled at him as I passed through the gate.

It took me a moment to cast my charm again, to go unnoticed as I walked through the heart of Hereswith, back through pockets of gossip and dismay and curiosity. I had just come upon the square when a strange, long scuff on the cobblestones caught my attention. It was a thin mark, as if caused by the tip of something sharp, and it led to a wagon parked not far from me.

I paused, chilled when I recalled Elle's nightmare. The knight had let the point of his sword drag over the stones. He had walked to the wagon where Elle had been hiding. Surely, this scuff mark was just a coincidence.

I crouched down to study it closer, rushing my fingers over the mark on the cobbles. I looked at the wagon, and I began to imagine perhaps the knight had been here last night, walking the streets and hidden beneath the water. But that would mean *two* different nightmares had descended last night—Archie's and Elle's—and that had never occurred. At least, not as far as I knew.

Before I could let that revelation unfold, someone tripped over me.

The impact knocked me down, and my charm of stealth broke as my portfolio went flying. Leaves of my drawings danced on the breeze, and I rushed to gather them before they were carried farther into the market. And through the cascade of parchment, I saw him kneeling on the cobblestones, also hurrying to gather my stray illustrations.

Phelan.

My face warmed when I saw him holding my drawings, these intimate pieces of my heart. He paused to study one, transfixed, and I snatched it from his hands.

He scowled, lips pursed as if he wanted to say something snide until he realized it was me and his expression softened. "Forgive me, Miss Madigan. I didn't see you."

I made no response but folded my now wrinkled papers back into my portfolio. When I continued to walk up the street, he rushed after me.

"May I walk with you?"

"I suppose," I said, and quickened my pace. He noticed and kept perfect stride with me, and all the people of Hereswith seemed to freeze, watching the two of us pass by.

"I know you must think very ill of my brother and me," Phelan began, slightly out of breath as the street took a steep turn. "But I do hope in time that you will come to understand why this happened."

His words infuriated me. I halted and spun. "I think I already understand, Mr. Vesper. You and your brother were raised wanting nothing. Two rich, spoiled brats of the aristocracy. And now that you are grown, you wanted a town to be warden of, so you rolled a die and landed on Hereswith. Quite a challenge, I might add, since it's rather far from your home and resides in the shadow of mountains. But I commend you both for your noble sense of duty and obligation, and while I don't think you will fit in well here, I hope I'm wrong, for the sake of the residents."

The shock in his eyes and the flush of his face were delicious to behold. I smiled as I continued on my way, thinking he would leave me alone. But he was far more stubborn than I anticipated and caught up to me again.

"I'll have you know, Miss Madigan, that I'm not staying in Hereswith."

"Oh, I see! So you assisted your brother in stealing the town and now you are abandoning it?"

"I have responsibilities elsewhere," he said in a near growl. As if I should care.

"Then don't let me keep you from them," I said, my father's cottage coming into view. Phelan relinquished me, coming to an abrupt halt in the street, and I walked the rest of the way home on my own.

But it felt like I was treading an endless nightmare, and it would end if only I could wake.

I didn't know where Papa planned to take Imonie and me, and the uncertainty gave me a stomachache as I waited in the yard, holding a mewling Dwindle in my arms. The wagon was parked at our gate, packed to the brim with boxes and crates and burlap sacks of our possessions. Most of the furniture remained behind in the cottage, as did the framed artwork and the endless pots of plants, all of which Papa used a scouring charm over, to ensure no trace of us remained. I had ensorcelled nearly everything from my room into one bag, using Mama's shrinking spell.

A crowd had gathered to see us off, most of them dear friends who had known me for half my life. Lilac Westin brought a bag of pastries, her eyes rimmed red. The Fieldings were there, the girls holding my books. And to my great shock, Mazarine. The disguised troll wore a modest dress of thick brocade and wielded an umbrella, to shield her skin and hair from the sunshine.

Papa was the last to emerge from our cottage. He carried the book of nightmares, and I watched as he delivered the tome to Lennox Vesper, who waited by a patch of daisies in the yard, Phelan at his side. My father gave him the book and the key to the cottage, and it was officially done and over. Papa was no longer warden of Hereswith, and we were homeless.

I buried my face in Dwindle's fur, to hide the tears that burned my eyes. I felt Imonie's hand on my shoulder, and her attempt to comfort me only made my emotions spin harder. I could feel the weeping in my chest, threatening to rise.

Oh gods, I thought. *Please don't let me cry here. Let me at least get out of sight of the Vespers.*

Despite my resolve, a sound slipped from me. The strangled sound of a girl trying to swallow a sob, and halfway succeeding.

Dwindle let out a disgruntled meow. I was squeezing her too hard, and when I lifted my face, my nose was running. A few tears had escaped, and I hurried to dash them away before anyone but Imonie could notice.

"And where will you be heading, Mr. Madigan?" Lennox was asking. He was a blurry shape at the corner of my eye, but I saw how he cradled the book of nightmares in an awkward stance. The weight of the book had caught him by surprise.

"Wherever the wind blows," Papa said.

He helped me and Imonie settle in the wagon bench before he climbed up himself. His hands trembled as they took the reins and he clucked to the horse, urging the gelding onward.

I wanted to look back at the cottage, at our friends, one last time, but I didn't. Because I feared I would break into hundreds of pieces if I did.

We didn't talk until eventide, each of us lost to our own thoughts until Papa drew the wagon off the road and we chose to camp in a copse of oak trees. Imonie built a fire and made a quick stew of wild onions, potatoes, and some summer sausage, and we gathered around the light and ate, our mood somber.

I had noticed the mountains were growing distant. My father was taking us east, and it made me feel lost. I wrapped a blanket around my shoulders as Dwindle curled up on my lap. And I looked for something I recognized, something to ground me. I found it on the dusky horizon, where the fortress in the clouds was carved into the mountaintop, so distant now I could hardly discern it. But it was a familiar sight and made me feel less adrift. Weary of the silence, I asked, "What do you think is up there? In the fortress?"

Imonie was sitting in the grass, knitting a shawl. "Nightmares. And the lost one."

"The lost one?" I echoed. It had been a long time since she had told me a mountain story, and she knew I was playing innocent in order to draw that tale out of her.

She was quiet for a moment, her focus seemingly on her knitting. But then she began to speak, her voice rich and vibrant.

"Over a hundred years ago, there was a woman who lived in the mountains, alone in a small house in the city of Ulla. In her younger years, she was a faithful lady-in-waiting for the duke's sister, but as she grew older, she preferred solitude, and she listened to the wind that blew in the morning and the evenings. Stories were wrapped within such gusts, and they kept her warm on the darkest of nights. She lacked for nothing and wanted nothing more.

"But a rap sounded on her door one summer midnight, when the moon was full and the wind was quiet and the air was warm. When she answered it, no one was there. No one, until she heard a wail and realized a large basket had been left on her stoop. And in the basket was not one baby but two.

"The woman had never cared for children. They were loud, messy, fragile, demanding. They were wholly dependent on their caregiver, and she did not want to be fastened to such responsibility. But nor could she be heartless and leave the babes on her porch.

"She brought them into her home. Two boys, perhaps only a month old. Ugly and floppy, and she did not know how to hold them. But hold them she did, and their weeping eased. She spoke to them, and they smiled at the sound of her voice. When they grew hungry, she filled a bottle with goat milk and fed them. For months, she sought their parents. For months, she tried to find a new home for them. But in the end, she chose to keep them with her.

"They were identical twins, she swiftly discovered as they grew. It was nigh impossible to tell them apart, and many days she confused them, until she came to learn their personalities. One was intelligent, drawn to books and quiet spaces, and the other was wild, adventurous, a boy who wanted to roam the mountains and drive stakes into rabbits. The quiet one she could raise, but her wild boy . . . the woman did not know how to tame such a heart, if such a heart could be tamed without breaking.

"For all their differences, they both held a vein of craftiness. This she learned when they began to play each other's roles. Her quiet boy would deceive her, acting as his wild brother to take his punishments. And the wild boy would act as his quiet twin, to avoid her wrath when he strayed too far.

"The woman had no choice but to send them both away to school in the city after a decade had passed. Let one become a warrior, she thought, and the other a scholar. And maybe when they grew into men, they would serve the duchy in mighty ways. But even if they did not, she would be proud of them, and she loved them each for their different strengths.

"Grow into men they did. They visited her often in the beginning, after their schooling was complete. Her quiet boy was devoted to his books and knowledge, and her wild one had fallen prey to love, wedding a beautiful girl of the summit. It was good in those days. And then her boys forgot her, distracted by the allures of life. A storm brewed on the horizon. The duke was a cruel ruler, oppressing his people. And it did not matter how much the woman prepared for it. The storm broke and with it the duchy, and her home, her land, was shadowed by the curse.

"She had no choice but to leave. All the people of the mountains . . . they could not stay there. The nights were treacherous, their dreams woven with terror. No one could step foot in the fortress, where the duke had been slain. In the pandemonium of leaving, she could not find her boys. *They are wise and shrewd*, she thought. She made it to the mountain doors, where the summit opens into a valley, and she waited for her boys there.

"Soon, they came. One passed over the threshold freely, into the grass. The other, however, could not. The mountain held him captive, and he could not leave its shadow. When the mountain doors began to close, the woman wept and rushed to her son who was bound to be lost to her, only to be held back by his twin. They watched the mountain doors close and seal, devouring brother and son. Those doors have not been open since, nor will they until the remaining wraiths—the heiress, the lady-in-waiting, the advisor, the guard, the master of coin, and the spymistress—all who once planned the duke's demise, return as one to break the curse."

I was silent, soaking in Imonie's tragic story. When she did not speak again, I realized she was done with her tale, and it left me hollow. I should have asked for a happier story, and I lay down in my bedroll, listening to the wind rake through the grass and the crickets chirp their starlit lullabies.

"Clem." Papa's voice caught my attention, and I turned to see he was holding a remedy vial out for me to take.

I reached for it, the glass cool against my palm, but I hesitated. "Do I still need to drink this now? Since we're no longer wardens?" That had been Papa's reasoning as to why I shouldn't dream at night. It would be difficult indeed to face my own nightmare in the streets of Hereswith. Dreams often revealed one's greatest vulnerability; dreams were doors that led into hearts and minds and souls and secrets.

"Best you do," my father replied, and I watched as he drank one himself before settling in for the night.

Even Imonie took a remedy. I followed suit, uncorking my vial and letting the bittersweet liquid rush over my tongue and coat my throat. A familiar taste, one I had been drinking every night since I could remember.

I lay down in the grass, my eyes growing heavy with exhaustion, and I looked to the mountains, now darker than night against the constellations. And I wondered what sort of things would haunt my sleep, if I ever gave my mind and heart the chance to dream.

Travel was miserably slow.

My father was in no hurry, Dwindle meowed the entire time, and our horse and wagon took a plodding pace as we traveled across the Bardyllis Duchy. But all too soon, the mountains faded away and we were surrounded by crop fields still golden with summer heat, pine forests, and rings of small villages reminiscent to Hereswith. We passed over the Starling River and I noticed the shift.

The dirt roads became cobbled, the forests surrendered to chains of houses, the quiet fragrance of the country gave way to the sounds and smoke and smells of habitation. I could see the haze of the capital in the distance, the sprawling and overwhelming city of Endellion, the seat of the duke's sovereignty, and I suddenly knew exactly where my father was taking us.

I turned to look at him, and his profile was set like granite, his eyes carefully avoiding mine.

He was taking us to my mother.

9

My mother's town house was in the northern quadrant of the city, in sight of the river that flowed through the capital like a silver vein. The last time I had been here to visit her was three years ago, when I was fourteen, and I had longed for Hereswith the entire summer I had spent with her. Longed for the mountains and the meadows and the slower pace of a country town. My mother had sensed the homesickness within me, and I think that was why she failed to invite me the following summer, or the following. We had gradually grown apart when I had chosen to study my father's way of magic instead of hers.

I felt a twinge of apprehension when I approached her door, and I could only imagine how my father was feeling as he waited in the wagon with Imonie, the afternoon beginning to melt into dusk. I rang the bell, cleared my throat, and smoothed the tangles from my hair, to no avail; I looked like a weary, dust-ridden, and windblown vagabond when my mother opened the door.

Her shock was tangible. Her eyes widened when she realized it was me standing at the threshold, and her expression softened.

"Clementine?"

"Hello, Mama," I greeted her with a hesitant smile. I was surprised by how much silver now laced her black hair.

"Where's your father?" she asked, her voice sharp with displeasure. But she gave me no time to reply; she glanced over my shoulder to see Papa sitting like a defeated warrior on the wagon bench. "Ambrose? Ambrose, come inside. You look weary. And Imonie. Come, the two of you."

My father eased down from the wagon, assisting Imonie. They began to gather boxes, which my mother rushed to assist with her magic, charming our possessions to glide themselves in through the front door to the parlor of her town house. After that, Papa insisted on taking the horse to the closest public stable, a block away.

I think he was avoiding the inevitable, which was having to tell my mother we had lost the town and currently had nowhere to go.

And so I did. While he was tending to the horse, I sat in my mother's opulent den that smelled of gardenias and patchouli. Dwindle rubbed up against my legs as I took the cup of tea Mama offered me, and I told her everything. Imonie sat beside me, adding a snort here and there in agreement, particularly when I relayed the arrival of the two magicians.

"The Countess of Amarys's sons?" Mama echoed, and her eyes slid to Imonie's. The two women seemed to hold a private conversation, which irked me.

I paused, uncertain. "You know of them?"

"Doesn't everyone in Endellion," she replied carefully. I couldn't judge her opinion of them, not like I could with Papa. "Her lands lie south of here, but the countess primarily resides in the city, where she has great influence. Her husband, the count, passed away years ago, but since then she has become a close confidant of the duke, in fact."

That only made my indignation flare. Why, then, would Lennox need to uproot my father and me? Why Hereswith, when he could have chosen any town, any village, any slice of the city to be warden of?

"So the sons challenged you and your father," my mother prompted.

I nodded and continued with the doomed tale, and my mother listened, her gaze resting on me and the scars that gleamed at my neck. She was quiet when I was done, and her silence made me feel uncomfortable. As if she was weighing what she wanted to do with us and our predicament.

"Will you let me and Papa and Imonie stay here for a little while? Just until we can find new work in the city," I asked, because I didn't know if she lived alone. If she had a lover or a companion, even though her house felt empty and quiet, full of golden trim that glittered in the shadows.

"Of course, Clementine," she replied, a lilt of offense in her tone, as if I were being absurd to assume otherwise. "It'll be like old times."

It would not be like old times, and we all knew it.

Papa arrived, letting himself in the front door. His footsteps were heavy as he approached, and he stood awkwardly on the threshold of the den, trying not to look at my mother. She rose from her settee, elegant in her lavender gown, her black hair swept back in a loose chignon.

"You haven't aged a day, Ambrose," she said to him.

Papa at last looked at her, unguarded, and I thought I saw regret in his eyes. They had parted ways seven years ago. I remembered how they had reached a point when all they did was bicker and argue. They held different ideologies about magic and the intent behind spells. My mother studied *metamara* and used its whimsy on the stage, captivating audiences as she transformed one thing into another. She believed magic should be fun and entertaining, and my father, with his rigid *avertana* opinions, believed magic should only be used in logical, practical ways. As a means to guard and defend others.

"Same to you, Sigourney," he said. "If Clem and Imonie can reside with you, I'll find lodgings elsewhere."

"Don't be ridiculous," my mother replied. "I live here alone, and this house has far too many empty rooms. Stay here for now."

He nodded but still seemed frozen on the threshold.

I suddenly felt exhausted by the weight of everything—worry as to where we would go, what we would do now, and the sheer amount of homesickness that pinched my lungs every time I drew a deep breath.

That first night in my mother's town house, I lay in bed and relived my new moon battle with Lennox and Phelan, over and over in the dark.

And I finally let myself cry.

Imonie merged into city life with ease, tending to the house and cooking for us. But my father and I were stricken and lost, perusing the classified column of the daily paper for possible work. There were no openings for a dream warden in the city, which seemed unbelievable to me, given how vast Endellion was. So many people, so many nightmares, so many streets. But I swiftly learned that territory was divided into small segments, and there were far too many magicians and not enough positions. A dream warden was a highly contested profession, my mother said when she saw both Papa and I were helplessly searching the ads.

"We could challenge someone this upcoming new moon," I said to him after dinner one night, when he and I sat alone by the fire. "We could win new territory here in the city."

My father studied the dance of the flames. "No, Clem. I won't do what the Vespers did to us."

And I understood why, yet I wanted to regain my position. I needed to be doing something here, for fear I might dissolve into dust.

"Then why don't we return to Hereswith and challenge Lennox? We would still have the advantage, Papa. We know the nightmares." But even as I said it, the words sounded unfeasible, desperate. Dishonorable. I couldn't envision my father lowering himself like that, even if I could—somewhat—see it of myself.

"I think it's time to put away nightmares and dreams and new moons," he said, to my dismay. When he looked at me, I saw that he had fully accepted defeat, that he was done as warden. "We're here now. There are many new avenues to take in the city. Let's put the past behind us and start a new life."

"A life without magic?" I asked, and I could scarcely comprehend it. That he would want to let all his skill and diligence go to waste, until his spells sank into the darkest place of memory, rusted from disuse.

"Perhaps it would be best, Clem."

I buried my opinions, but I was angry. At him, at the Vespers. At myself for losing a challenge I should have easily triumphed.

And the anger smoldered in me like a star.

"Come, you need a walk," Imonie said to me a week later. "I'm heading to the bakery and could use the company."

I hadn't left my mother's house in days, so I set aside my book and laced my boots, following her out the front door.

It was a cloudy, somber day. There was no wind, and the air sat heavy in the streets, stale and warm, even with October's approach. I was still adjusting to the noise, for it seemed like the city never slept, and I tried to find comfort in the bustle of carriages, buggies, and people hurrying on errands, but I only felt more isolated and out of place.

Imonie and I took a side street. We had been walking for nearly half an hour and had already passed two bakeries.

"Are you trying to weary me with a long walk?" I drawled.

"You know I'm picky about bakers," she replied tersely, and it only made me think of Lilac Westin in Hereswith and her renowned cinnamon rolls.

The street spilled us out into a wide thoroughfare. Thin rays of sunlight had pierced the overcast sky by the time Imonie found a bakery to her liking. I had spotted an artist's supply shop across the street, and I planned to meet back up with her after a moment of my own perusing.

A silver bell rang when I entered. At once, I was transported by the shelves of paper, sketchbooks, and canvases, by row after row of paint tins and brushes and bottles of linseed oil. Overwhelmed, I took my time admiring everything until a girl my age with curly brown hair appeared behind the sales counter.

"Can I help you find anything?"

"No, no I'm just browsing," I replied.

"Do you paint?"

"I draw."

"Ah, lovely! You can find those supplies in the next aisle over."

I thanked her and decided I should keep to what I knew best, and that was charcoal and pastels. But perhaps one day I would be brave enough to buy some paint, and a brush or two.

Eventually, I settled on a new sketchbook, and I made my way to the sales counter, where the girl was perched on a stool, reading a poetry book. I was reaching for my coin purse when the doorbell chimed and the girl's attention shifted.

"Lady Raven," she said, sliding off her stool to curtsy. "I have your order ready."

I turned to see a woman of the court, dressed in a dark silk gown. She looked to be my mother's age, with a few wrinkles catching the corners of her eyes, and her blond hair was swept up in a chignon, a net of diamonds holding it in place. Her lips were painted bloodred, and they were pursed, as if she did not smile often.

She approached the counter, her heels clicking on the floor as she rudely cut in front of me. She waited, tapping her fingers as the shopgirl set out a bundle of burlap. Lady Raven proceeded to untie it, her hands hidden beneath two lacy gloves, and she closely examined each item. Every brush tip, every tin of paint.

I glanced at the shopgirl, who had gone pale.

"It's everything you asked for, Lady Raven. Just as you prefer."

The lady finished her examinations and knotted the burlap. "Yes, everything looks acceptable. Thank you, Blythe." Lady Raven turned to depart with her order, and that was when she finally took note of me.

I stood, stark and silent, as her cold gaze swept over me. She studied my wild hair, the features of my face. And then she frowned and said, "You look familiar. Have we met before?"

"No, lady," I said, but my palms had become slick.

"Mm." She lost interest in me and departed the shop.

When I turned to the girl once more, setting my sketchbook on the counter to purchase, Blythe released a tremulous breath.

"I apologize for that. She's one of our loyal customers, and my father told me to always give her precedence when she steps into the shop."

"It's all right," I said. "I'm Clem, by the way."

"Blythe. Will I see you again here soon, Clem?" She handed me the sketchbook as I paid her for it.

"Most likely." I smiled and started to leave, but I smelled a trace of Lady Raven's perfume in the shop, roses and lavender, and it reminded me . . . "By the way, who was she?"

Blythe's eyes widened, as if I should have known. "Why, that was Lady Raven Vesper. The Countess of Amarys."

10

"Perhaps you could take a few art classes," Imonie suggested as she poured me a cup of tea the following morning.

"Where?" I asked, sitting at the table. An art class was enticing, albeit scary to contemplate, as I had never been instructed before.

"The university, perhaps?"

The thought of attending a school full of strangers made my stomach knot. "Maybe."

"Well, you need to find *something* to keep you occupied, Clem. Perhaps taking a class here or there might help you adjust, make some new friends."

I sighed, knowing she was right. Papa had already left for his new employment, working in the mines. A laborious task as far from magic as he could find. And my mother was still asleep, but I felt restless, aching for something. *The mountains,* I thought, *and home.* I longed for my life before the Vespers had stepped within it, and I wearily reached for the honey jar. I was about to melt a spoonful of it in my tea when the newspaper caught my eye.

Papa had been reading it, and there was a smudge of jam on the headline.

I reached across the table to take it and began leafing through the classified column.

Wanted—a caretaker for an elderly solicitor.
Wanted—a tutor in science and literature, for a young noblewoman.
Wanted—a dancer for the Disillusioned Tavern.

I turned the page, my heart heavy with discouragement until I saw the warden notices. Suddenly my hands were trembling, and my eyes raced across the entries.

Wanted—a warden partner for Lidia M. Lirrey, with the territory of 19 South Elm Street to 25 Reverie West. Experienced magicians only. Contact Ms. Lirrey at the Society as soon as possible.
Wanted—a warden partner for Phelan Vesper, with the territory of 1 Auberon Street to 36 Yewborne Street. All magicians are welcome to audition, and interviews will be held from eight o'clock in the morning until noontide at the Luminous Society Museum in Old Village, on Wednesday next. Contact Mr. Vesper for more details.

I felt heat rise in my face and I read it again, just to be certain it was the right Phelan. The pompous, impolite, selfish, tragically handsome Phelan. The aristocrat who had stolen my home and disgraced me. Bumping into his haughty mother the day before at the art shop had only roused the worst of my feelings. Toward him, toward Lennox. Toward a family that felt as if they could take whatever they desired and suffer no consequences for it.

My anger burned away to cold guilt for losing Hereswith. And then an idea came to mind.

I dropped the newspaper into the plate of eggs and cheese that Imonie had just set on the table. She was already staring at me with a cocked brow.

"I don't like that gleam in your eyes, Clem."

"Imonie," I said, and my mind reeled with possibilities. I could feel my magic wake, like embers being stirred back to life, and I grinned a slow, sharp smile. "Imonie . . . I have an idea. And I need your help."

If she had known what I truly planned to do, Imonie would have never assisted me. But I saw the longing for the mountains in her every time she glanced out the window and viewed nothing but brick walls, chimneys, and wrought-iron gates, and we crafted a plan. She had some estranged family in the city of Marksworth, and she asked my parents for a week's worth of vacation, to go and visit them in the neighboring province.

I made my case to accompany her, and my parents relented after they argued about me leaving the city. Papa said no, my mother said yes, and she thankfully won that spar.

Imonie and I bought a passage on a stagecoach, something that would fly along the roads of Azenor, but instead of taking us north to Marksworth, it took us west to Hereswith. Time was the most vital thread of the plan; I had only a week to get to Hereswith and back before Phelan held interviews for a partner.

"I wish you would tell me what you plan, Clementine," Imonie grunted as the coach jostled us back and forth.

I shifted my satchel of art supplies on my lap. "You'll know soon, Imonie."

"Your plan doesn't have anything to do with that Lennox Vesper, does it?"

"No. He won't even know we are in Hereswith. And we'll be back in Endellion on Tuesday, if everything goes smoothly."

"I'm not going to like this, am I?" She narrowed her eyes.

"I honestly don't know what you'll think, but I ask you to trust me."

She was quiet after that, watching the land pass by in a blur. We reached Hereswith in only three days. I had to pay the driver extra to let us disembark before we reached town, and then Imonie and I carried our satchels and walked through the valley into the forest that crowned Hereswith. Evening was falling, and the air was cool and sweet with the promise of autumn, the mountain wind rushing to greet us among the pines.

Imonie was savoring the fragrance, the gentle sway of the trees, until her nostrils flared and she stopped upright.

"Clementine."

I stopped to look at her in the starlight. She must have smelled it on the wind, the place I was guiding her. "Don't worry, Imonie."

"Whatever you plan to do upon coming here . . . you should change your mind. This is reckless, dangerous. What would your parents think if they knew?"

I didn't know what they would think about my decision, what they would do once they discovered what I had done. The uncertainty churned my stomach, but I had lost too much and come too far to turn around as a coward.

"I'm not changing my mind. I need you to wait here for me. I'll return shortly."

She didn't like that. But she heeded me, settling down on a log with the wind for company, and I continued to weave through the woods.

Soon, the pines grew sparse and I could see the lights of Hereswith, shining like fallen stars. I arrived at the mansion's backyard, a verdant garden meticulously maintained by one of the town boys, and I walked the gravel path to the back door.

My heart was hummingbird swift within me, and a tremor shook my bones as I arrived on the porch, as I lifted my hand.

I had a piercing moment of doubt. But I saw myself and who I wanted to become, and my confidence returned, limning my resolve.

I knocked on Mazarine's door.

She was exactly where I knew she would be—sitting on a plush divan in her library with the curtains drawn, candlesticks burning and dripping wax onto the floor. She was dressed in black velvet with an amethyst hanging at her throat, and she smiled when she saw me enter the chamber.

"Clementine Madigan," she greeted me. "I did not expect to see you again so soon. Although defeat does not suit you."

I wondered if anger had grown a film over my eyes, something I could not blink away, and I suddenly felt a sting of vulnerability. Her comment unsteadied me for a breath.

"I have a question for you, Ms. Thimble," I said, finding my courage once more. "I seek your knowledge."

"Do you? Sit and tell me what knowledge you hunger for."

I sat in my usual chair, the one where I had drawn her human face countless times. I kept my art satchel on my lap, feeling safer with something between us.

"What do you seek, child?" the troll whispered to me in a soft, enticing tone.

I studied her guise boldly. It was so skillfully rendered; she looked every bit of human as I was. Only the mirror had given her away. Only her reflection had betrayed her.

"The magic of disguise you're wearing," I began, and my heart was beating again, so fast it turned my voice into a wisp. "How did you weave it? How did you cast it? Is it *metamara* magic?"

Mazarine's grin widened. "And you desire to know this why?"

"Because I want to cast it on myself."

"Defeat does not suit you, and yet you think deceit would, Clementine?"

Her words provoked me, but my silence only amused her more. She leaned closer to me, her amethyst necklace swinging with her languid movements.

"You want revenge, young one?"

"I want what is mine," I said. "I want to regain what was stolen from me." And I had no doubt that one day I would win back Hereswith and call it home again. But I needed to bring the Vesper family to their knees in order to do so.

"And you believe disguising yourself will enable you to attain such things?"

"Yes."

She sat back, but she was reveling in my answers. "Do you know where I was born? I come from the mountains, from a duchy you can only imagine despite the fact that you lived for so long in its shadow. The magic I wear is not something you have ever encountered here, Clementine. It is old, ancient. I created this enchantment of disguise long before the cruel duke was assassinated."

I had always wondered how old she was. To know she had been alive before the Seren Duchy fell apart informed me that she was well over a hundred years in age, and I shivered. She had lived in an era that was nothing but legends now, and I sought to rectify it. Perhaps trolls had longer life spans than humans. But even as I tried to convince myself . . . something didn't feel quite right, as if time had turned sour in the room. As if Mazarine had stopped the hours from touching her, somehow.

"My magic is very dangerous, and it will require a great cost," she continued. "And I do not know if a human girl is strong enough to bear such a price."

She's trying to frighten me, I thought. *She's testing my mettle. Don't back down, don't be afraid. . . .*

"Then I suppose there is only one way to discover if your words are truth, Mazarine," I said.

"Perhaps. But I also do not give my knowledge and magic away freely," she countered, lacing her long, gnarled fingers together. "And I do not think you have enough gold or bone marrow to satisfy me."

"No, I don't," I agreed, choosing not to dwell on the bone marrow part. "But there *is* something I have that I think you will want."

She waited, watching as I opened my leather satchel. I withdrew a fresh sheet of parchment, a stick of charcoal, and she laughed.

"You have drawn me so many times, Clementine. Why would I want another portrait?"

"I have drawn you in *disguise*, Mazarine of the Mountains. This time, I will draw your true face."

Her humor melted, replaced by longing and the glitter of vanity. I had her, and I concealed my smugness as I continued to hold up the paper, waiting to be marked.

"But then again . . . perhaps you don't want any evidence of your true nature on paper," I said, and began to pack my supplies away.

"Wait, Clementine."

I paused, and she fought a war within herself.

"The portrait of my true face will be enough for payment," she eventually said. "But now the question I must ask is if *you* are willing to pay the cost of my disguise."

"Tell me the cost, then."

She poured a glass of wine. "I will take half of your heart and turn it into stone. It will divide you, and you will turn colder. Because half of who you once were will be no more, you will need to surrender half of something you love to hold the spell. Your art or your magic, most likely, since those are two things that have always been with you, growing alongside you year by year." She took a sip of her wine, but her gaze never left mine. "So what will you choose to give up, Clementine Madigan? Your art or your magic?"

I didn't want to relinquish either one.

For the troll was right: magic and art had been with me always. My two constants, my two greatest achievements. Both light and fire in my imagination, growing year by year alongside me, deepening and flourishing even in the hardest moments of life. And my dream of mastering *deviah* magic, when my magic and my art would coincide as one beneath my prowess, slowly began to die.

"My art," I whispered. "I will give up my art."

Mazarine nodded, but she wasn't surprised. She had known my decision and my weakness, as I had known hers.

"Then let it be done," Mazarine said, and rose from the divan. "Come and draw my portrait, and I will grant you my magic, a disguise of your choosing."

I still had one more burning question to ask her, but I held it on my tongue as I followed her to the mirror. She stood before the glass and I brought out my board and clipped the paper to it, sitting close enough so that I had a clear view of her reflection.

The sight of her was chilling.

Terrifying and magnificent—the elements of a nightmare. I began to draw her true face. I soaked in the wild silver of her hair and the traces of forest that grew within it, the rocky planes of her face, the sharp crookedness of her bloodstained teeth, the shining slant of her horns, the unquenchable pools of her eyes. She was fierce and terrible and yet wholly tame in that moment as I strove to bring her to life on paper.

My hand was aching when I was finished. I stood and unclipped the parchment and set it into her waiting palms. Mazarine's delight was nearly overpowering as she studied herself.

She said nothing, but her eyes were like dew, and she eventually looked at me again. She reached out and brushed my cheek with her cold knuckles.

"Wait here," she said. "I need to fetch a few things for your disguise."

I nodded, my voice hung in my throat, and I watched her depart the room. Thankful for the time alone, I resumed my seat and procured a new sheet of parchment and a fresh stick of charcoal.

I began to draw my final piece of art.

I designed my disguise, how I wanted to appear after Mazarine took half my heart away. An unexceptional face, an ordinary girl who would not garner a second look on the street. A few freckles, because I liked them, and bold brows because I had always wanted that in my own face. But the rest was plain. I traded my wild copper hair for sleek, long tresses the color of summer soil. A medium-brown shade that was rather dull indoors but boasted a hint of gold in the sunlight. No more gill scars in my neck or dimples in my cheeks. My eyes molted their dark brown for a shade of hazel. I gave up two inches of my height. The square cut of my jaw was narrower, and my skin would retain its pale shade.

I finished my sketch long before Mazarine returned. I was exhausted, so I closed my eyes and leaned my head back, resting until I heard the doors groan.

I rose to meet her.

At once, I was overcome by the stench. She was holding a goblet of something foul smelling, a cloudy liquid that made my stomach roil. I didn't want to know what she had cooked and blended to make it.

She seemed unperturbed by the smell, interested by the sketches I had made.

"Ah, your disguise," she said, admiring them. "Although I must say I am surprised."

"Why is that?" I asked, breathing through my mouth.

"I thought you would want to enhance your beauty," she said, arching her brow. "Most of your kind chase after such things. They want an attractive glamour, something to draw the eye and admiration to them. But not you."

"No," I whispered.

I wanted to be unremarkable upon appearance. I wanted to be underestimated, overlooked, on the verge of being forgotten. I wanted a trustworthy face that inspired friendship, a face that could draw out a secret. A face that one would never assume hid something vengeful beneath it.

It was time to speak my burning question. One forged from my greatest fear.

"How long will this magic of disguise last?"

"The longevity of this spell depends on you, mortal girl,"

Mazarine replied. "On how well you guard the stone half of your heart. Be vigilant and your disguise will last unto death. But should the stone within you crack . . . the rest will soon crumble, little by little, until your disguise falls away."

I dwelled on that for a moment. "But you said this enchantment will make me colder. So the chances of me cracking anytime soon are slim."

"It will make you colder. But even the deepest of ice eventually gives way to fire, Clementine."

Her answer satisfied me, and I nodded. I wasn't worried about my disguise failing me anytime soon.

"Although do keep in mind," the troll added, "mirrors are your greatest enemy. They will not lie for you, and your true reflection will always shine brightly upon them."

"Yes, I will be careful in their presence," I whispered.

A quiet moment pulsed between us. Mazarine extended the goblet, waiting for me to accept and drink.

My mouth went dry as I took hold of the cup. She murmured an incantation, one that was unfamiliar to me, a guttural language.

The room was suddenly too warm. My heart was fighting vibrantly in my chest, hammering against my bones. The pain of it breaking was harrowing, and I gasped, falling to my knees.

It felt like I was drowning again.

It felt like I was being cloven by an axe.

I couldn't breathe, and tears were streaming down my cheeks, but through the haze of my anguish, I saw Mazarine clearly. Her face was stark and amused as she held the rim of the goblet to my lips.

"You must take three swallows, Clementine."

I took the first, forced it down like the bittersweet remedies I had drunk all my life.

I took the second, and my heart was an instrument being strummed one final time. The melody trembled through me, a sorrowful ballad that echoed through every bend and corner of me. One that begged me to reconsider.

I took the third swallow, and the pain bloomed unbearable in my chest. I felt heavy, as if I had been filled with molten gold. I was both burning and freezing, and I quivered.

A moan escaped me.

The pain was too great, too bright.

I could not withstand it, and I surrendered to the embrace of darkness.

11

I woke to something tickling my face. It felt like cold dirt was on my skin, on my chest, weighing me down.

Annoyed, I began to lift my hand and brush it away, but my limbs were heavy, prickling with pins and needles.

My eyes fluttered open, but there was a film over them, a transparent material that moved when I breathed. *I should be panicking*, I thought. *I should be alarmed.* But my heart seemed unmoved, beating a steady pulse, and I calmly lifted my hands from the dirt and began to tear away the gossamer that was layered around my face.

I was lying in the forest. Moss, dirt, pine straw, and twigs clung to my half-buried body. I rose from the earth and stood shakily on my feet, brushing my clothes clean.

It took me a moment to remember what had happened. To recognize where I was.

I could see a glimpse of Mazarine's mansion through the pines. My leather art satchel was at my feet. I lifted my hands, studying them.

They trembled, but looked no different.

I noticed my hair. Long, sleek, and brown, flowing down my shoulders. I wrapped a tendril around my fingers, marveling at the sheen of gold that lurked within the threads when the sun touched it.

I rushed my hands over my face, felt the slope of it, the thick brows I had created, the thin lips. Then my neck, where the gill scars were gone.

I laughed, a raspy sound, and I wondered . . . how long had I been lying here? Sleeping, transforming in the shadows of the pines?

I quickly knelt by my satchel and opened the buckles. I sifted through the leaves of paper and found the sketch of my disguise. I would keep it, to remember what I now looked like, since a mirror would be of no help to me. I rolled up the drawing and tucked it into the pocket of my skirt, and then I buried my satchel. The art supplies were worthless to me now.

I walked through the quiet light of the forest, searching for Imonie.

She was where I had left her, although she was pacing, frantic. I stood between two trees and watched her for a moment, her distress so keen that she had not heard my approach. She was muttering a prayer, wringing her apron in her hands.

"I will *kill* that child," she said. "I will kill her whenever she returns to me."

"Imonie," I said, my voice deep and scratchy and yet still my own. I would have to remember to disguise it later, when I saw Phelan again.

Imonie startled and whirled, yanking a slender dagger from her belt. I didn't know she even owned a weapon, and the steel glinted in the light as she glared at me.

"Who are you?" she snarled, and I was briefly taken aback by her tone.

"Imonie," I said, and took a step closer to her. "Imonie, it's me."

She recognized my voice. Her mouth fell open. The knife tumbled from her grip. She suddenly looked grieved, like she wanted to weep.

"Clementine?"

I didn't respond, but I was satisfied. If the woman who had raised me had failed to identify me, then no one would.

The mountain wind rushed through the pines, tangling my hair.

And I smiled.

PART 2

Heart of Stone

12

I stood on the marble steps of the Luminous Society Museum, staring at the elegant colonnade. It was a quarter till noontide, and the sun was high in the cloudless sky above me. I had just returned to Endellion, and I was wearing my black-and-white striped skirt, my white chemise, my velvet bodice. The traditional clothes I once wore on new moon nights, when I had fought beside my father in the streets. It felt right to wear my old armor in this moment, even if the fit was slightly off now and the style was five years out of fashion by city standards.

I ascended the stairs to the heavy wooden doors, knowing I was almost out of time.

I had sent Imonie on to my mother's town house. She was still upset by my disguise, and I made her swear not to say a word to my parents. The confrontation would soon come, but I would think about it later.

The museum greeted me with a wash of cool, musty air. My boots clicked on the floor as I walked to the receptionist, a young magician decked out in a top hat and a brown jacket with a daisy tucked into one of the buttonholes.

"I'm here to be interviewed by Phelan Vesper," I said.

"You just missed him," the receptionist replied, frowning down at the schedule spread before him. "He finished early for the day."

"Did Mr. Vesper find a suitable partner, then?"

"On the contrary. He was woefully unimpressed."

I wasn't surprised to hear this. I remembered the way Phelan had first regarded me in the street of Hereswith, when he had narrowly avoided becoming Mazarine's dinner. He had been underwhelmed by me, or so he had appeared to be. I had spent many hours thinking about how I would snare his attention in this interview, hours I had spent jostled in the stagecoach, suffering Imonie's glares. And I knew his respect for me had not sparked until I had sunk his boat during the new moon challenge.

"Will you call him back?" I asked the receptionist. "The ad said he would be conducting interviews until noontide. And I'm here with minutes to spare. I think he will want to see me."

"Well . . . I suppose I can send word to him. Can you pay for a runner?"

I procured a silver half coin from my purse. The receptionist wrote a hasty message on a slip of parchment and hailed a messenger boy from the streets.

"It might be a while," he said, motioning for me to follow. "You can wait in the gallery." He led me down a corridor into a spacious room with a sad echo.

The gallery was empty save for a table and a chair set in the center of the chamber. The floors were checkered, and the walls were crowded with framed artwork. I stood in awe, craning my neck to study the paintings on the highest row. An unexpected pain shook me. I fell prey to longing for what I had surrendered.

I reached out to trace a gilded frame. My talent was gone, and I felt the aching pit of its absence. I gave myself a moment to experience the pang of regret, to study the beautiful muses of the paintings that surrounded me, whispering their stories in rich oil and sweetened shadows and careful brushstrokes. Paintings of monsters and magicians of old, of creatures and places and landscapes that appeared so vibrant I longed to step within them.

This regret would consume me if I wasn't mindful of its sharp edge. It would chip at the stone within my chest, and so I buried the feeling beneath the ice of my intention and stood in a patch of sunlight, waiting for Phelan to arrive.

It seemed like I waited an hour for him.

At last, I could hear sounds in the corridor, just beyond the gallery. Two sets of boots approached, and one belonged to him. I reached out with my magic, to catch the low conversation in the hallway.

"Who is this person?" Phelan was asking. "Do I know her?"

"I'm not sure, Mr. Vesper," the receptionist stammered. "I've never seen her before. Forgive me, I didn't think to ask for her name."

"But you're certain she's a magician?"

"Yes, sir. She cast no shadow. I *did* make sure to check that."

"Well, I hope she proves me wrong. I fear my expectations are rather low after this morning."

The gallery door opened. I stood like a statue, my breath suspended as Phelan stepped into the chamber.

He was dressed in a black jacket with coattails and a matching top hat, a pheasant feather tucked within its band. His waistcoat was crimson, embroidered with golden flowers, and his boots were spit polished, reaching to his knees. There was no rapier sheathed at his belt this time; the only thing he carried was a book. His dark hair was captured by a ribbon at the nape of his neck.

He took two steps into the chamber and then stopped, his gaze finding me at once.

I felt a bead of perspiration trace down the curve of my back. Why was he looking at me like that? I wondered if he saw through my guise, if he knew it was me. Although how could he? Not even Imonie had recognized me.

"Mr. Vesper?" I asked, pitching my voice deep.

"Yes. Forgive me, I thought . . . I thought you were someone else for a moment." He gave me a disappointed close-lipped smile and walked to the table and chair. The receptionist hurried to place an inkstand on the desk before departing the chamber, and Phelan sat and opened the book, taking a quill within his hand.

"Do you have any experience? Have you ever fought on a new moon before?" he asked, marking a new entry on the page.

"No, I haven't," I lied. "But I've always wanted to be a dream warden."

"Very well," he said, and leaned back in the chair, looking at me again. Dust motes spun in the air between us. "Prove to me that you would be my perfect accompaniment."

I had expected more questions from him. His lack of them was telling—he didn't expect me to last two minutes into this interview. He found me unremarkable, underwhelming, a face that melted into all the others he had beheld that morning.

I turned to hide the emotion that flickered through me. I was fulfilling the very role I wanted, and yet Phelan irritated me so greatly that I wondered how I would be able to work alongside him. How long would it take me to usher his family's downfall?

I would need to enact a stellar performance, and I thought about all the things I had learned from my mother, who flourished on the stage with *metamara* spells. Once, I had thought her tricks simple and harmless, mere whimsies to delight a crowd. She turned handkerchiefs into doves, pennies into fireflies, a sapphire bracelet into falling rain. She made it look effortless, and I stopped before a painting of ravens perched in a persimmon tree.

I suddenly knew what I wanted to do, my *avertana* magic yearning for a spar. I took what I knew best of both threads of magic, and I called the birds to me, coaxed them from the canvas into our realm. They emerged with a thunderous flap of wings, hovering around me like a storm until I whispered Phelan's name and they dove to him.

Phelan's eyes widened. He rose in haste, the chair flipping over behind him, and the ravens swarmed him, clawing at his jacket, his hair, his face. I heard him utter a curse of surprise, and I watched as he winced and outstretched his hand, cutting through wings and turning the ravens into feathers. They drifted to the floor in sad spirals.

I had already moved on to my next painting, one that boasted a knight in plated armor, wielding a great sword. I briefly thought of the menacing knight who had haunted Elle Fielding's dream and summoned this painted one forward. He was tall and slow at first, as if waking from a long sleep, but his footsteps made the floors tremble, and I urged him to Phelan.

The knight did as I wanted. I noticed how Phelan's handsome face drained white, as if he had seen a ghost. His eyes went wide and dark; his hands quivered as he raised them in a defensive stance.

The knight swung his sword and Phelan leapt back, almost a moment too late as my knight cut the table in half. Wood splintered and cracked. The walls shook, the frames rattling in protest. My heart beat cold and swift as I watched Phelan frantically cast a charm that rebounded off the knight's breastplate. The knight grunted and attempted another decapitation, unfazed by Phelan's magic.

Phelan was terrified, uncertain how to fell this knight. And he was no use to me dead or wounded. His fear, though, was intriguing and a touch satisfying.

I curled my fingers and the knight swayed, exposing his neck for a brief moment.

Phelan rushed to meet the weakness, his magic slicing the opponent's neck clean to the bone. Down my knight went, in chunks of armor, like a crumbling pillar of stone.

I wasn't finished yet, though. I stepped to the third painting, one that depicted four wolves running in a snowy landscape. The wolves came to me, docile as pups until I whispered Phelan's name to them. Their coats were thick, each a different shade of gray and glittering with snow, and they stalked to Phelan on silent paws.

He was surrounded, and yet he fought them boldly, even as their claws shredded through his sleeves and pants, and I saw his blood begin to well and drip.

Ease, I told the wolves. I permitted Phelan to vanquish them one by one, his magic radiant, growing in strength and accuracy, as if he at last had learned the steps to my dance. And then it was over. He had slain all four wolves, and they lay as snowdrift at his feet.

Panting and speckled with blood, he looked at me. Between us lay a carnage of magic and charms—black feathers that glistened blue in the light, pieces of armor, an abandoned great sword, icy swaths of snow. Phelan removed his top hat and raked his hand through his hair, and I saw how he bled, how he trembled. He was not badly wounded, his pride and confidence more shaken than anything else.

I gave him a moment, and I called the pieces of the paintings back to me. They returned to their frames, as if they had never seen our realm. Phelan watched as I reversed my charm. When the floor was clean—the poor desk would remain splintered, however—he set his hat back on his head, composed. He studied me closely, a furrow in his brow.

"Who are you?" he asked.

I suddenly was overcome with the urge to leave. How had I thought I could do this? Surely, he sensed it was me beneath the guise.

Before I could stop myself, I strode for the door.

"Please, wait," he breathed. "What is your name?" He reached the door before me, and he laid his blood-speckled hand on the wood. I stared at the brass handle, just out of my reach.

Reluctantly, I met his gaze. The words caught in my throat, and I reminded myself to keep my voice low. "Excuse me, Mr. Vesper. But I think this was a mistake."

"A mistake?" He chuckled and glanced at the disrepair of his clothes. And then he looked at me, how immaculate I was. "I think you are rather brilliant. And you're not here by mistake."

I remained silent, and he shifted his weight, his hand sliding away from the door.

"I offer the position to you. Take the afternoon to ponder it, but if you need help in deciding, join me for dinner tonight at my town house."

"I'll think about it," I said.

"Good," he replied with a smile, as if he already knew I had determined my mind. "I live on Auberon Street, house eleven, in the south quarter of Endellion. About a twenty-minute walk from here. Dinner will be at six." He opened the door for me. "I only ask one thing of you before you go."

I stepped over the threshold into the hallway, but I paused to glance back at him. "And what is that, Mr. Vesper?"

"Your name, please."

"Anna. Anna Neven." I spoke smoothly, as if I had said such a name endless times before. As if that name had always belonged to these bones, this spirit. The stone half of my heart.

"Then I will see you at six, Miss Neven," he said, and I hated how confident he sounded.

"We'll see," I countered.

I didn't slow my pace until I was back in the bustle of the streets and out of sight of the museum. I stopped by a fountain brimming with wishful pennies and sat down on its stone ledge, pressing my palm to my chest, where my heart beat its new, strange rhythm.

My plan was simple. Deceive Phelan. Take advantage of his resources while I positioned myself to uncover dirt on his family, because all noble families had secrets to hide. Set that secret free. Watch the Vespers fall, one by one, into disgrace, including Lennox in Hereswith.

I wasn't sure if I would ever reveal my true self to Phelan after it was all said and done, but one thing I knew for certain: things were going exactly as I hoped.

13

By five fifty-eight that evening, I was walking Auberon Street, rapidly approaching town house eleven. I hadn't gone home that afternoon but wandered the southern quadrant of the city until I worked blisters on my heels, waiting for the sun to set.

I had imagined Phelan's home to be drab and a touch eldritch, with an unpainted door and narrow windows and weeds in the garden. Town house eleven turned out to be unfortunately charming. It was three stories of gray brick with ivy growing up a trellis. The windows shone as if they had just been washed, framed by dark red shutters, and there was a gate off to the sinister side of the house, which led to a back garden.

The shadows were growing hungry on the street, and the lamps were being lit when I made my way to the door and knocked at six sharp.

It opened instantly, like someone had been waiting just behind the indigo-painted wood.

To my shock, it was an older woman. Her thistledown hair curled beneath a lacy cap, and she was dressed in a starched black dress and lace-trimmed apron. "You must be Anna Neven! Welcome, welcome!" She smiled and beckoned me to come inside, as if she had known me all my life. "We're so pleased you are going to be joining us!"

"Ah, yes," I said, and felt a brief flash of annoyance, because Phelan must have assumed that I would accept his partnership and told his housekeeper. But I swallowed the objection and stepped into the brightly lit foyer.

"By the look in your eyes, I don't suppose he told you about me," the woman said with a chuckle, and shut the door behind me. "I'm Mrs. Stirling. I cook and clean for him, and my grandson, Deacon, runs errands."

"How lovely," I said, thinking that Phelan didn't deserve such a cheerful woman to do his chores. Although if I was honest . . . I did have Imonie all my life to wash my clothes and ensure I was fed. So perhaps I shouldn't judge, although I was looking for something—anything—to give me reason to add another mark against Phelan. "And I suppose he didn't tell you that I'm still undecided in my decision of partnership?"

"He told me you were in the midst of deliberation, Miss Neven," said Mrs. Stirling, and her smile deepened, revealing a slight gap between her front teeth. "But after I beheld what you did to his clothes today . . . I do hope you will accept."

I couldn't help but laugh, true and heartfelt, even if there was only half a heart beating within me. "Then I am one step closer in accepting the offer, Mrs. Stirling."

"Good, my dear. He needs a magician such as you beside him."

A creak on the steps caught my attention. Phelan was descending the stairwell, drawn by the sound of my laughter. But he stopped when I looked up at him, and he seemed hung by uncertainty, to see me standing in his foyer. He had changed since our meeting earlier. His clothes were, once again, finely tailored and cut from the latest fashion, and his hair was damp, tamed by a ribbon. I could smell his aftershave from where I stood—a medley of pine and meadow grass, a fragrance that instantly stirred my homesickness—and I had to distract myself with my own raiment. I had chosen to wear the same clothes from before and had ensured they were wrinkled, and that my hair was unbrushed and loose, tangled down my back. I was quite disheveled in comparison to him, but it was deliberate.

I cast a bet as to how long it would take him to begin purchasing new garments for me. It was my intention to steal from his coffer, bit by bit, without him even realizing it. Just as he had stolen my home and livelihood. Just as he had made me pack up everything in a whirlwind with hardly a day to grieve over what I had lost.

"Miss Neven," Phelan said, and continued his descent. "Welcome. I do hope you're hungry. Mrs. Stirling has cooked all afternoon to impress you."

"Then she is in luck," I said, glancing at her. "I don't remember the last meal I ate."

"Oh, dear child! I have plenty for you, then, but I need to return to the kitchen. Phelan? Why don't you give her a tour, and then bring our guest into the dining room."

"Of course, Mrs. Stirling," he said.

We watched as she hurried down the hallway, and then I glanced sidelong at Phelan.

"Is this your house, or hers?"

That coaxed a slight grin from him. "It's mine by law, but it answers to her, I think." He noticed my clothes, wrinkled and gilded in dust, and the long snarls in my hair. I waited for him to say something about it—add another mark against him in my ledger—but he managed to quell his objection and said in a pleasant tone, "Come, Miss Neven. Let me show you around."

I followed him into the drawing room, a wide chamber with wainscoting and striped wallpaper, a plush rug that swallowed footsteps, a marble hearth, and an assortment of furniture. The tang of lemon haunted the air, as if Mrs. Stirling had just polished all the wood.

"This room is for visitors, and most evenings Mrs. Stirling and her grandson, Deacon, and I like to play a round of cards after dessert. You should join us tonight." He indicated the card table that sat between two couches, and I nodded, thinking I should definitely *not* play cards with them. My competitive nature would emerge, and who knew what I might do to win.

Phelan glanced at me, as if he read my thoughts. "I take it you like cards?"

"A little. I don't play very often."

He nodded but seemed unconvinced. I followed him through

the drawing room until I saw the great mirror hanging on the wall, positioned above the game cupboard. I froze, staring at the hungry glass. Why did he need such a large, obtrusive mirror in his drawing room?

Thanks to the thick rug, he didn't hear me come to a frantic halt, and his eyes were set directly ahead, where he was leading me to an open archway. I hurried past the mirror, praying he wouldn't turn. And I caught a glimpse of myself in the glass. A reflection of wild auburn hair and large brown eyes and pressed lips, as if I were holding a song in my chest.

"This leads to the library, where I do most of my work," he said, guiding me through the archway into a back corridor, which wound to a set of double doors with panels of stained glass.

I exhaled, following him into a spacious library. The shelves rose from floor to ceiling, carved from mahogany wood. There was a hearth, swept clean of ashes, and a desk in the center of the room, where a tome sat beside a vase of swan quills and an herbarium. His book of nightmares, I presumed, and I approached it, measuring its thickness, the tattered edge of its pages, the weight it gave to the room.

"How long have you been warden here?" I asked.

"For five months."

"So you have faced multiple new moons in your appointed streets?"

He hesitated, a shadow in his expression. "Not exactly. I've only faced one of the five."

I was intrigued by his response. "Why only one?"

"This most recent new moon I was away due to travel, so I hired an independent magician to cover the streets for me," he explained in a stilted voice. I knew *exactly* where he had been that moon, but I maintained my pleasant facade. "And on my first new moon . . . I was overwhelmed and wounded. It took me a while to recover, and while I was healing, my twin brother fought on my behalf."

Lennox, I assumed, and my lip almost curled in disgust. I was surprised to learn they were twins, because they looked nothing alike. An old story came to mind, the one Imonie had told me of the woman of the mountains and her twin boys. They had been identical, often switching roles to protect each other from punishments. I wondered what it would be like to so seamlessly change places with someone, fooling friends and family alike.

"Your brother must deeply care for you," I said. "I assume the two of you are very close?"

Phelan was quiet, and it prompted me to glance at him. His gaze was distantly set on the shelves of books behind me.

"Our relationship is one built on favors and debts," he replied, still avoiding eye contact with me. "And I swiftly learned that we don't work well together, and I needed a different partner on the new moon nights."

He needed someone to guard his back, which I understood. I had once guarded my father's, and he mine. Strange, that Phelan didn't want it to be his twin brother. Although Lennox was not a likable person.

"What were you wounded by?" I asked, my gaze drifting to his chest. To his perfect posture, which betrayed no visage of weakness, even as I knew my own magic had left lacerations on his skin earlier that day. Nicks and cuts that now hid beneath his garments.

"That I cannot tell you," he replied with a lilt of mirth. "Unless you accept my offer, Miss Neven."

"Touché, Mr. Vesper," I said, and turned my attention away from the intensity of his gaze to the book of nightmares. I considered it foolish that he'd left something so vital and important sitting in plain sight on his desk until I dared to trace its battered cover and was rewarded with a sting.

The shock of it made me wince more than the pain, but I yanked my hand away as blood welled on my fingertips.

"It bites," Phelan belatedly said as he walked to me, pulling a handkerchief from his inner pocket. "Here, I apologize. I should have warned you."

I nearly accepted his handkerchief, my blood welling like a string of red pearls, but I felt a warning in the pit of my stomach. I needed to be careful and give him no piece of me. No strand of hair, no drop of blood, no breath of mine. Nothing that he might use to divine my true nature, should he come to one day suspect I was not who I appeared to be.

I set my fingers in my mouth and licked away my blood, to which he arched his brow, as if secretly repulsed. My blood tasted like warm iron, and I cleared my throat, drawing my fingers from my lips and pressing them against my palm, urging the wounds to clot.

"How long have you lived here, Mr. Vesper?"

"For three years."

"But you have only been warden for five months. How did you come to earn the responsibility?"

"The magician who guarded this territory became a madcap," Phelan replied.

"A madcap?"

"A magician who seeks to find a way into the Seren fortress and break the new moon curse."

Oh, I had come across quite a few of those, milling around Hereswith, seeking information. I remembered how Imonie, Papa, and I had called them "vultures," and how much we had hated them. I remembered how I had thought Phelan and Lennox had been such people the first time I saw them.

"And how many inhabitants do you guard here?" I asked.

"Six streets fall beneath my care. A total of three hundred and five individuals."

An impressive amount for a young magician, I thought.

"And what about you, Miss Neven?" Phelan asked. "Where do you come from? Where do you currently reside?"

"Does it matter?" I countered with a smile. "My life has been rather dull up until this moment. I wouldn't want to bore you with details."

"It matters to me," he said, earnest. "If you and I work together . . . we can't be strangers."

"Of course not," I agreed, but was shifting away from him, my focus attracted to the window of the library, where a vast array of potted plants sat on a table. I recognized all the plants by name, and I brushed the variegated leaves of one. "Do you make your own remedies, Mr. Vesper?"

He had no chance to reply. I was suddenly aware of the glint of two eyes, peering up at me through the tangles of foliage.

"Hello!" a voice chirped, and I startled, my breath hissing through my teeth in alarm.

I watched, astounded, as a boy crept out of the dangling vines, standing before me with a click of his heels. His hair was a mop of tawny curls, his face was freckled, and his clothes were mud stained. He was missing his front tooth as he grinned up at me.

"Deacon," Phelan said with a sigh. "What have I told you about sneaking and eavesdropping?"

The boy glanced at Phelan, his smile fading. "I know, Mr. Vesper. It's rude and I'm sorry, but you told me it was impossible to sneak up on a magician. And I just snuck up on *two* of you!"

"Yes, and that was very dangerous," Phelan remarked. "You took us both by surprise. What if we had responded in another way?"

"Like with magic?"

"Yes. Miss Neven might have turned you into a mouse."

I gave Phelan a flat expression. "Is that the most imagination you have? I wouldn't have turned him into a mouse." And I brought my gaze back to Deacon, softened by his eagerness, his toothless smile. "I would have turned you into a hawk, maybe. A bird who could soar through the clouds. Or a wise fox who knows all the secret ins and outs of the house."

"Or a dragon?!" he cried hopefully.

"Alas, a dragon would not fit in this library. And you might catch all the books on fire," I said.

That made sense to him. He nodded, but his eyes were glazed, as if his mind was whirling with possibilities. "Have you ever turned a human into an animal, Miss Neven?"

"No, I haven't," I responded honestly. "That is very risky magic. It's not that difficult to turn a human into something else if the magician has the imagination and the right spell work, but it's far trickier to return the human back to how they once were. A change is made in the process, and it's easy to err."

"That does sound hard," Deacon mused. "Have you done it, Mr. Vesper?"

Phelan shook his head in a negative response and motioned for the boy to come closer. "Why don't you go and see if your grandmama needs help with dinner. Miss Neven and I will be right behind you."

"All right," Deacon said, but he gave me a smart little bow. "I'm very pleased to make your acquaintance, Miss Neven!"

I smiled, and warmth began to seep in my chest. It emanated a shallow ache, the sort of ache one feels when they have run too far, or when they are about to be reunited with someone they have missed for years.

An ache of stone being shifted, and I couldn't believe it. Not this soon. Not by the kindness I had met here, the welcome and the genuine smiles. Not by the sweet adoration of a little boy and his toothless grin. This would *not* be my undoing, I vowed, and struggled to steady my heart, dwelling on the fact that I'd once had such things until they had been taken from me.

I drew in a deep breath until the ache eased, but Phelan was regarding me intently.

"Are you well, Miss Neven?"

I forced a smile, although I could only wonder what lurked in my gaze when I looked at him. "I think I'm just hungry."

"Then come, let me take you into the dining room."

I trailed him out of the library, down the main corridor—my eyes seeking mirrors of all shapes and sizes. The dining hall was a narrow chamber occupied by a table, velvet-lined chairs, and a marble hearth alight with a fire. Mrs. Stirling was just setting down the last dish.

"Oh good, there you are. Come sit here, Miss Neven." She indicated the chair across from Phelan's.

Wonderful, I thought drolly as I surrendered to the chair. I would unfortunately have to look at him all throughout dinner.

Phelan waited to sit until Mrs. Stirling and Deacon had taken their seats. And then he reached across the table and poured wine into my glass flute.

"Potatoes?" Mrs. Stirling asked, offering the warm bowl to me.

I filled my plate, and the dishes were passed until everyone had taken a spoonful of everything. We fell silent as we began to eat; there was only the sound of cutlery and the crackle of fire.

I relished every bite, eating slowly. The last meal I had taken was dried meat and a plum on the stagecoach hours ago, offerings from Imonie's satchel. Thinking of her made me think of my parents, and my mouth went dry when I anticipated telling them what I had done. What I was doing.

"The food is delicious, Mrs. Stirling," I said, to distract myself from the apprehension. "Thank you."

The older woman smiled and waved off my compliment.

"Do you have any siblings, Miss Neven?" Deacon asked after wiping the edge of his mouth with his sleeve.

I saw the disapproving look Mrs. Stirling sent him before pointing to his napkin.

"No," I answered. Creating siblings, as tempting as that was, would only complicate my story. "Do you, Deacon?"

"I'm the youngest. I have two older sisters."

"That sounds fun. I wish that I had sisters."

"What about your parents?" the boy asked. "Your mama and papa."

"What about them?" I didn't like the idea of lying to a child. But he was certainly full of questions, and I felt my cheeks flush.

"Do they live nearby? Did they teach you magic?"

"I think that is enough questions, Deacon," Mrs. Stirling said. "Remember your manners."

Deacon looked downcast by the chiding, his attention returning to his plate as he pushed his peas around in a circle.

"It's quite all right," I said, reaching for my wine. "I never had the opportunity to know my father. My mother raised me. She was the one to teach me magic."

"I bet she is proud of you, Miss Neven," said Deacon, and I heard the longing in his voice. I had not sensed illumination in him, that unmistakable flame of magic that some of us were born with. But it was apparent that he wanted to become a magician.

"She would be, yes," I replied, and took a long sip of wine.

Deacon's mouth opened, ready to spout more queries, but

Phelan swiftly moved the conversation to other, safer things. I ate my fill, listening more than I spoke, but chiming in when it felt right, and Mrs. Stirling brought out chamomile tea and almond pudding for dessert. I despised almond pudding but swallowed every bite, washing it down with overly sweetened tea.

"Deacon, help me clear the table," Mrs. Stirling said, rising from her chair.

Deacon groaned but then asked, "Can we play Seven Wraiths tonight?"

Seven Wraiths, I thought with alarm. That card game my father had forbidden me to play. The one the Fielding girls loved, even with its enchanted consequences. All I could think of was Elle, terrified of a nightmare she had been given by losing the game. A nightmare that had frightened me as well. I could almost hear the heavy clink of the knight walking through the streets again.

"I think we should," Phelan said, also glancing to me. "Would you like to join us, Miss Neven?"

"I fear I need to return home," I said, standing. "But thank you again for the lovely dinner, Mrs. Stirling."

She smiled and nodded, but I could see the tension in her face. I hadn't shared my decision yet, if I was accepting Phelan's offer or not, and Deacon carefully began to stack the plates. When he came to take mine, he begged, "Please, Miss Neven! *Please* choose us! Mr. Vesper needs you."

"Deacon!" Mrs. Stirling called to him through the swinging kitchen door, mortified by his outburst.

I wanted to smile at the boy, to reassure him. But I worried about drumming up that ache in my chest again, and so I merely watched as he retreated into the kitchen with a pile of precariously stacked dishes.

Phelan cleared his throat and rose. "Let me see you out, Miss Neven."

I followed him back into the corridor, where I did find one small mirror hanging in a collage of paintings, gleaming mirthfully on the wall. But I didn't think it would be likely to give me away so long as I ensured no one trailed me into the hallway.

Phelan opened the front door. The night rushed in, encircling us with the fragrance of sweet cedar smoke from a nearby tavern. We stepped out onto the front porch, and the lantern light trickled over our faces.

"Do you need more time to consider the offer, Miss Neven?"

"No, I've decided. But there is one thing I want to ask you, before I give you my reply," I said.

"And what would that be?" he drawled, gazing intently at me.

I held his stare, even though I felt oddly vulnerable. I didn't know if I liked or disliked the way his attention was so rapt upon me.

"Why did you offer the position to me?" I asked. "You must have had plenty of other promising magicians at the interview today."

"I did. And yet all of them performed for me, as if they were on a stage. Not a single one engaged me as you did," he replied. "I confess, Miss Neven, that there was a moment when I thought your intentions were to kill me. And then I realized how absurd that was, and that you were testing me as I wanted to test you. You challenged me as if you were a nightmare on a new moon, and I knew then that you were the one that I wanted beside me."

His confession took me by surprise. "You must have some terrible nightmares haunt these streets."

Phelan paused. "I do. I've come to learn that they are treacherous on the darkest of nights."

Every street is treacherous, I wanted to say, remembering the gills that had scarred my neck. I resisted the urge to trace where they had once gleamed.

"Then I accept your offer, Mr. Vesper," I said. And before he could respond, I added, "When do we begin?"

"Tomorrow," he answered. "At eight o'clock sharp."

"Excellent. I'll see you here at eight." I took another stair down, only to feel his presence follow me.

"Wait, Miss Neven. Let me walk you home."

I pivoted and held up my hand. "That's not necessary."

Phelan glanced beyond me to the streets, dark patches punctured by the wavering beacons of lamplight. This was a quiet, aristocratic segment of the city, composed of families who were all home for the night. But there were other parts of Endellion that were dangerous to roam alone. I read the lines in his brow. He was worried about this, as well as curious to know where, exactly, I hailed from.

"Then let me call a horse and cab for you," he said.

"No, I truly don't need one," I insisted. "I prefer to walk, especially after that rich dinner." I took another step away from him and he held his ground. "Good night, Mr. Vesper."

I strode over the flagstone path to the gate and slipped out into the street.

I waited until I was three blocks away before I called my own horse and cab. It would have taken me all night to make the walk from the southern quadrant up to the north peak of the city, where my mother's town house resided.

Alone at last, I relaxed in the coach, the cushion smelling of cheap perfume. I leaned my head back and closed my eyes, exhaustion creeping over me. But Phelan's words continued to sound in my mind, like an instrument that would not cease playing.

You challenged me as if you were a nightmare on a new moon.

He had no idea.

14

The front door was unlocked. I let myself in, quietly latching the door behind me. I followed the threads of voices and candlelight into the kitchen, where my parents and Imonie sat at a table, waiting for me to come home.

My mother saw me first.

I stood on the threshold, where the firelight could wash over me, and I waited for her to ask who I was—a stranger in her home. She said nothing but her face went pale. She set her teacup down with a clatter in its saucer and that was when I realized she knew, somehow, that it was me.

"Ambrose," she said, but it was too late. My father was turning in his chair, to see what had transfixed my mother's attention.

He frowned and instantly rose, scaring Dwindle down the hallway.

"Who are you?" he asked, and while he was polite, I saw the

gleam of fear in him. He sensed it, too, and he didn't want to believe it.

"Papa," I said, and he flinched. "It's me."

He took a step back as if I had struck him. Imonie buried her face in her hands and my mother was frozen, watching us with bloodshot eyes.

"What have you done?" he cried, and his devastation was like a dagger in my side. "Clem . . . *what have you done?*"

"You may want to live your life without magic," I said. "But I don't. You may be content to live in the city, working in the mines, but I long to go home to Hereswith. I'm not done fighting for it, Papa."

My father tore his fingers through his hair. He shot a fierce look at my mother and asked, "Did you encourage this, Sigourney?"

"No," my mother said. "Whatever magic she used to transform . . . it was not mine."

Papa paced through the kitchen. "Why? Why have you done this?" he asked, coming to a halt before me. "You were perfect the way you were, Clem."

"This won't last forever."

"How long, then?"

"The disguise will break when I want it to," I answered, hoping my parents believed me. I didn't know for certain how easily this magic would relinquish me. If my spirit was cold, then it might take a long time to chip away the stone in my chest.

"You still haven't answered me," he said. "*Why* have you done this?"

"I want to know why they chose Hereswith, why they chose to challenge us," I whispered. "I want to know their secrets. I want them to feel the same pain as us—to lose something that means the world to them. To feel the sharp edge of their own selfishness."

"Who are you speaking about?" Papa rasped, but he knew.

"I've become Phelan's partner. He's a dream warden in the southern quarter of the city."

"Phelan *Vesper?*"

I nodded.

"He doesn't know it's you, does he?" Papa said, and he chuckled. The sound was familiar; I made the same kind of laughter when I was overwhelmed and furious and afraid. "This is very foolish, Clem. I know what they did to us was agonizing, but you must let it go. This will eat you from within if you don't, daughter."

Let it go.

He might have found peace by doing such, but I couldn't.

"Papa . . ." I reached for his hand, and for an anguished moment I thought he would jerk away from me. But he wove his fingers with mine, fingers that were now smudged and stained from work in the mines. A place he should not be, as if he wanted to forget and hide who he was. "Papa, I know you're worried, but I'm doing this because families like the Vespers need to know they are not invincible. That they cannot just come and steal someone's home for their own amusement."

His eyes flared. He dropped my hand and said, "Go to your room, Clem."

"But, Papa—"

"Please go. I need a moment."

He had never ordered me to my room before like this, and my face flushed as I spun and hurried up the stairs to my chamber. A candelabra was lit, and I sat on the edge of the bed, exhausted. It had been a long day. When my father refused to come see me, I washed my face and brushed the tangles from my hair, and I dressed in a soft chemise.

I climbed into bed and sat against the headboard. Beyond my window, the city still teemed with noises, and I longed for the peace and quiet of the countryside. I stared at the door, waiting, and it must have been sometime past midnight when I finally heard Papa softly rap on the door.

"Come in."

He stepped into the room, haggard and slow, as if his joints ached. I braced myself for the worst until I watched him cast a protective charm around the room, so no one could overhear us. No one, including my mother and Imonie.

Papa stopped at the foot of my bed. He stared at me a moment, like I truly had become a stranger in all ways to him.

"Tell me what spell you have planned to protect yourself," he said. "A spell that will shield you and give you the chance to flee when Phelan discovers it's you, and you've been deceiving him."

"He will never know it's—"

"*Clementine.*"

I swallowed. "I don't have one planned yet."

"Then that is the first order of business. I want you to have it prepared by the end of this week, for me to approve."

"Very well," I said, and my mind reeled with potential spells

I could spin for such an encounter. If I was truly in danger of Phelan harming me.

"Second order of business," Papa continued in a gruff voice. "You will obviously be working with Phelan every day as his partner. How do you plan to move to and from his house and here, without him discovering where you live? If he sees me or Imonie . . . your cover will be blown."

"Yes, and I have a plan," I replied. I knew he wouldn't like it, so I merely smiled, but I realized my dimples were gone, the dimples that he loved, and Papa only scowled at me.

"Explain the plan."

"It may take me a few days, but I'm hoping Phelan will give me a room."

"At *his* house?" Papa demanded.

"Yes."

"I don't like this, Clem. Not one bit."

"I know, but I'm a magician, Papa. You have taught me the best *avertana* has to offer, and I have faced many types of danger, and this . . . this is not something you should be worried about. It's bad luck to harm a guest beneath your roof, remember? And besides, it will give me an opportunity to drain his resources."

"Where is this coming from, Clem? *Draining resources?* This isn't like you."

He didn't know I had given half my heart away, and perhaps I would have felt shame in the past over his disappointment. But not now. I remained quiet, waiting for his acceptance.

He sighed. But when he looked at me again, I saw that I had won this argument, and he reluctantly nodded.

"You will cast a protective charm on your bedroom door every night?"

"Yes," I said, thinking I still had to somehow convince Phelan to even offer me a room.

"And the windows?"

"Yes, the windows as well. Don't worry, Papa."

"I will worry every moment that you're gone," he said, and I felt that terrible ache in my stone heart again. I had to glance away from him and how destitute he appeared. I played with a thread of my quilt until I felt composed.

"Is that all, Papa?"

"No. Once he gives you a room, you're going to tell Phelan that you will have every Monday night off, new moon permitting, and you are going to use your stealth charm to check in with me here. We'll have family dinner together so your mother, Imonie, and I don't worry ourselves to death."

"I can do that," I said.

"And one last thing, Clem." But he hesitated, and I sensed this was the reason why he had charmed the room, so no one could eavesdrop. "You mentioned that you're doing all this because you want to know why the Vesper brothers chose Hereswith. I want to know as well. I don't want you to risk yourself, but if the opportunity presents itself for you to . . . uncover this, I want you to share it with me on Monday nights. And if you come across any information about the countess . . . I would also like to know it, Clem."

"The countess? Why do you want information on her?" I asked, remembering the stilted moment I had met her in the art shop.

She had studied me with cold reserve and said, *You look familiar. Have we met before?*

"She's an old acquaintance," he answered, glancing away. The hair rose on my arms as I wondered what would make a selfish noblewoman interact with a rustic magician like my father. "We were never friends—I was far too lowly for that—but we worked together until we had a falling-out, years ago."

"Do you think she told her sons to take Hereswith, as a way to slight you?"

"I don't know," Papa replied, a bit too quickly for my liking. "Now, do you agree to my terms?"

I nodded.

"Good. Did you drink your remedy tonight?"

"Not yet," I said, but I reached for the small vial, which sat waiting on my bedside table.

"You're a warden again," Papa said. "It would be wise to continue drinking them every night. Particularly since your partner doesn't know who you truly are."

I didn't say that I had been taking them every night since we left Hereswith, as he'd asked me to. And because he seemed to be waiting, I drank the remedy. It went down like a secret, and even after all these years of swallowing them night after night, I still grimaced.

But I knew what Papa implied. It would be disastrous indeed if I strove to be a vengeful eye in Phelan's house, only to let a nightmare, of all things, betray who I was.

15

"Is your book going to bite me again?" I asked, standing in Phelan's library. It was my first day of work with him, our first day of tenuous partnership. It was going as well as could be expected. I had been half an hour late, due to a carriage crash on the lower north quadrant, and I had swiftly come to discover Phelan detested tardiness.

His back was angled to me as he watered the plants on the table, sunlight gilding his dark hair. "No, not today."

"But perhaps tomorrow?"

He glanced at me, noticing the wrinkles on my plaid skirt, my taupe shirt with brass buttons gleaming up the front. My hair was braided, at least, and he returned his gaze to the plants.

"You should begin to read. You have much to catch up on."

I sat at his desk and carefully opened the book of nightmares. I sifted through the most recent of entries, and quickly realized that some of them were written in dark gold ink, while the majority were in black.

"Do you have a reason for using different colored inks?" I asked.

"Yes. The gold entries are the active ones, dreams of people who currently reside here." If a resident happens to move away or dies, I charm their records into black ink, so I keep track of which dreams to study. He pruned a few wilted leaves and then went to work making a remedy. He chopped and scraped an assortment of leaves and petals into a glass flask, where it bubbled over a flame, casting an astringent aroma in the office.

"I suppose it's hard to keep track of everyone who comes and goes within your territory," I said after I had read a few of his entries. "The city is such a fluid place."

"Yes," he agreed. "Some nightmares unfortunately escape my records."

I left him to his task of straining and bottling the remedies, and I read through page after page of golden-hued nightmares. I began to jot down ideas for spells to counter them. The hours crept by. We worked in companionable silence, interrupted only by Mrs. Stirling bringing us a lunch tray of sliced rye bread, cold slabs of roast beef, cheese, and pickles.

Phelan and I sat across from each other at the desk, but I was too focused on eating and reading to attempt a conversation with him.

"Do you have dinner plans, Miss Neven?" he eventually asked.

"No." I kept my eyes on the page.

"Would you like to have dinner with me and two of my friends tonight? We can walk the streets this afternoon, so I can show you the territory boundaries, and then we can go eat with Nura and Olivette."

Nura and Olivette? I reached for my lukewarm tea, suddenly stricken with nerves. He had friends, which meant they would most likely ask me an endless stream of questions.

"I'm not sure. . . ."

"Do you have elsewhere to be tonight?" he asked, and I heard the curiosity in his voice. He wanted to know more of my history and was too polite to directly ask for it again.

I sat back, my fingertips stained gold and black from turning the inky pages.

"I'm not a very social person, Mr. Vesper."

"Neither am I," he quipped. "But I should warn you that if you put Nura and Olivette off tonight, they will insist on meeting you tomorrow night, and the night after that, and the night after that. . . ."

"All right," I said, waving my hand. "If your friends are so persistent, I'll join you."

"Excellent," he said, rising from the desk. "I have a few deliveries to make, but I'll return soon."

I watched him quit the library, the stained-glass doors latching behind him with a quiet click.

I waited a full ten minutes before I began to search through the drawers. I hoped to uncover correspondence—letters between him and Lennox, or perhaps him and his mother—and sifted through reams of blank paper, corked inkwells, bundles of quills, sticks of wax, candle tapers, a bronze stamp, an amethyst cluster, a sack of lemon drops. And then my fingers caught on a sharp edge of parchment. A square calling card. I drew it into the light.

By the seventeenth of November, it read in elegant handwriting. I held the card against a page in the book of nightmares, to compare it with Phelan's handwriting. The script was similar in slant and embellishment, but there were a few differences. I didn't believe Phelan had written this mysterious date down, but perhaps his mother had?

I returned the card to its place in the drawer. But my mind hummed with questions and thoughts. After a while, I decided to return to work. The next new moon was only eight days away, and I still had volumes to cover, new spells to forge in preparation.

I turned a crinkled page in Phelan's recordings, skimming until my attention was hooked by a particular nightmare. Stunned, I leaned closer until I could taste the dust of the pages, and I read Phelan's account:

> Knox Birch is standing in a great hall of shadows. At first, he does not know where he is, but by the creeping cold on his skin, he feels like he has been here before. When the sunlight begins to flood through the windows, he sees the banners dressing the stone walls—blue banners emblazoned with stars and moons—and he realizes where he stands: the fortress in the clouds. He can feel the great depth of the mountain beneath him, and it is strange how at home he feels in Seren, even though he has

never stepped foot in the mountain duchy.

Something evil happened here, he thinks.

But his memory wilts the more he attempts to remember why this place is cursed. And soon, he forgets those feelings altogether when the duke's throne catches the sunlight. Knox is alone in the hall, and suddenly, he desires to claim the empty chair. He takes the first step, believing that he will restore whatever has broken by making himself duke. He takes the second step, and then the third. And that is when a shadow emerges, hissing like wind through cracks in the mortar. The shadow fights him, impedes him.

Knox has no choice but to take the rapier that blooms in his hand and cut the shadow down. It lies limp at his feet, and he steps over it, his eyes on the throne. But another shadow interferes, wailing with such intensity that he cannot bear to hear it, and he pierces its heart. The second shadow crumples, and he steps over it, nearly to the dais steps, where the throne waits.

And yet a third shadow rises. It screams and fights him. He cleaves it in two, and it lies at his feet. At last, he thinks. He has defeated the challenges and he alone has earned the throne.

He claims the chair.

As soon as he is seated, the rapier in his hand

vanishes, and the shadows who are crumpled on
the floor are exposed for what they truly are:
his wife and his two daughters. They lie dead in
pools of blood, destroyed by his hand, and Knox
lets out a wail that never seems to end.

He wants to claw out his own eyes. He
wants to cut out his own heart. If only he had
seen them, he cries. If only he had seen their
faces, and not their shadows. . . .

The nightmare captured me, and I was shaken, desperate to escape its icy hold. Of all the dream records I had read in Hereswith, no one had dreamt of the fortress in the clouds. And yet I could still taste the brisk air of the mountain castle, feel the cold flagstones beneath my feet as if I had walked Knox Birch's nightmare. I closed my eyes and I saw a glimmer of blue on the walls, and I could hear the distant echoes of lives long lost. I wondered what it had been like before the curse. Why had the seven members of the duke's court killed him? Had one of them desired to take the throne from the Duke of Seren? Was the duke cruel as some of the legends spun him to be?

I couldn't bear to read another word.

And I shut Phelan's book.

Later that afternoon, I walked beside Phelan, learning the winding bends of the streets he guarded. The town houses were well maintained—some were extravagant with their ornate window casements and gates with finials dipped in bronze and lush gardens in the front yard. I wondered about the inhabitants who lived behind each door. The mere notion of trying to learn a horde of new names and faces was overwhelming, and I eventually looked upward, to the reassurance of the sky. It was overcast, threatening rain, and there was a slight chill on the breeze. I imagined Hereswith would have felt her first frost by now, and the leaves would soon change.

"Do you ever dream, Mr. Vesper?" The question slipped from me, soft and genuine.

"Do I ever dream?" he repeated, amused. He walked with his hands in his jacket pockets, and the wind stirred his hair. "You mean if I've experienced my own nightmare, Miss Neven?"

"Yes, I suppose that is the better question."

He was quiet, and when he slowed his strides, I slowed mine, to keep in pace with him.

"I've never dreamt," he replied, meeting my gaze. "But then again . . . I've never given myself the chance to."

I hated how his words resonated within me. I hated how his words could have been my own. I hated how they made me want to ask him more questions.

"You've taken remedies all your life, then? Even before you were a warden?"

He nodded, and a line creased his brow. "I know that must sound strange to you. But my mother, the countess, never wanted my brother and me to dream at night."

I drew in a deep breath. A vain attempt to quench my interest. "And why would she desire that? If I may ask, of course."

"You may ask, Miss Neven," said Phelan. "And I will answer

only if I may ask a question of you, which you must likewise answer."

I grimaced, loathing myself for letting him play me into a corner. "Very well, Mr. Vesper. You can ask *two* questions, and I will choose which one I want to respond to."

"Fair enough," he said, and guided me around a street corner. "My mother didn't want Lennox and me to dream because it meant we would need a warden to record our nightmares down in their book."

"And that's terrible, in her eyes?"

"Not terrible, but a vulnerability. A weakness," Phelan replied. "We would be dependent upon another, who would then know our dreams. And sometimes dreams are ridiculous, but most of the time . . . they reveal our innermost pieces. Our desires, our fears, our ambitions, our plans. Our past, even."

I mulled on that, thinking his mother must be very shrewd. If there were no dream records of their family, then I might have a harder time uncovering their secrets.

"Now," Phelan said, and I could hear the smile in his voice. "You must answer a question of mine."

"Go on," I said, bracing myself.

"Do you have any family in the city, or have you ever dreamt, Miss Neven?"

"I've never dreamt, either, Mr. Vesper."

That surprised him, and he glanced at me. "Really? Why is that?"

"Actually . . . let me take back my words for a moment. I have dreamt. *Once*," I lied, and I was amazed at how smoothly it rolled off the tip of my tongue. "When I was a little girl, I had a night-mare that frightened me so badly I was afraid to leave my room. So my mother began to give me a remedy every night, promising the monster in my dreams could never find me again."

He guided us down yet another street. I admired the old oaks that grew along the sidewalk, their gnarled roots working their way up through the cobblestones. "And does your mother still give you remedies, Miss Neven?"

"No," I whispered. "She passed away last spring."

"I'm sorry," Phelan said, and I was surprised to hear how con-trite he sounded.

We fell silent again until he stopped before a grand town house built of whitewashed brick. I gazed up at its navy shutters and crimson-painted door, its lintel made of carved marble.

"I wanted to show you this house in particular," Phelan said, reaching out to touch a wild tendril of ivy that grew on the iron gate.

"Why is that?" I asked.

"The duke lives here."

I examined the home with an attentive eye. "I thought the duke lived in the Blue Mansion, in the eastern quadrant."

"He does," Phelan replied. "The mansion is his primary resi-dence. But he has other homes located throughout the city. He never sleeps beneath one roof more than a week at a time."

"That's absurd," I laughed until I saw the arch of Phelan's brow.

"It's wise," he amended, glancing back to the town house. "Remember what I told you about my mother, and how she ensured my brother and I never dreamt? The duke has a similar dealing with nightmares. He doesn't want one magician to know all his dreams."

Rain began to fall. I watched as Phelan withdrew a tiny umbrella from his jacket pocket, and with an elegant flick of his wrist, the umbrella grew into its normal size.

"Shall we go to dinner?" he asked, opening the umbrella and holding it between us.

I hated that he stored tiny trinkets in his pockets. But hate could only last so long in the rain.

I stepped beneath the umbrella and we hurried to reach the tavern, elbows bumping in a stiff attempt to keep from touching each other.

The Fabled Tavern was three blocks away, a narrow building wedged between a tailor's shop and a jeweler. It was easy to overlook, built of drab gray stone with an arched entryway choked with wisteria. The corridor ushered us into a courtyard, whose open roof was charmed to catch the rain. Phelan left his umbrella by the coat stand, and I admired my surroundings. There was a reflection pool at the center of the courtyard, and fruit trees grew along winding stone paths. Cushions were spread out on the grass, and couples lounged with cups of tea and wine, listening as minstrels played stringed instruments from a pergola.

This was a watering hole for magicians, I swiftly realized. Good food, tea, wine, conversation, friendship, music, beauty. All the things needed to restore magic of mind, heart, and body.

"Follow me," Phelan said, and led me through the courtyard to an archway that swallowed us into the tavern's indoor seating.

It was a crowded, vibrant place, humming with conversations

and laughter. Tables and chairs were arranged over the blue tiled floors, and booths were carved into the walls. A host of lanterns hung above from the timber beams, bathing the tavern in low, warm light. The air smelled of herbs and sweet wine, and I noticed with alarm that there was a mirror behind the bar. But there were so many people gathered, and the light was romantically dim. I didn't fear my reflection, and I followed Phelan's winding path through the tables to one of the booths.

I saw Nura and Olivette before they saw me.

The girls were sitting side by side, their faces tilted close as they spoke to each other. One had a bob of white-blond hair, a rosy complexion with a sprinkling of freckles across her nose. Her companion had brown curly hair that brushed her shoulders, red-painted lips, and light brown skin. They were both dressed in bright colors, and my anxiety soared when they caught sight of our approach.

"Phelan!" the blonde cried with enthusiasm. "Hurry and introduce us! We've been longing to meet the magician who nearly killed you in the interview!"

"Of course you are," he humored her, but I saw a flush stain his cheeks as he turned to me. "Anna Neven, this is Olivette Wolfe and Nura Sparrow. Olivette and Nura, allow me to introduce you to my partner, Anna Neven."

"A pleasure to meet you, Anna," said Nura. Her voice was deep and smooth compared to Olivette's high pitch. "Come, join us."

I slid onto the bench across from theirs, and Phelan settled beside me.

"I want to know what inspired you to use the paintings in the gallery," Olivette said in a rush. "It was ingenious, but also very risky. How were you able to command someone else's art, Anna? Are you well versed in *metamara*?"

And so it begins, I thought with a twinge of fear. It was the same fear I felt when I saw a mirror, a cold shock that made my spirit coil. And yet I smiled and scrounged up an answer.

"It *was* risky. I won't pretend otherwise. But I've long been an admirer of art, and since I had heard that Phelan was very unimpressed with the other interviews he had held that day . . . I knew I needed to take a dangerous leap in order to catch his attention."

"Hmm." Olivette grinned, glancing from me to Phelan. "She knows you quite well, my friend."

"He's easy to read," I said with a nervous chuckle.

"Am I?" he countered, and I felt him look at me.

"Yes," I said, grateful that the waiter arrived, filling our goblets and setting down a platter of sliced bread, squares of cheese, olives, and an array of colorful jams. "Your eyes betray your thoughts sometimes."

"If that is so," Phelan said to me, his voice low with offense, "then read my eyes now. Tell me what I'm thinking."

I took a sip of wine before I met his stare. His eyes were dark, like new moons, and for all my bluster . . . I had no idea what thoughts haunted him.

"You're thinking that you're hungry, and the noise in this tavern is too loud for your liking," I teased, and lifted my goblet to him.

Phelan begrudgingly clinked his glass against mine, and the tension between us melted as we began to eat.

"Are you an artist yourself, Anna?" Nura asked.

"No," I replied swiftly. "I unfortunately have no such talent, but I love the work of others." And it was time for me to turn the conversation toward them. I smiled and asked, "How do you know Phelan?"

Olivette and Nura exchanged a glance.

"I've known Phelan for years," Olivette eventually replied. "We went to school together."

"And I met Olivette two years ago," Nura said. "When she was looking for a partner. She introduced me to Phelan not long afterward."

Olivette slathered honey butter onto a slice of bread. "Our territory is next to Phelan's, in case he hasn't told you yet. And we have a tradition of eating here at least once a month, before the next new moon."

"A lovely tradition," I said, and I meant it. I longed for this sort of camaraderie.

Our second course of food arrived, distracting us, and slowly, I became more comfortable, but I never let my guard down. If I was honest . . . I enjoyed Nura's and Olivette's company. Perhaps more than I should.

"You'll give us a warning if Phelan decides to go madcap, won't you, Anna?" Olivette asked suddenly.

From the corner of my eye, I watched as Phelan nearly choked on his wine.

"I'm *not* going madcap, Oli," he said tersely, as if they had argued about this before. "I told you. I'm not leaving Bardyllis or my streets for a long time."

Madcap.

Vulture.

I slid my gaze askance to look at him.

"You say that *now*, but you hear the gossip among our kind," Nura said. "The curse of the Seren Duchy has stood for a century, tempting every warden in the realm. An empty throne, a fortress cursed full of nightmares. Which of us wouldn't want to experience it?"

"It sounds dreadful," Phelan said in a flat tone. "And if the curse breaks . . . we'll all be without a job, won't we?"

The new moon curse dictated so much of our lives it was almost impossible for me to imagine living in a realm where nightmares didn't hold such power over us. But Phelan was right; if someone managed to open the mountain doors and ascend to the fortress in the clouds, and then furthermore break the century-old curse, the new moon would become a peaceful night. There would be no need for wardens.

"How can the curse be broken?" I asked. Not even the mountain descendants in Hereswith had truly known themselves, and their stories had been passed down to them from ancestors who had lived through the sundering.

"There are only rumors," Nura said. "But most madcaps believe it will come down to defeating a nightmare in the fortress."

"Phelan, I'm telling you," Olivette warned, pointing a speared olive at him. "If you so much as dare run off to the mountains without telling me and Nura, I'll kill you."

"You have nothing to worry over," he said.

"You talked about it once."

"Yes, once! When we were ten years old, Oli!" Phelan countered. "Do you even know how impossible it would be to reach the mountain summit? The doors are enchanted, and no one has been able to open them."

"It would be an adventure—"

"That would see us all killed," Phelan concluded.

"Anyway, Anna," Olivette said with a sigh. "You'll let us know if he changes his mind?"

"I promise," I said, and to her great delight, I clinked my goblet to hers and Nura's.

When Phelan and I left the tavern, it was half past eight and deeply dark, and while the storm had ceased, the streets were slick with water, shining like obsidian in the lantern light. A chill had crept into the air; it finally felt like October.

"Are you cold, Miss Neven?" Phelan walked in stride beside me. He kept his gaze fixed ahead of us, because the streets were still busy, but I sensed that he missed nothing. Not even a slight shiver of mine.

"I'm fine," I said.

We continued onward in awkward silence, but I was pleased to discover that I was beginning to recognize the crosshatching of streets. We took a turn onto a quiet lane; oak trees stood as sentries along the curb and it smelled like moss and damp leaves and musty stones. We were nearly to his town house.

"May I walk you home?" Phelan asked, just before we reached his gate. He finally looked at me. A thread of dark hair had escaped his customary ribbon. I wondered how he would look with his hair loose, unbound. As if he knew my trail of thoughts, he frowned. I smiled in return.

"No, but thank you, Mr. Vesper." I took a step backward, but my eyes remained on his. "I'll see you tomorrow, then?"

He said nothing, but the rain returned, a cold whisper through the oak boughs.

I was seven full strides away from him when I heard his boots on the cobblestones, chasing after me.

"If you won't let me walk you home, take my jacket, or let me call you a cab," he exclaimed, and I pivoted in surprise. "At least take the umbrella."

He withdrew the small trinket from his pocket and uttered the charm to return it to its natural size. And when he extended the umbrella to me . . . I accepted it, my icy fingers brushing his.

I didn't want it. For all I knew, he had ensorcelled it with awareness, and the umbrella would track me all the way home. But nor could I refuse it, not when the rain turned earnest, drenching my hair and blouse in mere moments. Not when he was staring at me with such intensity, as if he feared I would catch a cold and die on him.

"Thank you," I said, clearing my throat to hide how rusted those words sounded. "That is kind of you. . . ."

"If you think I'm kind, then I've fooled you," he said tersely. Shocked by his admission, I watched the rain drip from his top hat. "I'm no better than all the other nobles at court, and all of us play a game, Miss Neven."

For one heady moment, I feared that he had seen through me. I thought I might have fractured, due to feeling soft at dinner with his friends. I resisted the urge to touch my face, to ensure my disguise was sound.

"I'll see you in the morning," he said in an abrupt tone.

I left him standing in the middle of the street, keen to be gone. I waited until I was two blocks away before I hailed a coach, grateful to be out of the rain. My mind whirled, off-kilter from the strange words Phelan had said to me.

If you think I'm kind, then I've fooled you.

I closed the umbrella and propped it against the bench.

When the coach was three streets away from my mother's home, I disembarked. And just in case my suspicions were true . . . I left Phelan's umbrella in the cab.

16

Word soon came of a nightmare, something I had been anxiously awaiting as the days were beginning to pass and no sinister dreams had emerged. I was in the library, watering Phelan's plants, when he brought the letter to me.

"Do you feel up to collecting a nightmare, Miss Neven?"

I set down the watering can. "Indeed. Am I to go alone, then?"

"It's one of the duke's nightmares," said Phelan, holding up the letter. Its wax seal was like a drop of blood. "Lord Deryn has heard of my new partner, and so this is an invitation to meet you. I would accompany you, but my mother has called me to one of her council meetings on the west side of the city, and I fear it will take me most of the day."

"I can collect the duke's dream on my own," I said. And then I realized that Anna Neven wouldn't know how to divine a nightmare, and I made myself hesitate. "What if his nightmare needs divination? I don't know how to do that yet."

"It won't require divination," Phelan replied, leaving the duke's letter on the tabletop. "His Grace always recalls his dreams with sharp precision. All you need for this visit is the book of nightmares, ink, and a quill. Does that sound acceptable to you, Miss Neven?"

"Yes." I started to gather what I needed. My hands trembled, and I was struck with an unexpected bolt of homesickness. I could almost deceive myself, pretending I was back home in Hereswith, packing what I needed to visit the Fieldings. A day that was only weeks ago, and yet how distant it felt now.

"As I mentioned," Phelan said, breaking my thoughts and handing me a leather satchel to pack my things. I carefully slid the book of nightmares within it. "I'll be gone until dark. But you are more than welcome to remain here and have dinner with Deacon and Mrs. Stirling. In fact, she will probably be offended if you don't."

I smiled. "Then I'll plan to have dinner here." I buckled the satchel and slid its worn strap over my shoulder.

"Very good. I should go now, but perhaps tomorrow I can teach you how to divine a dream?" he asked.

I nodded, and we went our separate ways.

The duke was waiting for me in his drawing room. The chamber was wide and brightly lit. The walls were wainscoted, and thankfully no mirrors were present for me to sidestep around. Spires of golden candelabras were positioned behind couches and chairs. The hearth was cut from blue-veined marble, crackling with a slow-burning fire. Tasseled curtains framed the tall windows, which overlooked the front garden and the street. Busts of heroes sat in corners, and a small olive tree grew in a pot before one of the south-facing windows.

I paused to soak in the grandeur. And I smelled the duke before I saw him; there was a strange scent in the air, like rotting parchment, followed by the sweetness of bergamot.

"You must be Anna Neven," he said.

I startled and spun to face him. My old etiquette training surged, and I dropped a proper curtsy, although the weight of the satchel made me look clumsy.

"It's an honor to meet you, Lord Deryn."

"Enough with formalities," the duke said with a smile. The sunlight gleamed on his perfect teeth. "I am the one who is honored to meet you today. Phelan is destined to become one of the greatest magicians in Endellion, and I am pleased to know that he has found a good match."

Destined to be the greatest, was he?

"Come, join me at the table," Lord Deryn said, ushering me across the room to a round card table. A tea platter was set out for us, with ginger biscuits and small sandwiches.

I sat and carefully arranged the book of nightmares on the table while the duke poured us both a steaming cup of tea. He looked to be my father's age, his hair an ashy shade of brown and trimmed short. The silver in his beard caught the sunlight, as did the trio of emerald rings on his slender fingers. He was dressed in black and gold, and beneath the brief flutter of his jacket, I thought I saw a small dagger sheathed at his side. But perhaps I was mistaken.

"Have you always been a resident of Endellion, Miss Neven?" he asked.

I took the teacup he offered and busied myself with adding cream and sugar. But my palms were perspiring. Lying to Phelan was not difficult, due to our history. Lying to Nura and Olivette was harder because I liked them, as was deceiving little Deacon. But lying to the Duke of Bardyllis's face? I was weaving a dangerous web, one that might catch me. "I have, Your Grace. My mother was a seamstress in the west quarter."

"Oh? Where, exactly?" he asked, settling into his chair across from me. He took note of my garments, which made me stiffen. "I am always on the hunt for a good tailor."

I swallowed a scalding sip of tea. My toes curled in my boots, and I commanded myself to hold it together, to spin the lie. "My mother passed away this past spring, Your Grace. Or else I'm sure she would be honored to work for you. She was of the lower class and was not employed in one shop alone but drifted to wherever she could find work."

"I see," he said, and I thought he was studying me far too intently. "That is unfortunate. And your father? Was he the one to teach you magic?"

"I never knew my father. My mother was a magician and she taught me everything I know."

"You must have been very close to her."

I nodded and dropped my eyes to my tea. To my relief, Lord Deryn ceased asking me any further personal questions, and I prepared to record his dream.

"This nightmare occurred last night, Your Grace?" I asked, opening my ink and scrawling the date, his name, and his address on a fresh page.

"It did," he said, crossing his legs and lacing his fingers together over one knee. "The dream begins in the red room of the mansion. It is spring at midday; the sunlight is pouring in through the windows, and pots of flowers and green vines are flourishing in the chamber, and I realize my brother is standing among the foliage." He paused to give me time to catch all his words on paper.

"Do you dream of your late brother often, Your Grace?" I gently asked, thinking of the duke's older brother, who had died years ago.

"I do," he replied softly, as if the memory still ached. "Returning to the dream . . . he asks me to walk the streets with him, because he is weary of meetings and councils and being trapped indoors. I agree, and suddenly the room melts away and we are walking Verdaner Street toward the open air market. That is when I sense something is wrong. There are too many people, too many noises, too much movement. I tell Charles we should return to the mansion, but he is intent on something ahead of us, something I cannot see. I lose sight of him, but then the crowd opens up. I push my way through to step within the empty space, only to find my brother's neck cut open, and he's lying on the stones, bleeding out."

I wrote every word, the quill's nib biting into the paper. The ink turned gold as I wrote, some crafty charm of Phelan's, and yet I wasn't moved by the duke's dream. I couldn't begin to understand why it rolled off me like rain, as this sort of nightmare used to be the kind that roused my compassion.

Perhaps it was because the duke had dreamt countless nightmares of his brother's death before, recorded in earlier entries. Perhaps it was because I had read so many nightmares as well as encountered them in the streets on new moon nights that I had begun to learn the slant of them.

This nightmare felt fabricated.

I didn't believe Lord Deryn had dreamt it last night.

"I fall to my knees," the duke continued. "I hold him in my arms as he dies. And I watch as his face turns pale as bone, and he tries to say something to me, but I cannot understand his final words."

I finished the recording and gave the ink a moment to dry. I glanced over the sparkling porcelain of the tea, the untouched biscuits and sandwiches, and met the duke's gaze. "I'm sorry, Your Grace. This is a very upsetting dream."

He bowed his head in acknowledgment, and I sensed the deceit as if it were a diamond hanging from his neck, sparkling with each of his unsteady breaths, giving him away.

I closed the book and began to pack, but I waited to rise only after the duke had stood.

"I hope you will be prepared to face the new moon alongside Phelan this upcoming week?" he asked as he guided me to the front door. "You lack experience, do you not, Miss Neven?"

I gritted my teeth but managed a smile. "This is my first new moon, yes, Your Grace. But I have been studying and preparing myself."

Lord Deryn waved his frantic butler away. Alone, we stood in the foyer; I was keenly aware that the duke had positioned himself between me and the door. The cloying fragrance of his cologne washed over me again. Sweet and musty. My head started to ache.

"I am reassured to hear that, Miss Neven. But may I ask you a few questions before you depart?"

"Of course, Your Grace." My fingernails dug into the strap of the satchel, marking the leather with crescents.

"If Phelan is wounded on the new moon . . . would you abandon him in the street to save yourself?"

"I would never abandon my partner."

"Even if it meant your own pain or demise?"

My mouth was parched; I drew in a shaky breath, a medley of bergamot, old wet paper, and my intense desire to leave. "Even so, Your Grace. I'm not one to abandon my duties."

The duke took a step closer to me. I resisted the urge to shift backward, but I had a spell ready. One that would freeze him to the floor if he so much as tried to touch or threaten me.

"Are you aware that Phelan was wounded a few months ago, Miss Neven?"

"Yes."

"Did he tell you what wounded him?"

"No."

"Perhaps you should discover it, then. As you are his partner, he should confide in you."

"You don't know what happened, either?"

"He hails from a very secretive family. But I have no doubt

that you will soon be privy to the truth. Or perhaps encounter it on the new moon. If you learn of anything, Miss Neven, you will inform me, won't you? I pay well for information—riches, jewels, prestige. Position. If you wanted to be warden elsewhere, I could make it happen for you."

"Y-yes, Your Grace," I said, and the words were thick as thistle-down in my mouth. I felt numb as I sorted through the tumble of what he was asking of me, what he was offering me.

Did he know who I was? But how would he? I had never met or spoken to him before, when I was Clementine. And then I realized . . . he thought I was trying to climb the social ladder among wardens. Becoming Phelan's partner was a swift way to do so, in particular for a homely girl with meager beginnings.

At last, the duke unlocked and opened the front door for me.

I curtsied and swiftly departed. I felt his gaze as he watched me walk the stone path and slip beyond the iron gate. But I didn't dare glance behind to meet it.

I sensed he was coercing me, lying to me. A game among nobles.

And I was beginning to think he knew I was lying, too.

17

"You have to stay for Seven Wraiths!" Deacon begged me after dinner.

Night had just stained the windows, and I was anxious, waiting for Phelan to return from his council meeting. Suspicions of the duke and his fabricated dream continued to roam in my thoughts; I wondered if I should say something to Phelan.

"Maybe tomorrow night, Deacon," I said, carrying my plate into the kitchen.

Deacon intercepted me. "Please, Miss Neven!"

"Seven Wraiths sounds like a frightening game," I said in a teasing lilt. But my upbringing inevitably reared; all those times my father had told me how harmful the game was. That I should never play it.

"It isn't too scary," he insisted. "I promise. My grandmama plays, and she doesn't get scared."

"Deacon? Where are those plates?" Mrs. Stirling called from the kitchen.

"*Please,*" the boy pleaded.

"All right, but just *one* round," I said, and let him take my plate. "I still need to get home tonight."

"You should stay the night here, Miss Neven! I saw Mr. Vesper had a room prepared for you!" Deacon chirped before he slipped into the kitchen.

At last, I thought, weary of all the precautions I had to take in order to arrive at my mother's unnoticed. Weary, and yet something else pulsed within me, similar to the feeling I experienced before a new moon unfolded.

I stepped into the drawing room.

Mrs. Stirling had already stoked a fire in the hearth and lit the candelabras. The chamber was a dance of shadows, light, and the flash of golden trim, and I looked at the grand mirror hanging on the wall. As if it had set a hook in me, I walked to stand before it.

My reflection stared back at me. A face I had nearly forgotten. A face that felt like a stranger's now, as if a girl I had never met stood on the other side of the glass, watching me as I watched her.

You're not trying hard enough, said the girl in the mirror, touching a stray thread of copper hair. *You've been passive here, Clem. Do you expect this family's secrets to rise and meet you on their own volition?*

I turned away from the mirror, but my blood was coursing. I sifted through what I had gleaned so far. My father had once worked with the countess, and there was bad blood between them now. The countess was an artist. Her husband had died, years ago. The duke was fabricating nightmares and seemed far too interested in Phelan. Phelan had been wounded by something he was afraid to name and the duke was desperate to know. Lennox wanted Hereswith for reasons I had yet to learn. The seventeenth of November may or may not be a date of importance. But I didn't quite see how this all worked together or how I was going to regain control over my ability to return home.

My thoughts broke when Deacon arrived, wide eyed with delight. He made a beeline to the game cupboard, rustling around its shelves for a deck of cards. Mrs. Stirling joined us, bringing in a tea tray with sugar cream pie, and the three of us gathered around the card table.

I watched as Deacon expertly dealt five cards per player between a spoonful of pie.

"Do you know how to play, Miss Neven?" he asked, crumbs falling from his mouth.

"No, I've never played this game, Deacon. Why don't you explain the rules to me?"

"You know the legend of the mountain duchy, don't you?"

"Yes, of course I do."

"Then you know about the seven members of court who were cursed when the duke was killed?" Deacon queried.

"Yes. . . ."

"You know what they were cursed with, Miss Neven?"

"They cannot die or dream," I said.

"Right," he confirmed with a mischievous smile, as if this were a delightful fate. "So we call them *wraiths*. Anyway, there are seven wraiths in this deck. They're bad—if you draw one, you'll want to find a way to get rid of it by trading with one of us."

"Why don't you explain the game from the beginning, Deacon," Mrs. Stirling suggested.

"Oh, yes," he said, sheepish. "You have five cards in your hand, Miss Neven. Don't let me or my grandmama see them. You want to be able to discard one of your cards here, but it has to match in suit or in number. If you can make a match, you don't have to draw from the deck. If you can't make a match, you have to draw a new card, or you can try to trade a card. The goal is to be the first person to get rid of all your cards, but it's tricky, because you might have one of the wraiths in your hand. And that's the last thing you want at the end of the round. If you lose, you'll have a terrible nightmare when you fall asleep."

I studied the five cards in my hand. Two diamonds, a spade, and two of the wraiths. *Beginner's luck,* I thought with a snort, but then studied the first wraith card closer.

It depicted a middle-aged man dressed in blue robes. Moons and stars were stitched on the edges of his sleeves. His face was melancholy, his head bent, one hand over his heart, the other lifted as if he were in the throes of making a plea. His hair was blond until I tilted the card and the color changed to a fiery red. Or perhaps it was a cascade of blood, which began to drip from the ends of his hair, marring his raiment.

Breathless, I tilted the card again and his hair returned to gold, and the blood marks vanished.

A *deviah* magician had created these cards. A magician highly skilled in art who knew how to layer enchantment within the illustration. Something I once longed to achieve. I felt an ache in my chest and I quickly tamped it down.

The second wraith card surprised me further; it was completely blank, save for the title at the footer: *The Lost One*. But when I angled the card to the light, a scene bloomed on the parchment. Stone walls, blue banners, trestle tables. The grand hall of a castle, with an empty throne on the dais.

I had read about this place before, in Knox Birch's dream. This was the fortress in the clouds, the holding of the Seren Duchy. A chill snaked down my spine as I tilted the card again, watching the scene vanish once more, as if it had never been.

"Miss Neven!" Deacon scolded. "Now I know you're holding not one but *two* of the wraiths! Me and Grandmama won't want to trade with you this round. You have to keep them secret."

"Deacon," Mrs. Stirling warned. "Be nice. This is Miss Neven's first time playing."

I was hardly listening; I studied the first wraith card again. Inscribed at the bottom was the cursed man's title. *The Advisor.* "What are the titles of all the wraiths? It's been a long while since I heard the legend."

"The heiress, the advisor, the master of coin," Deacon began, listing them on his fingers. "The spymistress, the lady-in-waiting, the guard, and the lost one."

"And who is the lost one? I don't see them on the card."

Exasperated that I had now informed him of the exact wraith I was holding, Deacon said, "They are the one who was left behind in the fortress when the duchy fell. As punishment for killing the duke. Everyone else fled before the nightmares arrived."

I wondered if the lost one was just a myth, or if they still lived and breathed, alone in the abandoned fortress on the mountaintop. If they had ever stood on the parapets and looked down into the valley, down to where Hereswith had resided among lush grass and trees. And I remembered Imonie's story, the one she had told me just after we had left home. A legend about the woman with her twin boys and how one of her sons had been lost to the mountain, unable to leave its shadow. Imonie's tale had not stated why one twin was doomed to be trapped, but I supposed that legend complemented the game of Seven Wraiths. If the lost one was the assassin, the curse would not permit him to leave.

"Are you ready to play now, Miss Neven?"

"Yes, I understand the rules," I said. "Let's play."

Mrs. Stirling went first. She set down the three of hearts, to match the three of diamonds that sat faceup on the table, which provoked a groan from Deacon. My turn came next, and I laid down one of my diamonds. Deacon did not have a match for the discard pile and asked to trade a card with Mrs. Stirling.

A few more turns passed around the table, and then my wish was fulfilled: I drew another wraith card from the deck.

The Spymistress. A woman whose age was hard to decipher with her smooth, angular face and long white-blond hair. She was slim and sinewy, dressed in black and dark stained leather, and when I tilted the card, horns bloomed from her head, leaves grew within her tresses. A trail of smoke escaped her mouth.

I froze, gaping at the card. A troll. The spymistress of the fallen mountain court was a troll.

"Miss Neven!" Deacon cried. "You have to guard your face! Now I know you have another wraith card in your hand!"

My attention remained fixed upon the card, how the spymistress changed in my grip according to which angle I looked upon her. Human. Troll.

Mazarine.

I thought of her hoard of secrets, her clever disguise, the old magic she knew. How time seemed to hold no power over her.

Deacon and Mrs. Stirling beat me in that round of Seven Wraiths; I conceded with the advisor, the spymistress, and the lost one still in my hands. But I gained a morsel of knowledge, something that could only come from defeat.

Mazarine had once been the spymistress of the mountain duchy.

She was one of the seven cursed, which meant she could not die, nor could she dream. And if she could not dream, surely my father would have known.

All this time, a wraith from Seren had been living beneath his watch, in our town. And he had never said a word about it.

"Miss Neven? I have a guest room prepared just for you," Mrs. Stirling said to me after four rounds of Seven Wraiths, rounds I had encouraged so I could hold each of the doomed cards. To my own demise and Deacon's victory. "Mr. Vesper asked that I do so, in case you wanted to spend the night here."

I stood in the foyer. It was late—half past ten—and Phelan still had yet to return. I hoped he would stay away longer still.

"I'm not sure, Mrs. Stirling," I said. "I wouldn't want to intrude."

"Oh, my dear! You would not intrude. Mr. Vesper and I both worry about you walking home at night."

I hesitated, but eventually nodded. "I *am* rather weary."

"Come, let me take you to your room," she invited me, and began to ascend the stairwell. "Take care, though. These stairs tend to be slick on odd-numbered days."

The steps were a bit slippery, I noticed with amusement as I followed her to the second floor. The air smelled like roasting wood and evergreen, like meadow grass and the dust of old books.

"I've always loved this room," Mrs. Stirling said with a pleasant sigh as she opened a door, lighting a few candles. "It has a wonderful view of the back garden, and on clear days you can see the sunset."

I followed her into the bedchamber. The room was square, its wallpaper printed with climbing ivy. The bed was a good size, swathed in a canopy, and there was an armoire, a writing desk, and two windows trimmed with dark green velvet drapes.

And an oval mirror, hanging on the wall above the washbasin.

I stopped before I could pass by it, and Mrs. Stirling finished lighting the candles, reflexively spreading a stray wrinkle from the duvet cover.

"There's also some new clothes in the armoire, if you would like to change, Miss Neven," she said.

"Where do you and Deacon sleep?" I asked.

"Oh, we don't live here. I live four doors down and will be here before first light to get the fires started and breakfast cooked."

I hadn't realized that I would live with Phelan alone. I had assumed Mrs. Stirling and Deacon lodged here. This was certainly a detail to keep from my father, and I hoped he would understand that my plan had finally taken root, and not worry when I failed to show up tonight. Tomorrow was Monday, anyway. I would have the evening off to go to my mother's and explain the new arrangement to them.

"And you're certain Mr. Vesper won't mind me staying here . . . with him?" I inquired.

Mrs. Stirling smiled. "Not at all. Unless you feel uncomfortable with the arrangement, Miss Neven. And if that is so, I will sleep here tonight on the main floor."

"No, that won't be necessary," I rushed to say.

"Oh, Miss Neven," she said as if remembering something important, and reached into her apron pocket. "Best you take a remedy tonight, since you lost at Seven Wraiths."

I held out my palm and she dropped one of Phelan's vials in my hand. I proceeded to drink it, surprised by its sweetness. Honey with a hint of spearmint, and far more palatable than my father's recipe.

"Good night, Mrs. Stirling," I said, and waited until she had descended the stairs before I closed my door.

I went to the armoire first, curious to see what sort of garments hung within. There were a handful of colorful dresses, white chemises, embroidered bodices with ribbon laces, silk shirts, and skirts that seemed tailored to my size. Three different cloaks, to keep me warm on my walks. He had spared no expense. Pleased, I reached for one of the chemises. It was luxuriously soft against my skin, and I unbraided my hair and washed my face with lavender water before stepping into the corridor.

I listened to the strange sounds of the town house as Mrs. Stirling and Deacon left for the night, locking the front door. I listened to the walls pop and groan, as if the wood and nails had something to say to me. As if they knew I was here with ill intentions, and they protested my presence.

Quickly, I worked to set an alert charm on the front gate, so I would be warned of Phelan's approach when he returned home. I stepped into his room, where Mrs. Stirling had left a host of candelabras lit.

His bedchamber was modest, composed of earthen colors—greens and browns and grays. A mosaic of a forest graced one of the walls and a wardrobe sat in one corner, a writing desk in another. Stacks of books graced the floor, which I found surprising, since Phelan seemed to love tidiness. The curtains were drawn, and his four-poster bed was spacious, a canopy tasseled to the posts. A mirror hung on his wall above a wash station.

I went to his desk and sat down in a rickety chair, proceeding to open the drawers, minding how things were arranged. It didn't take me long to find the stack of correspondence, bound together with a red ribbon. A stack of letters, all of them addressed to Phelan.

Ravenous, I read the first one. A letter from the duke, and his handwriting was surprisingly crooked on the page, as if he had an unsteady hand.

Your debts have been paid. There is no need to thank me, but let's meet for tea this Friday, to talk about the new moon and how we can better prepare you.

Succinct and tantalizing. I wished there was more. The date read July 12. I folded it back into its envelope and moved on to the next. A bill, a receipt, a reminder about the dream tax, and how much Phelan's streets would owe. I passed through them all, the paper rustling beneath my hands. And then I came upon a small portrait.

The painting was of Lennox Vesper. He was young, perhaps thirteen, and he looked morose, as if the last thing he had wanted was to pose for a picture. The tone and style of art was familiar, like the feeling of crossing paths with someone I had met before, unable to recall their name. It tugged at my memory until I tilted the portrait, to study it closer. And Lennox morphed into Phelan.

I stared at this younger version of him. Still poised with a hint of sadness in his eyes, his dark hair bound by a ribbon. I watched him melt into his brother, and then back again, and I wondered what it would be like to have a twin.

It came to me then. The same artist who had illustrated the Seven Wraiths cards in the drawing room had painted the brothers' portraits. Phelan must know a *deviah* magician of art, and I was suddenly hungry to know for myself who created such wondrous portraits.

I continued to sort through the letters, sensing what little time I had left. A piece of parchment slipped from the stack, floating to the floor. I stared at it for what felt like an entire winter, and an icy finger traced my spine as I leaned down to recover it.

I recognized Phelan's writing. I had been reading it day after day in the book of nightmares, and I had come to know it well.

Stark and simple, the paper read:

Hereswith:
Ambrose Madigan, Warden.
Clementine Madigan, his daughter. Apprentice?
Partner?

I stared at my name.

Trembling, I tucked it away, burying it beneath a sea of wax-sealed envelopes and stray sheets of parchment and the two-faced portrait. I wanted more, though, even as my bones ached, and I was just opening another letter that looked to be from the countess when a chime sounded.

My alerting spell.

Phelan had reached the gate.

I was robbed of breath as I swiftly returned the contents to his desk, just as I had found them. But my hands quivered, and the tang of iron haunted my mouth as I rose, darting across his room, the firelight the only witness to my ransacking.

I shut my bedroom door just as the front door swung open.

I was already dressed for sleep; I climbed beneath my covers, sinking into the plush feather mattress. The light, I remembered a shallow breath later, and whispered a charm. The candles extinguished, one by one, leaving me in the cloying darkness of an unfamiliar room in my rival's house. Slowly, I slid down beneath the coverlet, my hair pooling beneath me on the pillow.

I heard Phelan's heavy footsteps as he ascended the stairs. He paused at the top, as if he sensed me in the guest room. I remembered belatedly that I had promised my father I would cast a ward on my door, on the windows.

Phelan retreated to his bedroom across the hall from mine, shutting the door behind him with a quiet click.

The house fell eerily silent.

My heart would not cease its strange, uneven beat. Was it becoming more stone, or cracking into more flesh? I couldn't tell, but it hurt to breathe deeply. I burned cold with fear and fury, and when I closed my eyes, all I could see was my name, bending to his handwriting in dark, bold ink.

18

"Someone arrived home late," I said, stepping into the dining room the following morning. Phelan was there, sitting in his customary seat. His dark hair was freshly washed and slicked back, and he sipped tea without making a sound, reading the morning paper while methodically cutting into a wedge of quiche. He was dressed formally, as he always seemed to be.

"And someone decided to sleep in my guest room last night," he countered with an arched brow, looking up from his paper.

His eyes traced my body. My hair was braided into a crown, and I was wearing one of the dresses he had had tailored, a simple yet elegant forest-green dress with flora and fauna embroidered on the bodice in golden thread. I waited for him to say something, and when he didn't, I sighed and relented to sit, reaching for the teapot.

"I won't take advantage of your hospitality again, Mr. Vesper,"

I said, filling my cup. "It was a one-night-only arrangement."

"Were you taking advantage of it, if I offered it to you?" he said, returning his gaze to his paper. But his attention was still preoccupied by me, and I didn't know if that was a good thing or a very bad thing. "You should stay here, Miss Neven. It would be easier for both of us, I think."

"For both of us?" I echoed, cutting a huge slice of quiche.

"Yes. I worry about you, since you refuse to tell me the neighborhood you live in or let me pay for you to take a horse and cab home every evening," he said in a flat tone, as if he didn't care that I kept secrets from him. Which made me think he did, rather deeply. "And there is that other matter."

"What other matter?" I asked. "Are you going to charge me for the wardrobe? You spent far too much on the garments, Mr. Vesper, and I might be indebted to you for years."

"No. The clothes are a gift, Miss Neven. I speak of how you are late for work. Every. Single. Morning."

I took a long sip of tea to hide my smile. I was purposefully late, just to irk him. "I'm afraid I cannot help that, Mr. Vesper. Every morning, there is some sort of carriage crash, and every market I have to pass through is so crowded one can hardly breathe, let alone move at a satisfactory pace."

"You could either leave home earlier, wherever that might be, or reside here."

"Hmm. A difficult choice."

"Should we flip a coin then, Miss Neven?" he said with a hint of sarcasm, snapping the wrinkles from his paper.

That was when the word first bloomed in my thoughts. *Exposé.*
I could write an essay on the Vespers, detailing how horrible they
were. I could submit it to the paper, anonymously. But I would
need more content than just detailing how they had stolen my
home. I needed to find the dirt they were hiding beneath their
perfect veneer.

"What's the cause for that smile?" Phelan asked, and I realized
that one had crept over my face.

I never had the chance to reply. The doorbell rang once, twice,
thrice. A harbinger of an impatient guest.

Before Phelan or I could so much as move, the table shuddered
between us, and Deacon crawled out from beneath it, leaping to
his feet with a flush of guilt.

"I'll get the door, Mr. Vesper!" the boy cried, and bolted down
the hall.

Phelan hefted a deep sigh but remained seated, pouring himself another cup of tea.

I was taking my first bite of quiche when I sensed the visitor's presence, like a winter shadow had fallen over the table.
And then I saw him from the corner of my eye, standing on the
threshold.

"Lennox?" Phelan said with surprise, rising to greet his brother.

I had thought about the moment when I saw Lennox Vesper
again. Thought about it so many times that it often made me feel
ill. But in my imaginings, the encounter had always happened in
Hereswith. Not in Phelan's town house, and not so soon.

It took everything within me—every breath, every thought,

every beat—to refrain from exposing my true self.

But my merciless heart grew hungry.

I took a long sip of tea, my gaze fixed on the upside-down print of Phelan's newspaper, but I watched the brothers from my peripheral vision.

"Lee," Phelan said again, walking to meet his brother on the threshold. "Why have you come? I wasn't expecting you."

"Who is that?" Lennox asked, and I felt the prickling of his stare.

I had no choice but to glance up at him and smile as if I had never seen him before.

"I'm Anna," I said in a pleasant tone. "Anna Neven."

Lennox stared at me for another awkward moment, and then he slid his heavy-lidded gaze to Phelan.

"Anna, this is my twin brother, Lennox," Phelan hurried to say, as if he was embarrassed by Lennox's rudeness. "Lennox, this is Anna Neven, my warden partner."

"A word, Phelan?" Lennox said. "In private." He vanished down the hall, his footsteps sounding in the direction of the library.

Phelan hesitated, glancing at me.

"I'll be fine here," I said.

I listened as Phelan rushed down the corridor, waited until I heard the door shut. I tossed down my napkin and rose, following them all the way to the latched doors of the library. I made sure not to stand before the stained-glass panels, where my silhouette might be noticed by them. Carefully, I coaxed my magic beneath the doors, where I could glean their voices.

"I'm disappointed in you, little brother. You couldn't find a prettier partner?" Lennox asked. "She's so plain. I would grow weary of looking at her every day."

Phelan was silent. When he spoke, his voice was clipped with anger. "Why have you come here, Lee? The new moon is only four days away. You should be in Hereswith."

"Hereswith," Lennox scoffed. "What a joke of a town."

"We have our agreement."

"Yes, yes, I know. I would take the town, you would continue work in the city. I'm tempted to switch our places."

I bit my lip. If the brothers switched places, I would be able to return to Hereswith. I would be home, but my father would not. . . .

"There will be no switching places," Phelan said coldly. "You wanted the town. You now have the town. We don't deviate from the plan."

"The people despise me. All they do is talk about Ambrose Madigan and his daughter with that fruit name."

"Remember your purpose, Lee. You won't have to be there for much longer."

"Yes, I know, *I know*," Lennox barked. "Which is why I'm here, Phelan. There's a problem. Dreams are missing from the book of nightmares."

"As we expected there to be."

"Not exactly." Lennox paced the library. The wooden floors groaned beneath his weight. "The whole purpose of us taking Hereswith was to find the dreamless sleeper. We expected one or two people to have nightmares absent from the record. An obvious and simple path to follow. But there are *nineteen* residents whose dreams are absent, by my reckoning. Nineteen! How am I supposed to find the one out of nineteen by November? That Ambrose Madigan was a wily one, as if he knew one day we would come, seeking the troll. He has protected her well."

My mind reeled.

By November.

My father protecting a dreamless sleeper.

Mazarine.

I remembered how she had asked me on the last new moon, *Tell me, Clementine . . . have you read one of my nightmares recorded in your father's book?* Had she been trying to prepare me for this? Had she foreseen what was coming? I sought to understand Papa's motive in protecting her. Was it simply so she could live in peace, or was someone hunting her? Someone like the Countess of Amarys?

The brothers continued to talk. "Honestly, Lee . . . that's not so difficult. Given that one of those nineteen was the actual warden. You should be able to discern which of the remaining ones are taking remedies every night, and which one is the actual dreamless sleeper, especially since Mr. Madigan has departed."

"Of course, I didn't expect Ambrose Madigan to dream!" Lennox snarled. "He was a warden and we do not risk encountering our own nightmares in the streets. But his daughter, whatever her name was . . ."

"Clementine," said Phelan.

The sound of him speaking my name was like an unexpected kiss on the mouth. I thought of it written on a stray sheet of parchment, tucked away in his desk like a secret, and gritted my teeth.

"Yes, *Clementine*," Lennox said. "She never dreamt, either."

"Which is not unusual, given she was her father's partner."

"She was not his partner but his *apprentice*, Phelan. She should have had a nightmare or two in that book, especially since she had been living there since she was eight years old."

A lull in conversation. My breaths suddenly sounded far too loud, and I feared the brothers had sensed my eavesdropping. I took a silent step back, my stomach in a knot, when I bumped into something. *Someone*, I realized, and turned to see Deacon lurking directly behind me, also eavesdropping.

I swallowed a curse. But now that I realized he was with me . . . well, I might as well linger a few minutes longer. I held my finger to my lips and Deacon grinned, delighted that I was joining him in his crime. We crept closer to the doors.

"Perhaps she drank remedies every night," Phelan said. "Her father was a warden, so perhaps he didn't want to encounter one of her nightmares in the streets on the new moon."

"Yes, I can see your point," Lennox grumbled. "But still . . . something doesn't sit right with me, Phelan. And that brings me to the next debacle: I've lost them."

"Who?"

"The Madigans! I set a charm on their wagon, to track where they went, as Mother desired. Ambrose must have sensed it and rerouted my enchantment. All this time, I believed they had settled in another town, a place called Dunmoor, not far from Hereswith. But they never stepped foot in that village. I've completely lost them, and Mother will have my head for it."

"Can you summon Mr. Madigan?"

"He scoured the house before they departed, so no. There's hardly a bootlace I can use."

Phelan sighed.

I was suddenly very thankful my father took such precautions.

"I'll see if I can locate them from here," Phelan eventually said. "You should return to Hereswith and gather any information about where they went from the residents."

"You're not going to inform Mother, are you?"

"No. *You* will be the one to tell her if we have truly lost them."

"Fine. If that is the way you want to play this . . . I should tell you that *he* was in a Hereswith nightmare, and not too long ago, either."

"What?" Phelan's voice was sharp. *"Who?"*

"You know who I speak of."

"What happened in the nightmare? What did he do?"

"Ah, unfortunately I can't tell you the details, brother. Such are the rules of wardenship, remember? Unless, that is, you want to switch places with me and take this dull little village off my hands."

Silence crackled. I resisted the urge to ease my spell further into the room, for fear of the brothers sensing my intrusion.

And then Phelan said, "Get out."

"Come now, Phelan. You should—"

"Get out of my house."

I urgently motioned for Deacon to follow me into the drawing room, and we rounded the corner just as the library doors burst open.

The mirror, I remembered with a hiss.

I dropped to my knees and crawled on the floor, and Deacon mimicked me, thinking I was trying to be covert. I slithered on hands and knees across the rug until the looming threat of the mirror had passed, and then I bolted upright and settled into one of the high-backed chairs, Deacon close behind me. He collapsed on the divan, and we both reached for a book to hold, pretending to read as Lennox and Phelan emerged into the foyer.

Lennox opened the door but paused to glance at me again, and I saw him shake his head, as if disappointed in his twin. My knuckles drained white as I held my book, the words swimming on the page before me. But then at last he departed, and Phelan slammed the door and leaned against it, as if he were overwhelmed.

I didn't look up at him until he walked into the drawing room and stood directly before my chair.

"Is everything all right?" I asked.

He was pale, and his eyes were distant when he met my gaze. "Yes, perfectly well. Deacon? Will you go and help your grand-mama in the kitchen?"

Deacon, who was trying to make himself invisible, groaned in protest but quickly obeyed, leaving Phelan and me alone in the drawing room. "I apologize for my brother, Miss Neven."

"What are you apologizing for?"

"That he is such an ass."

I shut the book and set it aside. "Don't apologize for him, Mr. Vesper. Although I suppose I will have to prove my salt, then, won't I? On the new moon."

"Why would you have to prove yourself?"

"Because I think your brother believes I'm destined to be a bad partner for you." I waited for Phelan to make a remark, but when he remained quiet, I added, "Why didn't you and your brother become partners? Surely the two of you would make a strong team?"

"On the contrary," Phelan was swift to respond. "I don't like working with him. We have fought together a few times before, and I hated every moment of it."

"Oh. I'm sorry to hear that," I said.

Phelan paced the drawing room and eventually returned to the foyer, where he retrieved his top hat and cloak from the rack.

"Are you going somewhere?" I asked, standing.

"Yes, I'm afraid something unexpected has come up and I must attend to it." He knotted the cloak draws at his neck and looked at me. "Will you stay here, Miss Neven? In case a request to record a nightmare comes in the post? With the new moon so close . . . sometimes the dam breaks and the dreams swarm."

I laced my fingers behind my back and nodded.

"Thank you," Phelan said, his voice soft with relief.

I watched him depart, felt the draft of crisp morning float into the house with his leaving.

And I sat back down for a moment, to gather my thoughts. A slight tremble racked my hands, and I stared at the inner curl of my fingers, wondering what I should do.

Because I knew why Phelan had left.

He was searching for my father and me.

19

I fetched a few nightmares, but the remainder of the day proved to be a boring Monday. Phelan was still gone by the time evening arrived, and I took great care with my stealth charm as I traveled to my mother's town house for my first night off.

Imonie's cooking greeted me in the foyer, and I all but groaned as I shed my cloak and followed the smells into the kitchen. My mother was setting the table, and Imonie was stirring a bubbling pot of stew. The warm air smelled of fresh bread and rosemary, and I drew it in deeply.

"Ah, there you are," Mama said, rushing to me as if I had been gone for weeks and not a mere day. She framed my face and studied me closely, and I almost blushed beneath her attentiveness. "I presume Phelan offered you a room?"

"Yes," I said. "My plan has gone off without a hitch."

"Take care, Clem," Imonie said, waving a wooden spoon my way. "Pride always sets a snare."

I sighed at her dourness but nodded, taking my seat just as I heard Papa descending the stairs. He looked weary, and even though he had just taken a bath, his fingernails were still dirty from working in the mines. I tried to imagine what it would be like, laboring from dawn to dusk, hidden from sky and sun. Working by the strained light of a lamp, swinging a pick and forgetting that you had once been a great magician.

It is almost like he is hiding from something, I thought as he sat across the table from me. And while questions swarmed my mind, I held my tongue, waiting.

"Is something wrong, Clem?" he asked. He was grumpy, which meant this conversation might go south if I wasn't careful.

"No. I'm here for my weekly dinner and check-in, remember?" I replied, explaining that I now had a room. He nodded, and while I talked, Papa noticed my nice clothes. He scowled but said nothing about them, to my relief.

Dinner wasn't what I expected. I thought it would feel effortless to return home and be with my family, in a place that felt more familiar than Phelan's town house. But to my shock, the air was tense, and conversation felt unbalanced, as if the four of us didn't know what to speak of.

I waited until dessert and tea before I brought up my news.

"The Vesper brothers were sent to Hereswith to find Mazarine."

Imonie nearly dropped the teapot. My mother froze with a fork in her hand, and Papa merely stared at me, as if he had imagined my announcement.

"Lennox is currently irritated," I continued, "because you have made it difficult for him to find who he seeks, all due to how you withheld more dreams from your ledger than he expected. Nineteen dreamers total, in fact."

My father raised his hand. I sensed my comment had offended him, and he said, "I have broken no laws of wardenship. I have recorded *every* nightmare that was dreamt during the time I was guarding the residents."

"That may be so, Papa. And perhaps you anticipated this happening someday, and you prepared years for it. But I want to know why. Why are you protecting Mazarine?"

"Mazarine Thimble?"

"Don't pretend. I know she's the spymistress of Seren. She's a wraith, and I want to know why you were shielding her."

"I was ordered to."

His quick response shocked me. "By who?"

"That I will not tell you, Clem."

I held his stare, suspicious. I had never doubted him before, and my breath turned shallow.

"Both Lennox and Phelan are hunting us, Papa, with the hope that we will identify the troll. And I think the countess ordered her sons to find Mazarine by November seventeenth," I said. "Does that date ring any bells to you?"

Again, the silence was thick enough to drown in. I glanced from Papa to my mother to Imonie. Why were they acting so strange?

At last, Papa dropped his gaze as he viciously cut into his pie, and said, "I have no idea what that date means. But thank you, Clem, for the news. I hope you're being very careful."

"Yes," I said, but I felt no better for having shared what I had learned. And even though Imonie's chocolate pie was my favorite, it suddenly tasted like ash in my mouth.

Phelan was home when I returned to his place later that night. I followed a trail of light into the library and found him sitting at his desk, his face buried in his hands, jacket thrown over the back of the chair. His cravat was untethered from his neck, his waistcoat unbuttoned down his chest, and he had cast off his boots. His socks were surprisingly mismatched. It was the most undone I had ever seen him.

I stopped just within the threshold, uncertain if he wanted my company until he raised his head and looked at me.

"Long day?" I gently inquired.

"Hmm." He reached for a teapot and poured two cups.

I drew up a chair, keeping the desk between us, and I accepted the cup. I studied him in the candlelight, the lines on his brow, the pallor of his face.

"I know this is none of my business," I began. "But if you tell me what's ailing you . . . perhaps I can be of assistance, Mr. Vesper."

He sighed and leaned back in his chair. "I'm looking for someone."

"Really? Who?"

"A magician."

"He must be an old friend of yours?"

"*She* is not an old friend."

"A former lover, then?"

He nearly choked on his tea. "No, not a lover. A rival would be a better term. She despises me."

"Ah," I said, pleased as I realized he was talking about me. "Why are you seeking this rival, then?"

"She possesses knowledge of something that's very important."

"And you think she would tell you as soon as you found her?" I countered. "Given that the two of you are not friends."

Phelan leveled his eyes at me. For a moment, I feared he had sensed my wicked amusement, savoring this humiliating moment of his, but he exhaled a long breath and said, "You're probably right, Miss Neven. Even if I found her, she wouldn't want to tell me anything."

"You could enchant her to tell you," I nonchalantly suggested, curious to know if he would do such a thing.

"No," he said swiftly. "That sort of magic is illegal and deplorable. But perhaps there is another route I can take."

I was wary as he stood and walked to his bookshelves. He pulled a leather-bound book with an illuminated spine, and turned through its pages until he found a loose square of parchment, tucked safely within the leaves. I watched, horrified, as he set that parchment on the desk. It was one of my charcoal drawings.

I went hot and cold all at once. This little drawing of mine was about to expose me.

How had he stolen it?

And then I remembered. The day we had collided on the street, when I had been studying the knight's sword mark on the cobblestones. My portfolio had fallen open, my drawings scattered in the wind. Phelan had helped me collect them, but I hadn't noticed him pilfering one.

I quelled my trembling and forced a calm mask over my face. I took the drawing in my hand, studying it as if I had never seen it before. My blood felt like molten gold, simmering in my veins. My chest ached as rock scraped against bone, and I determined in that split moment that this was a game I must win. I detached all emotion from my artwork.

"Is she an artist?" I asked, sounding as if I was only vaguely interested.

"Yes."

"She's not that accomplished. Why would you steal her artwork?"

"I . . . *what*?" Phelan frowned at me. "No, I didn't steal it."

"She gave it to you, then?"

"Well, no."

"Then you stole it." I set the drawing on the desk and leaned back in my chair. I drank the tea, hoping it would ease my dread.

"I found it," Phelan said. "A few weeks ago, I bumped into her on the street and some of her art came loose from the folder she was carrying. I helped her recover her pages, but it was not until after we parted ways that I found this one hung up on a bush farther down the road, carried by the wind."

"Why didn't you return it to her, then?"

He was pensive. I was coming to learn that I didn't like it when he was so silent.

"Never mind that." I stood so I could mirror him. "You have a way to find her now. Use this piece of her art to summon her to you."

"Yes, I was thinking to do such," he said, rubbing his chin. His gaze remained on my drawing, transfixed.

I needed him to do it *now*, while I was in the room with him. I couldn't afford to have him summon me when I was away.

Perspiration began to dampen my dress. I prepared for anything to unfold, readying my protective spell in case his summoning broke my disguise and I needed to flee. The enchantment waited on the tip of my tongue like a drop of honey.

I decided I should sit and settled into my chair. "Do it now, while you still have a few days before the new moon comes again. Summoning her will undoubtedly require much of your reserves."

"Have you ever summoned someone before, Miss Neven?"

"No. You?"

"Never. But perhaps you're right," he said. "I should summon her now, while you're here with me."

"And why is that?" I asked. "Do I need to protect you from her?"

He laughed. I realized I had never heard his laugh before. The sound was bewitching, even if it held a hint of scorn. "Yes, you might. She'll probably set a curse upon me when she realizes I've summoned her in such a way."

"Then maybe you should practice on me before you cast."

"Practice for what?"

"The words you will say to this magician when you summon her.

How will you explain yourself? You're about to burn her artwork."

Phelan groaned and paced the library. In and out of the firelight, the candle flames wavering with his apparent distress. "I don't know what to say to her."

"Well, that *does* present a problem," I said. "You need to have that figured out. What have you done to this magician? Why does she hate you? Is it justified?"

Phelan stopped, his back angled to me. "Yes. I stole her home, her territory. I disgraced her."

I rose and took a step closer to him, my blood singing. "Then you should start by apologizing to her. Genuinely. And then by telling her why you did such a terrible thing to her. And then ask for her forgiveness, preferably on your knees, for burning her drawing. Perhaps she will grant it to you."

He was silent, but he turned and stared at me with a ferocity that made my breath hitch.

He said, "That sounds a bit excessive, don't you think?"

"I suppose it depends on how badly you want to win her over."

"I don't want to 'win her over.'"

"Then what do you want?"

"I want to apologize," he said. "And I want to change what she thinks of me. Then, hopefully, speak candidly with her about the information I need."

"Do you remember what you once said to me, Mr. Vesper?"

He was quiet, regarding me.

So I continued, "You told me that you are not a *kind* person. So why go through all the trouble of apologizing?"

"Have you ever wanted to change someone's opinion of you, Miss Neven?"

"Not really," I replied. "You care very much for what others think of you."

"Don't you?"

"Does it look like I care?" I said, opening my arms.

His eyes searched mine, as if my secrets hid within them. "If you don't, then I wish you would bestow such magic upon me. I would like to not care as much as I do."

I approached him, ignoring how he tensed when I moved to face him, when only a slender space of air remained between us. Rain began to tap on the windowpanes. The night felt heavy and swollen with the storm; the shadows gathered knee deep in the corners of the library.

"If you want to learn," I murmured, "then it begins here." I laid my hand over his heart. "It begins when you acknowledge and respect who you are—scars and mistakes and victories and accomplishments all accounted for." I let my hand slip away, fingertip by fingertip, and watched his deep inhale, as if I had left a scorch mark behind. "Now. Summon her."

I returned to the safety of my chair.

Phelan cleared off his desk. He set my drawing over the center of the wood, along with a silver bowl, a moonstone, a knife, a candlestick. He next selected a spell book, leafing its ancient, crinkled pages open to a spell of summoning.

I watched as he read it, once, twice, as he began to utter the rivers of incantations.

He placed my drawing in the silver bowl and cut his palm with the knife. His blood dripped into the basin three times, marring the parchment, mingling with my art. Next, he held the moonstone over the wavering candle flame, until the stone seemed to come alive, a vein of light pulsing within it. He opened his bloodied palm and the stone gently lowered itself into the bowl, as if gravity had thickened. The moonstone came to rest over his blood and over my drawing. Smoke rose, a dancing blue tendril. The air smelled like cloves, like the wind from the mountains.

It was beginning.

"Clementine," I heard Phelan call. His voice echoed, resounded in my bones. *"Clem, will you answer me? Will you meet with me?"*

He was making no sound with his lips. The conversation was in our spirits—silence in our ears and yet thunder in our minds. His eyes were focused on the smoke as my drawing broke into flames, and my eyes were focused on him, the way the light washed over his face. His lambent eyes as he waited for me to materialize.

I prayed he would not look at me in that anguished moment when I felt the magic tug in my chest. I waged war against the overwhelming urge to rise and answer him.

Sweat beaded my brow, slipped down my back like a taunting fingertip.

"Clem," Phelan called to me again, his voice sharp and beautiful as glass in my mind. Reflecting prisms of color in every direction.

I forced my answer down, down in the tangled vines of my lungs and the wild briars of my being. And yet the tug turned bright and painful. I discreetly braced my feet on the legs of the chair. I held to the armrests, my knuckles strained white.

Hold to the chair, I ordered myself. *Don't move, don't rise, don't utter a sound. Don't answer him.*

The flames rose with crackling intensity, but just as swiftly as they rose did they begin to die. Once my drawing turned into ash, when the spell had nothing more to devour, it would end.

"Clem!"

I closed my eyes, trembling.

If he had only looked at me, he would have known. He would have realized that his magic could not summon me because I was already present.

But his gaze remained on the fire, and I was nothing more than a distant constellation in that moment, gleaming at the edges of his sight. When the flames surrendered into cold smoke, he let out a tremulous breath, slamming his palm on the wood in defeat.

I opened my eyes and looked at him. Phelan was ashen. Sweat dripped off his chin, and his eyes were bloodshot.

"Where is she?" I asked. My voice felt like sand in my throat.

He remembered me, at last. His gaze found mine and he sighed, lowering himself to his chair.

"I don't know. I must have done something wrong."

If there was ever a time for me to reveal myself to him . . . it was now. After this moment passed, things would change between us. I could feel it like the gradual shifting of a season, like autumn giving way to winter snow.

But I was silent, unyielding.

There was too much I knew—he and Lennox wanted to find

Mazarine—and so much I didn't know—what did they plan to do with Mazarine? If I revealed myself to him now . . . I wasn't sure what would happen, and I couldn't take that risk.

I left him in the library, my drawing burned into ashes and my heart beating far too swiftly for my liking.

20

The day of the new moon arrived like any other, save for the fact that I slept in that morning until I was rudely woken by Phelan knocking on my bedroom door.

"Miss Neven?" His voice melted through the wood as he knocked again. "Are you awake?"

I groaned and blearily took note of the daylight that snuck in through a crack in the curtains. It couldn't be later than nine o'clock, and I grumbled as I slipped from the bed, my hair a long, tangled mess down my back.

I opened the door to glower at Phelan, who had claimed I could sleep as late as I desired the night before, in preparation for battle.

To my immense annoyance, he had already showered and dressed. He smelled of soap and spicy aftershave and morning air. He had obviously taken a walk, and had probably already eaten breakfast as well.

"Yes, what is it, Mr. Vesper?" I sighed, and watched as he took note of my dishevelment.

He was speechless for a moment but quickly recovered by remembering what he held in his hands: a rapier.

"Are you sword trained, Miss Neven?"

I stared at the rapier he proudly held and arched my brow. "*This* is why you have woken me from the sleep you promised me last night?"

"I thought you would be up by now," he replied. "There's much to do to prepare for tonight."

"Yes, and I will be useless to you if I'm tired," I snapped, and then remembered myself. "Forgive me, Mr. Vesper. I'm rather grouchy until I've had my tea."

He smiled. A true, brilliant smile that warmed his eyes and made my stomach coil with warning.

"As I've learned, Miss Neven. Here, return to bed. I've brought breakfast to you, as well as your own rapier."

I stepped back and watched, utterly astounded as Phelan leaned the rapier against the door frame and reached for a tray of gleaming breakfast platters, which had been waiting in the corridor, just out of my sight.

"Will you please sit, Miss Neven," he said, taking the first cautious step into my room. "Before I drop this?"

Wordlessly, I returned to bed, and Phelan set the breakfast tray down before me and proceeded to remove the lids, exposing a bountiful breakfast of poached eggs, buttered toast, sliced fruit, diced potatoes with herbs, and a teapot with plenty of cream and honey to suit my appetite.

"Am I to expect this every new moon morning?" I asked as he poured me a cup.

"Perhaps," he teased. "Although the last thing I want is to reward your decadence of late morning sleep."

I rolled my eyes and added a dash of cream to my tea. "Well, then I suppose I shall soak in this grand gesture of yours now, since it may not come again."

"Do as you like, Miss Neven," Phelan said, returning to the threshold, where he had left the sword. "And then once you have eaten and dressed, meet me in the library for a lesson with your new rapier."

"I cannot wait," I said dryly, to which he only smiled again as if exceedingly pleased with himself and shut my door.

I was halfway through breakfast when I remembered the mirror that hung on my wall, and how I had completely forgotten the threat it posed to me. Phelan obviously had not caught sight of my reflection, but it was a sobering reminder of my foolishness. How I had let his thoughtful gesture distract me.

I finished eating and dressed, and I found Phelan in the library, sitting on the edge of his desk, leafing through a book.

He closed it the moment he caught sight of me, and rose with his perfect posture, only a thread of his dark hair defiantly falling across his brow.

I sensed the radiance about him, how his magic teemed in his hands. He was very anxious about this upcoming night, I realized, and I gave myself a moment to imagine what it would be like to fight alongside him instead of against him on a new moon.

The image seemed natural—the two of us on the darkest of nights moving in tandem, and I thought back to our new moon battle in Hereswith, only a month ago—and the ache in my stomach woke again, a flutter of warning.

"You never answered my question from before," he said.

I stopped halfway to him, a square of sunlight on the floor between us. "Oh? And what was that?"

"If you've ever been sword trained."

"No," I lied. My father had taught me how to handle all manners of weapons.

He held out a rapier for me to take. I closed the last of the space between us and took hold of the hilt carefully.

"You prefer to fight with weapons rather than spells on the new moon?" I asked.

"Spells always come first," Phelan replied. "But I've learned it's good to be armed as well."

I secretly agreed, remembering how I had once worn my weapon belt on new moon nights. How a blade had saved my life last time, when I had nearly drowned in a nest of lily pads and snakes.

I listened as Phelan introduced me to the rapier, instructing me on how I should hold it in my hand. When he demonstrated a few stances and thrusts, I mimicked him with ease.

"You have good form," he said with a hint of scrutiny.

"I'm a swift learner," I replied, and then took a daring slash at him.

Phelan was too slow in guarding himself. The tip of my rapier brushed his face and he lurched back with a hiss. I watched a line of blood well on his right cheek before he dropped his weapon and turned away from me.

"Oh, I'm sorry! Here, let me see it . . ." I followed him, setting my rapier down with a clatter.

He continued to evade me, face averted. "It's fine. I'm fine. Don't bother."

I didn't like him running from me. I reached out to snag his sleeve, guiding him to the desk. He surrendered, sitting on the edge of it, his palm pressed to the wound. Blood seeped through his fingers and I had a moment of panic, thinking I had cut open his face until he lowered his hand.

It was only a nick, but it was profusely bleeding.

"It's not as bad as it seems," I said. "Do you have a—"

He reached into his waistcoat pocket, and only when I felt his knuckles brush against my bodice did I realize how close I was to him. But I remained where I was, standing between his legs, and he knew what I wanted. He found his handkerchief, offering it to me with a wry smile.

"Don't smile," I scolded. "You're making the bleeding worse."

He winced as I pressed the handkerchief against the cut. I moved my other hand to the back of his head, my fingers weaving into his hair. He stiffened, as if I had pierced him to the bone. When I met his gaze, I found that his eyes were dark and inscrutable, riveted to my own.

"Is this punishment?" he whispered.

Yes, I wanted to say. Punishment for stealing my home, for burning my artwork. For not being as I expected.

"For what?" I countered, pressing harder on his cheek.

"For waking you too early?"

I tried to hem my laughter, but it escaped in a rush. "No, of course not. This was nothing more than an accident."

But I sensed that he struggled to believe me. And I realized that I hadn't laughed in a very long time as a soft ache bloomed in my chest.

"Who taught you how to handle a blade?" he asked. When his hand slid over mine . . . I was the one to turn rigid. The heat of our skin meeting seemed to burn right through me—a spark of wildfire.

"No one," I said, pulling away from him. "You should keep pressure on it, until the bleeding eases."

To my surprise, he was silent as I strode across the library. But I suppose he didn't like the thought of me running from him either, and his voice chased me just as I reached the doors.

"Where are you going, Miss Neven? Surely you are not conceding this spar to me."

I tarried on the threshold and cast a languid glance his way. "I won this round, Mr. Vesper. And I'm going for a walk."

Autumn hung golden in the air as I wandered. It was October sixteenth, and it felt as if a year had passed since I had lost Hereswith, not a mere month. I explored the streets' winding bends and corners until I felt as if I could walk their paths with my eyes closed and the sun was beginning to set.

I paused on the curb of our territory line, watching as a slight breeze rustled the oaks and people hurried home early, carrying parcels and packages from the market. Soon, this city would feel dead and empty, stricken with terror.

I was lost in such thoughts when I recognized Olivette and Nura walking toward me, hand in hand.

I reflexively turned away from them, wishing I had worn a hat or carried a parasol like some people of the city did, to hide beneath. I was surprised by the regret that suddenly welled within me. Regret that tasted bitter in my mouth, because I longed to befriend them, and yet I couldn't risk such a relationship.

I started to walk away, but Olivette saw me, and it was impossible to act as if I had not heard her bellow.

"Anna? *Anna!*" She frantically waved to catch my attention.

"Hello," I greeted her, and approached them. "So good to see you both again." And then all words fled when I saw what Olivette wore buckled around her waist—a leather weapon belt with two sheathed daggers. The twin to the one my father had gifted to me, years ago.

Nura noticed my stare and said, "It's tradition. Oli likes to walk our streets with her weapons before the new moon rises."

"It's for good luck," Olivette added.

"It's . . . a very nice belt," I stammered. "Where did you get it?"

"My father made it for me," Olivette replied. "If you like it, I can see if he can make one for you."

The sad fact was my own belt was at my mother's, tucked away in one of my trunks. Phelan would unfortunately recognize it; I remembered how he had studied my hips, the way my daggers had shone at the dinner table in Hereswith.

"Oh, no," I said. "But thank you for the offer."

"Would you like to join us?" Nura asked.

"I probably shouldn't. I was walking Phelan's streets, to reacquaint myself before tonight."

"They're your streets now, too," Olivette said. "And where is Phelan?"

"He already had his walk this morning. I would have accompanied him, but I was still sleeping."

"Ah, yes, we only just woke ourselves," Olivette confessed with a disarming smile. "New moons are the *only* morning Nura will let me sleep in so late."

I returned the smile. "Yes, well, I only had until *nine* until Phelan woke me for sword lessons."

"He's very anxious about tonight," Nura said, exchanging a concerned glance with Olivette.

"Is there a reason why he should be?" I asked.

"Did he tell you about his first new moon here? How he was wounded?" said Olivette.

"He briefly mentioned it."

"I think that's why, although he refuses to tell us what, exactly, wounded him so badly."

"And we don't feel it right to press him about it," Nura added. "But it worries us. It's been a year since a warden was killed on the new moon in this part of the city, but it does happen occasionally."

I chewed on my lip a moment, wondering. Phelan had mentioned his near death to me the first night I had shared dinner with him, when he had striven to win me over, but he had not further regaled me with details. It seemed everyone was anxious to know what had happened: Nura, Olivette, the duke. Me.

"Don't worry," I reassured them. "I'll guard his back tonight."

Olivette appeared relieved, but Nura appeared a bit doubtful.

"Good luck tonight, Anna," Olivette said.

"Same to you." I waved farewell to them.

I hurried back to Phelan's town house, the temperature dropping with the sun. A shiver nipped at my bones as I closed the front door behind me. Mrs. Stirling was in the kitchen, preparing dinner. The fragrant aromas embraced me in the corridor, and for a staggering moment, I was back home in Hereswith, and Imonie was cooking and setting the fine porcelain on the table. A place for me and a place for my father.

I laid my palm over the pain in my chest. I was learning how certain things were threats to the stone half of my heart. They were like swinging hammers, eager to form a crack within me, and I was struggling to know how to filter them into my life. Things such as memories of home, Deacon's smile, Nura's and Olivette's friendship. The way I sometimes caught Phelan looking at me.

I forced the memories haunting me into dust, until my homesickness was nothing more than a tiny trace, and I headed to the library. But Phelan wasn't there. I cast an inquisitive net of magic throughout the house, but I failed to sense his presence. He was gone, and I sat at his desk to read through the book of nightmares, only to discover the old tome was absent. *He must have been summoned to fetch a last-minute dream*, I thought, and leaned my head back in the chair, closing my eyes.

Just for a moment, I told myself, and drifted off to sleep.

I woke to the sound of Phelan speaking my name for the second time that day.

"Miss Neven?"

I jerked awake, rubbing a crick in my neck. He stood before me holding the book of nightmares, top hat perched slightly crooked on his head. His face was flushed from cool air, and the cut on his cheek had scabbed at last. Only a thread of sunset filtered through the library window; the rest of the room fell to shadows.

"Dinner is ready," he said, gently setting the book on the desk.

"I'm sorry," I croaked, my voice clogged from sleep.

"For what?"

I indicated the book of nightmares. "For being away. I should have accompanied you to fetch the dream."

"You didn't miss much," he said, removing his hat and tossing it onto the desk. "A recurrent nightmare, and one that is more bizarre than it is frightening."

I continued to rub the stiff muscles of my neck as I followed him into the dining room. Mrs. Stirling had set a feast of steaming platters on the table.

I took my seat first, and then Phelan sat across from me. There were only two places set at the table, for me and for him, and when Mrs. Stirling bustled into the dining room with a pitcher of chilled cider, I asked, "Are you eating with us tonight, Mrs. Stirling?"

"Oh no, my dear," she replied, filling our goblets. "Deacon and I return home early on these nights."

The nightmares wouldn't bloom until the clock struck nine, but I felt the anxious energy in the housekeeper as she set down the pitcher and smoothed the wrinkles from her apron. She was eager to be home with her shutters and doors locked against the night.

"Is there anything else I can provide for you, Mr. Vesper? Deacon and I have tended to all the windows, as well as the back door."

"No, Mrs. Stirling. You have outdone yourself, per usual. Thank you."

She curtsied and gathered Deacon and her cloak. "Good fortune to both of you tonight," she said. "I hope it is an early and effortless night."

"Don't worry, Mrs. Stirling," I said. "I'll take good care of Mr. Vesper."

I felt Phelan's gaze on me, but I resisted meeting it, smiling at Mrs. Stirling and Deacon instead.

"Good, very good," she murmured, scratching her eyebrow. "Don't worry about the plates after you eat. Just leave them on the table. I'll clean them in the morning."

And she was gone, Deacon in her shadow.

I returned to my meal, eating in companionable silence with Phelan.

It took me a moment to rouse my courage, but I finally did. "Are you going to tell me what wounded you moons ago?"

"I've thought many times on this," he said. "How to tell you of that night. But I can't find the words, Miss Neven."

"Oh." I was disappointed with his response, but I hid my feelings and finished my dinner. Silence frosted the table between us.

"I want to prepare you, but I'm uncertain as to *what* we can expect tonight, Miss Neven," Phelan said, breaking the quiet. "I apologize that I can't tell you more. Because of that . . . stay close to me tonight."

Stay close to me.

"I have already promised three of your friends that I will keep you safe tonight, Mr. Vesper," I whispered. "I suppose that means I have no choice but to knit myself to you, to ensure I don't break my own word."

That provoked a small smile from him. The scab on his cheek pulled, as if it wanted to break open again, and I wondered how long that mark would be there, reminding him of me every time he looked at it. He drank the rest of his cider, but he didn't touch his food again. I noticed his face grew wan as the hour progressed, that a sheen of perspiration had formed on his brow. And when he rose and carried his plate into the kitchen, I stood and followed him.

We put away the food in the icebox and washed the dishes, which was sure to evoke Mrs. Stirling's wrath the next day, as we had disregarded her command, but the action of doing something so simple seemed to calm Phelan.

We had another hour to burn.

Phelan built a fire in the drawing room hearth and I made a pot of tea, and we shared it before the crackling dance of the flames. Silent and pensive, waiting for the hands on the clock to tick their path to nine o'clock.

At a quarter till, Phelan rose and left the room.

I braided my hair out of my eyes and checked the buttons on my boots. I retethered the ribbon laces of my bodice, until I felt a pinch when I breathed deeply. I missed my weapon belt and my daggers; seeing Olivette's had stirred up emotions I'd thought I had buried. When Phelan returned to me, he had our two rapiers in hand. I accepted mine and belted it at my waist, a tremor of anticipation coursing through me.

"Shall we?" he asked with an elegant flourish of his hand, as if he were asking me to dance with him.

I was calm until that moment, when my memories crept back over me. The firelight of a cozy cottage, the fragrance of cherry galettes warm from the oven, my father leading me out into a star-dusted night, to the market green of Hereswith. My longing was keen; I wavered for a moment, thinking I might fracture.

I missed those old days. I wanted to return to them until I finally acknowledged that such a thing would be impossible. My life had changed seasons; I could never go back to how things had been. And when I met Phelan's dark gaze, my nostalgia melted away, leaving me standing in a world I had made.

We walked to the foyer with five minutes to spare. I followed Phelan out into the moonless night, as if I had done it a hundred times before.

21

Auberon Street felt cold and dead, like the crooked path of a graveyard. I walked beside Phelan, fog beginning to pool in low places, waiting for the clock to strike nine. I could feel the tension in him when our elbows accidentally brushed; his face looked ghostly pale in the lantern light.

I reached out to touch his arm, and he stopped, as if I had burned him.

"Mr. Vesper," I said, "it's going to be all right. This will be over and done with before we know it."

He sighed and turned to regard me. We had two minutes remaining until the new moon unfolded. The wind was beginning to intensify.

"You must be wondering why I'm so anxious," he stated. "It has to do with the truth that I don't deserve to be here."

I frowned up at him, thinking now was not a good time for

such dramatic statements. "Why not?"

He reached into his jacket for his pocket watch. "Because I wasn't born with illumination. I wasn't born with the magical flame, like my twin brother was. Everything I've accomplished I've had to learn. It took me many grueling years of lessons."

I almost laughed at his ridiculous statement, but thought better of it, as that was something Clem would do. Anna, on the other hand, would be impressed.

"Then that only solidifies your place and accomplishment, Mr. Vesper," I said. "You've earned the right to be warden here."

His watch chirped, and I knew the time had come. He slipped the golden orb back into his pocket and looked at me, whispering, "We can talk more about this afterward."

I wondered if he had even heard my compliment. He turned away from me, so that our backs were aligned.

We watched the street, my gaze fixed on the southern end while his scanned the north.

It was the sort of quiet that makes you fearful to breathe too loudly. The fog continued to gather, and my feet were cold in my boots as I strained to see through the mist.

Was this the element of a nightmare? I racked my mind, trying to recall if I had read any entries in Phelan's book that were made of fog.

"Look to your right, Miss Neven," Phelan said, and while his voice was calm, I knew the nightmare had begun.

I looked to see the row of town houses, shuttered and bolted with only stray beams of firelight slipping through the cracks.

And then I saw it, a heraldic banner unrolling from the roof, covering the house's face with a proud bolt of blue. Silver moons were stitched upon it, and diamonds winked like stars in the fabric.

"That's the mountain duchy's banner," I breathed, my memory surging.

"So it is," Phelan agreed, and we watched as more banners and tapestries unrolled from the roofs of houses around us, flapping slightly in the breeze.

The cobbles beneath me hummed, and I glanced down to watch them become large, smooth flagstones in shades of copper and gray, freshly swept. The air smelled of fresh sun and sweet red wine.

I knew where this dream had taken us. Phelan and I were standing in the fortress in the clouds, in the hall of the mountain castle.

"A dream of the Seren Duchy," I said.

"Did you ever read Knox Birch's most recent nightmare in my book, Miss Neven?" Phelan asked.

"Yes," I whispered, and I remembered it with a shudder. Mr. Birch had dreamt of the Seren throne and had unknowingly cut down his wife and two daughters in his hunger to claim it. "Do you see the duke's chair?" I asked, unwilling to take my eyes from the southern end of the street.

"Yes," he said. "It's ahead of me."

"Then Mr. Birch will be coming from my direction."

"Do you want to trade places?"

"No," I said, but I drew my rapier. "I'll tell you when I see him approaching."

I had yet to meet Knox Birch in the flesh—I had only read the account of his dreams—but I knew he lived one street over. I waited for him to appear, my palms slick with sweat.

At last, a man emerged from the darkness, striding through swaths of fog. He reminded me of my father, middle-aged and tall, with hair the color of a faded penny. His eyes gleamed gold, as if he was haunted, and yet his face was cold and merciless, like nothing could break him from his ambitions.

"He's coming," I said.

Phelan turned, and I felt a swell of cold air wash over me as he put some distance between us.

"He cuts down three shadows," he reminded me. "I suspect you and I are two of them."

I thought the same, but I had no time to agree with him as a woman with a pale, sorrowful face and long hair materialized from the shadows. Knox's wife, I realized, and she boldly intercepted him, pleading, "Please, Knox . . . please don't do this. Choose us, *choose us.*"

A rapier bloomed in his hand. He cut her down quickly, his blade piercing her core. She fell with a sickening thud, crumpled as a rag doll on the flagstones, her blood spreading beneath her like a crimson cloak. I knew he saw only a sinister shadow. He didn't see her until the end, when he got what he thought he wanted: a place in the duke's chair.

I was the next barricade in his path.

I drew in a deep breath and cast a spell net over him, one that would slow his movements. I sought the key of the dream—the crux to break the nightmare—and thrust my rapier at him, aiming at his heart. He blocked it, his movements like honey warming over fire, returning to their previous swiftness. We continued to circle each other, lunging and parrying, until the cross guards of our blades met; I was in the throes of uttering another spontaneous charm to freeze him to the stones, but the force coming from him slung me back and away. My hand tingled from the jar of clashing steel and I bit my tongue, my charm dissolving. I stumbled but Phelan caught me, ushering me behind him while I regained my balance.

I watched as he engaged Knox in a fraught spar, eager to rejoin the fight.

A new spell was rising within me like a song. I took a step forward and winced when I felt a sudden blaze of pain. My belly stung with the movement, and I glanced down to see the bottom half of my bodice hung open, its ribbon laces sliced into dangling shreds. I laid my hand over the torn fabric and felt something warm and sticky. My blood, I realized with a pang of shock, staring at its red stain on my palm. Knox's rapier must have grazed me, but the cut wasn't deep, to my immense relief. Although a few inches deeper and he might have given me a mortal blow.

I returned my focus to Phelan, sparks blazing along his rapier as he continued to fight. Knox wasn't slowing or wearying; he was like a storm, gathering strength, pushing us closer and closer to the dais and the throne. And when he nearly cut Phelan in half, I cast another charm to slow him down. As soon as Knox felt my enchantment hinder him, his face snapped toward me, furious. I met his gaze as steadily as I could, even as it intimidated me. Within his eyes, gold shone like two coins catching the light.

"His eyes," I said to Phelan, my voice ragged. The gold in his eyes had become a film, preventing him from seeing through the veil of his greed. "The dream's weakness *is his eyes*."

Phelan heard. He had to lurch back to avoid being skewered by Knox's blade, but the momentum swung around in his favor. He aimed and thrust the point of his rapier into Knox's left eye, and the gold that covered his pupil burst and ran down his face like ichor.

Knox went still and then gasped—his moment of realization—before falling to the ground in the puddle of his wife's blood.

Phelan withdrew his blade, watching the nightmare reach its harrowing end.

I stood a few paces behind him, staring at the blue banners on the town houses, the moon and stars and the promise of mountains, waiting for them to melt away, for the nightmare had been championed. But the banners remained as stubborn fixtures, and the flagstones and the duke's chair refused to fade. The elements of the nightmare were firm and solid in the street.

Something wasn't right.

Phelan was breathing heavily behind me. When I glanced over my shoulder, I saw he was still staring at Knox and his wife, their bodies refusing to vanish on the stones, and I had a sickening thought that perhaps it had all been real, that Phelan and I had in some way been fooled.

Had there been more to the dream, and Knox Birch had failed to divulge it to Phelan?

"Mr. Vesper . . ."

My voice died with the wind. The world around us became silent and still, as if we were trapped in a painting of a forgotten place, and then I heard it—the clink of armored feet approaching. A heavy, methodical gait that made the flagstones tremble beneath me. Silvered footsteps I had once heard before in a dream that didn't belong to me, but a dream I had divined.

"My gods," I whispered. It felt like a bone was wedged in my throat as I waited for the knight of Elle Fielding's dream to appear, his footsteps growing louder, louder, the dream rippling around me like it was under duress.

I forgot where I stood, where I was. I forgot about Phelan at my back, my entire being focused on this inevitable meeting.

And then the knight appeared, the fog swirling around him.

I had only seen his legs and feet in Elle's dream, when she had been crouched beneath the wagon. Now I beheld his entire self, fully covered in steel-plated armor that was splashed with blood. He was tall and broad as he walked with purpose, striding toward us. But it was not the blood or the long sword that he unsheathed at his side that coaxed my horror. It was the helm he wore, a helmet forged with tapers at its brow. Seven sharp points crowned him. I couldn't see his eyes, but I felt his piercing gaze.

Terror held me until I felt a warm hand take hold of my arm, drawing me back.

"Get behind me, Miss Neven," Phelan said.

As soon as I felt his presence, his magic's illumination overlapped with mine and bolstered my courage. I inhaled a deep breath, flexing my hand.

We walked backward in unison, to give ourselves more time to hammer a plan together. The knight followed with his steady pace; he seemed fixed on that gait. He couldn't run, but neither could he slow. We were faster but he was persistent, and I was uncertain about his weakness.

"Who is this?" I whispered to Phelan as we continued to walk backward, our eyes trained on the knight.

"I don't know. But he's the one who wounded me, months ago."

"You fought him?"

"Yes. Weapons are useless against him, as are any offensive spells."

I didn't quite believe Phelan, and I cast a disarming spell on the knight. My magic hissed into smoke when it met his breastplate, and he continued following us, undeterred. I tried again, desperate, to no avail.

"Save your magic, Miss Neven," Phelan said dryly.

"He must have a weakness." I studied the knight's armor. "He can't be wholly invincible."

Phelan was quiet, but then he said, "There are two of us and one of him. I will slip behind while you engage him."

I nodded and threw a blast of light at the knight's feet, to cover Phelan's movements. But it was futile; the knight sensed Phelan's presence and turned with him, swinging his sword. Phelan ducked and rolled, barely missing the edge of the blade, and I surged forward, anger smoldering within me. I roused that fire and funneled it, and my magic streamed toward the knight, striking him in the spine and limning his armor as if he had been electrified by lightning. He hesitated, and I took that moment to study the plates of steel and chain mail, searching for a golden scale or link that I could puncture and usher his demise. There was nothing, and he pivoted so swiftly he took me by surprise.

I lurched back in response and saw his sword arcing for me. Everything suddenly slowed. My motions, my breath, my heart. A warning prickled at the nape of my neck, and this horrible encounter felt strangely peaceful. This moment before death. This moment before the knight beheaded me.

I felt a hand on my ankle, a warm hand that pulsed with both life and terror. It yanked me so hard that I went down on the flagstones with a jar, my rapier tumbling from my hand. The knight's sword whistled harmlessly above me.

Phelan, I thought, dazed from hitting the ground. His magic clung to my ankle and he pulled me quickly to his side, over the stones.

I scrambled to my feet, swallowing the tang of iron, and I wiped the blood from my lip and watched as Phelan resorted to his rapier. The knight's blade broke Phelan's like it was made of glass.

Phelan stumbled back, but his opponent followed. I roused my magic just as the tip of the sword caught the front of Phelan's waistcoat. I heard the fabric rip, heard his grunt of pain, and he was hurled up and away as if he had been struck by a giant's hand.

I kept my eyes on the knight, despite the nagging temptation to look at Phelan. I heard him hit the flagstones behind me, and I coaxed the light of my hands to flood the knight's helm. His focus shifted to me, and I suddenly became aware that I was too close to him. I was within his striking range, and I had no choice but to flee to where Phelan was sprawled in the center of the street, his blood blooming like a rose across his torn waistcoat.

"Phelan," I breathed. "*Phelan*, can you stand?"

We only had moments before the knight reached us. His heavy tread began to sound again, and I reached down to haul Phelan up to his feet.

His eyes were glazed, but he responded as I supported his weight, his arm draped over my shoulders.

"To the house, Miss Neven," he said, his voice wispy as if he was about to faint. "If you please."

I wildly searched for his house, my bearings lost in the fray. I knew it must be nearby—we hadn't strayed far from it when the nightmare manifested. And then I saw house eleven, with its gray brick and climbing ivy, three doors away, and my relief nearly crushed me as I began to haul him to the front gate, the knight hounding us.

Don't look behind you, I ordered myself, even though I wanted to see how close the knight was to catching us. *Don't look down*, even though I wanted to see how much blood Phelan was losing.

My eyes on the door, Phelan limping at my side, the knight hounding us. This new moon was unraveling around me.

I dragged us through the gate, up the path and porch steps, the lantern light flickering as if beckoning us to hurry, hurry, *hurry . . .*

"The key," Phelan moaned. Of course, he had locked the front door when we had departed, and I frantically searched his pockets. He was steadily bleeding, and it coated my hand as my fingers darted from pocket to pocket.

The front gate creaked behind us; the knight was in the yard. Cold air washed over my back, like winter had arrived early. The ivy on the trellis withered; frost spangled the shutters. At last, I found the iron key, tucked within the inner pocket of Phelan's jacket, and I struggled to unlock the door, my hands numb, trembling.

"Miss Neven," Phelan whispered into my hair. *"Anna . . ."*

He was begging me to rush, because the knight was only steps away from cutting us both down.

I kicked the door open and heaved Phelan inside. Every fiber within me burned from exertion; I had to let Phelan go. He slid to the hardwood floor, groaning, and I turned to see the knight ascending the porch stairs, four steps away from us. From *me* as I stood on the threshold, watching his approach. An unspoken challenge glimmered like an enchantment between us, waiting to be inhaled and spoken.

Who are you? I wanted to ask, but my voice was a splinter in my throat.

"Anna," Phelan panted. "Anna, lock the door."

My ears roared. The floor seemed to tilt as the knight stared at me, as I stared at him. I thought I saw the sheen of his eyes in the slits of his helm. The sheen of something alive and angry and ravenous. The knight lifted his sword in one hand, but with the other he reached for me.

"ANNA."

Phelan's desperation dashed my suspended thoughts. I didn't know when I would have this chance again, when I would encounter this knight and his mysteries face-to-face. And that uncertainty was a thorn in my pride.

We couldn't beat him; we had lost this battle.

I slammed the door shut.

22

I closed my eyes, sweat dripping down my temples, and I pressed my ear to the door. The knight hadn't moved. He stood at the threshold, unable to pass over it since the door was locked.

I struggled with my desire to remain in safety and my hunger to oppose the knight again.

Someone wheezed behind me.

I turned to behold Phelan, lying on the foyer floor. He was watching me, his face blanched and furrowed with pain. His hand was pressed over his abdomen, where his blood was pooling.

A slender, cold part of me was satisfied to see him brought low, wounded, and humbled.

But then I knelt at his side and I took hold of his hand, drawing his bloodied fingers away, and those jaded feelings in me were eclipsed by worry.

"Can you help me up the stairs?" he rasped. "To my bedroom?"

I nodded and pulled him up to his feet. With me supporting his weight, we laboriously ascended the stairs with the assistance of my magic.

A lone candle burned in his bedroom. The fire in his hearth had died into embers, and I walked Phelan to his bed and eased him down on the mattress. I swiftly roused the fire back to a crackling dance and lit a few more candelabras, so I could examine him in better light.

I inevitably glanced at the mirror that hung over his wash station. If he sat up in bed, the glass would catch his reflection. And I would have to walk past it to leave the room. I felt trapped and annoyed, and struggled with my temptation to shatter the mirror.

A moan slipped from Phelan.

It drew my attention, to where he was lying in bed, his back slightly arched as he struggled to unbutton his waistcoat with one hand. I needed to leave now while he was preoccupied, to harvest an herb from the library and make a potent tonic that would render him unconscious. Then I would tend to his wound and my own, which I had all but forgotten about in the cascade of adrenaline.

I started for the door.

"Where are you going?"

I halted on the rug, just before the mirror, and met his gaze. "To the library, to make you an herbal tonic."

"I don't want an herbal tonic. I need you to stitch me up."

"Then you're going to want something for the pain. Lie back down. I'll return in a moment."

Phelan stared at me. "I don't trust you."

"What?" His words caught me by surprise.

"Come here, Anna."

I had no choice. He was watching me like a hawk, as if he could see through me, and I took a wide berth to his bedside, staying just out of reach of him and his mirror on the opposing wall.

"Why don't you trust me?" I asked, my voice low and far rougher than I intended.

"Because you want to slip away," he said. "You want to open the door and face the knight again without me."

I let out a huff of breath. "Fine. I was tempted to, yes."

"I forbid it."

"You *forbid* it?" I echoed with a hint of laughter. "And how do you propose to do that, lying in bed, wounded like a fair nobleman in war?"

"All right," he said. "I can't forbid you, but I ask that you stay here and help me. The knight will no doubt challenge us another new moon, but in this moment . . . I need you."

I need you.

His candor softened the hard edges that hid within me.

"Lie back down," I whispered, and he obeyed. I waited until his head rested on his pillow before I moved to stand at his bedside. Gently, I undressed him. I slid his arms from his jacket. I unbuttoned his tattered waistcoat, unknotted his cravat, and eased him out of his shirt. Once his chest was naked, I surveyed the damage.

His wound wasn't deep, but it was long, cutting across his stomach. I saw another scar, one that ran from his heart down to his hip, as if he had once been sliced open, and I couldn't help myself. I traced it with my fingertips.

"Did he do this?" I asked. "The knight?"

"Yes," he whispered, and his blood continued to trickle out. I took his rumpled shirt and pressed against the wound, and Phelan winced.

"How do you want me to stitch this?" I asked.

"In my wardrobe," he said, his voice hoarse with pain. "In the bottom drawer. You'll find my medicine box."

I hurried to fetch it, and Phelan remained still, staring up at the ceiling as I opened the wooden box. There was a pack of needles, dark thread, rolls of linen, a few small jars of healing salve, and antiseptic.

I cleaned the wound first before threading my needle, planting stitches along his skin. I had done this once before, with a cut on my father's arm, and while this wasn't a new experience, it was one that still made my heart quicken, to see Phelan's wound close beneath my fingers. To watch a different sort of magic spill from my hands.

"I've noticed something about you," he said just as I was finishing.

He was quiet until I looked at him. I was pleased to see some color had returned to his face.

"Your name," he said. "*Anna Neven*. You can spell both of your names forward as you can backward."

I cut the thread and wiped the lingering traces of blood from my fingers. "My mother was fond of palindrome names."

"Hmm."

I spread healing salve over my handiwork, and the fragrant smell of herbs began to drift in the air between us. I watched the steady rise and fall of Phelan's chest as he breathed.

"It's not your real name, is it?" he said.

I smiled as if he was ridiculous, finishing with my ministrations. "Of course it is. Why would you doubt me, Phelan?"

"Because you have told me so little about yourself."

"That doesn't make me a liar."

"No, but it gives me moments of doubt, Anna. And I . . . I don't want to doubt who you are."

I didn't know what to say. I couldn't afford to have him doubt or suspect me, and I did the only thing I could think of, the only thing that felt natural. I traced the hard cut lines of his stomach, the contours of his bare skin. I traced his scar.

"You doubt me in this moment, Phelan?"

He made a low sound that seemed forged from both pleasure and irritation and grabbed my hand with his, to halt my caress. "You wanted to leave me here, floundering on my bed!"

"I wanted to fetch you a tonic to dull your pain, you fool!" I leaned down closer to him, so that our mouths were a breath apart. My braid had come partly unwound in the battle, and my hair fell around us. "Now, I'm going to the library to harvest some herbs, and make you a tonic that will help you sleep. You will stay here and trust my word and not move, and when I return, you may ask me anything you want and I'll answer you."

He was silent, but he continued to hold my hand, pressed

against his heart. I could feel the frantic beat, pounding against my palm. A rhythm that made me realize things had started to shift between us.

I didn't hate him as I had before. How could I after this harrowing night had bound us together, in fear and courage and wounds?

And while his face had been difficult to read in the past . . . I saw the lines in his brow fade the longer he regarded me, our breaths mingling. I saw the shock of hope, tender and fragile and surprising as a flower breaking winter ground, rise within him.

I was beginning to think he liked me—Anna, not Clem— more than he let on.

When I stood, he released me. I took my time putting his medicine box away and gathering his clothes off the blood-speckled rug, because he was intently watching me, and I needed him to close his eyes before I passed the mirror.

At last, his eyes drifted shut, and I hurried by the mirror and out the chamber, down the stairs to the library. It was dark and solemn as a tomb, the air thick with the musty fragrance of books and the loam of plants, and I took a moment to drop my guard. To gasp in relief and lower myself to my knees. To lie prostrate on the floor and sift through the events of that night—in the streets and in his bedroom.

But all too soon, I made myself rise and light a candle.

Every muscle in my body felt sore and tense, and I kneaded a knot in my shoulder as I approached the plant table. I gathered what I needed, a recipe that was similar to making a remedy but without the fuss of draining plant pulp. I added a hearty dose of fiddle's spark, an herb that brought on swift, deep slumber. There was no chance of Phelan drinking this and not succumbing to sleep within a few moments.

I carried the tonic back up the stairs, pausing in the middle of the staircase to glance behind me at the front door, to the bronze handle that winked in the dim light. I wondered if the knight still stood on the threshold, waiting for me to answer the challenge he posed, but I forced myself to continue my ascent.

Phelan was just as I'd left him, his eyes closed until he heard me step into the room.

I hastened past the mirror and set the cup of tonic on his bed-side table. I realized I couldn't linger beside him, not with the glaring reflection of my secret, and I awkwardly stepped away, far from his and the mirror's reach.

"Thank you," Phelan said, but I detected a hint of mockery in his tone as he struggled to sit upright on his own.

I pretended to be distracted by the piles of books he had on the floor, kneeling to study their titles, to touch their worn covers.

"What did you put in this, Anna?" he asked after a moment, stifling a cough.

I glanced up to see his lips pursed in disgust. "It'll aid your healing and sleep. Drink all of it, Phelan."

I listened to him struggle to swallow my tonic, and I angled my face away, so he wouldn't catch my smile. I eventually felt the sting in my skin, and I knew that I could not ignore my own wound any longer.

Gingerly, I stood and turned to speak to Phelan, surprised to see his eyes were closed, his head slightly inclined back against the wooden headboard.

Well, then. My tonic had accomplished its purpose.

I walked to his wardrobe to retrieve the medicine box again. A stool sat in the shadows beside the furniture, and I drew it into the candlelight and took a seat upon it, my back to Phelan. I slowly unlaced the last of my bodice's ribbons and let it fall to the ground with a whisper. Next, I eased my chemise off my shoulders, down to my waist, so I could examine my wound.

A shallow scratch arced above my belly button, already forming a scab.

I reached for the antiseptic and was cleaning it when Phelan spoke.

"Are you wounded, Anna?"

I paused, a hitch in my breath. Here I was sitting half-naked in his room, when my tonic should have dragged him into dreamless sleep. I glanced over my shoulder to look at him still propped up in bed, his eyes heavy lidded but regarding me with attentiveness.

"No, just a scratch." I returned my focus to the cut, but I felt his gaze linger on me and the bare curve of my back. I was comfortable in my skin, and I didn't mind his attention, not as I probably would have if this had happened a month ago, or even a week ago.

I drew my chemise up to my shoulders and knotted its drawstring tight. The bodice was ruined, so I left it in the pile with his bloodied clothes.

"Ask your one question, Mr. Vesper," I said. "Unless you want to wait until tomorrow, when you have a clear head and will remember my answer."

"I have a clear head," he said, but his words were slurred as he fought the cloying effects of the tonic. "Come, sit here, Anna." He patted the bed beside him, and I merely stared at it, the mirror still a threat.

"Lie down, and perhaps I will."

He heeded me, easing his head to his pillow, his boots close to dangling off the bed.

I approached the other side and sank into the feather mattress beside him, a few generous hand widths between us.

"Ask your question, Phelan."

His eyes were closed but he smiled. "I want to know your real name."

"Mm, very well, although I think that's a sorry thing to waste your one question on."

That prompted him to crack open his eyes and look up at me. "Which means I have asked a very good question, because you don't want to answer it."

He was beginning to read me rather well, which stirred my apprehension. I resolved to be more careful around him. And I hadn't thought of myself as performing a role, but I should have, from the moment we'd had our interview.

"Anna Bailey is my true name," I said. "I chose *Neven* for myself after my mother died, to hide me from a few of her old acquaintances who might give me trouble. She had some old debts that she never paid before she passed away. That's why I haven't told you much about me."

"You could tell me who she owes a debt to, and I will pay it."

I frowned. "No, Phelan. I don't want you paying my mother's debts."

Go to sleep, I thought with desperation, and listened as his breaths pulled deep, his eyes closing more and more with each stubborn blink. I delayed a minute more, just to be certain he was asleep this time, before I began to edge my way off the bed.

"Don't leave, Anna," he whispered. "Stay here with me."

I wondered if he truly wanted my company, or if he was worried about me slipping away into the night without him. But I lingered.

Eventually, though, I couldn't deny my weariness. I found a dreamless remedy in Phelan's side table and drank it, surrendering to the soft embrace of the bed. And I fell asleep at his side.

23

"Miss Neven? *Miss Neven!*"

I woke to the shock and horror of Mrs. Stirling. She stood at the foot of the bed, her face blanched as she stared at me. Why did she look so upset? I wondered, groggily wiping the drool from my lips.

And then I realized this bed was unfamiliar, and Phelan was sleeping close beside me, his chest exposed and scarred and sewn up, his fingers entwined with mine. . . .

The memory of the new moon flooded through me and knocked away the last gossamer of sleep.

"Mrs. Stirling. Don't worry, he's all right," I started to say, but my voice died when I saw another figure step forward. One that sparkled with diamonds and moved with terrible grace. I recognized her. We had crossed paths in the art shop last month. The countess. Phelan's mother. Her blue eyes studied me with icy reserve, and I suddenly felt as if I were naked.

"Miss Neven, this is the Countess of Amarys," Mrs. Stirling rushed to introduce us, but she couldn't smooth away the tension in the air. "Lady Raven Vesper."

"It is an honor to make your acquaintance, Miss Neven," the countess said with a smile, which only made her eyes burn colder. I noticed she cast no shadow on the floor. "My son spoke very highly of you when I saw him last week."

My mind went blank as I held her stare. I was acutely aware of the bloodstains on my chemise, the wrinkles in the gauzy fabric, the snarls in my hair. I knew I appeared like I had just risen from the gutter, and I swallowed, uncertain how to save this first impression of myself.

Phelan, of course, blithely continued to sleep, and I regretted giving him such a strong tonic.

"My lady," I said, and slipped hastily from Phelan's bed, as if the coverlet had caught fire. "Your son fought valiantly last night but was wounded. I felt it best to stay beside him until morning."

"And I thank you for your diligence, Miss Neven," said Lady Raven. "I can handle it from here, and I would appreciate if you kept my son's wound a secret."

I dropped a crooked curtsy, feeling as if every one of my bones had come out of socket. Mrs. Stirling hesitated before granting me a gentle nod, but I departed as swiftly as I could, retreating to the safety of my bedchamber.

I sat in the shadows until my cheeks had cooled, and I opened my curtains and my shutters, basking in the morning light. I washed my face and shattered the mirror that hung on the wall because I was weary of seeing myself. I watched the cracks in the glass spread into a glittering web, until Clem was broken into an array of pieces, and yet I still didn't feel satisfied.

I needed to get out of this house, and I swiftly dressed and brushed the tangles from my hair, quietly descending the stairs.

I emerged onto the front porch, standing in the very place the knight had stood only hours ago. I shivered in the sun, longing for home. To rest in a place where I didn't have to pretend. And I cast my stealth charm and began to walk north.

Imonie was shocked to see me at the door. She had the town house to herself, and was in the middle of scrubbing the hallway when I arrived.

"What happened?" she asked, tossing down her bristle brush to greet me.

"Why does everyone assume something terrible has happened every time they see me?" I asked, exasperated.

Imonie pursed her lips, but I noticed how her eyes flickered over me, from head to foot. As if ensuring I was hale. "Well, it *was* the new moon last night. I take it you were victorious?"

I only sighed.

Her eyes narrowed. "I think this conversation calls for tea. And a hot breakfast. Come here, Clem."

I followed her into the kitchen, thankful that she didn't ask questions while she cooked, but that she listened as I rambled on about the night. I wanted to tell her of the knight but refrained, and perhaps it was only because Phelan had seemed so intent on keeping it a secret. I was on my second cup of tea when I confessed, "I saw the countess this morning. I just so happened to be sleeping in Phelan's bed when she arrived."

Imonie's face paled. "And why were you in Phelan's bed?"

"Nothing happened. He was wounded and he asked me to stay with him."

Imonie eased into the chair across from mine. She wrapped her fingers around her teacup, her eyes glazed in fear. I had never seen such a thing in her—she kept her emotions as guarded as she did her past.

"I want you to stay away from her," she said.

"Who? Lady Raven?"

Imonie nodded. "She's dangerous, Clem. She will stop at nothing to get what she wants."

"How do you know that?" I asked, breakfast suddenly like lead in my stomach.

"Have you ever heard about the Count of Amarys?"

"Her husband? No."

"That's because he's dead," Imonie said. "Been dead for almost sixteen years now. There was much speculation at the time he died. One day he was fine, the next? He fell sick. He died three days later, bloated and choking on his own blood. The countess was a young mother to two boys, and it all seemed rather tragic until rumors began to fly that the Duke of Bardyllis was the boys' true father, and not the count. And that perhaps the countess had poisoned her husband to get rid of him."

I gnawed on my lip, processing Imonie's story. This would be perfect for my exposé on the Vespers. "Do you think she killed her husband?"

Imonie wiped a wrinkle from the tablecloth. "Yes, I do. She poisoned him."

"But why?" I asked. "Why would she kill him? She hasn't gotten with the duke since then."

"Perhaps the count had come to know too much about her. Perhaps she wanted to raise her boys on her own. Perhaps she had simply tired of him. Perhaps he was in her way." Imonie shrugged. "No one knows, so that's why I'm telling you to give her a wide berth."

That did nothing to reassure me. Not when I recalled how Lady Raven's gaze had been icy, beholding me in her son's bed.

"Papa said she's an old acquaintance of his," I said.

Imonie snorted. "Yes, and why do you think he's now working in the mines and has given up magic and wants nothing more than to evade the Vesper boys?"

I wasn't sure, so I remained quiet.

Imonie began to gather the plates, carrying them to the wash bin. I thought the silence would continue to hang between us, but then she looked at me and said, "He doesn't want the countess to find him."

I was relieved to see the countess's carriage was gone when I returned to Auberon Street. The minute I stepped into the foyer, Mrs. Stirling met me with a sigh of relief and a tray of tea and biscuits.

"There you are, Miss Neven. Gave us all a fright, wondering where you had gone!"

"I'm sorry," I said, flushing when I realized I had been absent most of the day. I'd honestly thought no one would care. "I went for a walk."

I was worried that Mrs. Stirling would have that reserved gleam in her eye, the same from that morning, when she found me in Phelan's bed. But she only nodded and extended the tea tray to me.

"Do you mind carrying that up to Mr. Vesper?"

I accepted it and carefully ascended the stairs.

Phelan was sitting upright in bed, loose papers spread before him. He was intently reading, his hair damp from a bath. He was wearing clean clothes, my stitches hidden beneath his shirt. It almost felt like I had merely imagined the events of last night. As if it had all been a dream.

"Did Deacon find her yet?" Phelan asked, presuming I was Mrs. Stirling.

"He didn't need to," I replied, drawing his attention.

I stood on the threshold holding his tea tray, and for a moment, he and I stared at each other. Words seemed to be lost between us.

"I thought . . . ," he began, but his voice faded.

"That I had run away?" I finished with a teasing cadence.

He hesitated—where, indeed, did he think I had gone?—but withheld whatever he wanted to say or ask me.

"Come in, Anna." He dropped his gaze to the papers before him.

That afforded me the chance to slip past the mirror, and I set his tea tray down on his bedside table, mindful of the new jars of herbs that now sat by his glass of water.

"I see the doctor has been here," I remarked, watching as Phelan gathered his papers into a heap.

"Yes. And my mother."

"I know. I met her this morning."

Phelan's eyes darted back to mine. "Did you? She failed to mention that to me."

"No, I don't think she would have," I said, wandering to the window. The curtains were tasseled back, the shutters were open, and I stood in a stream of sunlight, watching the street below. "I was in bed beside you when I met her."

"Oh."

I couldn't resist glancing back at him, how he flushed and hurried to pour his cup of tea, thankful for the distraction.

"Do you remember anything from last night?" I asked.

Phelan took a sip, but his gaze found mine again. "I remember everything."

I had to break our stare first. My skin warmed when I thought about how I had touched him last night, how he had seen my bare back, how he had asked me to stay with him.

"I need to tell you something, Anna."

I braced myself. Surely, his mother had convinced him to dismiss me, and I waited for it to come, for Phelan to let me go. He set his teacup in its saucer. He was drawing this out, to no doubt make me nervous.

"What is it, Phelan?" I asked, impatient.

"I'm going away," he said.

I gaped at him, unable to hide my shock. "To where?"

"I can't tell you. But I'll return in a week or so, and I need you to remain here. To record the nightmares that may emerge and to give the portion of dream tax to the duke's collector, who will be arriving any day now to claim it. I also need you to discreetly pass on a payment to a friend. You will note that there is a purse with a red ribbon in the safe, where I store the money. When they stop by to 'borrow a book,' I need you to ensure they receive that money."

I was quiet so long that he frowned, concerned.

"Anna?"

"Yes, I will do these things for you," I said, inwardly shaking myself. "When do you leave?"

"Tomorrow."

"This must be a trip of great importance, since you should be at home, recovering in bed."

He refused to answer, returning his attention to his stack of papers. I sensed that his mother had given him this order.

And then the realization hit me like a strike to my body, and I turned to the window quickly, before Phelan could see the emotion ripple across my face.

I knew where he was going.

Hereswith.

24

T hree days after Phelan departed, Lord Deryn called.

I found him waiting in the library, standing before Phelan's bookcase, intently studying the volumes on one of the shelves. He pivoted when he heard me enter, a well-practiced smile on his face.

I smelled the bergamot of his cologne. A sickly sweetness, mingling with that odd scent of molded parchment. And I knew he was here for me, not the tax.

"Miss Neven. It is good to see you again."

"Your Grace," I said with a curtsy.

"Forgive me for calling so unexpectedly, but I wanted to speak to you. Please, sit."

I obediently lowered myself into the chair, but my dread kindled. A few spells rose to mind, in case I needed to cast them on a whim.

"I wanted to inquire about this last new moon," he began, taking Phelan's seat behind the desk. "Was it my nightmare that materialized?"

"No, Your Grace."

He waited for me to elaborate, and when I didn't, the duke raked his fingers through his beard.

"I know you cannot tell me which dream manifested," he said. "Forgive me for asking. But I need to know how Phelan was wounded."

"How do you know he was wounded, Your Grace?"

"I have ears and eyes everywhere, Miss Neven. Nothing happens in this province that I do not know about."

His words were unsettling, but I was determined that he would never know how much he rattled me. I sighed as if relieved and leaned closer to him, my elbows impolitely resting on the desk.

"I'm happy you already know of it, Your Grace. Did the countess inform you?"

"No, she did not." There was no emotion in his face, in his voice when he spoke of her. The monotone only made me more suspicious of their relationship.

"I confess that I have been worried about him, especially since his mother sent him away. He should be resting in bed."

The duke didn't rise to my bait. He made a noise of contemplation and then said, "What wounded him? An element of the nightmare, or something beyond it?"

I was quiet, wondering if he was accusing me of being a poor partner.

"Choose your answer carefully, Miss Neven," the duke warned in a voice like honey. At last, the threat I was anticipating. "I want the truth, even if that gives me no choice but to remove Phelan from this post. Or you, for that matter."

He doesn't want Phelan in danger, I realized, and then saw this as my chance to have Phelan's aspirations and accomplishments shattered. I could tell the duke Phelan was weak, vulnerable. But even if my desire had originally been to see Phelan lose his home and sense of purpose . . . I was now tied to him, and I didn't want to relinquish what I had gained just yet. I reveled in being a warden again.

"Phelan and I vanquished the nightmare," I said. "But then something else emerged. Something unexpected and malevolent. It wasn't recorded in his ledger."

"What was this unexpected thing, Miss Neven?"

I hesitated.

The duke sensed it and softened. "You will not betray him by telling me."

Oh, but I certainly felt like I would be. Phelan hadn't told two of his closest friends. He couldn't even describe it to me, his partner. It was almost like Phelan had been ordered not to speak of it.

"I think you should ask Phelan when he returns, Your Grace."

Lord Deryn smiled and leaned back in the chair, but his gaze never left mine. "I am going to tell you something, Miss Neven. Something not many people know, and yet I am going to trust you with this secret."

I sat frozen, hating how eager I was to hear what morsel the duke had to offer me.

"Phelan was not born with illumination," he began. "He was not accepted into the Luminous School until I waived his entry. In fact, he failed every single entrance exam, but I saw the potential in him. I gave him a place in the school, I funded his education, and I ensured he received this portion of territory when he was ready to become warden. I have had a hand in shaping him into the magician that he is despite the fact that I have no light in my bones, and it would be a shame to see my investment lost before its time."

I listened, and his words began to spark thoughts I had never entertained before. The duke had been married years ago, but his wife had died not long after their vows. He was a widower, childless. Heirless. And if the duke had played such a quiet but steady hand in Phelan's upbringing—if he thought of Phelan as an *investment*—then the duke had greater plans for him. Whether Phelan knew it or not remained to be seen.

"You plan to name him as your heir," I whispered.

The duke was silent, studying me with sharp intensity, as if he had underestimated me before now. "Yes, Miss Neven. You must not breathe a word of it to him or any other, you understand?"

"I understand, Your Grace."

"And I want to know what is threatening him on the new moon nights."

I could see no other way to avoid it.

I told the duke about the knight.

He listened with a scowl. "This sounds like someone who can control and influence nightmares."

"I've never heard of such a thing," I said, transfixed by the imagining. "How is the knight able to do this?"

"Something, or some*one*, is providing him with a door to enter the dreams on the new moon."

"Who would have such power? A magician?"

Lord Deryn was pensive for a moment. "I do not know, but you will not be able to vanquish him in the dream realm. You will have to locate him in the waking world and defeat him here."

"Not a small feat," I said, but I was surprised by how eager I was for this challenge. I wanted to uncover the knight's secrets. His purpose. His source of power. Even if that entailed me working with someone like the duke.

"Indeed, it is not," Lord Deryn agreed. "But if you can find a way to remove his helm in the nightmare . . . you would see his face. And if you see his face and describe it to me, I would be able to locate him in the province."

The duke was not making a suggestion; he was giving me an order. I thought about the places I knew the knight had appeared: Months ago, on Phelan's first new moon as a warden. Hereswith, the night before Phelan had arrived. And then again on one of Phelan's streets, this October new moon. This didn't feel random to me; it felt like the knight was after Phelan, and it chilled me.

"If the knight arrives on this upcoming new moon, then I will find a way to do that, Your Grace."

"And you will come to me at once with the description, Miss Neven."

I nodded, although my mind was whirling, remembering how the knight had almost beheaded me and sliced Phelan open.

"You have a concern, Miss Neven?"

I met the duke's gaze. "Yes. The knight is a formidable opponent, immune to magic and blades. I don't know how Phelan and I will manage to remove his helm without suffering damage to ourselves."

Lord Deryn steepled his fingers together and pressed them to his lips. "If magic and weapons are useless against the knight's armor, that must mean the armor was forged by a *deviah* magician."

That hadn't crossed my mind. But now that it had, other pieces began to fall into place. Wild speculations. I wondered if the card game of Seven Wraiths somehow influenced the ability of the knight's armor. If both of them were tied to nightmares, and both of them made by *deviah* magicians . . . perhaps they were linked, somehow.

"There is a smith not far from here," Lord Deryn continued. "He is one of the best in the province. A *deviah* who can layer enchantment into steel. I will have him forge something that will help you both."

"If it's armor, it will be more of a hindrance than a help, Your Grace. It will only slow us down, and we must be swift."

"It is not armor, Miss Neven," the duke said, rising from the chair. "I will put the order in, but the smith will most likely want to meet with you about measurements."

"Very well, Your Grace. And what shall I tell Phelan about where this gift arrived from?"

"Tell him it is from me." He fell silent, pensive. But his gaze remained on me. "Phelan speaks of you often, Miss Neven." And I didn't know why he would say such a thing until the duke shocked me further by adding, "Would you want to be a duchess?"

"No."

"A reflexive answer, Miss Neven. As if you have contemplated it before."

The truth was I had *never* thought about it, but the duke was making me anxious. What I did know was the last thing I wanted was to be a pawn in a noble's game.

"If I ever became a duchess," I said, "it would be by my own choice and merit, and not by marriage."

"Ah, you could become the Duchess of Seren, then. That throne is open to anyone who could ascend the mountain and break the new moon curse."

"Which I hear is not nearly as simple as it sounds," I said. "The mountain doors won't open unless all the wraiths are together. And who knows where the seven of them are hiding these days, if that legend is even true."

"How do you know this?" he asked sharply.

I bit the inside of my cheek, the pain my punishment for speaking so freely. "Just a rumor, Your Grace. My mother used to tell me a few mountain stories when I was a girl."

The duke's calculating silence continued to roar.

I felt the urge to state, "I'm not a madcap, if that's what you truly want to know."

"I think we all are madcaps, in one way or another. And a warden like you already has all the training one would need to defeat whatever nightmares lurk in that old mountain fortress," the duke countered, arching his brow. "But as you said, Miss Neven. The wraiths are but a myth. Faces in a card game meant to frighten young children. Now, then. I have taken more than enough of your time today."

I rose, thoughts muddled by all he had said to me, and began to follow him to the library doors until I remembered the dream tax. "Your Grace, the tax . . ."

He paused and gave me a smile, one that crinkled the corners of his eyes. I wasn't fooled by the gentleness of his demeanor. I saw the glint of greed within him. "My collector will arrive later today, Miss Neven. The money never passes through my hands, not until it has been marked and accounted for."

I curtsied and waited until Mrs. Stirling had seen the duke out, and the house fell quiet once more. But I could smell a trace of the duke's cologne again, and I opened a window to let the potent fragrance escape. The library seemed to soften in relief that the duke was gone, and I approached the hidden safe in the wall.

I whispered the spell into the dust motes and watched the safe's door appear in the wall with a mercurial gleam. The door conceded to yawn open beneath my hand, recognizing me, and I stared at the bundles of coins that rested within its belly.

A small portion of this money was mine, for Phelan and I took a percentage and split it between ourselves. *My first proper paycheck*, I thought before locating the bundles Phelan had set aside for the tax collector.

Four bags, each the size of a cantaloupe, swollen with coins. I studied them, one by one, and felt their weight in my palm.

So much money, I thought with a disbelieving heart. *So much money.*

Two days after the duke's visit, I received a request from the smith to come to his shop. It was a tricky place to find, and I walked past it twice before I finally found the shop door, which was so unremarkable that it nearly blended into the brick wall.

The doorbell rang when I entered. The shop was composed of a small chamber, smelling of leather and iron and cleaning oil. Swords of all kinds were displayed on one wall, as well as axes and daggers. A few suits of armor caught my attention. I paused before a steel-plated set that reminded me of the one the knight wore, only far less sinister. Indeed, I felt as if I had stepped back in time. All these weapons and armor . . . not many people possessed such things anymore. They were figments of the past. And the air was dusted with nostalgia, with the memory of fading things.

"May I help you?"

I turned to see a middle-aged man with thinning brown hair and sharp eyes, a pair of wire spectacles perched on his hawk nose. He wore a leather apron, and his hands were covered in grime.

"I'm Anna Neven," I said.

"Ah, yes. I need to take your measurements." He hurried behind his desk and found a spool of measuring tape.

I had told the duke that armor would slow Phelan and me down considerably. And I wanted to protest until the smith measured my height and my left arm, studying my shoulder and the way I stood.

"You're not making armor?" I asked.

"No. A shield."

A shield would *be helpful*, I thought. Although I remembered how the knight's sword had shattered Phelan's rapier like it had been composed of glass. It could just as easily sunder a buckler, but I held my doubt.

"How long have you been practicing *deviah*?" I asked.

The smith glanced at me, a suspicious arch in his brow. "Long enough, I suppose."

"Were you a warden before?"

"No. But I am familiar with *avertana*."

"Do you often create enchanted armor?"

He gave me an exasperated expression. "Do you often come into shops and ask a hundred questions?"

I blushed. "I'm sorry. I just find your vein of work quite fascinating."

That mollified his gruffness. *Slightly.* "Creating enchanted armor is extremely difficult, even for the most experienced magicians. It would take years to achieve one suit. Now, then, Miss Neven. I'll deliver the shields to Mr. Vesper's town house when they are ready." He wrote down a few notes, which I took as his way of dismissing me.

I began to leave the shop when something caught my eye. A leather weapon belt, hanging overhead. It was the twin to the one I had possessed, the one my father had purchased for me when I began to fight at his side on the streets of Hereswith. The twin to the one Olivette had worn the other day.

My breath caught.

The resemblance was uncanny, undeniable. Papa must have bought it from this shop.

"Another question, Miss Neven?" the smith asked, noticing my rapt attention.

I wondered if this smith was Olivette's father, remembering how she had told me that her father had made the weapon belt for her. And I opened my mouth to ask more about the belt, to tell him I knew Olivette, but something gave me pause. A warning, as if I had felt a draft. "No. Good day to you, sir."

That afternoon, I began writing my exposé at Phelan's desk. I used his ink and quill, and a blank journal I had purchased, and started listing the things I wanted to include:

—The countess buys art supplies (for herself?) and is a magician. Potential deviah?
—The countess poisoned her late husband, the count, because . . . ? (She was bored of him/she had a liaison with the duke/he had uncovered a secret of hers she wanted to keep buried.)

—Lennox and Phelan may or may not be the duke's children.
—Phelan failed his entrance exams, holds no illumination, and would have never become a magician if it wasn't for the duke's influence.

"Miss Neven?" Mrs. Stirling opened the library door. It startled me so badly my quill shot across the page, and I hastened to close my journal. "I'm sorry to interrupt, but a visitor has come to borrow one of Mr. Vesper's books."

"Yes, give me one moment and then send them in, Mrs. Stirling."

She nodded and left. I hurried to charm my journal so no one but me could read it before opening the enchanted safe, retrieving the purse with the red ribbon. It was swollen with coins, and I wondered what Phelan had set this sum aside for.

A creak sounded on the threshold.

I spun to greet the visitor, only to stiffen in shock. Words froze on my tongue as I stared at the girl from the art shop. Blythe.

She gave me a tentative smile, tucking a stray curl behind her ear. "I'm so sorry to interrupt you, but I'm here to borrow one of Mr. Vesper's books. He said you could help me."

I swallowed my shock, as well as the hope that she would remember me. I was in disguise, and I had nearly forgotten it.

"Y-yes, of course." I walked to her and extended the coin purse.

Her delight was tangible. She beamed at the purse, cupping it with both hands. "Oh, this is so much more than I thought it would be! Please thank Mr. Vesper for me!"

And what am I thanking him for? I wanted to ask. "Of course."

"Thank you," Blythe whispered again, sliding the purse into her leather satchel. "My brother is a warden of a few streets that have fallen on hard times and cannot pay the duke's tax. So Mr. Vesper's donation is much appreciated."

"Phelan will be pleased to hear of it," I said, struggling to hide my surprise. This side of Phelan was new to me. And I didn't like how it made me doubt my prior assumptions of him.

"I also have a message, for you to give to Mr. Vesper," Blythe said. "A few weeks ago, he asked me if I had seen someone named Clementine in the art shop. I told him there had been a pretty girl named Clem with red hair, and he wanted me to inform him if I ever saw her step foot in the shop again."

"And has she?" I asked, clearing my throat.

Blythe shook her head. "No. But the strange thing is his mother, Lady Raven, *also* asked about the girl. She wanted me to follow Clem home the next time she visited the shop. I thought Mr. Vesper would be interested to know his mother is also looking for her. I hope Clem is not in any sort of trouble."

"On the contrary," I said with a slight grimace. "Perhaps they want to commission her."

"Perhaps. Well, good day to you . . ."

"Anna. Anna Neven."

"Anna," Blythe said.

I remained standing in the library long after she departed. The shadows grew long, gnarled roots around me.

The Vespers knew I was in the city. And I thought of the spell I had planned, in case Phelan discovered who I was. The spell my father had insisted I have prepared.

At the time I created it, I had believed that I would never have to cast it.

Now? I was no longer sure.

25

Phelan returned after a week and a half's absence, and he brought the first frost of autumn to the city. I reunited with him in the library that evening, where he stood before his shelves, frantically leafing through a book. And when that failed to entice him, he set it down and reached for another, his fingers swiping through the pages.

"You were away longer than you said you would be," I greeted him, closing the library doors behind me.

Phelan turned. His hair was tousled, his clothes uncharacteristically wrinkled from the journey. "Yes, forgive me, Anna. I hope things were uneventful here?"

"Quite," I said, joining him before the shelves. "The dream tax has been passed on to the collector. And I gave the red ribbon purse to your contact. She was very thankful for the amount."

"Good. Did she have any other messages for me?"

"She hasn't seen your old rival Cordelia—"

"Clementine," Phelan corrected me.

"Yes, whatever her name is, in the art shop."

He sighed and carelessly dropped a book on his desk. "Just the news I wanted to hear."

"What else have you done to try and locate her?"

"I've contacted a few art shops and checked her Luminous Society files," he said. "There's not much there to glean, as both of her parents are highly private people and paid to have their records guarded. But it seems her mother is proficient in *metamara* and performed stagecraft, so I've begun to check with theaters in the area."

My pulse skipped. I had never thought about him tracing my mother to me, because she went by her stage name, and had been doing so for nearly a decade, since she split with my father. Despite that, I was tempted to dismiss myself and send an urgent message to my parents, but I quenched the impulsivity and chose to take another route.

I lingered in the library, watching him draw book after book from his vast shelves.

"What are you looking for? Aside from Clementine, that is."

"A certain volume," he said. "I can't remember its title, but it has an essay on trolls that I need."

"Trolls?" I echoed, thinking of Mazarine. "Why is that? Did you encounter one?"

"Perhaps." Phelan sounded distant, resuming his search.

I watched. There were moments when Phelan looked at me or when our skin brushed and I felt something electric pass between us. I told myself it was merely from two enemies being in close quarters, until I realized that I had—unfortunately—come to miss him during the time he was away. But more than those unsettling feelings . . . I needed to distract him from Mazarine, from hunting me and my parents.

"This house is far too quiet at night without you," I said.

That brought him back to me. He met my gaze, and I wondered what he saw in my eyes, because Phelan smiled.

I took a step back, and it was like we were bound by an invisible tether, because he suddenly forgot about the mess of books around him and took a step forward.

"Leaving so soon, Anna?"

"Well, you're knee deep in books," I said, waving my hand. "We can talk more tomorrow."

"Talk more about what?" he asked. "The fact that you missed me?"

I suddenly couldn't tell if he was humoring me or deadly serious. "I never said that I missed you. I said that it was *quiet* here."

He took another step closer. "Then let me be the first to confess. I missed you."

"I have no doubt."

"I should have taken you with me."

I tried to imagine that scenario—going to Hereswith with him. Staying in my old house with him and his brother. Walking streets I knew like the lines on my palm, and pretending it all meant nothing to me.

"You should have." My voice was husky, full of longings he would never understand.

"And I'm weary of trolls and dusty journeys and missing Clementines and having to deal with my brother's snark," he said, and the space between us closed a little more.

I had to tilt my chin to look up at him. "And what can I do about that?"

"Distract me."

He shouldn't challenge me with such a thing. I could give him all sorts of distractions, and I raised my hand and grasped the ribbon that held his hair at the nape of his neck. Slowly, I pulled it loose, and I listened to his breaths quicken as his dark hair spilled around his shoulders. Not once did he look away from me as my hands deftly unfastened the top two buttons of his waistcoat. My fingertips traced the faint scar my rapier had left on his cheekbone.

I stepped back to regard him. "Yes, you look much better as a rogue."

Surely, that comment would offend him. But he laughed, and the sound was golden, incandescent. I longed to hear it again, as soon as it melted away.

"Come, the distraction is not over yet," I said, inviting him to follow me from the library. "Go set a pot of tea to boil, and then meet me in the drawing room."

"What for?"

"That would spoil the fun, now, wouldn't it?"

He only arched his brow, but a smile lingered on his mouth. And I hated how I suddenly wanted to taste it.

Phelan took the corridor to the kitchen; I stepped into the drawing room and found the cards. I stoked the fire in the hearth and lit a few candles by magic, and then I sat in a high-backed chair and waited for him to arrive with the tea. He must have used magic as well to prepare it, because he arrived sooner than I anticipated. The mirth that had been in his eyes just moments ago waned when he saw Seven Wraiths laid out on the table.

"Honest to gods, Anna . . . I'm tired of this game," he said, setting the tray down. "It's all Deacon wants to play, night after night, and—"

"As I know," I replied. "But I have something important to say to you, and I think it will help if we are holding the cards."

He only sighed and poured us each a cup of tea, settling into the chair across from mine. I had a strange feeling that he would do just about anything I asked of him, and it made my hands tremble. He watched as I dealt, and the silence was thick as we studied our cards.

I wanted to gather as many of the wraiths as possible and was delighted when I drew the heiress, a young woman with long dark hair and sorrowful blue eyes, a white dress accentuating her lovely figure. A golden belt was cinched at her waist, where a small dagger was sheathed in a bejeweled scabbard. When I tilted the card in the light, tears of blood streamed down the heiress's cheeks, marring the ivory sheen of her gown. It was a disturbing sight, one that made me forget where I was until Phelan nudged my foot beneath the table.

"It's your turn, Anna."

"Will you trade with me?" I asked.

To my surprise, he did. I gave him the eight of clubs, and he gave me another wraith. The guard. He was decked in armor, his face obscured by a helm. But when I tilted the card, flames began to lick up his body, melting the steel into quicksilver, and I could see his face, screaming in pain. . . .

"You are *terrible* at this game," Phelan drawled.

I ignored him and asked, "Do you know who illustrated these cards?" I had an inkling that his mother had painted them. I had seen her buying supplies in the art shop—a place I now wished I had never step foot in. She cast no shadow. And there was that uncanny portrait of the twin brothers, tucked away in Phelan's desk.

"Yes, I do."

"Who is it?"

He shifted in his chair. I sensed his discomfort, and his voice was wary when he said, "What's this really about, Anna?"

I laid down my cards, faceup, so Phelan could see them. The two wraiths caught the firelight, gleaming as if they breathed, as if they lived, trapped on the paper.

"I think the enchantment surrounding these cards is giving the knight a way into dreams that are not his own," I began.

Phelan frowned, contemplating. "Go on."

I couldn't tell him that my conclusion had not only come from the duke, but also from Elle Fielding in Hereswith, who had lost a round of Seven Wraiths and suffered a nightmare for it. A dark dream where the knight had trod. The cards and the armor, both made from different *deviah* magicians, were somehow linked together by nightmares. I just did not know *how* yet, and I hoped

Phelan would give me insight.

"We know that whoever loses this game will have a nightmare as punishment," I continued, tracing my fingertip over the burning guard, the weeping heiress. Both who had betrayed their duke a century ago. "I think the nightmares spawned by this game are providing doorways, or portals, for the knight, who is wearing enchanted armor, to physically pass into them."

Phelan, frowning in contemplation, set down his cards to mirror mine, and I saw that he had been holding the spymistress. Mazarine. Her horns flared and then vanished, and I swallowed the questions I wanted to voice, questions that would betray all the things I shouldn't know.

"My mother painted these cards," he confessed at last.

"I noted that she is a magician when I met her in your bedroom," I said carefully. "I didn't realize she is also an artist."

His gaze flickered to mine. "Not many people know of her skill. She hardly speaks of her *deviah* magic to me."

"Have you ever asked her why she paints these cards?"

"No."

"Does she know that the knight has wounded you twice, now?"

"Yes, of course she knows." He was becoming agitated with my questions.

I swept the cards off the table and shuffled them. Phelan watched me with hooded eyes as I dealt us a new hand.

"Your mother is making these enchanted cards, unaware that she is also giving someone the chance to wreak havoc on the new moon," I said. "You and I need to discover who the knight is, and what they want. Perhaps they are simply seeking a challenge, but perhaps they have a bone to pick with your mother. Hence why they have attacked you twice now, Phelan." And why the knight appeared in Hereswith, the day before the brothers had arrived. As if the knight had known they were coming.

Phelan looked pale in the firelight. "You think the knight will come on the November new moon if one of us loses at cards and dreams tonight?"

"Yes," I said. I didn't tell him that I believed the knight had specifically targeted him, and that it was vital we discover who this vengeful person was before they killed him.

"Then whichever of us loses must also choose to forgo a remedy, in order to dream tonight, Anna."

"*Yes,*" I said again, softer. I bit my lip. I couldn't afford to be the one to lose and dream. I needed it to be him.

He stared at me for a long, uncomfortable moment. I didn't look away from him; I held his eyes as he held mine. Even as he seemed to steal my breath.

"Very well." He picked up his cards, as did I. And my hopes were dashed when I saw that I held three different wraiths. The advisor, the lost one, and the lady-in-waiting. If I was going to win, I would need Phelan to trade cards with me three times.

He refused to trade at all.

I lost with the three wraiths in my hands, and when I surrendered them, faceup on the table, Phelan fell quiet.

"Another round," he murmured, and worked to shuffle and deal.

I didn't want to acknowledge what he was doing, or why. But

he purposefully lost the second round.

Defeated, Phelan rose with a weary groan and drained the last of his lukewarm tea. "Take a remedy tonight, Anna. I'll be the one to dream. Surely, the knight will be *delighted* to use my nightmare as a doorway this upcoming new moon."

To my shock, I stood and said, "No. Let us both dream tonight."

Perhaps it was because of the late hour, somewhere long past midnight when reality begins to blur into recklessness. Or perhaps it was because we were both exhausted. Or because I liked him more than I wanted to, and the thought of him suffering through the night so I wouldn't have to vexed me. Or perhaps it was merely because I had never allowed myself to dream at night, and I longed to experience it.

"All right," he agreed.

Together, we banked the fire and extinguished the candles, ascending the stairs to the second floor. There was an awkward pause before his door; Phelan stalled for a moment, holding a candlestick. The solitary flame carved shadows on his face; pinpricks of light shone in his eyes. I knew he wanted to say something else to me, and so I also tarried on my threshold.

"I'll leave my door open tonight," he finally said, darting a glance at me. "If you need me, call and I'll come to you."

I nodded and slipped into my chamber, shutting the door behind me. But I stood there for what felt like years, stiff with apprehension. And I decided to open my door and leave it that way, just as Phelan had left his, and I prepared for bed.

I lay down in the dark, drawing the coverlet up to my chin. If

I dreamt of my old life—of a girl with auburn hair and charcoal-streaked fingers, walking the streets of Hereswith—I would break all laws of wardenship and fabricate a nightmare to record in Phelan's book. And if this nightmare happened to spawn on the new moon . . . then I would be exposed and I would flee, as Papa had prepared me to do.

I drifted into sleep before I felt wholly prepared for it.

When I woke hours later, the sheets were crumpled around me, the night pitched dark and cold. The hour before sunrise. It was not a nightmare that had startled me awake. It was the emptiness. The howling quiet. A terrible sense of unease crept over me.

I hadn't dreamt at all.

I sat forward in bed with a gasp.

I was chilled to the bone; I trembled, full of aches I had never felt before. It was as if I had slept in a snowdrift on midwinter, and I struggled to rise. My fingers and toes were like ice.

My sleep was dreamless, although it shouldn't have been. My mind was hollow, but I told myself it was nothing to worry over. Nothing to worry over as I left my room and crossed the hallway, to where Phelan's door sat open with invitation.

I took two steps into his chamber and then halted, as if I was truly losing my mind. I shouldn't be here. I shouldn't seek him out for comfort.

"Anna?"

He was awake, as if he had been waiting for me. I listened as he shifted in bed, sitting forward. "Anna, are you all right?"

"Yes," I replied, and the lie sat in my mouth like glass.

Something that would tear me up as soon as I swallowed it. And I said, "No. No, I'm not."

"Do you want to join me? There's room for both of us."

I already knew there was room in his bed. I had slept at his side once, and it had been one of the best nights of sleep I had experienced since leaving Hereswith.

I couldn't see in the dark, but I surrendered and felt my way to his bed. I listened as he moved the blankets, as he fluffed a pillow, as he made space for me.

I eased into the warmth of his bed. The sheets were like silk, steeped with pine, meadow grass, rain, and spices. The smell of his skin and his soap. And the ice I had felt upon waking dreamless began to melt. The bed was generous enough that we could both lie side by side without a chance of touching, and I relaxed, sinking into the feather mattress. But I could sense him, how slim the distance was between our bodies. If I reached my hand out to the gentle darkness, my fingertips would brush his shoulder. His hair. The line of his jaw.

I felt safe lying beside him. As the tingling left my limbs, I asked myself why I didn't dream. A voice echoed in my memory, as if in reply. *Tell me, Clementine . . . have you read one of my nightmares recorded in your father's book?*

Mazarine's words, haunting me weeks after she spoke them. And then it was like she was speaking to me, because I heard her whisper, *"Have you read one of your* own *nightmares in your father's book?"*

"Anna?"

"Mm?"

I was thankful he spoke, breaking me from my reveries. I listened to him breathe, wondering if he was about to tell me what nightmare he had dreamt. If I would need to write it down for him. And when the silence deepened like a canyon between us, I thought he had drifted asleep until he spoke again, and his confession echoed through me. . . .

"I dreamt of nothing."

26

"It must have been the cards," I said later that morning, watching Phelan pace the library. "Perhaps the enchantment has worn away in them, from being passed through so many hands."

"No," he said. "Those cards will never lose their enchantment. Not while the curse still lives on the mountain."

"Do you think the curse will ever end?"

"I don't know, Anna."

I fell silent. I hadn't told him that I was also dreamless. As far as he knew, I had suffered a nightmare while he had suffered nothing. And if I was honest, there was a piece of me that wanted to tell him the truth. To confess and watch the furrow in his brow ease. But I feared it would make me too vulnerable.

"How does your mother create the cards?" I asked. *How does she enchant her illustrations with nightmares* was what I truly wanted to know.

Phelan stopped pacing. His back was angled to me; his attention was fixed on the frost-laced window. One would never think he had experienced a bad night; he was impeccably dressed, and his raven-dark hair was held by his customary ribbon. But his eyes were bloodshot and distant. Even when he looked at me, I sensed he was far away.

"I'm not sure. I know very little of *deviah* magic." He sighed. The sound could have come from my own lips, as if our worry was the same. "I need to go tend to a few things. You can have the rest of the day off, Anna."

He left in a rush, grabbing his top hat and coat from the rack on his way out.

For a moment, I didn't know what to do with myself and this unexpected day of freedom. And then I smelled the aroma of Mrs. Stirling's cooking drift down the hall, browned butter and golden crust and strawberry preserves, and I knew exactly where I wanted to go.

I went to see Imonie.

She had the town house to herself again. Mama was at the theater, Papa at the mines. I sat on a kitchen stool with Dwindle purring on my lap—even in a different shape, my cat knew me. Bright October sunlight flowed in from the windows as I watched Imonie bake. It almost felt like the Vespers had never happened to us and we were back in Hereswith.

Almost.

"It looks like they've been feeding you well," she said as she kneaded dough on the counter.

"The food is good," I replied. "But I do miss your galettes."

She tried to hide how much my comment pleased her; only a hint of blush warmed her cheeks. "If I had known you were coming, I would have a whole tray ready for you."

I smiled, but I said nothing else for a while, the words suddenly feeling too heavy to speak. I would have been content to simply sit silently in Imonie's presence until she looked at me with her keen eyes.

"What's troubling you, Clementine?"

It was a relief to have someone I trusted, someone who knew me in all my shades, ask me a direct question.

"What does it feel like when you dream, Imonie? Do you dream every single night if you don't take a remedy?"

"It's been a long while since I dreamt," she replied, returning her gaze to her dough. But her attention remained fixated on me. "Once, when I was younger, I dreamt vividly every single night. The good dreams were like sustenance, feeding me all throughout the following day. And the bad ones? Well, I think you know what nightmares are like, Clementine."

I mulled over her reply, and then asked, "Is it common to wake up and forget what you dreamt the night before?"

That brought her eyes back to mine. Sharp and probing. "Why do you ask, child?"

"I'm merely curious."

"Then yes. Sometimes."

The stiffness in my shoulders eased. I stroked Dwindle's calico fur and thought perhaps that had been the case for me last night. But the longer I tried to convince myself, the weaker it felt. Because both Phelan and I should have been battered by nightmares. And nightmares were not the type of dream to be forgotten come sunrise.

"There's something I want to tell you, Clem," Imonie said, wiping her hands on her apron. "The other week, when you came for Monday night dinner. You asked if November seventeenth held any significance."

"And does it?" I prompted, my interest catching.

"It doesn't in Bardyllis, but once, long ago, that date meant something in Seren. It was a night of feasting, when the people of the mountains lit fires and ate their favorite foods and danced beneath the stars. It was the last feast of autumn, because the snow comes early in the mountains."

"Why didn't you mention this to me when I first asked?"

Imonie glanced away. "You know speaking of the mountains grieves me, Clem."

She was about to say something else, but the front door creaked open, and we both turned, surprised to see my father appear on the kitchen threshold.

"Papa!" I greeted him.

He stopped upright and gaped at me a moment, and I noticed that he had washed the grime of the mines away, and that his hair was brushed, and he was wearing fine clothes.

He wasn't pleased to see me.

"Why are you here, daughter?" he asked in a brusque tone. "Shouldn't you be with Phelan?"

I slowly rose from my stool, setting Dwindle on the floor. "And shouldn't you be at the mines?"

Papa glanced beyond me, to look at Imonie, but by the time I spun around, their silent conversation had ended.

"Forgive me, Clem," my father said gently. "You're taking a risk by coming here in broad daylight. I didn't expect it."

"I haven't forgotten my stealth charms."

"Come, sit with me in the drawing room."

I moved to follow him until I smelled something odd. It was faint at first, and I told myself it must be coming from the kitchen. But when I stepped into the drawing room and could still taste the bergamot and parchment in the air, I halted, watching my father sit in a leather chair.

"You've been with the duke," I stated.

Papa gazed up at me, his face frozen. His lips hardly moved as he asked, "What makes you think that?"

"You smell like his cologne."

"Don't be ridiculous, Clem."

"Don't *lie* to me!" I cried. The emotion welled, sudden and fierce. It took me off guard, and I drew in a deep breath to calm myself. "What does he want with you?"

My father continued to stare at me; his face was like a stranger's, cold and suspicious. I couldn't read him, and fear sparked within me.

"Sit down, Clementine."

"Was he the one who ordered you to protect Mazarine?" I asked. "Does he hold something over you, Papa?"

"Yes, and that's all I can say to you of the matter." I hadn't expected my father to reply. So when he did, it nearly made me keel over. He rose and approached me, cradling my face in his palms. I could smell the bergamot on his skin, as if he had shaken the duke's hand.

"Did you make a bargain with him, Papa?" I asked in a hoarse voice. *Please*, I thought. *Please tell me no. . . .*

My father only studied me, as if he was desperate to find a semblance of his daughter in my disguise. "You've met the duke, Clem?"

He was turning the conversation on me. I tried to step away but he held me steady. "When?" he asked, and I heard a thread of worry within his voice. "What did you meet with him about?"

"Papa . . ."

"Answer me."

"To record a dream of his. Weeks ago."

"Is that all?"

"Yes." But I had hesitated, and Papa had heard it. He knew I was lying.

"Clem," he whispered. "What else happened?"

I had always trusted my father. And I saw how naive that was of me. To never question him, to always tell him everything.

"That was all," I said, and I felt the stone of my heart settle. As if it would never crack and relinquish me. "But perhaps you should tell me why *you* met with the duke."

"I don't want you to worry over this, Clem," he said. "All is well. What I want you to do is continue playing your role as Phelan's partner safely and shrewdly. Do you understand?"

I nodded, even as his hands continued to cradle my face, firm within his grip.

"Good," he whispered, and his fingers fell away. "Now, then. Do you have any news about the countess?"

I did. I knew that she was a *deviah*, and she had been creating enchanted cards for Seven Wraiths. I knew that she was trying to keep Phelan's new moon nemesis an absolute secret, for reasons I could only marvel at. I had an inkling she had once had an affair with the duke, and Phelan and Lennox were the offspring of that liaison.

But if my father would not be forthright with me, then why should I be with him?

"No news, Papa. But Phelan is searching the theaters, seeking Mama."

"I'll let her know," he said. "You should return to your post before you are missed."

I let him walk me to the door, Imonie slipping a few cheese pastries into my hand. My father and I paused in the foyer, and I knew he wouldn't open the front door until I had cast my stealth charm. But I delayed; I was still hungry for answers.

"What would happen if I ceased taking remedies at night?"

Papa frowned. "That would be a foolish thing to do, Clem."

"But what would happen if I *did*?" I insisted. "Would I dream, Papa?"

He was silent, but his stare held mine for a long moment. "You would dream, daughter. And there is no telling how terrible those dreams would be."

I cast my stealth charm. He opened the door for me, and I slipped out of the town house without another word. I walked a few blocks before I came to a stop near the river, and I stood on the mossy bank for a while, acknowledging the truth like a bruise on my skin.

My father was deceiving me.

I didn't drink a remedy that night.

I lay in bed with the door open, like it had been the night before. As Phelan's was, on the other side of the hall. As if some channel had been forged by our dreamless slumber, and if I dared to rise, its current would guide me to him.

I stared up into the darkness, afraid to fall asleep, afraid to discover what awaited me on the other side. Afraid of the answers that I sought.

I slept beneath the shadows of a canopy, beneath the watch of the stars. I woke to the fragile light of the sun. And I was cold again, as if I were in an empty cavern, or lost on a winter sea.

There was nothing for me to experience in sleep, despite what my father had sworn.

Again, I hadn't dreamt.

27

The shields arrived.

I had honestly forgotten all about them, and Phelan and I stood side by side in the library, staring at the two shields laid out on the desk. The larger one was for him, made of dark, glistening wood and silver studs. Its companion was smaller, crafted from a red wood with golden accents. The one the smith had made for me.

They were beautiful, and when I traced the edge of mine, I felt a chill in my hand. I tasted mist and rust and salt in my mouth. Enchantment that was forged deep into the essence of wood and steel.

"Why did these arrive?" Phelan asked tersely. He had been in a foul mood since the day before, and I could only assume it was due to his dreamless sleep. "I didn't order them."

I cast a careful glance at him. "The duke had them commissioned for us."

"Please tell me you didn't, Anna."

"That I didn't *what*, Phelan?"

"Tell the duke about the knight."

I was silent. Phelan groaned and dragged his hands down his face. "He knows too much and all but owns me. I don't want to be any more indebted to him than I already am!"

I remembered what the duke had said about Phelan. *His investment.* I dared to wonder if Phelan was his son, but I would never breathe that assumption aloud. At least, not yet.

"You don't like the duke?" I asked.

"I won't say that I *dislike* him," Phelan replied. "But he is everywhere I turn. Watching me, advising me. Ordering me." He paused, and a light of realization flickered through him. "He came here while I was away, didn't he? Did he force the truth about the knight from you, Anna?"

"No, but he was concerned about your well-being."

Phelan groaned again and walked to the window, to gaze beyond the glass. "Well, then. I suppose we have no choice. The shields it is."

"The shields are to protect us while one of us removes the knight's helm," I said, and Phelan turned to stare at me. "We need to identify whoever it is."

"Removing the helm will be impossible."

I sighed at his pessimism and lifted my shield. It was heavy, but not to the point where I would be unable to wield it. I slid it onto my arm and met Phelan's stare. "I think you and I can do it."

"He might not even appear this upcoming new moon."

"Why? We've been playing Seven Wraiths every night. We've all but rolled out a welcome rug in our dreams, inviting him to the streets on the new moon."

"But I still haven't dreamt."

I glanced at him. "Were you able to speak to your mother about it?"

Phelan never answered, as we were interrupted by Mrs. Stirling, who brought in a pot of slippery elm tea and a pile of letters that had just arrived in the post.

Phelan and I sat at the desk, drank tea, and sorted through the correspondence. Most were nightmare requests, and I made a list of names we needed to visit.

"This one is for you," Phelan said, handing a thick envelope to me.

I accepted it with reservation. Who would write to me? And then I saw the golden wax seal, and I slowly opened it, slipping out an exquisite invitation.

Lady Raven Vesper was inviting me to a dinner party, following the next new moon. November seventeenth.

I stared at that date until it swam on the paper. Imonie's words flooded back to me: *It was a night of feasting, when the people of the mountains lit fires and ate their favorite foods and danced beneath the stars.* Did the countess know this? Was this all some coincidence of dates? I didn't think that it was, and I must have been staring at the invite too long, because Phelan asked, "Would you like to attend it with me, Anna? As my date?"

My heart quickened at his offer. I hated that it did; I hated that

I wanted to go with him. I winced, swallowing the pain and the desire, and dropped the invitation on the table.

"I'm fairly certain your mother loathes me," I replied.

"She doesn't loathe you."

"I have nothing to wear."

"I'm afraid that excuse won't do, Anna. I'll provide you with something."

"Of course you will."

"Is that a yes, then?"

Yes. "No."

Phelan leaned across the desk and said, "I know you dislike this sort of thing. As do I, but my mother has given me an order, so I cannot escape it. And I told her I would not attend without you."

That caught my attention. "She *orders* you to attend dinner parties?"

"Not often. But this time, yes." And he smiled, as if that would help change my mind.

It was not the charm of his smile, but the enticing thought of seeing the countess again, in her mansion. I would have access to her private residence—a *deviah* magician with a multitude of secrets—and I knew this opportunity would not come again. It was the perfect chance to glean more information for the exposé I planned to write about the Vespers.

"Very well," I conceded. "I will go as your date, but only if I am the one to remove the knight's helm on the new moon."

His smile melted into a scowl. I waited for him to protest, but instead he extended his hand across the desk and said, "I agree to your terms."

I hesitated only a beat before I reached out and let my hand slide into his.

We shook on it.

The moon waxed.

Phelan and I gathered nightmares. We walked the streets in the evening with our shields on our arms, growing accustomed to their weight. We planned strategy, we planned a dance with the knight, we planned for the unexpected and the expected.

The moon waned.

I no longer drank remedies at night. I never dreamt, and I refused to dwell on what that might mean. I blamed it on the tattered state of the cards; I told myself the magic of the game was weak and worn. I never asked Phelan about his nights, but I knew he wasn't dreaming, either. I knew the long, dreamless nights were wearing him down with worry, because I felt it too. How it made one crave warmth, to feel something other than numbing emptiness.

Sometimes, I found myself concerned for him, and how distant he was. Something had changed within him; he seemed guarded and preoccupied. I occasionally wished that I had been honest with him about my own sleep. For despite how close I felt to him now, my lack of vulnerability had built a wall between us.

Two nights before the November new moon, he came home late from visiting his mother. I was already in bed, but I heard the front door slam, followed by a crash that shook the walls.

My pulse leapt in my throat as I grabbed a robe and flew down the stairs.

I found Phelan in the throes of dismantling the library. I stood, stunned, as he viciously swiped his books off the shelves. Volume after volume was hurled to the ground, until the floor was nearly covered in exposed pages and scuffed covers. He took to his desk next, completely unaware of me. There was a whirlwind of fluttering papers and quills and shattering glass, ink spilling like dark blood.

"Phelan," I said, but my voice was nothing more than a rough whisper.

He went to the window, where his potted plants were arranged. He took each one in his hands and hurled them against the wall. Vines and flowers went limp in clumps of soil. I dared to step closer to him.

"Phelan."

He froze, at last hearing me. When he turned, I saw that his eyes were red rimmed, and his cheeks were flushed, from anger or from weeping, I didn't know. But I had never seen him like this.

He released a sharp breath when he met my gaze.

I wanted to ask him what had happened. But I couldn't find the words. They lodged in my throat as I stepped over his ruin.

"Anna," he said. His voice was hoarse; he no longer sounded furious, only sad. "Anna . . . you should leave."

I halted. "Leave?"

He set down the pot he had been about to toss. "Yes. Get far away from me, my family."

My fingers curled into fists as I wondered if he had discovered my true identity. He hadn't mentioned Clementine Madigan since the day I'd conveyed Blythe's message, but I sensed he was still searching for me.

"You would tell me to leave two days before the new moon?" I asked, incredulous. "Why?"

Phelan turned away, surveying the damage he had wrought. "I can't tell you why. But I want to give you the opportunity to leave while you still can."

I stared at him, stunned, as he began to pick up books and set them back on the shelves.

The volume of nightmares was sprawled in the middle of the floor; I retrieved it, smoothing the pages that had bent. Phelan paused, watching as I walked the tome to his desk and set it down.

"Remember that night you told me that you weren't *kind*?" I asked. "Well, in case you failed to notice, neither am I."

"Anna," he began, desperate. "You sh—"

"No, listen to me! I have invested too much time, sweat, and blood in you and your streets for you to dismiss me over some family matter you refuse to divulge. I'm not going anywhere, Phelan Vesper."

I left him to clean the library on his own, but I sat in bed by candlelight, too anxious and angry at him to sleep. I reached for my journal and reread my exposé, eventually turning the page to write what Phelan had said to me earlier: *Get far away from me, my family.* I stared at those words, and I wondered what had inspired them. I needed to know—his mother must have done something awful—and I shut the journal.

My door was open, as it had been every night, and yet I was

still surprised to see him appear, standing on my threshold long past midnight. He had never come to me in the dark as I sometimes did to him, to lie close enough to feel his heat but far enough that we never touched.

We stared at each other for a long, fragile moment. A moment when I wondered if he was about to ask if he could sleep in my bed, and I felt terrible warmth course through me.

"You're right," he said. "I'm sorry."

"For what?" I would never be above making him grovel.

"That you had to see my fit, downstairs. That I told you to leave." He paused, but his eyes shone like gemstones in the firelight. "I need you. And if you had departed as I first wanted, I would have soon come after you."

I shivered, but I refused to dwell on how his words made me feel, like I was sugar melting in tea. I needed to know what his mother had done to upset him. "You can talk to me, Phelan."

He was quiet. His gaze dropped for the briefest of moments, down to my throat and the loose neckline of my chemise. "I know. Good night, Anna."

He left, striding to his bedroom across the hall. I thought it was probably for the best and slid into the safety of my cold sheets.

28

The November new moon arrived, at last. Phelan and I walked the cold, darkened streets with shields on our arms, waiting for the dream to arrive.

The trees were succumbing to bareness, limbs creaking in the wind and leaves gathering on the cobblestones, damp and golden and fragrant beneath my boots. I could see my breath, a steady plume of smoke, and I felt the chill of the air bite my cheeks.

It began to drizzle.

The streetlamps cast hazy circles of light and I shivered as moisture gathered in my hair, beaded on my raiment. A dankness settled into my bones. My shield sat snug on my arm, but the uneven weight of it was agitating my shoulders.

Phelan said nothing as he stood at my side, but he frequently checked his pocket watch. We hadn't discussed the library dismantling again, or what had driven him to do it. In fact, he had kept me at a polite distance, and I hated to admit that his reserve bothered me.

I could barely see his face in the darkness, but when he looked at me, his eyes were bright, almost feverish.

"This weather is granting us a disadvantage," he said.

"As long as we stay close together, we should be fine," I replied. But I couldn't deny that he was right about the disadvantage: the streets were slick from the drizzle and patches of leaves. We continued to wait as the rain began to fall steadily, soaking through our clothes.

"If something goes amiss," Phelan began to say, "I want you to retreat to the house and lock the door."

"I'm not retreating and leaving you."

He never responded, because the nightmare manifested in the streets with a sudden and fierce gust. It blew us both off our feet. We sprawled on the wet cobblestones, breathless and wide eyed and clumsy with our shields.

"What was that?" I asked, scrambling to my feet, my gaze peeling the darkness.

We both heard a clatter behind us. The sound of something climbing up a trellis, rattling the shutters of a nearby house.

I turned. It looked like a man upon first glance, but then I saw that he was some manner of demon, with pale, scaly skin, sinewy wings, and long talons in place of nails. His eyes were lambent and he hissed when the shutter remained locked against him. He flew to the next window, seeking to unlock it. I was alarmed, to see a figment of a nightmare so intent on breaking into a house.

"Is this a child's nightmare?" I asked Phelan, because I failed to recognize it.

"Yes. The demon comes and takes the child through the window," he replied.

We would have to climb after it on the trellis, which would be difficult with our shields. Phelan shed his buckler in the street and I followed suit. Together, we approached the town house.

"Is there anything else that happens?" I asked.

He waded through a bush to reach the base of the trellis, taking hold of the lattice. He glanced at me and said, "No. Just the demon and the kidnapping."

The demon finally noticed us.

He hissed from his perch on a second-story window ledge before flying to the next house.

"We'll have to be more discreet." Phelan headed to the path that wound to the backyard.

But the demon had his eye on us now, watching with a taunting glare.

"Wait, Phelan," I said. "We need to set a trap for it, or else we'll be chasing it from town house to town house until dawn."

Phelan paused. "What sort of trap?"

I was already taking a step back, returning to the street, my eyes on his house.

"Anna?" He hurried after me.

"I'm going to sit in my room with the window open and the shutters unlatched," I said, breathless. "You need to be in the backyard, prepared in case the demon manages to drag me out the window."

I waited for him to protest. To my surprise, he didn't. I slipped in the front door and locked it behind me, and Phelan went to the garden in the back, where he could see my bedroom window.

I hurried to light a candle in my chamber. I opened the window and unlatched the shutters, and I drew a chair up center to it and sat.

The rain continued to fall, a quiet melody. I was frozen to the bone, waiting to hear the demon's claws rap on my shutters.

It didn't take long.

The demon burst into my room with needles of rain. He expected to find me in bed, so I had a moment of surprise to cast my magical net. He screeched and flung himself against the wall, attempting to cut through the binds I had draped over him. They held, and I watched for a moment, until the demon had tired himself. I sought the golden key, thinking it should be somewhere on the demon's body. A place to stab him.

There was no golden weakness.

But from the corner of my eye, there was an alluring gleam.

I turned to my open window, the casement slick with rain. There was a hint of gold at the edges, and I suddenly understood, although it seemed very reckless.

I didn't give myself another moment to doubt. I called my magical net back to me, felt the corresponding recoil like a whip striking my hand. But I gritted my teeth through the shock of pain and leapt for the demon as he made to flee through the window.

He hissed as we glided into the night, as if I was suddenly a great hindrance to him, and I thought about being a child dreaming this nightmare. I thought about how the entire crux of this dream was that the child was terrified to let the demon carry them out the window. And yet how it was the key to ending it, to awaken.

The demon dissolved into smoke beneath me.

I was flying, falling, tumbling. I aimed for the closest roof and eased myself down with a slowing spell, but it was still a rough landing. I hit the shingles, knocked a few loose as I slipped, scrambling for purchase. I cursed the rain and my temerity, thinking of all those lessons when my father had instructed me to be cautious.

Those lessons felt as if they belonged to another life, another girl.

I hung from the gutter and eased my way to the corner of the house, where I could drop down to a trellis. Halfway in my descent, the lattice groaning like it wanted to break, I heard Phelan on the ground beneath me.

"Are you all right, Anna?"

I paused to glance down at him. The rain sat on his face like tears. His dark hair swept across his brow in a terribly endearing manner.

"I'm fine. The demon is gone." And the lattice responded by finally cracking beneath me. I was suddenly spilled into the darkness below, into Phelan's frantic arms.

The impact sent us sprawling into a bracken patch. My hands delved into the damp soil above his shoulders, my legs straddled his waist, and I felt every point of contact between us. The heaves of his breaths beneath me. How his warmth chased away the cold nip of the night.

I attempted to slip off him, stiff and awkward in my drenched clothes. He grasped my waist, tightening his hold on my hips as if he wanted me to remain. Or perhaps to simply cease moving.

One of his hands rose to carefully tuck a thread of tangled hair behind my ear. So he could behold my face in dim light. And when his thumb traced my lips, as if he had imagined kissing them . . . a gasp escaped me. I felt a hint of pleasure and pain, both lurking deep in my chest. I winced as if a needle was prodding my heart.

"Anna?" he whispered, uncertain.

I instantly shrank away, realizing this was foolish. To allow myself to be so close to him and enjoy it. His fingertips grazed my jaw as I retreated. I refused to acknowledge the confusion and chaos of my feelings then, but I knew I would have to later, like a sunburn appearing on my skin.

"We should go," I said, successfully sliding off him this time. "Another battle awaits us."

That sobered him. Maybe the knight would come, and maybe he wouldn't. But lying in a garden entwined with Phelan Vesper was a bad idea, either way.

We returned to our original post, the streets empty and lamplit, gleaming with rain. I fixed my shield upon my arm, preparing for the second leg of the night. My adrenaline was beginning to ebb. I felt sore and weary, and my drenched clothes were chafing my skin.

It's almost impossible to judge time on a new moon night. I don't know how long Phelan and I stood there, our breath like clouds, our skin pebbled from the cold, our shields waiting on our arms.

But it felt like hours until the silence was broken by an unexpected sound. Someone was singing in the distance, a slurred chorus that echoed off the town houses.

Phelan and I both whirled to look behind us. In a ring of lamplight, I saw a man stumble. I could see he had a bottle of wine in his hand, and he continued to sing, defiant and foolish and utterly unaware of himself.

"Gods above," Phelan said, exasperated.

"I take it he's not part of the nightmare," I said, but I felt a jolt of worry. It was always dangerous for residents to wander the streets on the new moon, even after a nightmare had broken. I had heard horrible stories of how magicians had inadvertently slain innocent mortals who had been in the streets, because the wardens believed they were part of the nightmare. Of course, this typically only happened to magicians who were unprepared, those who did not study and memorize their nightmare ledger.

"It's Allan Hugh," Phelan groaned. "And no, he's not part of the nightmare. He's very real."

"You should do something," I whispered, thinking it would be disastrous to have a drunk Allan wandering the streets if the knight appeared. "Can you take him home?"

But even *that* was a risk—to make Allan's wife have no choice but to unlock her door on this capricious night.

Phelan sighed. "Yes, he lives one street over. I'll take him there now. Will you—"

"I'll wait here for you," I said.

Phelan must have heard the resolve in me. I was not about to trail him and this drunk individual. He nodded and began to run up the street, splashing through puddles, calling for Allan's attention.

I watched until they had vanished into the darkness. I soaked in the silence again; I closed my eyes and leaned my head back, face upturned to the sky.

And that's when I felt it. A tremble in the cobblestones beneath me.

A shift in the wind around me.

The rain eased, as if nature was retreating, hiding.

I opened my eyes and watched the knight appear.

He was unchanged. He walked his same steady, heavy-footed pace. His armor was still bloodstained. His helm still inspired a blaze of terror in me. He drew his sword and the tip of it rang on the stones alongside him, a warning for me to run from him.

I walked to meet him, shield ready on my arm.

I'm faster, I reminded myself. *Stay out of his reach and if you stumble, remember the shield.*

He took his first swing at me. I danced out of the sword's path. I would wear him out, and I taunted him again, stepping close to provoke him, darting away from his reach. He swung, I evaded. I believed I could continue doing this until dawn, and I had every intention to until the knight feigned a move and I misread him. He turned and caught me by surprise, but my reflexes saved me.

I swung my shield around to block. His sword lodged within the wood and I expected my buckler to crack in two, but it held firm, suddenly illuminated as its enchantment stirred. I was drenched in golden light, and the knight bent to it, to me. I stumbled backward, and his sword came with me, embedded in my shield. I was amazed at the sight of him disarmed.

He seemed stunned as well.

And I claimed that moment of surprise, just as I had done with the demon. I swung my shield and the hilt of his sword at his chest, and the blow rocked him from his feet. He went down with a grunt on his back.

"Anna!" Phelan shouted from a distance, and I knew he was running to me. But I didn't spare him a glance.

I let my shield slide from my tingling arm and stood over the knight, my foot on his chest. He was dazed. Frozen on the cobblestones. I knelt and removed his helm.

The streetlight spilled over his face. A face I knew alarmingly well.

It was my father.

29

I couldn't breathe; I couldn't move. I hovered above the knight and stared at his face—familiar and yet hauntingly strange in the darkness of the new moon. A face that was beloved to me. And yet there was no recognition within him as he stared up at me. His eyes were unforgiving and sharp as flint; his auburn hair was lank in the rain. His mouth was pressed in a hard line, and vengeance burned within him like stars.

I recognized him, and yet part of me denied it.

My father appeared younger with the shadows playing over his features. Startled, I realized I had seen him like this before. On the night when the Vesper brothers had arrived to Hereswith and Papa had been sick. He had asked me to glamour him to look hale, and as I cast the spell, I had caught a glimpse of his younger self.

Before I could demand why he appeared this way, what he was doing, how he had walked into this nightmare, my father reached out and took hold of my throat. His grip was fierce, unrelenting. I gasped and clawed at his hand, but my fingers were useless against his armor.

He is going to kill me.

The thoughts burst in my mind as the world tilted. I struggled; I viciously fought him, and it only made my blood thrum faster. I could hear Phelan shout my name again, his boots echoing on the street as he ran for me. My sight was dimming, my lungs burning. And yet I held my father's vicious gaze, unwavering, and rasped, "Papa . . . *Papa!*"

My father grew still.

He stared at me, his eyes widening like he had woken from a dream. Before I could rouse another strangled word in my throat, he released me, hurling me up and away from him as if I were weightless. My hair streaked across my face as I glided through the rain, as I hit the cobblestones with a painful jar.

Phelan reached me a moment later.

His arms came about my body, drawing me up and holding me firm against him. At first I thought I didn't need his strength until I realized that my feet were numb.

"Anna? Anna!" Phelan turned me toward him.

I gasped a broken, terrible sound. My neck throbbed as I leaned into him. My voice emerged, weak and brittle. "Where is he?"

Phelan glanced beyond me to where the knight had been just moments ago.

"He's gone, Anna."

I didn't believe him. I looked to where I had seen my father, gleaming in bloodstained armor. Where my father had almost strangled me.

It was as Phelan said. The knight had vanished, retreated. But his sword remained lodged in my shield, and my shield lay on the cobblestones. A testament to what had happened.

I felt my awareness fading and I bit my lip until the pain sharpened me.

Stay awake, stay awake . . .

Phelan's breath was labored as he led me to his house and ascended the porch stairs. He bore me inside and kicked the door closed. The sound reverberated through my body and I could see the concern in his expression, a wrinkle of fear on his brow.

He carried me upstairs, past my bedroom, into the lavatory. He spoke and the candles ignited, washing us in rosy light. Gently, he set me down on the tile floor, propped up against the cabinets. I knew there was a mirror, directly above me, and it hovered like a blade about to fall.

If I wasn't so drained, I would have shattered it.

Phelan knelt and drew my hair away from my neck, studying the column of my throat. I imagined bruises would soon bloom.

"I'm fine," I said, and I wanted to send him away but couldn't find the strength. His fingertips traced my neck up to my jaw, to the arch of my cheek. A soft caress that made me ache. He held my face in his hands, and I closed my eyes, surprised by the surge of trust I felt for him. I breathed deeply until I had calmed myself. Slowly, I could feel my limbs again. Slowly, my fear faded, and a bitter coldness replaced it. The ice seeped into my chest.

I opened my eyes.

Phelan was watching me intently. Whatever shone in my gaze made his hands fall away.

"I'm going to draw you a warm bath," he said, reaching for the handles. Water began to flow from the faucet, and he cast a heating spell over it. The chamber became warm, steamy. Lavender intoxicated the air.

I could have fallen asleep, propped up against those cabinets, lulled by the sound of running water.

But I continued to see my father's hauntingly young face, feel his hand on my neck, choking me.

"Did you see the knight's face?" I asked.

Phelan was still on his knees, tending to the tub. A jar of bath crystals was in his hand, and he poured them into the water. "No, I didn't. But you did, Anna?"

"Yes," I whispered, and Phelan waited until the tub was full before turning off the faucets. He returned to me, on his knees.

"Did you recognize the knight?" he tentatively asked. "You seemed to hesitate when the helm was removed."

"I've never seen him before," I lied, and Phelan nodded. But I thought I saw his eyes shutter, his jaw flex.

"Do you need me to help you into the tub?"

I almost laughed until I realized how shaky I was. I tried to unlace my bodice, but my hands were trembling. "If you could help me undress . . . I can do the rest."

He did so with great care, unbuttoning my boots first. He slipped them off my feet one by one. He unlaced my bodice and drew my skirt down, and I could hear him breathing, deep and steady, like his heart was pounding. Soon I was sitting in my damp chemise and my knee-high stockings, and he hesitated before he reached beneath the hem of my undergarment to find the top edge of my right sock. I felt his fingertips trace my skin as he slowly pulled the wool down my leg, leaving goose bumps in his wake.

I closed my eyes as he reached for the second one, and I was wondering if I should let him completely undress me when he paused, my stocking pooled around my ankle.

I looked at him, brow arched. He was frozen, staring at something on my left calf. Two scars made by fangs, on a night not unlike this one. When I had nearly drowned and had pulled myself into Phelan's boat. They were scars I thought he would never see, and so I had left them when Mazarine transformed me.

He met my gaze. I couldn't read the thoughts that lurked within him—if he suspected I was not who I appeared to be—but nor did I have the energy to reassure or lie to him.

"I can handle it from here," I whispered, and waited for him to slip away, the door latching behind him. I drew myself up with help of the cabinets, kicking off my left stocking. I let my chemise fall away and I stepped into the bath, sinking into the warm water with a tremor.

Alone, at last, I indulged the softer side of myself. I covered my mouth and wept.

I don't know how long my mind whirled before a wave of misgivings crashed on me. I embraced the pain and finally relived my father's betrayal, seeking to make sense of it. How long had he been hiding enchanted armor, and why was he stepping into nightmares? What power was he channeling to do it? Why had he not recognized me? Why had he appeared to look twenty years younger?

I wiped away my tears, my neck aching from his brutal hand. And then I studied my own palms, my fingers, the length of my brown hair. All of them lies, a facade that I had made for myself.

"Oh my gods," I whispered, watching my hands quiver. My father must also be wearing a disguise. He was two-faced, as I was. How old was he, truly? Why would he need to hide his face? His age?

I would have to go to him and insist he answer my questions. Questions that threatened to burn through me, questions that I wanted to hone into swords and pierce him with.

He had lied to me. He was a hypocrite. *He had nearly strangled me.*

I laid my fingers over my neck; I felt the stone half of my heart grow colder than the ice on the mountains.

I would have to take him by surprise at the mines that evening, when he left his shift. And while I felt too restless for it, I slept most of the day. Late afternoon sunlight crept through my curtains when I woke, and I saw that Mrs. Stirling had left a tray of food by the bed. It must have been hours ago, because the tea and soup were cold.

I rose and dressed, avoiding my reflection in the shattered

mirror. My neck was sore; I imagined the bruises were beginning to show on my skin as I silently crept down the stairs.

I paused in the foyer, listening. I reached out with my magic, mindful to go gently, or else I might gain their attention.

Mrs. Stirling was in the kitchen. She stood at the counter making dumplings. Flour was on her apron, on her face. She sang beneath her breath. Farther down the corridor, I sensed Phelan in the library. The doors were open, and he sat with the book of nightmares cracked before him. He was so still he could have been hewn from stone as he stared at the page. His worry hung in the air like a thundercloud. And then beyond the back door, in the garden, was Deacon. He was supposed to be gathering herbs for dinner but he was preoccupied with whittling a stick into an arrow.

I called my magic back to me and slipped away from the town house, careful to make no sound.

I hurried down the street, fighting the sensation I was being followed. It eventually overcame me so greatly that I did pause and wait in the alley between two shops, to see if anyone was trailing me. Phelan, most likely. But I never saw him, and I imagined I was simply being paranoid, after discovering that my father was not who I believed him to be.

I called a horse and cab and traveled to the northwest point of the city.

I lingered in a shadow by the mine yard, waiting for dark, when my father's shift would be over.

It seemed like I waited an eternity before the miners began to file out of the earth, their faces streaked with grime. My father was at the end of the line, his head bowed, his boots dragging. I intercepted him, grasping hold of his shirt and tugging.

"What—?" He let out a startled sound until he realized it was me. He followed me to an alley, and his concern nearly smothered me.

"Has he discovered you? Do we need to flee?"

I gaped at my father. He acted as if nothing had happened the night before. As if he had not tried to strangle me.

"Clem," he urged, impatient.

"Who are you?" I countered coldly.

He blinked, taken aback. I could just discern his face—the face of a forty-seven-year-old man who I had implicitly trusted—as a nearby lamp limned us with faint light.

"What?"

"You heard me," I snapped.

"I have no idea what you mean, Clem."

"It's Anna. And you do know, Ambrose." I drew my hair away from my neck, so he could see the bruises.

The shock and fury on his face were electrifying. My father reached for me but I evaded him, my stomach knotting. I was going to be sick. I was shaking, fuming. My anger was so keen it felt like I might break apart.

"Did he do this?" he demanded, his voice trembling.

"No, Phelan did not do this to me. *You* did. Last night."

"Last night?" he whispered, bewildered, and then he realized it had been the new moon. "Wait a minute, Clem. *Wait!*"

But I had already taken a step away from him. When he moved to follow, I held up my hand and he halted.

"Where did you get the armor? What spells are you casting to step into the dreams? Why did you wound Phelan twice? Why are you disguising your face?"

He stared at me as if I had lost my mind. I felt trapped in an upside-down world with him, one where nothing made sense, and all I could hear was my own uneven pulse, beating like a drum in my ears.

"I have no idea what you speak of, Clem!"

My eyes burned with angry tears. "I know you're wearing a glamour. One that makes you look far older than you are. And I want you to stay away from me, in both worlds. The waking as well as the new moon realm. Stay away from Mama and Imonie. Do not come near me or Phelan again, or I will have the duke eviscerate you. Do you hear me?"

"Daughter, please," he said, stepping nearer to me. "Explain to me what happened. Did you see me in a dream?"

For a moment, I almost believed him, that he had no recollection of last night. But I wouldn't be deceived by him and his act.

"Don't come any closer to me!" I warned. "Did you not hear me? I don't *trust* you. You are vile and deceptive and I want no part of you."

I turned and began to stride away.

"Clem! *Clem!*" he shouted, which only fueled my anger as he recklessly exposed my cover.

I gathered my stealth charm about me, slipping from his reach and his sight. And yet I couldn't resist. I glanced over my shoulder to see my father on his knees in the street, dazed as if I had just given him a mortal wound.

30

It was late when I returned to the town house. Mrs. Stirling and Deacon had departed for the night, and I found Phelan sitting in the drawing room before the fire, a glass of wine in hand.

"Miss Neven," he greeted me as I joined him in the room. I should have known then that something was wrong, but my mind was trapped in a daze. "Are you all right? We were worried about you."

I sank into the chair across from his. "I'm fine. I went for a walk. I apologize for missing dinner." I met his gaze, shocked when I saw that his dark hair was unbound, brushing his collarbones. Why was he regarding me in such a way, as if he were memorizing me?

"Is there something on your mind?" he asked.

"No." It was strange how his eyes, slowly taking me in, made me ache to be known. To not have to hide and pretend and feel this rock in my chest.

"You know you can confide in me, Anna."

Let it crack, I dared myself. *Let yourself fall and come undone and be who you want.*

"I know."

The enticement lasted for a minute before I regained control of myself, glancing away from his intensity. I watched the safety of the fire. And I realized I was just like my father, cut from the same cloth. Deception and secrets and vengeance and lies ran thick in our blood.

"Can I tempt you with a round of Seven Wraiths?" Phelan asked quietly.

"I'm sick of Seven Wraiths," I replied, pinching the bridge of my nose when I inevitably envisioned my father in that blood-stained armor.

"Then grab another game. I think it'll take your mind off whatever is troubling you," he said. "At least for tonight, while you are here with me."

I sighed but conceded to look at him once more. His gaze was on my neck. On my bruises, I realized, and I watched as his knuckles drained white.

"Very well," I said, and rose.

I was glad to turn away from him, walking to where the cupboard sat against the wall, just beneath the mirror. I crouched to avoid its taunting gleam, opening the cabinet and sifting through the other board games until I found one that seemed promising. I stood without a second thought.

I hadn't heard him move.

I hadn't sensed his presence, not until it was too late.

Phelan stood behind me. I met his stare in the mirror, and his shock sent a pang through me.

He beheld me as I truly was, the girl he had first met and championed. Neither of us moved or spoke. It felt as if ice had fettered my ankles, sprouted in my chest, making it difficult to think through the frost that gleamed between us.

And then he broke it with his voice—the ice and the uncertainty and my entire facade.

"Clem."

The sound was beautiful and terrible, piercing me like an arrow. I felt a crack in my chest. It wasn't deep; it was only a hairline break, the stone faithfully holding to my heart, even as the pain swarmed. I pressed a fist to my breast, clenching my teeth until I thought they would chip.

Hold yourself together. Don't crumble like this.

I did the first thing that came to mind. I hurled a spell at him, even though he hadn't moved or threatened me. No, all he seemed capable of doing was staring at my reflection, stricken.

Vines rose up from the rug. Thorns and leaves and indigo blossoms. They wove together in a whispering rush, and my intentions were to trap him, to form a cage about him. It would give me the time I needed to flee, but when I thought about running . . . I had nowhere to go. For that had been my father's plan all along, and it was now worthless in my eyes. And when I saw the pain and betrayal in Phelan's face . . . I could not entrap him. I reined my spell back a fraction, so that my vines would form a wall between us. A barrier.

He studied it for a moment. My impulsive defense.

I watched through the gaps in the vines and leaves as he slipped a dagger from the inner pocket of his jacket. He began to cut through my enchantment, hack by hack, and it gave way to him. Flowers sundered beneath his blade, their petals cascading to the floor. The vines snapped and recoiled; the leaves hissed into steam as he dashed through them. My spell held valiantly, giving me the time I needed to run.

Run, I thought, and yet I couldn't move.

My desire ran dark and deep. I wanted to face him again, wholly known. I wanted to answer his challenge.

I wanted to clash with him.

And so I waited and watched him work through my enchantment. My thorns dragged over his face, leaving bright scratches behind. They clawed at his hair, at his clothes, and when he finally emerged on my side of the wall, he looked the most disheveled I had ever seen him. He looked untamed, half wild.

He stared at me, panting, blue petals and silver leaves in his hair. He tossed his dagger aside.

Slowly, we circled each other, our gazes holding as if we were both prey, both predator.

Say something! I wanted to shout at him. His silence was overbearing, crushing. I couldn't read his thoughts.

And then he smiled, but it was scathing. Sharp and unfamiliar.

The sight of it sent a thrill through me.

I hurled another spell at him, an arc of light. He was ready for it, taking it in his palm, dissolving it into shadows. For all my disguise, he knew me well, and that was maddening. I struck him again, again, but he caught my spells effortlessly, as if he knew exactly what to expect from me. He turned my fire into smoke, my wind into dust, my light into shadows. He accepted everything I gave him and yet he didn't retaliate. He refused to counter my moves, and I didn't know if he was waiting for me to tire myself or if he simply didn't want to risk hurting me.

This would never end. The two of us circling, me striking, him absorbing.

I turned away from him, frustrated that he wouldn't spar with me, and he caught me around the waist. I tripped over my own vine, snaking across the floor, and down we went. We tangled, our limbs entwining and our hands catching and our breaths mingling.

I saw it in his eyes, at last. The shock of my deception was wearing thin, and the realization kicked in like a second heartbeat. I watched his eyes darken when he remembered my interview, how I had attacked him. When he remembered all the lies I had spouted to him. When I had told him to get on his knees and apologize. When he had tried to summon me and thought he had failed.

"I should have known it was you," he whispered, his mouth dangerously close to mine.

His skin flushed with anger, indignation. I was satisfied to see it, to know my vengeance had run its course. That I had hurt him as he had once hurt me.

We rolled on the floor, caught up with each other, unable to separate ourselves as if a spell had bound us, and I finally emerged on top. I straddled his waist, held him beneath me, and before I knew it, I called his abandoned dagger. The weapon came willingly into my hand; I set its glittering edge to his throat and he went still, his gaze fixed on mine.

And I thought . . . *Is this who I am becoming?*

I didn't recognize myself in this tenuous moment.

"Clem," Phelan said. *"Clem . . ."* He dared to take a gentle hold of my wrist.

I recoiled from him. I tossed his dirk away; it landed with a plink in the rug. I slid off him and stood, trembling.

He sat forward and rose with fluid grace, putting a safe distance between us.

I felt him stare at me, a heated moment I was reluctant to acknowledge. But soon the draw to meet his eyes was irresistible. I glanced up and held his gaze, unrepentant.

I knew I had wounded him, deeply. He lowered his guard; he looked devastated.

"I hope you enjoyed every moment you played me a fool," he said.

"Phelan," I whispered, but my voice turned to ash in my mouth.

"I hope you achieved whatever it was you wanted. I hope all your lies were worth it." He took a step back; I felt the space between us like a chasm had formed in the floor.

I felt completely hollow.

"Bravo, Miss Madigan." Phelan held out his arms to grant me a mock bow. He spoke a charm beneath his breath. I had never heard it before, and I tensed until I realized it was not directed at me but at him. I watched him fade away.

He was gone.

Alone, I sank to the floor, to the remains of my vines and thorns and withering magic.

31

He didn't come home.

I sat in the library at his desk, watching patches of sun travel across the floor. I waited for him, words gathering in my chest, building like water behind a dam. Words I wanted, *needed*, to say to him. An explanation. An apology, even. Maybe. But Phelan never returned.

My disguise still held firm as my own skin. When I drew a deep breath and held it in my chest, I could feel the small crack within me. I wondered how much longer I had until the stone half of my heart shattered. If I could suffer a few more blows before the spell relinquished me.

Mrs. Stirling found me at noon, concern creasing her brow. "Miss Neven? May I ask what happened in the drawing room?"

I had cleaned it the best I could, but my vines had left a few fissures in the wall and the mirror. "A slight altercation, Mrs. Stirling."

Her eyes widened. "I hope no one was harmed?"

"No, all is well." The lies still flowed smoothly from my mouth. Gods above, I sounded just like my father.

She nodded but didn't seem convinced. "A package has arrived for you."

At first I thought it must be from Phelan. Something ominous, something to make me pay for all my deceit. But Deacon carried in a narrow clothes box and set it carefully on the desk before me.

"What is this?" I asked, wary.

"Your dress, Miss Neven," Mrs. Stirling said. "For the countess's dinner tonight."

Oh. That was tonight. It was the seventeenth of November, and I had hardly known it.

I rubbed my brow, keenly distressed. But I tempered my feelings before Mrs. Stirling or Deacon could detect them, and I smiled. "Thank you. Have you heard from Phelan this morning? He left early, before I woke."

"Yes, Miss Neven. He wrote and said he would be away for a few weeks."

"Oh?" A few *weeks*? I paled at the thought, wondering where he had gone.

"Did he . . . did he not tell you?" Mrs. Stirling asked kindly. She finally inferred that the "slight altercation" had been between us and that I was completely in the dark.

"He didn't. But no matter. I'll tend to things here while he's away." I granted her and Deacon a smile, but it was weak, and they saw through it.

"Oh, and you received a letter." Mrs. Stirling reached into her apron pocket to extend an envelope to me.

I accepted it, immediately recognizing the duke's crest.

"Let us know if you need anything, Miss Neven," the house-keeper said as she herded her grandson from the library.

I scowled as I opened the duke's letter. I was not surprised by his message, succinctly written:

> Miss Neven,
> I surmise that the new moon was a success.
> Please send me a detailed description of
> the man in question, as soon as possible.
> Lord Ivor Deryn
> Duke of Bardyllis

I held the duke's letter over a candle flame and watched it burn. I was not ready to expose my father. And yet I didn't know what I was waiting for, either.

I stared at the clothes box, but refrained from opening it. I quickly gathered my cloak and departed, heading to the town house that Olivette and Nura shared a few streets over.

They were sitting in the dining room still wrapped in their robes, eating a late brunch. I was suddenly overcome with strife, wondering if Phelan had revealed my deceit to them. . . .

"Anna!" Olivette greeted me warmly. "Come join us! There's plenty."

Her vibrant response was a relief. But Nura sensed my distress, even as I sought to hide it. She set down her teacup and bluntly said, "What's wrong?"

I hesitated on the threshold. "I was wondering if you two had seen Phelan today. Perhaps he dropped by this morning?"

"Phelan?" Olivette echoed, glancing to Nura. "No, he hasn't."

"And he hasn't sent a letter in the post to you?"

"No," Nura said, rising. "Did something happen?"

"Yes," I breathed. "We got in an argument."

"During the new moon?"

"No, afterward. He left and I haven't seen him and I don't know where to find him." What was *wrong* with me? I sounded desperate. If I didn't know better, one would think I had feelings for him, and I cleared my throat, embarrassed.

You are afraid he will expose you, I told myself. And there was a kernel of truth in that statement. He now held something over me, and I was uncertain what to expect from him. If he would use it against me. If I should go ahead and reveal myself before he did.

Nura reached out to gently take my arm. "Here. Sit and eat. Things always feel worse on an empty stomach."

I sat. My shoulders were sore; my knees ached. I drank a cup of tea and relented to eat a few bites of egg and steak, Olivette watching me with obvious concern.

"Do you want to tell us what you quarreled about?" she whispered.

I set down my fork. "I . . . no. It was foolish, though. And he is quite angry at me."

"That is so hard to imagine," Olivette said. "I don't think I've ever seen Phelan angry! He's so mild, so even-tempered."

Until he met me, I thought.

"It's natural in our line of work, Anna," said Nura. "Partners will inevitably butt heads. You shouldn't beat yourself up over it. I'm sure Phelan is taking the time he needs to sort through whatever has come between you. But you'll see him tonight, to smooth things over with him."

I frowned. "Tonight?"

"At his mother's dinner. He wouldn't miss that."

"He wouldn't?"

Olivette smiled. "Of course not! His mother gives him an order and he follows it, every time."

"Oli," Nura warned. "You shouldn't speak of the countess like that."

"What?" Olivette shrugged. "It's the truth."

I stood, suddenly overwhelmed by nerves. "I probably shouldn't go tonight."

What if he planned to expose me at the dinner? But the more I imagined it . . . would Phelan do something like that to me?

"What? Yes, you should come, Anna," Olivette insisted. "You can ride with us tonight!"

I was silent, contemplating all my options. To go, to stay. To run, to confront. Nura stood beside me. Gently, she drew the hair away from my neck and saw my bruises.

"Is this Phelan's doing?" she asked in a low, sharp voice. One that made me shiver.

"No, it wasn't him," I replied. "An unfortunate result of the new moon."

Olivette gasped, also seeing the bruises from across the table.

"Anna! Oh my gods, what happened?"

"It's nothing," I said, taking a step away from them. "I'm perfectly fine." And it was a good reminder for me to glamour the bruises until they healed. "I think I will ride with you tonight to the dinner, if you don't mind."

"Of course," Nura said. "We'll come pick you up at half past five."

I left before they could press me for further answers, retreating to Phelan's town house.

I rested most of the afternoon, but soon my uneasiness swelled, and I prepared for the countess's dinner.

The dress Phelan had tailored for me looked to have been spun from gold. It rushed off my shoulders and softly held my curves, tiny jewels sewn along the hem and the neckline. I had never worn something so beautiful. It felt like sunlight on my skin, warm and soft. Alluring.

I glamoured my bruises and then touched a few lank strands of my hair. I decided to braid it into a crown, weaving within the plaits a golden ribbon that I found in my wardrobe.

The sun set. The stars were beginning to smolder in the sky when Olivette and Nura arrived. I sat on the bench across from them, rocking with the sway of the cab, and listened to them talk. A low, pleasant stream of conversation, one that I failed to join, because my thoughts were distant, roaming.

"My father will be so delighted to finally meet you tonight, Anna," Olivette said.

I blinked, returning to the cab. "Your father will be at dinner tonight?"

"Yes."

"How many people will be here, do you think?" I asked nonchalantly, but my dread rose. Something was going to happen tonight, and it wasn't going to be pleasant.

"I'm not sure," Olivette said, glancing at Nura. "This is the first time we've been invited to one of the countess's dinners. They are selective affairs, though. Many of the upper class hope to win an invitation."

That did nothing to ease my sense of foreboding.

All too soon, the carriage arrived at the countess's mansion.

It was a grand estate, out of reach from the street by a long, private driveway. The house was built of creamy stone and a gray shingled roof, three storied with large mullioned windows, creeping ivy and multiple chimneys. The front doors were on the second story, and two curved staircases blossomed from the courtyard up to the entrance. Through the dusky light, I could see a long stretch of shallow water to our left—a reflection pool—and the hedges of a garden.

I followed Nura and Olivette out of the coach and up the stairs.

A butler took our cloaks and led us deeper into the mansion, to a spacious ballroom, where the floors were blue-veined marble, the ceilings arched and coffered. Hanging chandeliers burgeoned with silver wrought leaves and candles.

Music haunted the air, and servants milled about with flutes of sparkling champagne. I expected to see a crowded room, a night full of people I could lose myself among. But it was a small, intimate party.

Nura and Olivette drifted toward the musicians, but I remained standing, soaking in the grandeur of the room. And I couldn't help myself; I looked for Phelan among the black jackets and top hats.

He was nowhere to be seen, and I buried my disappointment just as the countess caught sight of me.

"Miss Neven," she said, and I sank into a deep curtsy. "I am honored you have accepted my invitation."

"Thank you, lady. The honor is mine."

"Come, take a turn around the room with me," she invited. "We are still waiting on a few more guests to arrive, but let me introduce you to an old friend of mine in the meantime."

I fell into a stilted stride beside her and soon realized she was taking me directly to the duke, who was standing beside a man I recognized—the smith who had created the shields for me and Phelan.

"This is Lord Deryn, the Duke of Bardyllis," the countess said. "And this is Aaron Wolfe, the most renowned smith in the province, as well as Olivette's father."

"Miss Neven," the duke greeted me with a languid smile. "A pleasure, as always."

"Your Grace." I curtsied, and then looked at Olivette's father. "Mr. Wolfe."

"I shall leave the three of you," the countess said suddenly, as if it had been her task all along to deposit me at the duke's feet. And perhaps it had been, I thought irritably as I watched her stride across the room.

"Were the shields a success, Miss Neven?" Mr. Wolfe asked.

His face and voice were so carefully guarded that I couldn't tell if he was surprised to see me here tonight.

"Yes, Mr. Wolfe. Thank you."

The smith nodded, and there was an awkward lull until he glanced at the duke and said, "I should go say hello to my daughter."

I wanted to beg him to stay, to not leave me alone with the duke, but I held my tongue. When Lord Deryn stepped closer to me, I flinched.

"I trust you received my letter today," the duke said in a low voice, offering me his arm.

I hesitated, but only for a breath. I rested my hand in the crook of his elbow and permitted him to slowly walk me around the edges of the room.

"Yes, Your Grace. I apologize that I have not had time to write a response."

"You saw the knight's face?"

"I did."

"Can you describe him to me?"

I envisioned my father's face. The words rose to illustrate him, but I couldn't speak them. Even with his betrayal, I couldn't find the desire to expose him. "No, Your Grace. I fear it was a dark night. It would be impossible for me to describe it in detail to you."

"Then we are in luck," the duke said, coming to a stop.

I glanced up at him, but his gaze was elsewhere, cutting across the room.

"Did the knight perhaps look like that man?" he asked,

indicating a new dinner guest.

I turned to see who he spoke of, and the hair rose on my arms.

My father stood just within the ballroom, speaking to the countess. Clean, his beard trimmed, his hair slicked back. He was not a miner but the magician I had always known him to be. He wore a top hat and white waistcoat and black jacket with a rose in his lapel. On his arm was my mother, dressed in a bloodred gown overlaid with a net of black stones. And trailing them was none other than Imonie, wearing a blue dress with lace sleeves, her steel-blond hair swept up in a loose bun.

I froze, but my mind flooded with anger, shock, a multitude of questions.

What were they doing here?

My silence was answer enough for the duke.

"Good, Miss Neven," he said, amused. "I am glad Mr. Madigan could whet your memory. Now, if you will excuse me."

My hand slipped from his elbow as he rejoined the countess. I continued to stand, stranded. My father sensed my stare, his eyes rising to meet mine.

He appeared just as surprised to see me, his mouth going slack. If not for my mother guiding him away, distracting him with a flute of champagne, I'm sure my father and I would have fought in the countess's ballroom, ruining my guise for good.

Even Imonie paused, setting a tense gaze on me. I almost went to her; she had always been my refuge, a safe place for me to call home. And yet tonight she was like a stranger.

Ignore them, I told myself. *You have never seen them before. . . .*

The ice thickened in my chest. I was cold, calm, poised. A girl with a stone trapped in her ribs. And then I felt his stare.

My eyes scanned the ballroom until I found Phelan nearby, standing in one of the archways, draped in shadow, watching me. I wondered how long he had been leaning against the frame, observing my precarious walk around the room. But the moment our gazes met, the glittering, firelit world faded around us. There were only shadows and a path that connected him to me, a path that felt treacherous to walk in the sense that it might undo me.

His face was smooth of expression, his eyes inscrutable. I wanted to know what he thought of me, when he had started to suspect I wasn't who I claimed to be. And I didn't know if he planned to expose me, or if he would ever forgive me. I told myself not to care, but a small fracture was within me now, and my regrets began to trickle through it.

Even the deepest of ice eventually gives way to fire, Mazarine had once told me.

I turned away from Phelan, unable to look upon him a moment longer.

I found my way back to Nura and Olivette, who were in high spirits.

"Oh, there's Phelan," Nura said, looking beyond me.

"Why isn't he joining us?" Olivette wondered, waving him over. "Have you spoken to him yet, Anna?"

"No."

Nura exchanged a swift glance with me before saying, "I'll go speak with him."

She left me and Olivette, and I tried to focus on conversing with her, but my worries tugged, and I watched Phelan speak to Nura across the room. He was saying something solemn to her. She frowned, listening. And then she glanced back to where Olivette and I were standing, and I thought for certain he had just exposed me.

"Shall we go speak with your father?" I asked Olivette with a hint of desperation, lacing my arm with hers. But no sooner did we begin to approach Mr. Wolfe did my parents begin to speak to the smith, and I came to a halt.

"What's the matter?" Olivette asked.

"Do you know those people? The ones speaking to your father?"

She studied my parents. Papa looked up at me, held my gaze for a beat too long.

"The woman is Sigourney Britelle, one of the most esteemed performance magicians in the province. Have you ever been to one of her shows, Anna?"

"No, I have not."

"Phelan should take you to one soon, then," Olivette said. "As for the man . . . I've never seen him before, but he seems familiar with her." She paused and then added with a hint of anger, "And he keeps looking at you. Do you want me to say something to him?"

"No, but thank you, Olivette." I narrowed my eyes at Papa. He finally ceased glancing at me with that worried gleam.

Sweat began to bead my skin and I reached for a flute of champagne, a tremor in my hand.

I watched Imonie next from the corner of my eye, and when the countess walked a loose circle around her . . . my dread turned into a leaden thing, weighing me down. Their conversation didn't look friendly; I openly observed as the countess finally ceased her predatory walk about Imonie, and their lips moved but I couldn't read them from where I stood.

Why would someone as haughty as Lady Raven invite my parents, Imonie, me? Why would she invite someone like Olivette's father, who worked with his hands and kept to the shadows? Why would she invite Nura and Olivette? I couldn't make sense of this dinner party and the odd mixture of guests, and it only heightened the sense that something was wrong.

Nura returned to us. I struggled to focus on her, waiting to feel her scathing glare, for her to expose me for the fraud I was. It never came; she was too preoccupied with Olivette. She wove their fingers together—brown and white—and whispered, "Come here, Oli. We need to speak."

I watched them retreat to a quiet corner of the ballroom. I felt bare, alienated. I drained my champagne and decided I would leave. This night held nothing promising or good for me, and I didn't care if I offended the countess.

I turned and nearly stepped into Phelan.

"Going somewhere, Miss Neven?" he said, cordial but cold. The cadence he would give to a stranger.

"Yes. I'm going home. Wherever that might be." But I didn't step away. I stood facing him, so close I could smell the spice of his aftershave. "Will you let me pass, Mr. Vesper? I know I'm the last person you want to see tonight."

"You read minds now?"

"Yes. For three gold coins."

"You seem to have already emptied my pockets," he said. "Or else I would pay."

"Go ahead, then, Mr. Vesper."

He arched his brow. "Go ahead with what?"

"Expose me. Reveal who I am. That's why you told your mother to invite my parents and Imonie here tonight, no? Take your vengeance on me and let's call a truce. We can part ways and you never have to see my deceptive face again."

He smiled, but it wasn't gentle. It was a wince, as if something within him ached, and he leaned closer to me. "I know you believe this night is about you, Miss Neven. Let me assure you: it's not. And you can leave now if you want. I won't stop you. But you will come to regret your impulsive departure when the sun rises."

"You speak in riddles," I said, breathless with anger. "Why are my parents here?"

"You will discover that soon enough," he replied. "If you choose to remain."

It was a challenge. One he knew I couldn't resist.

The dinner bell rang.

I followed the stream of guests into the dining hall, surprised when Phelan chose to sit beside me. The table was long and narrow, sparkling with fine china and glasses and silver candelabras. Once everyone had taken a seat, I noticed that two chairs were empty.

"Two more guests will be arriving later," said the countess, as if she had heard my thoughts. She was the last to sit at the head of the table, the duke to her left, Imonie on her right, and only once she had taken her seat did the servants file into the dining hall bearing the first course.

It was a thick green soup I had never seen before. It was also chilled, and I didn't know what I thought about it when I forced a spoonful into my mouth.

Nura and Olivette also seemed disgusted with the green mystery. They were sitting to my left, and I watched from the corner of my eye as they took only a few polite sips. My father, who had somehow managed to sit directly across from me, drank the entire thing, savoring it.

Conversation flowed quietly. I didn't even try to engage with Phelan. He, too, was often silent, speaking minimally when the duke attempted to draw him into a discussion about dreams.

The second course arrived. Another strange dish I had never tasted before, but it looked to be roasted poultry on a bed of sautéed greens and buttery porridge, with pickled beets on the side. I didn't know how to properly eat it, so I watched my father, who once again acted as if this dish was one of his favorites. Were these recipes from Seren? I was too shy to ask, but it was the only explanation I could come up with, especially when I recalled how Imonie told me the significance of November seventeenth to the mountain duchy.

Course after course was served. All of them were bizarre and unfamiliar, and I struggled through this seemingly endless dinner, thankful that no one took much note of me. I was beginning to believe that Phelan had fooled me into staying when the dessert was delivered, a lemon pudding with berries and cream, and Phelan leaned close to me, to whisper into my ear as one does to a lover.

I didn't move as his lips brushed my cheek.

"Something is about to happen tonight," he said. "You must not expose who you are. Hold your act."

And then he leaned away from me, as if he hadn't spoken such dire words, dipping his spoon into the pudding.

My father was watching us, though. I lifted my eyes to his, and the tension eased in his face. As if he also knew what was about to unfold and he was waiting for it. . . .

The doors opened with a bang, startling half of the table.

The candlelight flickered as Phelan's brother, Lennox, entered the room. He looked windswept, his clothes wrinkled, his cravat knotted crookedly as if he had arrived here in great haste. He wasn't alone. Mazarine accompanied him. Mazarine in her human disguise.

My breath left in a rush. My body tensed until I felt Phelan's hand on my knee, beneath the table.

Hold your act.

The countess smiled and rose. "At last, you have arrived, my son. And I see you have brought our guest of honor."

"Indeed, Mother," Lennox said with a triumphant smirk. "Ms. *Mazarine* Thimble of Hereswith."

I couldn't take my eyes from her. There was a trickle of blood flowing from her lip, and her silver hair was snarled. It was almost impossible to believe that she had been bound and brought roughly into the city. Mazarine, a bloodthirsty, dangerous creature of the mountains. But in this moment, she had been tamed. Her hands were fastened behind her back.

"Perhaps you would like to sit and join us, Mazarine," the countess said. "Or perhaps you would like us to call you by your true name."

Mazarine smiled. It was frightening, even with her human face. "I will not sit and eat at your table, even if you tried to serve the best of Seren foods. Call me by my name, heiress."

Lady Raven stared at the troll. The only evidence of her displeasure was the tightening of her jaw. "Welcome, Brin of Stonefall. It has been a long time since last we met. Ambrose Madigan has shielded you well the past decade, but alas, all good things must come to an end."

Mazarine spat on the table.

Lennox took a fistful of her hair and yanked her head back, and I felt compelled to rise until Phelan tightened his hold on my knee.

Even my father gave me a sharp glance. One that ordered me not to interfere or respond.

I watched, but my mind was reeling.

"You have us all together, Lady Raven," Mazarine—*Brin*—said with a malicious gleam in her eyes. "Why delay? Prove your point."

The countess lifted her hand in response. An emerald ring gleamed on her finger.

Five servants, who had been standing against the wall, stepped forward. They no longer held platters; they held daggers. And they moved in unison, approaching the table.

Mazarine was stabbed first. A servant plunged the blade into her chest, where it met her bone with a *crack*. The troll laughed as dark blood ran down her dress, as it seeped into the silver tangles of her hair.

Next, Aaron Wolfe. Olivette's father. He didn't fight or protest as a dagger split his heart. He seemed to welcome the mortal blow, and Olivette lunged to her feet, overturning her chair, screaming and screaming and screaming. Her father didn't even look at her. He closed his eyes, sorrowful, peaceful. As if he were already dead.

The blood dripped from his chair, pooling on the rug.

My heart pounded in my ears.

An uneven rhythm.

I trembled.

Phelan's hand remained warm on my knee, holding me steady, holding my guise in place. I drew in slow, deep breaths, but the air was full of copper, the metallic taste of blood.

The duke was next. He didn't fight it either but surrendered to the blade. It pierced his broad chest and he only sighed, complaining how the countess had just ruined his best waistcoat.

When a dagger found Imonie's heart, I nearly rose from the table, to lunge across it to reach her. *No, no, no,* my thoughts rang, until she looked at me and gave the slightest shake of her head. I had seen that look before plenty of times; she was scolding me, even as her blood marred her blue dress.

Stay there, Clem. I read her thoughts. *Be patient, be shrewd.*

And then my father.

The last servant approached Papa's chair. A noise of distress slipped from me when I saw the flash of the blade. The dagger sank deep into my father's heart with a wet thump, down to the silver hilt. His blood rushed forward, fast and bright like a rose had bloomed over his breast. It sprayed over the white tablecloth, speckling the china and the candelabras in crimson. I watched its cascade, numb with shock, waiting to feel my face crack like an eggshell. Because I sensed it rising; somewhere deep within me, Clem was screaming in my bones. Furious to escape. Witnessing Imonie's and my father's murder was going to shatter my disguise.

This is the end of me. My lips parted, full of ragged breaths, as if I had run for hours.

But my father remained upright. Soon his blood slowed and then ceased altogether, leaving only a red stain on his waistcoat. He sat in his chair and breathed with a pierced heart. My mother remained at his side, eyes closed and her face pale, but even she was not surprised. She wasn't protesting or reacting to the violence that was unfolding around the table.

I couldn't fathom it. I prepared myself to see Papa slump in the chair. To gasp his last breath. But the dagger held no power over him.

My father cannot die.

Olivette continued to weep, but Nura held her in her arms. Nura had known this was coming, I realized. That was what Phelan had whispered to her earlier that night, and Nura stared at him now, both furious and fearful. But Phelan's focus remained on his mother, who stood at the head of the table, calmly watching the demise of her dinner guests.

I waited for Mazarine the troll, Mr. Wolfe the smith, Lord Deryn the duke, Imonie, and my father the magician to drop dead. But they continued to breathe, sitting in their blood-soaked raiment. Waiting. Their gazes strayed to the countess.

Mazarine laughed, and the sound broke the brittle tension in the room. "You have proven who we are, Lady Raven," the troll said. "Now prove yourself to us."

The countess didn't hesitate. She took the last dagger from the servant who waited beside her chair and she plunged the blade deep into her side.

I felt Phelan flinch, but he said nothing. Beneath the table, I reached for his hand. Our fingers intertwined.

The heiress, I thought, studying the countess. And then I dwelled on her companions—the wraiths who I had held as cards in my hands. Her companions, who she had commemorated by painting them, over and over, lending her magic and her sorrow to a card game. They had been mere illustrations to me in those moments when I had been playing a game, and I had never dared to believe that I would one day sit at a table with them, beholding their accursed state of being. I had never contemplated that I was the daughter of one of them.

The advisor, I thought, staring at my father. *He was the mountain advisor.*

And Imonie? I wasn't sure what her title was among the wraiths, but all my life, I'd believed what she had told me—that her ancestry was rooted in the mountains, but she had been born in Bardyllis. Never had I imagined she had been part of the court that had sundered Seren. That she had been there when it fell apart.

My childhood, my entire life, had been built upon lies.

"Welcome, old friends," the countess said. "It has taken me years to find some of you, thanks to Brin of Stonefall's magic of disguises. But here we are, reunited after so much time apart."

"What do you want with us, Lady Raven?" the duke asked, yanking the dagger from his chest. "I was quite happy in Bardyllis. So were you."

"Happiness never lasts for our kind," the countess said before glancing at my father. "Ambrose's twin brother, Emrys, has withstood the curse for a hundred years on the mountain. We left him behind a century ago, the lost one of our alliance. He has carried the curse and walked the fortress in the clouds as penance for slaying my brother, the Duke of Seren, but now Emrys has found his way out.

"He walks dreams on the new moon, taunting us to come home. Twice he has wounded my son, and by the vengeance of his blade, I no longer had a choice but to gather you all to answer his challenge." She held up her chalice of wine, as if preparing for a toast. "We scattered like chaff when the curse began. We went our own ways and sought to live our own quiet lives. I lost track of you, as you did with me. But the time has come, my old friends. It is time we returned home. It is time we remembered ourselves and dreamt again. That we no longer wake from cold, dreamless slumber. That we live and feel as mortals do. That we die when the time comes. For we have dwelled hidden and forgotten in this province for far too long."

She paused, and I was suddenly hanging on to her every word. I felt them resound in my soul, in the dreamless depths of my being. "It is time for us to return to the mountain. It is time for us to end the curse."

PART 3

Mountain of Dreams

32

I stood in the foothills of the Seren Mountains, on the edge of Bardyllis province, savoring the cold bite of the wind as the sun set. It had taken our party a full week to travel from the city to the border, but now we were here, full of anxious thoughts and a heavy sense of foreboding.

We would approach the mountain doors the next day. Part of me hoped the doors would refuse us entrance, but Imonie had once told me that they would open if all the wraiths approached together.

I studied the fortress in the clouds, carved into the summit.

I had been traveling with the Vespers' party, everyone believing me to be Anna Neven. Save for Phelan and my parents and Imonie, all four of whom I hadn't properly spoken to since the countess's bloody dinner. I had an act to perform, and I ignored my family. But at night, when I was alone and embraced by darkness, my anger burned so bright it felt like a fever was ravaging me. Lie after lie, my parents and Imonie had fed me, allowing me to grow up beneath deceit.

I didn't want to even look at them.

But I knew I needed to eventually speak with Imonie and my father, whose twin brother I had mistaken as him. I needed more information about this mysterious uncle who had almost strangled me on the new moon, and I deigned to ask the countess more about Emrys during our journey.

"He's Ambrose's identical twin, and the mastermind behind the assassination," Lady Raven had said to me. "He slayed my brother and the mountain made him pay for it, holding him captive while the remainder of us left. If he wasn't so coldhearted, or better yet, if he hadn't tried to kill my own son, I would feel pity for him."

"Who made him the armor?" I had asked next. To say I was nervous to meet Emrys once we ascended was an understatement. He had only released his hold on my neck when I had called him "Papa," and I surmised it was because he realized I was his niece. Which meant he knew who I was, and I couldn't afford to be exposed as Clementine Madigan yet.

"Why, Aaron Wolfe made the armor," the countess had replied, as if I were daft to not realize it.

We had been traveling in a coach together. Phelan and Lennox were in another, as Phelan was still avoiding me as much as I was avoiding my own family.

"How old were you when the curse happened, Lady Raven?"

"That's impolite to ask, Anna," the countess had replied stiffly, but it only confirmed my suspicions that she was wearing an aging glamour, just like my father. To look older than she was, even though she had lived well over a century. In fact, most of the wraiths had become magicians—the countess, my father, Mr. Wolfe. Imonie never had, but then again, Imonie wasn't wearing an aging charm to fool unsuspecting people. I was almost certain of it.

I had then dared to press my luck and asked her, "Who is that other woman in our party? I think her name is Imonie."

"Ah, yes, *Imonie*," the countess said with a hint of malice. "I once called her by another name, long ago. She was my lady-in-waiting before the curse. She used to dream with me about how we could make Seren a better place if my brother was off the throne. And gods, I remember . . . I remember the day she told me twin boys had been left on her door stoop. She did not know what to do with them, and I told her to take them to the orphanage and wash her hands of them. Someone else would eventually want them. But no. She kept them and I knew they would grow up and break her heart, as children are prone to do."

One of those twin boys had turned out to be my father. And I had not pointed out that the countess herself had borne twin boys, and that life sometimes had a twisted sense of humor.

"Regardless," Lady Raven had continued, clearing her throat as if the memories still haunted her. "Imonie hid from me a long time after the curse, when we wandered the province and tried to make new lives. I recommend that you stay clear of her. She's as slippery as an eel."

That conversation had happened days ago, but I was still mulling over it.

I sighed and turned away from the mountains and my recollections. Our party was setting up camp, and I walked to where the Vespers' servants were rushing to erect the tents. I had a tent of my own, as did Lennox and Phelan, although the countess ensured to set her tent between ours. As if she had anything to worry about. Phelan had hardly looked at me this past week, speaking to me only at a polite minimum. Most of the time, I didn't care. But then there were other moments, usually at night when I watched the moon begin to wax, when I felt the sting of his dismissal.

I longed for the way it had once been between us.

I had tried to speak to him. One evening, I found him standing alone a few yards from camp, and I had joined him.

"I know why you came home angry that night."

He had glanced at me, and I waited, hoping he would talk. That we could settle this rift between us. Of course I didn't truly know why he had stormed home and destroyed the library that evening weeks ago, but I could imagine that was the day his mother had told him who she was, who *he* was—the son of a wraith—and that she was gathering up her erstwhile companions with the intention to return to the mountain.

"Perhaps," he had said before walking away. "But I don't want to talk about it with you, Anna."

His words still stung when I recalled them, but I also couldn't fault him for being angry at me. I swallowed that memory and watched the first star break the dusk as I returned to the camp.

Tents were pitched in a ring with a fire in the center. Olivette and Nura were currently struggling with their tent, until Nura gave up and enchanted it to rise. My parents and Imonie were already camped as well, Imonie beginning to cook dinner over the flames. And then there was the tent for Mazarine, who everyone gave a respectful berth, and the duke's.

I drifted to a log beside Nura as she began to chop carrots for a stew. I helped by peeling a mealy potato, and I waited until Olivette, who was tending the fire, rose to fetch more sticks.

"Have you figured out who is who?" I whispered to Nura.

She knew I spoke of the mountain court—the seven wraiths— and was quiet for a breath, but her eyes darted around the bustle of the camp. Some of the wraiths were obvious; others, I was still trying to identify.

"I believe so," she began in a low tone. "Mazarine is the spymistress, obviously. The countess is the heiress. I think the woman called Imonie once served the countess as her lady-in-waiting." She paused to dump her carrot rounds into a cast-iron pot. "I think Olivette's father is the advisor."

I held my tongue. I believed that was *my* father's former position, but I was still uncertain.

"And what about the duke?" I whispered.

"The master of coin," Nura said without hesitation, and I nodded.

"But what I'm wondering," I began, lowering my voice a shade more as one of the Vespers' servants tossed a split log on the fire, "is how the master of coin was able to worm his way into being

Duke of Bardyllis. If he can't age, and wasn't born into the Deryn family, then how did he manage it . . . ?"

"It's a mystery," Nura agreed, "and I think there is some old magic at play here. The duke is obviously disguised, as Mazarine is. Maybe she fashioned a glamour for him to appear just like the real duke, so the master of coin could seamlessly take his place without anyone realizing there had been a swap."

It alarmed me to think the master of coin had been wearing a full-blown guise, just as I had been. That he had been masquerading as a well-known, beloved person—Lord Deryn. But this would explain why the duke had ordered my father to guard Mazarine, over a decade ago. Because if something happened to the troll, then the duke's disguise would surely crumble.

I discreetly glanced up from my peeling to catch sight of him on the other side of the camp, speaking to Phelan.

"His Grace certainly pays a great deal of attention to Phelan," Nura said sharply.

"I've noticed that as well."

She glanced at me. "You and Phelan are still at odds?"

"He refuses to speak with me."

"Well," Nura said, scraping her second batch of sliced carrots into the pot. "Sometimes conflict can't be resolved with words alone. Sometimes it requires settlement of a different sort." And she gave me a shrewd smile.

A burst of laughter escaped me.

"Ah," she whispered. "You have drawn his eyes now."

"Is he hurling daggers my way?"

"On the contrary. He looks immensely jealous of me, as if he longs to be the one who made you laugh."

I smacked her arm, which made her chuckle.

"Don't tease me, Nura."

"If you doubt me, then look for yourself, Anna."

I did, unable to resist. As soon as my gaze touched his, Phelan languidly glanced away, back to the duke, as if I didn't exist.

"Oh yes," Nura said, also noticing. "You have certainly gotten under his skin. Whatever did you do, my friend?"

I focused on my potato peeling, thinking if she knew the truth . . . she would despise me. "Perhaps I enchanted him, and the spell has broken."

Olivette returned with an armload of branches and dropped them before us, and I didn't realize she had been crying until Nura leapt to her feet.

"Oli? Oli, what is it?"

Olivette glanced at her father, who sat on a nearby rock. Mr. Wolfe froze, stricken. He made to rise and approach until Olivette turned away.

"I'm not going with him," she announced, dashing tears from her cheeks. "He's lied to me my entire life. Why should I believe anything he says now? Why should I risk myself by returning to some cursed mountain fortress?"

"Come, let's chat." Nura took a gentle hold of Olivette's hand, guiding her away from the camp.

I hesitated until I saw the sheen in Mr. Wolfe's eyes, and I stood, following Nura and Olivette. I could relate to Olivette more than anyone else in this camp. Her words could be my own, as if she and I were reflections of each other. And I wanted to say, *I understand how you feel. My childhood has also been built upon lies.*

I considered confessing to them—these two girls who had become my friends. What if I opened my mouth and told them everything? That I was a girl named Clem who had lost her home and wanted Phelan to pay for it. Would they still trust me afterward? Would they hold my secret?

Don't be a fool, I told myself.

I quietly approached Olivette and Nura.

"Shh, Oli. It'll be all right," Nura was saying, drawing Olivette into an embrace. "We don't have to ascend if you don't want to."

I wondered if seeing the mountain had churned up these feelings in Olivette. To realize how close we were to returning to a place that our parents' sins had cursed a century ago. The sight of it had done so to me. I felt as if my blood was singing. It was nearly impossible to sleep at night.

"This isn't *my* curse," Olivette said vehemently. "It's *theirs*. They're dragging me into it, and you, Nura, and even you, Anna! And everyone is still holding so many secrets, and no one knows who to trust or what awaits us when we reach our destination. I . . . I can't do this anymore!"

She buried her face in Nura's neck and sobbed.

My gaze drifted to the meadows that lay south. Hereswith was not far from here, perhaps half a day's travel. I was so close to home and yet it felt as if all along, I'd belonged here at the footstool of the mountains.

I knew why the wraiths wanted me and Phelan and Lennox and Nura and Olivette to accompany them. The legend claimed that nightmares roamed the fortress in the clouds. It was the heart of the new moon curse, and all of us were trained to fight such dangers. But it didn't make the uncertainty any easier to bear.

Olivette finally wept the last of her tears, Nura stroking her hair.

"I know much has changed lately, Oli," she said. "But your father is a good person. Perhaps he wanted to tell you who he was, but he didn't know how."

Olivette was silent, but she was listening.

"And he's doing the right thing," Nura continued, framing Olivette's tear-streaked face in her hands. "He's partly responsible for this curse, and he's now returning to hopefully see its end. And if we are successful . . . then the Seren Duchy can be restored."

"And who will take the throne?"

Nura paused, but she glanced at me with an unspoken request.

"Who would you want to see on the throne, Olivette?" I asked.

Olivette was quiet for a beat, wiping her nose on her sleeve. "I don't know, but not me. I don't want it. What about you, Nura?"

"I don't want it, either. Not without you." Nura tightened her embrace. "But don't you remember how you once wanted to be a madcap, Oli?"

"Gods, don't remind me."

"You thought it would be a grand adventure to see the fortress in the clouds. So did I, after I met you."

Olivette's gaze drifted to the summit. "And now I realize how foolish I was to want that. We could all die tomorrow, up there in that dank fortress. It took me this long to realize how much I love Endellion. And those music classes we thought about taking? I don't want to die before learning how to play the flute, Nura."

"We aren't going to die, Oli," Nura whispered with a smile. "After this is over, you're going to learn how to play the flute, and I'll learn how to play the violin."

I decided to give them a few moments alone and walked to the fire, the stars gathering overhead as the dusk deepened. Soon, Olivette and Nura returned, and I remained on the Wolfes' side of camp with them, even though I made sure I ate the food the Vespers' servants had prepared.

No one talked much that night. Not even the duke, who had strangely seemed the most affable out of our traveling party.

We continued to sneak glances at the mountains, at the fortress. It was dark; there was no visage of life in the stone, and yet all of us knew my uncle resided there, walking those corridors, waiting for us to return.

The lost one.

I wondered if he would challenge and kill us on sight.

"Lady Raven," the duke finally drawled. "Since you are the one who has so generously collected us all and dragged us across the province to the mountain . . . what is the plan for tomorrow? How are we to prevail?"

Lady Raven took her time in responding, holding her goblet up for a servant to refill with wine. "We'll approach the mountain doors tomorrow morning. They'll open, because all of us are present. And then we'll ascend and speak to Emrys."

"What if he doesn't want to speak?" Mr. Wolfe asked. "He nearly killed your son, Raven. *Twice*."

"I know what he did, Aaron," she snapped. "He attacked Phelan to prompt me to act. That is all."

"Good thing we have plenty of wardens," Mazarine said wryly from where she sat in a shadow, crunching on chicken bones. "The nightmares will no doubt run rampant."

"We are prepared," the countess insisted. "All of us are here and ready. There is nothing to worry about."

"But someone is missing from our party," Mr. Wolfe said. His statement made me glance around the fire ring. Everyone was accounted for.

"Who do you speak of?" Nura asked.

The smith glanced at my father. "Where's your daughter, Ambrose?"

Everyone froze either to gape at my father with surprise or regard him with suspicion. I played the act, looking at him with an arched brow.

Papa calmly ate the last spoonful of his stew and set his bowl aside. Imonie, who was visibly anxious at the turn of conversation, took his bowl and began to wash it. My mother sat on a rock nearby, her long dark hair boasting a blue sheen in the firelight, her face sorrowful.

"Yes, where is Clementine?" the countess asked. "I've heard so much about her. Should she not be here with us? Both of my sons are. Aaron's daughter is here. Where is yours?"

"I don't know where my daughter is," Papa said. "After our town was lost to us . . . she was angry with me and ran away. I haven't been able to locate her."

"You don't have any tricks up your sleeve, do you, Ambrose?" the countess queried with a laugh. "Although perhaps I should also ask the same of you, Ms. Britelle? Since you are a seasoned stagecraft performer."

My mother narrowed her eyes. "What are you implying, lady?"

"That you have schemed for Clementine to arrive at the mountain fortress after we have ascended and taken all the risk and danger."

Mazarine snorted and cracked open a new chicken bone. Thankfully no one paid her any heed but me.

I told myself to inhale, exhale. To not draw any attention. But my body was wound tight and I think Nura sensed it, sitting beside me.

"Clementine has no idea who I truly am," Papa answered. "I have withheld my past from her. And when she does discover it . . . the last thing she'll want is to be anywhere near me."

His words dampened the mood of camp. My father stared into the flames, as if his only daughter was truly lost. But through the fire and the dancing shadows and the starlight, I felt someone watching me.

I lifted my gaze to meet Phelan's.

This time, he did not look away.

33

I couldn't ascend the mountain the following morning without speaking to my father in private. The questions were devouring me. And I remembered the things I had once said to him, when my heart had been wrung by betrayal.

You are vile and deceptive and I want no part of you.

I retired to my tent and waited for the camp to fall quiet. I cloaked myself with stealth and slipped into the night, cautiously approaching my parents' tent.

I hesitated a beat. I was anxious to enter unannounced, because I was uncertain about the status of their relationship. I had been surprised that my mother chose to accompany my father on this journey, given their past.

But perhaps love was not something easily forgotten, even when it had burned down to ashes.

I was beginning to understand why their marriage had unraveled all those years ago. My father was deathless, dreamless, cursed. A magician of the mountains. And my mother wasn't. She was of Bardyllis; she would age and die. She could dream.

And yet she had guarded his secret.

As Phelan was guarding mine.

I slipped into their tent without stirring the canvas.

They had not gone to bed yet, to my vast relief. But they sat close to each other, a few candles burning around them, casting monstrous shadows on the tent walls. My father startled when he saw me materialize.

"Clem," he rasped, and I held my finger to my lips, silently rebuking him.

"Anna," my mother said. "We were just speaking of you."

I drew a deep breath, burying the resentment and bitterness that bloomed within me. I told myself that I would handle this conversation as Anna would, as an outsider with little emotions attached, and whispered, "I don't have long, but we need to talk, Ambrose."

He nodded, glancing at my mother. She rose, brushing the wrinkles from her dress, and said, "I'll keep watch."

She departed, touching my shoulder on her way out, and I took her place on the ground, facing my father.

He cast a quick spell; I sensed his magic drifting around us like feathers. Enclosing us in the tent, so our voices couldn't be overheard.

"What can I expect when we stand in the mountain fortress tomorrow?" I asked.

"I don't know, but I imagine my brother will greet us." He paused, his gaze drifting to my neck. He was remembering the bruises that had been there, inspired by Emrys's hand, and he said, "I'm deeply sorry that he hurt you on the new moon."

"I thought he was you."

My father smiled, but it gleamed with pain. "You would have known who he was if I had told you the truth from the beginning."

"Yes, the truth would have been nice," I said, my skin flushing. "You and your brother are the twin boys in Imonie's story." I remembered that tragic tale of hers. At the time, I hadn't realized she was sharing a glimpse into her own past. "You and your brother . . . she raised you, didn't she?"

"She did."

I studied my father's face in the candlelight—lean and handsome and yet creased with sorrow. I wondered if he had been Imonie's quiet boy. The lover of books and knowledge. Or if he had been her wild boy. Reckless and untamed and full of challenge.

"How old are you, Papa?"

He chuckled. "Well, I was twenty-five when the curse fell. But I've been alive for nearly one hundred and twenty-seven years now."

"Can I see your true face?"

He hesitated but nodded. I watched as his glamour melted away, and I saw him as he was, frozen in time as a young man. And even though I was prepared for the sight, it was still strange to behold.

"It's one of Mama's spells, isn't it?"

"Yes," he answered, and the glamour returned. "Without it, I was unable to stay in one place too long, for fear of people becoming suspicious of my agelessness."

"Why did you choose to become warden of Hereswith?" I asked. "Did you want to be as close to your brother as you could? Even as the curse kept you apart?"

He was quiet for a moment, but his brow furrowed. "Yes and no. I do miss my brother. Some days, it is nearly unbearable. But I was also given an order to protect Mazarine."

"The duke's order?"

"Indeed."

"He's wearing one of Mazarine's guises."

"He is. As you know well yourself."

"And he must have killed the real duke quietly," I surmised. "And then had Mazarine enchant him, so he could replace Lord Deryn without anyone knowing there had been a swap."

My father was silent, but I saw how my spoken revelation softened his eyes.

"How did you get dragged into this, Papa?"

"The duke found me by chance years ago, even though I had tried to melt into Endellion society. My marriage to your mother was on the rocks by then, so when he offered me Hereswith with a few terms attached, I took it."

We both heard a sound beyond the tent. A nightingale's call.

I knew it must be a warning from my mother, and yet there was still so much more I wanted to ask my father.

"The countess thinks we are scheming," I rushed to say. "She's concerned about me arriving. Why?"

"Because for the era of the curse to fully come to an end, a new duke or duchess must claim the mountains and reinstate a court," Papa said. "The Countess of Amarys no doubt thinks I am going to try and position you as sovereign. I believe she has similar plans when it comes to one of her two sons."

I held his stare, wondering what my father saw within me. If he saw light or darkness. If he saw truth or deceit. If he would make a case for me to rule or if he thought me too reckless, too ambitious.

And I . . . I didn't know what I wanted. These thoughts were new to me; they swarmed like a hive, and I didn't want to entertain them for too long, for fear they would overcome me.

Another bird call.

I stood but lingered, because I had one more question.

"Papa . . . why can't I dream at night?"

"Because of me, Clem," he said, rising to his feet. "Because of the curse in my blood. It runs through you, daughter."

Did that mean the mountains owned a part of me? That I had a place among the clouds? Would I dream again, once the curse was broken? Where did I truly belong?

I felt divided, yearning for Hereswith and my old life. But that had been a life built upon a facade. And so I acknowledged the other half of me, which secretly longed for something new and dangerous.

Papa must have read my slant of thoughts. He continued in a low voice, "You inherited the curse, but something else as well. You also have a claim."

"A claim?"

"To sit upon the throne."

"Is this what you want for me, then?"

"Mere weeks ago, I wanted you to lead a normal life," he said. "One where you could draw, paint, become a *deviah* magician if you wanted. I sensed the countess was hunting us when her sons arrived in Hereswith, and I fought it as long as I could. I tried to keep us from being discovered by her, so our lives could move forward here. But everything has changed now. We've been drawn into this century-old conflict, and you are the only one I would see end it."

I stared at him. "How can I trust you now? After all the lies you have raised me beneath? In what world would I believe what you are telling me? In what world would I follow you up the mountain?"

My questions wounded him. Agonized, he reached for my hand. I sidestepped his touch, a knot in my throat. There was a warning in my chest, a painful scrape of stone against tendons.

"Listen to me, daughter. When we ascend the mountain tomorrow, alliances will be formed. Not all of us are promised to survive. If you want to throw your lot in with the Vespers, then by all means, you are grown and your own person. But if you want to take the throne, you have my support, as well as the duke's."

"The duke's?" I remembered how my father had met with Lord Deryn one afternoon not so long ago. How his hand had smelled of bergamot. A cologne the duke must wear to hide his true scent—that rotting smell of parchment.

"For years I protected Mazarine for him," my father said. "And now the time has finally come for me to call in a favor; he will support your claim to Seren, should you desire it."

Another bird call, this time more insistent. I didn't want him to see how his words had affected me and I asked, "Was the Duke of Seren good or cruel?"

Papa had never told me mountain legends when I was a girl. Imonie had occasionally, and her myths had depicted the duke as an oppressor. But I wanted to hear what my father thought.

"He was cruel, Clem. A man bent by selfishness. But that doesn't absolve me for what I did. What I planned as a member of his court. And it's all the more reason why I refuse to see someone unworthy take the throne again."

I nodded and slipped from the tent. I tried to put myself in his place, in Imonie's place. What would I do if I was in the court of a cruel person? Was it right to kill them? I kept to the shadows, tossing off my stealth charm halfway to my tent.

I entered through the canvas door. I heard the clink of beads, the rustle of fabric, and I startled to see the countess standing there.

"Lady," I said, rigid with shock. I felt a spasm of fear that she had uncovered my journal with my exposé, which was sitting just behind her, tucked away in my satchel. What would she do to me if she read it?

"Where were you?" she asked.

"Visiting the privy."

"For ten minutes?"

"I had to walk a good way to find a private place," I said. "Your servants mill around the camp like ants."

She was pensive for a moment, as if weighing my voice for a lie.

"May I help you with something?" I asked.

"You and my son have quarreled," she stated tersely. "What about?"

"I think you should ask him, lady."

"I have, and he will not tell me." She pulled her fur cloak tighter about her, but her eyes never left mine. "Whatever has come between you . . . you need to settle it before we arrive at the fortress tomorrow morning."

I sighed. "What is this truly about, Lady Raven?"

"Phelan cares for you, Anna," she said, and I couldn't help it: my mouth fell open, drawing a snicker from her. "Do not act so surprised. Any fool could see it."

"Any fool could see he can hardly bear to look at me."

"That may be, but I know my son very well. And when he does allow himself to look at you, there is an ocean in his eyes," the countess said. "I will not see you usher his downfall."

"His downfall? Lady Raven . . . I am his *partner*." A partner who had once schemed of gathering all his family's dirt and publishing it in the paper. A partner who had once drawn his blood with a rapier and reveled in his groveling.

She wasn't wrong to doubt me.

"Partners have turned on each other before," she countered. "I want you to swear allegiance to my family. Your vow will come into great importance when we stand in the fortress hall tomorrow, when the curse realizes we have all returned to the place of our betrayal."

The last thing I wanted was to swear my allegiance to the Vespers.

364

My father's words rang in my thoughts; I had his support, as well as the duke's, although I was reluctant to believe it just yet. I could most likely also garner Mazarine's support. But I didn't know if I desired any of it. I hoped I would have a better sense of what to do and what I wanted when I reached the summit.

In the meantime, I held an advantage, and I wasn't afraid to play it.

"I will swear my allegiance to you, Lady Vesper," I said. "I will fight on your behalf until the curse is broken and the mountain duchy is restored."

"Good, Anna. Come, kneel before me and give me your vow."

I did as she wanted.

I knelt among the blankets and furs of my makeshift bed and held out my right hand. She unsheathed a small dagger from her belt and bestowed a quick, shallow slice to my palm. The wound stung as I spoke my vow to her.

"I, Anna Neven of Endellion, pledge myself and my magic to your service, Lady Raven Vesper, Countess of Amarys. I will serve you and your family from this moment until the curse breaks on the mountain and the Seren Duchy is restored. Should I break my word, you have the power to bring me harm by whatever way you see fit, according to my betrayal."

She nodded, pleased with my words.

I rose and she wrapped the wound on my hand with a strip of cloth torn from one of the blankets.

"The first thing I ask of you is to make amends with Phelan," she said. "You once guarded his back on the new moon nights in Endellion. I would ask it of you again."

"You believe someone in our circle would harm him?" I asked.

She nodded, and I could sense she was warring with her words. To tell me or to withhold what she thought. When she continued to hesitate, I said, "The duke, perhaps?"

"The duke and I do not often see eye to eye, but he would not hurt my son," she replied. "I do not trust Ambrose Madigan."

"The magician? Is there a reason, lady?"

"His loyalties are questionable," the countess replied. "He was once very close to his twin brother. They were inseparable before the curse. I would not be surprised if he chose to defend his brother instead of restoring the duchy."

"I'll keep that in mind, lady, as well as watch over Phelan," I said, and I hated how her statement about my father planted a seed of doubt in my mind. "Although your son tends to hold grudges. I don't know if he will ever forgive me."

"Oh, I have no doubt that he will," she said.

I watched her walk to the tent entrance, the night wind stirring the canvas as she departed.

I stood for a moment longer, contemplating all the paths before me.

Anna Neven might have given her vow to the Vespers. But Clem Madigan's allegiance remained to be seen.

34

We rose early with the sun and prepared to ascend, leaving our tents pitched, as if we would soon return for them. The Vespers' and the duke's servants would remain behind, tending to the camp. I didn't carry much: a satchel stuffed to the brim with several changes of clothes, green apples, a wedge of cheese, the journal with my exposé notes, an inkwell and quill. My father had snuck a dagger to me, and it was hidden in its leather sleeve, tucked away in my boot.

I walked with the Vespers' party through the long, frosted grass, my father, mother, and Imonie leading the way. We were silent, pensive. All too soon we reached the mountain entrance.

Two great wooden doors sat before us, thrice the height of a woman, arched and latticed with iron. I thought about how long it had been since the passage or the lift inside had been used.

"And how are we to open these doors?" Lennox asked with a huff.

"The doors will open on their own, since all six of us are together again. Emrys, the seventh, is already here, of course," Mazarine said from the back of the line. "Approach the doors, Ambrose."

My father closed the distance between us and the entrance, and just as the troll predicted, the doors creaked open on their own, streams of dirt cascading from the stone lintel above. The mountain seemed to rumble, as if recognizing the broken court that stood at its feet. The twin doors came to a rest, gaping open like a mouth, eager to swallow us. The passage was dark; I could smell damp stone and rich earth and rotting wood.

"Brin," the countess said crisply, pivoting on her heel to regard the troll. "Why don't you lead the way?"

Mazarine snorted, but moved to the head of the line, passing my father with a polite nod.

"Do you need fire?" he asked, but she didn't answer.

She stepped into the darkness of the passage and vanished, and we waited, uncertain.

"Should we follow her?" Nura whispered from behind me.

No sooner did she speak the words than fire bloomed in the passage. Torches bracketed on both walls ignited one by one.

We followed Mazarine's path. I could feel the heaviness in the air—cold, quiet, sentient air. The floor beneath our boots was swept clean, set with stone. The walls on either side were recessed and carved with moons and suns and people. Relics of the duchy that had once dwelled here.

This place felt like a tomb.

The passage opened up into a vast, cavernous chamber. From the faint reach of the firelight, I could see wagons full of cobwebs and crate upon crate, stacked in clusters. A storeroom of sorts, or once a place of trade, and it felt vast, endless. I stayed nearby the Vespers, but my eyes roamed my surroundings with its high ceilings that melted into darkness and the stone pillars that stood like trees. I kept waiting to come across skeletons, thinking it must have been pandemonium when the curse unfolded here.

"Ah, here is the lift." The countess's voice broke the heavy silence.

Mazarine had already located it. The troll stood beside a sleek platform of wood, its railings made of iron; she studied its pulley and gears. Lanterns burned at the four corners of the lift, granting light to see. "It is still functional."

My father joined Mazarine's side, examining the lift's operation. "Yes, it looks just as we left it, all those years ago. It hasn't aged a day."

"Enchanted," Olivette whispered in awe.

"Cursed," Nura added.

Mazarine glanced up from the lift to study us, her eyes catching the firelight like those of a cat. "Ambrose was brave enough to lead us to the doors. I took it upon myself to lead us into the passage. Now it is your turn, Lady Raven of Amarys, to be the first to take the lift."

I watched a shadow dart across the countess's face as she frowned, but then she seemed to have a change of heart and smiled.

"Of course, Mazarine. My family and I will be the first to

return to the fortress. It is only fair. Come, Lennox and Phelan. And you too, Anna."

I followed them onto the lift. I remained near the railing, but my palms were slick with perspiration as I imagined being toted upward, into the darkness and unknown, on this piece of shaky wood.

The duke stepped forward to unexpectedly join us. "I will ascend with you, Lady Raven," he announced gallantly.

"How kind of you, Your Grace," the countess replied, but I heard the twist in her words. She didn't want the duke to accompany us.

"Are we ready?" Mazarine drawled.

The countess nodded.

The troll shifted a lever and the lift began to groan and shake. The chains tightened and rotated through a great wheel, and up we went.

I held on to the railing and looked down at my parents and Imonie.

They were staring at me, worry and fear drawn in their faces. I was being carried away from them, out of sight, and I felt a twinge of anxiousness.

I glanced away from them first, casting my eyes up to the darkness and the unknown.

It was a slow but steady rise.

We began to pass by different stone landings, silent and shadowed, but the lift did not stop. We continued to inch upward, the chains ticking like a heartbeat, and I knew we were in the fortress, surpassing the lower floors. No one spoke, but I sensed the duke watching me. I ignored him, and kept my eyes on the wall of stone, waiting for us to reach our destination. The darkness was gradually fading around us, as if we were ascending from night into day.

The lift jerked to a halt and I stumbled backward into Phelan. He grasped hold of my arm, steadying me, and he didn't let go until the countess took the first step off the lift, onto the highest landing of the fortress.

Sunshine streamed in through skylights in the ceiling. The floors were set with stone, smooth and polished and accented with small blue jewels. The landing opened up into a wide chamber that broke off into four different corridors.

We stood in the sunshine and drifting dust motes, staring at each of the passages, and behind us I could hear the lift beginning to lower with a loud clang.

"Mazarine has inadvertently given us an advantage," said the countess. "We should explore before the others arrive. See if we can locate Emrys." She glanced at me. "Anna, you will go with Phelan. His Grace and Lennox will come with me."

"Should I not accompany Anna and Phelan," the duke dared to say, "since you and I are familiar with these passages, and they are not?"

Lady Raven's annoyance was nearly palpable. But she nodded at the duke and said, "Very well."

She and Lennox took the western corridor, while Phelan and I followed the duke into the eastern one.

Lord Deryn and Phelan both had rapiers sheathed at their belts, and their hands strayed to the hilts as we walked deeper into the silent fortress. I didn't sense danger, only sorrow and cobwebs of memories. Vibrant tapestries dressed the walls, pleading to be admired after so many years missing a beholder.

I paused before one, captivated by its quaint beauty. It depicted a view from the mountain fortress, overlooking a lush valley. The longer I stared upon the tapestry, the more I felt as if I could step into this scene and find myself in a sun-drenched meadow, cradled by the mountains. . . .

I began to reach out, my fingers touching the finely woven threads.

"Miss Neven," the duke said, breaking my reverie.

I glanced to where he and Phelan waited a few paces away, both of them regarding me.

"Please stay close to us," he said. "I do not know where Emrys is, and I do not wish to risk losing you to him."

The duke led us to the fortress hall, a place Phelan and I had both walked on the new moon, in Knox Birch's nightmare. The scene the countess had painted on the card of the lost one.

It felt strange to stand in a place I had seen dimly before as a bewitched reflection.

But I recognized it. The blue banners of heraldry on the walls, the arched windows, the multiple hearths, the tables and benches. The dais. But the duke's throne was missing, and I exchanged a discreet glance with Phelan.

"We shall sit here and wait," the duke said, drawing out a bench at the nearest table.

"What are we waiting for, Your Grace?" Phelan asked.

"For the others to arrive. I do not know why your mother thinks wandering around is an advantage, Phelan."

I struggled to understand her reasoning as well, and I conceded to sit at the table, eager for my parents and Imonie and the Wolfes to arrive. Phelan remained standing, too restless to sit. He paced the hall, the click of his boots echoing off the walls.

I waited until Phelan was out of earshot before I addressed the duke.

"What is it like, Your Grace? To return home after so many years away?"

He glanced at me from across the table. I couldn't help but wonder what his true face looked like. "It is bittersweet, Miss Neven. My thoughts and heart are full of memories."

I thought about the conversation I'd had with my father the night before. The duke had given my father Hereswith, but with orders. And I didn't know what the duke wanted, but it seemed he was the countess's opposition. I didn't trust the countess either, although I did Phelan.

I trusted him because he was protecting me by keeping my true identity a secret, for unknown reasons.

Although sometimes I imagined that I knew why, when Phelan looked at me.

"What was your position in the mountain court?" I asked, and the duke gave me a toothless smile.

"You have not uncovered that yet, Miss Neven?"

"I have my suspicions."

"Which are . . . ?"

"You were once the master of coin."

He studied me closer. "Not the guard, or the advisor?"

"No." And I remembered how many coins Phelan's territory had paid to satisfy his dream tax.

Does he truly want to break this curse? I wondered, because once the curse ended, so did the new moon nightmares. There would be no need for wardens and the dream tax. Perhaps the duke had lied to my father about supporting my claim.

Phelan eventually grew weary of pacing and joined us at the table, sitting a few hand lengths away from me. That ended my conversation with the duke, and we waited for the others to arrive.

Mr. Wolfe, Olivette, and Nura finally appeared in the hall, and not long after them my parents, Imonie, and Mazarine arrived.

"Where is the countess?" Imonie asked with a concerned frown.

"And Lennox?" Nura added, noticing that he was also missing.

"They are exploring the fortress," I replied, and I saw the suspicion in my father's face.

"We should not progress without them," said Mr. Wolfe, rushing his hands through his wispy hair. "We need to make plans as one."

And so we waited.

I was beginning to wonder if Emrys had slain them both in some shadowy corridor when the countess and Lennox appeared, no longer toting their bags.

"Ah, good," Lady Raven said, taking note of everyone. "We are all gathered here."

"Where were you?" my father snapped.

She cast him a surprised glance. "I was reacquainting myself with my old home, Ambrose. My former quarters are exactly as I left them."

Papa opened his mouth to say something else, but a loud bang stole our attention. We glanced to the dais, where a hidden door had been opened and shut without our notice. There stood Emrys, watching us with jaded eyes.

He wasn't wearing his enchanted armor, as I'd half expected him to. He was dressed in blue robes stitched with silver moons, with a dark shirt and trousers beneath. His auburn hair fell across his brow, just like Papa's, and his mouth was set in a firm line, also like my father's. I stared at him, amazed by the resemblance. If my father dropped his aging glamour, it would be difficult to tell them apart from a distance.

"Emrys," Papa greeted him, slowly approaching the dais.

"Hello, brother," Emrys said, gazing down at him. "It has been a long while. And yet look at you. Wearing an old face like a man with something to hide."

My father's shoulders drew back, tense. This reunion felt fraught, icy. I swallowed and hoped I could evade Emrys's attention.

"I see you have brought your companions," Emrys continued, regarding the rest of us. We remained close together around one of the tables. No one spoke; we hardly dared to breathe.

Emrys's gaze found Imonie and lingered on her. His mother. Imonie, who stood quiet and still, as if she had anticipated this moment for years and now that it had come . . . she didn't know what to do, what to say to him.

She remained silent, and I ached for her. I wanted to wrap my arms around Imonie and bury my face in her dress, to breathe her in as I had done as a child. Oh, how she had loved me, the granddaughter she could not claim in word because of her and my father's secrets, but she had claimed me in love. And that love had given me a warm, safe childhood, despite the pain of my parents' separation. That love had clothed me and fed me and raised me, protected me.

I hadn't fully appreciated her until this moment.

Emrys opened his mouth, and I expected he would greet her. But different words spilled out, and his eyes coldly passed over her to Phelan, to the Wolfes. To the duke. "At long last, the traitorous court is reunited. I hope your lives in Bardyllis have been idyllic, a dream. Was it you, Ambrose, who gathered and rallied our alliance to return?"

"It was me," the countess answered, and boldly took a step toward him. "I found those who wanted to be forgotten. Your brother, for one. As well as the spymistress and the master of coin. The three of them would have continued on for another hundred years if you had not found a way to haunt the new moon. And so it is I who answered your summoning, Emrys. I have brought us back to end this curse."

"Raven," said Emrys, his eyes shifting to her. "You have not changed either. Do not lie and claim that you returned to ease my suffering."

The countess acted like he had struck her. Her face went pale; her eyes glittered like she craved to stab him.

"You are perhaps looking for the throne," Emrys continued, motioning to the empty dais. "The chair your brother once graced as duke, before you plotted to kill him, Raven."

"*We* plotted to kill him, old friend."

Emrys only smiled, but there was no kindness within it. I wondered if walking this fortress, abandoned and alone for an entire century, turned a heart into stone, deeper than Mazarine's old magic. "The throne does not appear until nightfall," he continued. "When it appears, your dreams will manifest. Be ready, for they will be eager to cut you to the quick."

"Dreams?" my father echoed.

"You have not dreamt since you left," Emrys said. "That has changed now. You stand in the mountain where the crime was committed, where the curse hooked your souls. Your dreams, then, will now return when you sleep. And there are no remedies here to keep them at bay. Nor will these corridors and this hall be safe when the sun sets. If you do not wish to encounter the nightmares, remain in your room with the door bolted. But if you want to end the curse, one of you must break the dream and claim the throne."

His words wove together all the stray pieces of my wonder, questions, and dread. We would dream, and our dreams would roam this place at night, just like they did on the new moon.

What would my mind spin and create, now that it could?

"Oh, and one final warning," Emrys said, raising his hand. "Your deathless state is no more in these halls. You can bleed and feel your life ebb; you can feel the mortal sting of a blade. It would be a shame, indeed, to watch a number of you fall before the curse breaks."

A hush settled over the group. The wraiths looked shocked to learn this. I snuck a worried glance at my family.

"Go now and rest," Emrys said. "What little daylight you have remaining should be used to prepare for tonight. Bread, meat, and water will appear in your room by magic every evening an hour before sundown. I am sure I will see some of you in the hall when darkness falls."

I waited for the duke to rise first before I stood, hoping to remain hidden in the group. My father and the countess returned to us, and I had to remind myself to follow her instead of Papa.

Emrys's gaze found me just before I left the hall.

With a chill, I realized he knew exactly who I was.

35

I chose a bedchamber across the corridor from Phelan's, near the countess's grand suite. The room was small but clean with a trio of windows, a bed with a feather mattress, a wardrobe in one corner, and a fireplace where enchanted flames burned. I unpacked my bag, eating one of my apples while I hung my clothes in the wardrobe. Who had once dwelled in this room? I wondered as I eventually sat on the edge of the bed. Blankets were folded at the foot of it, and a wolf pelt was draped over the middle.

I tried to judge the time of day by the slant of light on the floor and surmised it to be around one in the afternoon. And then I waged a war with myself: to fall asleep so I could last the night, or to resist, for fear of dreaming.

I eventually decided I would at least lie down. I stared at the ceiling for a while until my eyes felt heavy.

The bed was soft beneath me, the fur warm across my legs.

I drifted to sleep before I knew it.

I am in Endellion.

I walk the streets I guard with Phelan, and I don't know what I look like—who I appear to be—until I pass by a gilded mirror in a storefront. I'm Anna in the reflection, and it surprises me. I lay my hand over my breast, covering my heart. The stone within me holds, emitting a heavy permanence. It has grown into my flesh; it cannot be removed, nor will it ever crack and crumble.

I suddenly feel lost, within myself and in the streets.

I turn, struggling to breathe, until I see Aaron Wolfe's shop. I step inside and walk among the swords and axes and armor. I approach the leather weapon belt but it is something else that captures my attention. A slender dagger with a jeweled hilt. As I reach for it, Mr. Wolfe appears. Olivette's father.

"How much for the dagger?" I ask him.

"The price is the secret you hold," he replies.

And I know if I take this dagger within my hand, it will cut me, and Anna will bleed away.

Mr. Wolfe disappears, and I am left with the decision, to bleed or not.

I choose not to, and it's not because I am afraid of the pain but because I hear the pounding of an anvil in the distance. I follow the sound through a back door, down a dark tunnel that makes me shiver, into a workroom.

Mr. Wolfe is nowhere to be seen, but something claims the center of the chamber.

I approach it cautiously, a warning ringing in my mind. It's a full suit of armor, standing upright, waiting for someone to step

within it. As I draw closer . . . I recognize it. This is Emrys's armor,
the one he wears on the new moon, trespassing into nightmares.

Fresh blood drips from it. I watch it spill down the breastplate,
pooling on the floor. I hear something move behind me and I whirl to
find Mr. Wolfe standing in a doorway, framed by light, staring at me
with shadows in his eyes.

"Whose blood is this?" I ask.

He doesn't answer, but an axe gleams in his hands.

"Whose blood is this?" I ask again, louder.

He takes a step closer to me, the floor creaking beneath him.

I startled awake.

It was twilight, and my clothes were drenched with sweat. I had no idea where I was. Not until I sat forward and studied the sparse chamber that held me.

Trembling, I slipped from the bed and warmed myself at the fire, although the dream's chill lingered in my mind. Why on earth had I dreamt such a thing? Olivette's father, of all people. I quickly ate a few bites of bread and meat that had appeared on my table as Emrys foretold, washing it down with water.

I donned my boots and then sat on the edge of the bed, waiting for night to arrive. That's when I noticed a folded slip of parchment sitting on the floor, as if it had been snuck beneath my door.

I rose and picked it up, suspicious until I recognized Imonie's handwriting.

Be patient, be shrewd.

I smiled, remembering how she said this to me every new moon. But the warmth of the memory faded when I realized what she was saying to me.

Don't get yourself killed, Clem.

I took the dagger my father had given me into my hand, pacing the room, anticipating what was to come.

The night deepened.

Ready, I approached my door, but my fingers paused on the iron handle. What if it was my dream that materialized in the hall? I shouldn't have let myself sleep this first day. I had already failed on the *shrewd* part of Imonie's message.

I stepped into the corridor with such thoughts nipping at my mind, catching a glimpse of Phelan up ahead, striding through the candlelight toward the hall.

I wasn't surprised to discover he was venturing out to encounter the night's offering, but I did wonder how many of us would. Six of us were wardens, but that didn't mean all of us would roam the fortress, seeking out what could be our own nightmare.

I followed him through the winding passages, past door after door, tapestry after tapestry.

When I reached the entrance of the hall, though, I hung back, concealed in a shadow. I had a clear vantage point of the hall and could see Nura and Olivette limned in firelight as they paced, waiting for the dream to appear. I sensed Phelan was nearby, but I could no longer see him.

I tarried in the shadow, the stone wall rough and cold against my back.

"I'm not surprised to find you here," Phelan said, his voice emerging from the darkness on my right.

"I could say the same about you."

We stood in awkward silence together, close enough to sense the other but far enough away to have no chance of touching.

"Did you sleep this afternoon?" he asked.

Did you dream was what he meant.

"Yes," I replied. "Did you?"

He was quiet for a beat, and then said in a husky voice, "Yes. I did as well."

Another round of silence. I watched as Nura and Olivette grew weary of pacing the hall, choosing to sit on the edge of a table. They hadn't slept; I could see the exhaustion in their faces.

"Is your brother coming to fight tonight?" I asked.

"I don't know."

You should, I thought, biting the inside of my lip. I didn't desire to see Lennox take this duchy and restore it back to life. But I had no doubt he would believe himself to be the best candidate.

I was opening my mouth to say something snide when I felt a rush of air. Phelan was in the shadow with me, and our arms brushed as he whispered, *"Anna."*

He had never said my faux name like that, with urgent awe. And I swiftly learned why, when I saw the dream that manifested in the hall.

I was walking the streets of Endellion.

I stopped before a mirror in a storefront, to look upon my reflection.

This was my dream.

Heat spread through me like a fever. Mortification and dread unfurled in my thoughts, and for a moment I could only stand and helplessly gape as I watched my nightmare overtake the hall. I started to rush forward, only to be stopped by Phelan.

"Wait," he hissed into my hair.

I froze until I remembered that Olivette's father appeared in the dream as a sinister force. And Olivette was in the hall, watching everything with wide eyes.

I pulled away and Phelan let me go.

I entered the hall; I stepped into my dream.

It was like treading a river, one that deepened with each step. The currents tugged me toward myself, this terrifying flesh-and-blood copy of Anna. What would she do if I caught her attention, if our eyes met? What would *I* do?

I was relieved that I had not taken that bejeweled dagger, that I had not exposed my true self. Nothing about this dream gave me away as Clem, although it did mention my secret and it raised suspicions about Olivette's father.

We had nearly reached the end of the dream. The armor shone and dripped blood.

"Father?" Olivette cried, staring at Mr. Wolfe holding the axe.

I knew she was caught up in this dream just as I was, struggling to tell what was real and what was fantasy. She saw her father and thought it was truly him, arriving to assist in fighting the nightmare.

"Olivette!" I called to her, hurrying to close the gap between us. My friends didn't know this dream like I did. I was the only one who held the advantage.

The sound of my voice drew dream Anna's and Mr. Wolfe's attention. The moment they looked at me, I was overwhelmed. I sank to my knees, dazed as if I had been struck across the face.

Nura was the one of us who responded.

She cast a defensive spell as Mr. Wolfe approached with the axe. Her magic arced with blue light, finding its mark in his chest. The smith stumbled back but did not fall. It roused his anger and he moved faster.

"Wait, Nura," Olivette shouted. "It could be him!"

"This isn't your father, Oli," Nura said, hurling another charm to slow him down.

I could feel my pulse in my ears as I rose.

Olivette was shouting and Nura's magic was teeming in the air, scorching Mr. Wolfe's clothes, burning his skin. But he continued to press us, swinging his axe.

Nura blocked it with a charm and attempted to wrench the axe from his grip. Her magic rebounded and tossed her back a few yards. She landed lithely on her feet several tables away, and I saw the tension in her face as Olivette attempted to speak to Mr. Wolfe's phantom.

"Father, lower the axe," she said.

He swung.

Olivette gasped and lurched backward, scrounging up a magical shield, but the edge of the blade sliced her raised forearm. Nura launched herself over the tables, teeth bared as she struck

Mr. Wolfe again with more force. He stumbled, granting her enough time to ease Olivette up and away safely out of his range.

Phelan appeared. He engaged with the smith so Nura could continue retreating with Olivette, who was weeping, her forearm leaving a trail of blood on the flagstones.

We were all so distracted by Mr. Wolfe's attack that we forgot about Anna.

I glanced to where the shade of myself continued to stand by the bloody armor. I saw the gleam of gold at Anna's breast, the jewel she wore about her neck.

I was the key to ending this dream. My stone heart was the weakness, the break. It had to be broken, and as soon as I realized this, Anna began to retreat from the hall.

I pursued her.

I didn't realize Phelan was chasing after me until I was about to slip out the side door Anna had vanished through. I felt his magic encircle me, slowing me down.

"Wait," he panted, reaching my side. His magic loosened, and I spun to look up at him. "Let me come with you. Let me guard your back."

I entertained the temptation, because the more I realized I would have to give my phantom a mortal wound, the stronger my reservations grew. But when I looked at Phelan . . . I knew he would struggle in wounding this reflection of me as well.

"Help Nura and Olivette to their chamber and lock the door," I said. "Quickly, before Mr. Wolfe reaches them. I will meet you there after I bring this to an end."

My words struck a chord between us.

We glanced at the dais, where the duke's throne had appeared, illumined by a stream of moonlight. Emrys stood beside the regal chair, an observer as the night unfolded. His face was like marble, unreadable, but he was watching Phelan and me, watching Nura, Olivette, and Mr. Wolfe. Watching and waiting to see if this dream would break.

I slipped from the hall; Phelan didn't follow me this time.

The corridors were cold and dark, punctured by the flickering light of sconces. I followed the trail Anna left for me, sounds of her boots on the stone floors, a flicker of movement as she rounded corner after corner. She was leading me deeper into the fortress, down to the very heart of the mountain. In my dream, I had felt lost. And that sensation welled within me once more.

I must have chased her for an hour, through every vein of the fortress.

I walked through the dark kitchen, through dusty storerooms, through the armory, where swords and crossbows and shields hung on the wall, glinting in the dim light. Through a library with endless shelves of musty books. Through rooms and suites long abandoned.

I stopped in the main corridor, thinking she was about to bring me back into the hall. I stood ragged, bewildered. Surrender was softening me until she appeared at the end of the passage, waiting for me to follow.

I no longer ran. I walked, which gave me the chance to draw my dagger from my boot. I slid the steel free from its leather sheath and held it in my hand, following Anna into a spacious suite.

I knew at once this was the Duke of Seren's chambers.

The moon was setting, but the last of its silver light streamed in through the open balcony doors. The wind sighed, stirring the curtains. Anna came to a halt, a strange mark on the floor between us. It was wide and dark. Old blood that had dried long ago.

"This is where it happened," she said to me, meeting my gaze. "Where the Duke of Seren was murdered. Where the curse was cast. His sister always believed she was the true heir, not him. And when she hatched a plan to be rid of her brother, six other court members readily joined her, never dreaming of what their ruthlessness would inspire."

The golden jewel gleamed at her chest. I let out a long breath, the dagger slick in my hand.

"Why have you brought me here?" I asked.

"Because you need to see it," she replied. "You need to stand on the same ground where the crime was committed."

"Did my uncle kill the duke?"

She chose not to answer. I could hardly discern her face—the face I had drawn for myself months ago.

"They say the duke was a cruel man," I said.

"Does that excuse the court of the murder they plotted? Lady Raven may have first spoken the idea aloud, but it lived in the other six hearts."

I was quiet.

"Go on," she taunted me when my hesitation continued. "Strike me and bring about the end."

"You act as if you're not a part of me," I said. My hands shook, much to my dismay.

She smiled. "Of course I'm a part of you."

Knox Birch's nightmare suddenly came to mind. He had wanted to claim the throne of Seren, and he had cut down his wife and daughters to do it. He had sliced through his own heart and had not even realized it until afterward, when the blood stained the ground, when he had obtained his desire at an unthinkable cost.

But there is no other way, I thought. The dream had to be vanquished so the throne could be claimed and the curse broken. I wondered if the greed shone in my eyes like a film as I prepared to pierce Anna's heart. I wondered if one had to become a monster in order to end the curse.

I took a step closer. One moment, it was just her and me. The next, a rough hand yanked me backward. I collided with someone's broad chest, the point of a dagger prodding my side, just beneath my ribs. A little more pressure, and it would pierce me.

I froze when Lennox hissed into my hair, "Did you think I was going to let you be the victor here, Anna? Do you truly believe you are the one destined to break the curse? You, a girl from the gutter who never deserved to be warden with the likes of my brother. You shouldn't even be here."

I didn't reply. But I thought on the past, when he had defeated me for Hereswith. When he had stolen my home, all because I had hesitated.

I stared at phantom Anna, whose eyes slid to Lennox as he held me roughly against him. Behind her, the balcony doors sat open, eerily as if they had been left that way a century ago. The sun was just beginning to rise, the mountains incandescent with gold.

And I dared to spin and turn, risking the dagger he held at my side. It cut through my dress; I felt the blade bite my side, but I forgot the pain as I cast a repelling spell at him with deadly accuracy.

Lennox was blown off his feet, hurled up and away to the other side of the room. He slammed into the wall and for one wild moment, I thought I had killed him. I only felt a tiny bit of remorse.

He slid to the floor with a grimace, his eyes shining with fury as he charged again. I dodged the spell he spouted at me; I effortlessly danced around the green fire he created, and we met in a clash that robbed our balance.

On the cold, bloodstained floor, I struggled to slow him down. Because he was crawling to reach Anna, and it was a race to break the nightmare before the sun did. The light was creeping ever closer through the window and doors, and I bared my teeth and dragged Lennox by the ankle back to me. Among the scrambling, I thought I saw the glistening of bones, lurking beneath the duke's bed. As if a skeleton had been swept beneath it.

Lennox was dazed, but he fought me until I disarmed him. I flung his dagger away and held my blade at his throat.

"Anna . . . ," he whispered, suddenly trembling. "Anna, think of Phelan. He will come to hate you if you wound me."

"*Wound* you?" I taunted.

"You mean to kill me?"

I stared at him, but from the corner of my eye, I watched as the sunlight inched closer to where Anna stood. She was becoming transparent, about to melt away.

"Do you know I swore allegiance to your mother?" I asked, pressing my dagger deeper into his neck, just to see him squirm beneath me. He let out a yelp when a bead of blood welled. "You *fool*! I'm fighting on your family's behalf, but if you get in my way again . . . I won't hesitate to cut you down."

"All right, all right," he panted, lifting his hands. "Get off me, will you?"

Around us, the room became illuminated. Dust and cobwebs and the patina of memories. The shadows gave way to light.

Anna sighed. She turned into a wisp of smoke, victorious. The nightmare had slipped through my fingers.

And the curse remained to be broken.

36

I couldn't stop shivering.

I fetched a fur-lined cloak from my bedroom and laced it tightly at my collar before I knocked on Olivette's door. Exhaustion was heavy as a millstone on my shoulders; I waited for someone to answer. I could hear murmurs within the chamber, and then the lock was unbolted and Nura cracked the door.

"Anna?" she asked, glancing beyond me.

"It's me," I reassured her, and she welcomed me inside.

Olivette was sitting upright in bed. Phelan stood before one of the windows, framed by sunrise, and Mr. Wolfe was tending to the fire.

All of them looked at me when I entered. I stopped, feeling my vulnerability like a burn. I could hardly look Mr. Wolfe in the eye.

"How are you, Olivette?" I asked, my voice hoarse.

She held up a bandaged forearm. "I'll be fine, Anna. It wasn't bad."

"It only required twenty-five stitches," Nura said pointedly.

"And thank gods you could sew it up without a hitch," Olivette replied, just as sharply. I sensed the two of them had quarreled, but it was centered on the fact that Nura had nearly witnessed her partner's dismemberment.

"Is it safe to assume you did not break the dream, Anna?" asked Mr. Wolfe.

"Unfortunately. I failed." I felt Phelan's stare from across the chamber, but I didn't lift my eyes to him.

"You didn't fail, Anna!" Olivette cried.

Ah, sweet Olivette, who only saw the good in people. I smiled at her, but it sat on my face like a wince.

"Is there anything I can do for you?" I asked, eager to wash away the stain of my dream.

"Can you brew a pot of tea from thin air?" Olivette asked, and I laughed.

"How I wish." The meat, bread, and water once a day was fine, I supposed, but I couldn't deny that I craved a good stout tea.

"That's what I want the moment I leave this mountain," Olivette stated with a sigh. "A pot of tea with cream and honey. And some blueberry scones."

I caught the worried expression that crossed Nura's face as she gazed at Olivette. We might be on the mountain for a while.

"Miss Neven?" Mr. Wolfe gently drew my attention. "May I speak to you in private for a moment?"

I nodded, but my throat was narrow as I followed Olivette's father into the corridor.

"Nura and Phelan told me the details of the dream," he began with a stammer. "I feel like I must apologize, Miss Neven."

I stopped walking so I could face him. "No, Mr. Wolfe. Please, don't apologize. The dream was mine. You are not at fault."

He sighed, struggling to believe me. I imagined it was horrifying to see your daughter dragged into a room, crying and bleeding from a wound your phantom had given her.

"That may be, Miss Neven," Mr. Wolfe said. "But there was truth within it."

I wondered if he was hinting at my secret—the price for that bejeweled dagger. And then I recalled the armor.

"You forged the armor that Emrys used to walk the new moon," I said.

He nodded. "I made it long ago. But the inspiration for it has always been betrayal. I began my service to the duchy as a guard, but my mind was given to other things, mainly the spells of *metamara*. Transforming one thing into another. My father was a smith, and as I held no other skill but to protect and guard, I began to learn how to craft armor and weapons. I soon joined Raven's inner circle, only because her brother the duke wanted me to create more and more weapons that I felt were dangerous and wrong. And Raven was the only one who was powerful enough to protect me from her brother's bloody whims.

"She asked me to make enchanted armor. The seven of us who desired to see the duke gone had formed an alliance, and we were to draw stones, to see who would give him the killing blow. Whoever was selected would wear the armor, as a way to protect their identity and themselves from any magic the duke might cast in defense. So I began to forge it, and I thought all would be well with the plan, but none of us realized how slow the armor would make us. And to kill the duke . . . one would have to be swift.

"I completed the armor, but we never used it. I left it in a storage closet in the castle armory, locked away. I forgot all about it when things fell apart, when I fled to Bardyllis."

I was silent, thinking on his words. I envisioned the duke's chamber, the bloodstain on the floor. The bones beneath the bed. And I wanted to know who had been the one to kill the duke.

"Who drew the stone?" I asked.

Mr. Wolfe glanced away from me, as if he could not bear to look me in the eye. "What do you mean?"

"Who drew the stone to assassinate the duke?"

"Emrys did."

I retreated to my chambers. The sun streamed in through the arched windows, and the floor was bitterly cold beneath my feet as I removed my boots.

My mind whirled, thinking of stones and armor and what the wraiths must have been like before the curse had fallen.

I had just pulled the ribbon loose from my braid when a knock sounded on my door.

"Come in," I said.

The door opened. Phelan stood on the threshold, hesitant until I motioned for him to step inside. He did, shutting the door behind him. His boots were scuffed from the nightmare, his trousers ripped at the knee. His cravat and jacket were abandoned. His shirt hung slightly open at the neck draws, and I remembered the scars on his chest.

"We need to talk," he said.

I waited for him to speak and began to unwind my braid with my fingers, my hair coming loose in rich waves. He watched me, transfixed, until I asked, "What did you need to talk to me about?"

"This is Mazarine's magic, isn't it?"

I knew he spoke of my disguise, and I looked away from him, bracing myself for this conversation. One that had been brewing between us for well over a week now. I sealed the door and windows with a quick spell to hold our conversation private. "Yes."

"Can you tell me why?"

"Why I donned a disguise and became your partner?" I walked to the small round table by my hearth, where a pitcher of water sat. I poured myself a glass but didn't offer one to him. "I was angry. You and your brother arrived without warning and challenged my father and me for my home. You won it, fairly, and yet I couldn't let it go. The way you both disgraced us. How we were now homeless."

He sighed and dragged his hand through his hair. "Why did you come after me? What did you intend to do, Clem?"

I made myself take a long swallow of water, but I was trembling, torn between my desires. To be shrewd and continue withholding things, or to let the truth unfold. I set down the glass and drew my cloak tighter around me, as if it could protect me from the discomfort of both choices.

"Did you plan to kill me?" he asked.

"Honestly, Phelan! Do I look *that* merciless to you?"

He stared at me. "I don't know what I see in you."

"I wanted to disgrace you, as you had done to me," I confessed, walking to him. "I wanted to hurt you and your family, to make you feel the things that you had inspired in me. I wanted you to be devastated. And I wanted to win my home back."

He stiffened, as if my words had cut him. But he held my gaze, insistent. "Did you ever plan to reveal to me who you were? Or were you going to up and leave me without word, without a trace?"

"I wanted to tell you. Eventually."

"To bask in your victory, I suppose."

"Yes." I sounded callous, and I watched Phelan flinch.

"So Anna was all an act?" he asked.

"In some ways," I replied carefully. "But in others, no. I was and still am exactly who I was before. Even in the moments when I was with you as Anna . . . I was Clem."

"Did your father put you up to this?"

"No. It was all my doing. My decision."

"And do you feel the same as you did at the beginning?" he asked. "Do you want to see me devastated? Disgraced? Do you want to hurt me, Clem?"

How should I respond? I was suddenly terrified to be vulnerable in his presence, uncertain where such a path might guide us.

"No, Phelan. You were not who I thought you to be at the beginning," I said, my cadence clipped with frustration. "You turned out to be different. And I wanted to despise you. I wanted to throw more kindling on my hate and yet you gave me nothing to burn, because you are simply too good. Even now, you are too *good*."

I shoved his chest for emphasis. He didn't budge, but his hands rose to capture mine.

"How so?" he said. "I told you I wasn't kind."

"You gave me a room when you thought I had nowhere to go. You clothed me and spared no expense. You listened to me when I began spouting wild claims about Seven Wraiths and the knight. And even after you realized who I was . . . you protected me," I said. "You should expose me now. I don't know why you are holding my secret like it is one of your own."

"And yet perhaps I will expose you," he said. "In time."

I froze, my hands still caught in his. "Are you threatening me now?"

"If my dreams are a threat, then yes." He fell silent, as if he wanted me to find the explanation in his eyes. I couldn't see it and pressed him for more.

"What are you speaking of?"

"I dreamt of you yesterday, Clem."

My divided heart all but stopped.

"I dreamt of you," he whispered again.

"A nightmare, I presume?" I countered, unable to help myself.

He smiled. "That I won't say. Although you may see it whether I want you to or not." He paused, his mirth fading. "Do you understand what I'm saying to you?"

I stepped back, suddenly overwhelmed. My hands slipped from his and I walked about my chamber, in and out of the light. His dream might be the one to materialize tonight. Apprehension took hold of me like a claw.

"How did you see me in your dream?" I asked.

"In both ways," he answered. "I saw you as Clem. And I saw you as Anna."

"That won't necessarily expose me," I said, breathless from the shock of his confession. But when I met his eyes from across the room . . . I realized that it would. Whatever his dream held, it was going to reveal my secret.

"I'm sorry, Clem," he murmured, and he did sound contrite, as if he could control what his mind created in sleep.

I almost laughed. "We have never dreamt, you and me. All our lives, we have been void of dreams until now. And at last, we dream, and your first is tainted by a treacherous girl who you must despise."

"I would not trade such a dream," he was swift to say. "Not for me, not for the world. Not even to break this curse. But for your sake in this strange game we find ourselves trapped within . . . I would."

"Well," I said, glancing out the window. "Thank you for the warning. Although perhaps you'll dream of something else this afternoon."

"Perhaps." But he didn't sound confident. And I was swiftly learning that our dreams were intent on unmasking us and our plans. Our secrets, our past. What we hoped for.

What we desired.

An awkward lull beat between us. My face felt hot when I pressed my hands to my cheeks, and I wondered if I was getting ill.

"I should go," Phelan said. "Let you get some rest."

I turned and watched him leave, the door latching quietly behind him. I was still staring at it two breaths later when the door unexpectedly swung open again, Phelan's gaze finding me instantly.

"I wanted it to be you," he said, his voice deep, rough-hewn. "When I returned to the museum for that final interview . . . gods, how I wanted it to be you."

And he had gotten his desire, only not how he had envisioned it.

I took the first step to him, and it broke the storm that had been building between us. He met me in the center of the room, and I had enough sense to flick my fingers and charm the door shut before we collided.

His hands grasped my waist, drawing me to him. I took hold of his collar, my mouth hungry to taste his. Our lips met, cautiously at first as we explored each other. My fingers drifted into his hair as I drank his sighs, his breaths. His hands moved to the curve of my neck; his fingertips traced the dip of my collarbones. I arched into him as he pressed me against the wall.

Vaguely, I heard an inner voice remind me that I was held together by stone and ice. Vaguely, I remembered my disguise, and I told myself that I had not come all this way as Anna only to break now into Clem.

My heart sang a vibrant ache; the pain branched through me, a sharp warning that stole my breath.

"Phelan," I gasped, my fingers tightening in his hair.

He drew away. Cold air washed over me.

I opened my eyes to meet his gaze, afraid that he would see me come undone. But he was looking at my side, where he had pushed aside the drape of my cloak to touch me. His hands fell away; his right palm was smeared with blood.

"You're bleeding," he whispered frantically. "You didn't tell me you were wounded."

I had forgotten about the swipe his brother had taken at me, hours ago. And everything seemed to crash over me at once: my exhaustion, my worry, my desire.

"Come here." Phelan guided me to the bed, easing me down to sit on the edge of the mattress. "Let me tend to you."

"Do you mean to undress me again?" I asked wryly.

He wasn't amused by my humor. "You might need stitches, Clem."

I winced, feeling the wound with each breath. "And what are you going to stitch me with?"

"I brought my supplies."

"Then perhaps you should fetch them."

He stroked a tangle of hair from my brow. His thumb grazed my cheek to find my mouth, tracing my parted lips before he brushed them with his own. A soft, fleeting kiss. Heat flared through me as I watched him depart.

Alone, I inhaled the solitude and pressed a fist to my chest, aching. It took me a moment to regain my composure, and I rushed my fingertips over my face, measuring my disguise. It was still intact, holding fast. But I sensed the frays along my edges. It wouldn't be much longer now.

I stripped and examined my wound, arcing just over my hip bone. It wasn't deep, but it was steadily bleeding again, most likely reopened when Phelan had pressed me against the wall.

A knock on my door. "Anna?"

It was him. His voice made everything leap within me, breathless.

"Anna?"

I swallowed and reached for a clean chemise. It was wrinkled from being shoved in my satchel, but it was soft against my skin as I unlocked the door.

Phelan stepped inside, carrying his medicine kit.

"I can stitch myself," I said, reaching for it.

He withheld the box, glaring at me. "Are you serious?"

"As the grave. Hand it to me, please."

"You're pushing me away from you. Why?"

I hesitated, even as I longed to tell him everything.

"No more lies, Clem," Phelan whispered. "We have both held our secrets long enough. Tell me what is troubling you. Tell me how I can help you."

It was strange how those words of his struck deeper than his kiss. I wavered, leading him back to the bed. I lay down and let him stitch my wound, because I knew that I needed him to do it. And this was a good opportunity to get the answers I still needed from him, as he wouldn't be able to up and run if I asked something he didn't want to answer.

I stared up at the ceiling while he stitched my side. "How long have you known of your mother's plans?"

He exhaled, as if he had been waiting for it. "I sensed she was up to something when she gave me and Lennox orders to take Hereswith and study the book of nightmares for a dreamless sleeper. We suspected she was looking for a particular wraith, but I didn't realize her full intentions yet. When she finally told me that she herself was a wraith, and that she had located nearly all of her kind and planned to return to the mountain and break the new moon curse . . . I was furious. That was the night you saw me tear apart the library. It made me question everything . . . who she was, who I was. What was to come for all of us."

I bit my lip against the sting in my side. "When did you realize who I was?"

"When I saw those scars on your leg," he replied, cutting the thread. "That entire day, I kept telling myself it was ridiculous, that there was no way you could have fooled me for so long. But I started to examine every single one of our interactions, and I realized I should have seen it, right from the very beginning when you viciously attacked me at the interview."

I struggled to hide a smug smile. "I wasn't *vicious*."

Phelan was silent so long it prompted me to look at him. As soon as I did, he leaned so close that our lips almost touched. "You were indeed *vicious*," he breathed, but pulled away before I could kiss him. "That's why I wanted you. And then after the new moon, you snuck from the house. I followed you, all the way to the mines. I saw you speak to Ambrose and I knew without a doubt it was you."

He wiped my stitches with antiseptic, the air between us full of static. And then I whispered, "Why didn't you reveal me to your mother?"

Phelan glanced away, repacking the medicine kit. "I thought about it, at first. I was so angry at you for deceiving me. But I couldn't do it. Every time I approached her about it . . . I couldn't speak the words."

I felt like he was withholding something else. Why wouldn't he meet my eyes when he answered?

I chose to be vulnerable in that moment, hoping it would encourage him to be the same, and sat forward, my stitches pinching my side. I took his hand and I laid it over my chest, where my heart was beating. Phelan's eyes widened at first, uncertain of my intentions until I said, "My heart is only mine by half."

He continued to kneel before me, pensive, his eyes studying me as his hand continued to rest against my breast. As he felt the uneven song beneath my skin. "And where is the other half, Clem?"

I told him the truth, about Mazarine's tonic, and what I had to surrender. I told him half of my heart was stone and my disguise as Anna was dependent on its survival.

"That night when you caught my reflection in the mirror," I said. "When you said my name . . . the stone within me suffered a crack. And I don't regret that it did, because I had forgotten how vital it is to be known for who you are, and not for who you pretend to be. I had forgotten how good it is to be seen, even with flaws and scars. I *wanted* you to see me. But I can't risk it now. Not until the end comes. You are making it more difficult for me because I've grown fond of you, in the most impossible of ways."

There was a long beat of silence. I was suddenly eager to know his thoughts, but I was too proud to beg for them.

I waited, full of blazing tension, watching him.

"Then I will guard you until the end, even if that means I must do it from a distance," he said. His fingers traced down my arm to twine with my own, lifting my hand to his lips. To kiss the hollow of my palm, as if sealing me with a vow. "Rest now, Clem."

He relinquished me and stood. I sensed he was anxious about the things I had shared with him, but he hid his emotions well.

"Do you need anything before I go?" he asked, halfway to the door.

I studied him, wondering how this had happened to us. I yearned to say one word to him. *Stay.*

But I shook my head, surrendering to the cold bed.

"No."

He left.

I soaked in the silence of the mountains, drawing my fingers through my tangled hair. Phelan had become my greatest alliance while also becoming my greatest threat. And a few strands of auburn now shone among the golden brown of my hair.

37

Imonie had slipped another message beneath my door.

I found it as soon as I woke from my afternoon sleep, still heavy from dreams of Hereswith.

This time, she wrote: *The master of coin?*

I stood and puzzled over it and why she had sent it to me. I contemplated going to her; she and I still needed to talk. But I knew it was too dangerous for me to be in any way associated with her, especially since I had cast my lot with the countess. And I winced whenever I imagined asking Imonie why she'd lied to me all those years. I honestly knew what her answer would be: to protect my father and the life he had built in Bardyllis.

To protect *me*, until the right time came to tell me the truth.

I burned her message, as I had with the one the day before. I couldn't risk having them lying around my room, and as I watched the parchment curl into ash, I realized what she was trying to tell me.

She wanted me to take the throne. And she must be doubting the duke's—*the master of coin's*—agreement with my father to support my claim.

I threw on my charm of stealth and walked the corridors, my eyes keen to find the duke. I eventually located him in the fortress's garden, meandering among tangles of shrubs. I stood behind the courtyard doors and watched him through the glass windowpanes. He paused to gaze at the astounding view that rolled beyond the garden walls—an overlook of the mountain city of Ulla, built in tiers with houses of stone. Abandoned and empty now, with nature overtaking it.

I needed to speak with him, but I couldn't do it in the open, where the countess might see.

I hastened to the duke's chambers. His door was locked, but I picked it easily enough with a charm. I settled in a chair where I had clear vantage of the door, my stealth still cloaking me, and waited.

A quarter of an hour later, the door opened.

The duke entered the chamber, wholly unaware of my presence. If he had been more attentive, he might have noticed the odd wrinkle against the wall panel. A break in the pattern. But as my luck had it, he was too preoccupied.

I gave him a moment to cross the floor. He came to a stop before the mirror, and he gazed at himself. From where I was positioned, I could only catch half of his true face in the reflection.

He was old. Much older than his disguise. His hair was long and silver, his face pale and crinkled as parchment. There was a scar on his brow, and a beard covered his face, gleaming like frost.

He sighed.

I understood a fraction of that feeling, and I watched as he turned to his refreshment table, as he poured a glass of water.

The cup was halfway to his lips when my voice broke the silence.

"The water is poisoned, Your Grace."

The duke startled.

He dropped the glass and I watched it shatter, the harmless water spilling across the floor. I released my charm as he turned, finding me instantly sitting in the chair against the wall.

"Miss Neven," he said, and he somehow managed to sound pleased to see me. Although he was an exquisite pretender. "You have taken me by surprise."

"Forgive me, Your Grace. I thought it best that I give you warning."

"And who seeks to poison me?" he asked, glancing down at the puddle.

"I will tell you, but only if you honestly answer two of my questions first."

He laughed, a deep robust sound. "Very well, Miss Neven. Come, why don't you take a seat next to me, and we can share what little bread and meat I have remaining, unless it is poisoned as well?"

I rose and joined him at the table, but I declined the meal.

"Your food is safe, but I'm not hungry."

He nodded but seemed to hesitate before breaking the brown loaf. "Ask your first question, Miss Neven."

I waited until he had taken a bite. "Do you want the new moon curse to end?"

"Of course I do," he answered, but he spoke too swiftly. "The nightmares have haunted us long enough in Bardyllis. My people are weary of them. They are a great inconvenience every month."

"Even if the dream tax fills your coffers?"

He narrowed his eyes at me but took another bite of bread. "That tax not only serves the betterment of the land, but pays magicians like you, Miss Neven. Do you want to do such dangerous work for free?"

"Wardens deserve to be paid," I said. "But the tax on dreams is excessive and unnecessary."

"I suppose that means you are in favor of breaking this curse, Miss Neven," he stated. "At the cost of losing your profession and income."

"I'm in favor of breaking it," I replied.

I had never imagined I would find myself in the throes of ending the new moon curse, and the duke was right—to see it broken would change my way of life. But I wanted the mountain duchy to be restored. I wanted the realm to be healed. I wanted my father and Imonie to feel less like wraiths and more like humans again.

I wanted to do something beyond fighting nightmares, moon after moon, trapped in a vengeful cycle.

"Then that settles your first question," he said. "Ask your second."

"Who do you support when it comes to new sovereignty?"

"Ah, we have at last reached the meat of the matter," the duke said, and as if to make a point, speared the roast with his fork. "This is not easily answered, Miss Neven. There are many factors at play."

"Such as?"

He chewed, and I knew he was giving himself time to form his answer. "I think the members of the original court have been given our chance and we squandered it, didn't we? I am in favor of one of the children ruling."

"Lennox, Phelan, or Olivette?"

"There is another one."

"Who?"

"Ambrose's daughter." The duke cut another slice of meat. "Clementine Madigan."

"A strange name," I mused.

The duke only arched his brow and ate his roast.

"Well," I said. "Where is this girl?"

"You heard Ambrose the other night at the camp. She's missing."

"Then she is not a candidate for the duchy," I replied simply. "So we shall set her aside. Who, out of the three present, would you support?"

"*You* could also take the throne, Miss Neven. We talked about this before. One doesn't need a claim to rule Seren, although it does help garner approval and protection."

And that was when it hit me: what I wanted, and what I didn't. I stared at the duke and said, "I don't want to rule."

"Very well." He sighed and set down his fork. "You know of my investment."

"You speak of Phelan." Who was a human, not a sum of money. But I held that comment between my teeth.

"Phelan is for Bardyllis. I only need his signature on the papers to officially deem him as my heir."

"Are he and Lennox your sons?"

The duke didn't seem shocked by my blatant query. He only smiled and said, "You are not the first to wonder that. But no. They are not."

"You must have some agreement with the countess, then," I said, and watched how his expression shifted. It was only a minute change, but enough to inform me that I had struck a nerve. "And that agreement must have been forged long ago, because it seems as if the two of you don't see eye to eye now."

"The countess has always been ambitious," he answered. "I've known her her whole life. She only makes decisions that serve her interest in the end. Phelan as duke is one of them, because she thinks he is her weaker son. She thinks she can manipulate him and rule through him. And you see . . . she has always wanted to rule. She never got over the insult that her brother was deemed more fit to be duke, and not her. Ever since then, she craved power."

"Then who do you think she wants to see rule the mountains?" I dared to ask. "She was the one who was so keen on seeing this curse overturned."

"My dear girl," the duke said, and reached for my hand. "*She* wants to rule the mountains. She always has. A century has not changed that ambition of hers."

I slipped my hand away from his hold. "But the nightmare must be broken before she can claim the throne."

"And her two sons are wardens, aren't they?" he said. "She will have Phelan and Lennox break the dream and she will claim the right to rule."

I was quiet for a moment. And then I said, "Do you want to see her reign?"

"I have already told you that I think our court has had its moment."

"Then would you support Olivette Wolfe? Or Nura Sparrow?"

He chuckled. "Olivette has made it quite clear she wants nothing to do with the mountains. She is Bardyllis, through and through. As for her partner . . . I fear I do not know much about her to say if I would support her claim or not."

He wasn't wrong. I sensed Olivette was uncomfortable here. She longed to return to Endellion. I sensed Nura did, too. And it didn't feel right to put such weight and responsibility on them now, not when Olivette was still reeling from her father's secrets and had been wounded by a nightmare. Not when both girls had outright said *I don't want it.*

"You dislike Lennox?" the duke asked.

I did my best to keep my face neutral. "He's not who I envision for the mountains."

"But Phelan is."

"Yes."

The duke sighed. "As I said, Miss Neven, he is—"

"For Bardyllis," I finished the phrase. "And Bardyllis is a well-established province. Anyone could be polished and trained to be sovereign over it, to inherit the land from you. But that is not so when it comes to Seren. Its people have been scattered for a hundred years. Its fortress has been abandoned. Its court broken and cursed." I paused, hoping my words were finding their mark with the duke. *The master of coin.* "I don't know how long you've been disguised, Lord Deryn. I don't even know your true name, and I won't ask for it. But I want you to consider releasing Phelan from Bardyllis and supporting his claim for Seren. You say he is your heir, and yet your blood is of the mountains, not of the meadows and the coast. This fortress was your first home, Your Grace. Remember where you have come from."

He was pensive, listening. I wondered how easy he would be to sway, if he would remain faithful to the bargain he had agreed to with my father, or if he would shift course. I knew my wisest action was to let him simmer on what I had said.

I rose from the table.

"Take the remainder of the day to mull it over," I said. "But if you do decide to join me in supporting Phelan's claim, come to the hall at sunset and raise your glass to me."

"I shall consider it, Miss Neven," he said with a nod. "Now, then. Who sent you to poison me?"

I began to walk to the door, but I turned to regard him one final time. I caught a glimpse of his true reflection in the mirror.

An old, shrewd man was he.

But two could play that game.

"The countess, of course," I said, and departed without another word.

38

Eventide fell.

I began to prepare for the night. I washed my face and braided my hair, hiding the auburn strands. I donned a plaid skirt, a fresh chemise, and a black bodice to lace over it. The clothes I felt most comfortable in. I drew my stockings up to my knees and put on my boots, my dagger tucked in its hiding place, and then ate the meal that appeared on my table. Pumpernickel bread and a roasted hen and water still cold from a mountain stream.

I was one of the first to reach the hall that night.

The Vesper brothers were present, leaning against one of the trestle tables. I made a point to avoid looking at Lennox, but my gaze drifted to Phelan. He was already looking at me; I took three deep breaths before I broke our stare, walking the length of the hall.

Every minute that passed heightened my worry. The potential

manifestation of Phelan's dreams was the root of it, but there was also the possibility of my parents' dreams, or Imonie's, or even Mazarine's to expose me. I didn't know if they dreamt of me or not, and it made me anxious.

As soon as I thought about Papa, he appeared in the hall, dressed in his best and prepared to fight. I shared one fleeting glance with him, and then we both ignored each other.

Nura and Olivette did not arrive, and I presumed they were resting that night, safe in their bedchamber.

I watched the last of the light fade through the windows and was surprised to see the duke enter the hall, just as I'd requested. He held a glass of water, and he meandered over to Phelan and Lennox, speaking a few words with them.

Perhaps he had only come here to taunt me. But then the duke met my gaze from across the hall and lifted his glass to me.

I acknowledged him with a bow of my head, just before he departed.

Alliances were not carved in stone, it seemed.

Phelan noticed our exchange, but only because I was never far from his attention. And I couldn't help but notice his every detail in return. The garments that fit him perfectly: fawn-brown trousers and knee-high boots, a waistcoat embroidered with the phases of the moon, a cravat, a black tailed jacket, and a rapier sheathed at his belt. His dark hair was loose, just as I preferred.

The countess entered the hall next, to my shock. She wore an ink-black dress with a fur draped diagonally across her body, cinched tightly at her waist with a belt of gold. A dagger was sheathed at her hip. I wondered why she was there—she was a magician, but not a warden—and I made my way over to Phelan's side after Lennox had vacated their table.

"Your mother is planning to fight tonight?" I asked.

"She plans to watch," Phelan replied. "But your—" He caught himself, clearing his throat. "Mr. Madigan is joining us, I see."

"Yes," I said, keeping my voice low. "I hear he was once a great warden."

"I believe he still is," Phelan said gently.

"Phelan," I whispered, and I wanted to ask if he would claim the chair should the dream break tonight. He was the hope of the mountains, because Olivette and Nura didn't desire it, and Lennox was crooked in heart, and I was full of contradictions and lies. But I lost my courage; the words wilted within me.

He waited, but his mother approached us, and the moment was lost.

"Ah, I am glad to see you here tonight, Anna," the countess said.

"Yes, Lady Raven," I replied. "I'm ready to fight beside Phelan, per usual."

She smiled, but the warmth failed to reach her eyes. "May I have a word with you, my son? Over here with your brother?"

Phelan released a soft sigh, one that I knew expressed his reluctance, but he accompanied his mother back across the hall to where Lennox stood.

I took note of the three of them, plotting in a shadowy corner. My father, who walked the aisle alone. And then there was me, caught between the two, full of hope and doubt and plans of my own.

The night arrived at last. The shadows in the hall sweetened until the multiple hearths ignited with enchanted flame, casting streams of light across the floor.

It took a while for the throne to materialize on the dais. But once it appeared, Emrys arrived to stand beside it like a magistrate at court, and the nightmare was not long to follow.

I watched the hall shift, molting its tables and benches and heraldic banners. The floors rippled into white marble with threads of blue; the timber beams in the ceiling sank to become arched and coffered. Chandeliers bloomed, glittering with silver leaves and candles.

I recognized this place. It was the ballroom at the countess's mansion in Endellion.

I glanced across the way to look at Lady Raven. Her face was stark, her eyes wide with dread.

This was one of her dreams.

I hung back at its edge and watched.

The phantom countess stood in the center of the ballroom, and beside her was a man, tall and trim with thick dark hair. He reminded me of Phelan, and I knew this was her brother, the Duke of Seren. The magician who had cursed this court and the new moon, whose bones now gleamed beneath his bed.

The phantom countess startled to see him. "What are you doing here, Isidore?"

"You are not pleased to see me, sister? Not even in dreams?"

She was quiet, but I saw how she traced her belt, seeking the hilt of her dagger.

Isidore noticed and smiled, fearless of her. "You cannot kill me in this realm."

"I was not seeking to."

"Then what is this blood on your hands?" he asked.

The countess glanced down to see she had smeared blood on her dress. She held up her hands, and they trembled as blood dripped from her fingers and gathered on the floor, inch deep.

"Shall we see all the people you have killed, and those you hope to end?" drawled Isidore, and with a sweep of his hand, more people appeared in the ballroom.

There were ten victims in total, counting the Duke of Seren, and I didn't recognize any of them, but the air grew tense when they looked at the countess, the woman who had set their deaths in motion. I saw a flash of red hair, long and loose and wild, as a girl walked across the ballroom through the blood.

I felt a stitch in my side when I saw her face.

It was me.

Clem.

And I didn't know why I was in the countess's dream. Not until I stood beside the Duke of Seren and the truth sank into me like a blade.

The countess planned to kill me.

I glanced around the nightmare, seeking Phelan. I couldn't locate him among the fantastical gleam of our surroundings, but I longed more than anything to behold his face in that moment. To see if he had known of his mother's plans.

Whatever else the dream had in store was altered, because Lennox stepped forward to walk among the victims, his rapier drawn and his hand up, ready to cast. He should have been more patient, I thought with gritted teeth. Now he had interrupted the nightmare, and it would run its own reactive course. I would never know how the countess's dream truly ended, if she succeeded in killing me.

But perhaps it didn't matter. Lennox was focused on Clem; he wove his way through the victims to reach her, and I realized that she wore the golden jewel around her neck, just as Anna had the night before. The weakness was me and my stone heart, and I swallowed a curse, irritated that the dreams here seemed fixated on exposing my secret.

Phelan appeared, trailing his brother. "What are you doing, Lee?"

Lennox paused to glance over his shoulder. "She is the key to breaking this dream. Don't you see it?"

Phelan gazed at Clem. His eyes were dark and filled with longing, and I wondered what thoughts ravaged him as he looked at my phantom.

Clem was silent and pale, rooted to the bloody floor like a statue. The sight of her stillness made me nervous, and I took a step deeper into the dream.

"This is not her, you know," Lennox taunted, sensing his brother's attachment, and prepared to pierce Clem's chest with the tip of his rapier.

"Wait, Lee!" Phelan struggled through the crowd, who began to turn on him. The peaceful guise of the ballroom shattered, and Phelan had no choice but to divert his attention to defend himself.

My father stepped forward, entering the fray. I watched him strike down one of the countess's victims with a beam of light. He cut the Duke of Seren in half, unrepentant, and Isidore gasped, melting into smoke.

The countess must have been waiting for her brother to be conquered, for she interfered at last, her face flushed from the mortification of watching her dream on display. She ignored the phantom of herself and the teeming violence, and withdrew the dagger from her belt.

"Kill her," she ordered Lennox, nodding at Clem.

My eyes drifted back to Clem, and my body coiled with energy, preparing to impede the countess should the dream break. I watched this phantom of myself, who continued to stand, docile and gentle, and I wondered if I would go down quietly, if I would do nothing while Lennox attacked me.

Lennox drew back his sword, preparing to strike Clem.

And she waited until he had begun his forward thrust, the rapier glinting in the light. She moved her hand in a terribly familiar way, a movement I had performed many times, and her magic caught the blade before it could pierce her breast. The rapier submitted to her, bending back on itself to sting its wielder, and Lennox went wide-eyed in shock, emitting a scream as his own blade punctured his shoulder.

How pleased I was in that moment.

I stood in the shadows and watched with satisfaction as Clem flicked her fingers and hurled Lennox back. He landed on the floor with a groan, his rapier still lodged in his shoulder, and he mewled in pain, blood soaking his clothes.

The countess turned bug-eyed, glancing between her son and Clem.

"Phelan!" she cried, shrill. "Come and finish this."

Phelan's clothes were shredded. There was blood splattered across his waistcoat and hands, although I didn't believe it was his. His hair was tousled, dark threads of it framing his face. He stopped fighting, and I could tell he was weary by his shoulders, how they curved inward. His old wounds must be hurting him.

"Come here," the countess said, sharper, and he obeyed.

Phelan walked to her in a heavy gait. My father continued to fight the remaining phantoms in the dream, but his attention was now split, divided between what he battled and the sight of Phelan approaching his daughter.

"Go on," Lady Raven prompted. "This is yours to vanquish."

Phelan stared at Clem, his breaths ragged. He held up his rapier, pointing to her heart, to that promise of gold. The nightmare's fault line.

He froze in that stance, but his arm quivered.

Gradually, he lowered his sword and said, "I cannot do this."

"Yes, you can," his mother encouraged him. "This is just a phantom. Whatever power this girl holds over you . . . now is the time to break free, Phelan."

He took a step nearer to Clem, unable to look away from her.

From me, I thought, and a warning rang deep in my bones.

I moved silently, drawing closer. Blood soaked the hem of my skirt. It rippled in my wake, and yet no one noticed my approach. No one but my father, who had finished slaying the rest of the dream's phantoms and was sore for breath.

I wasn't sure what to expect from Clem, if she would treat Phelan with the same regard as she had Lennox. My stomach clenched when Phelan gently reached out to her.

I saw the shift in her expression, the cold glitter in her eyes. There was no love, no forgiveness, no mercy within her. Vengeance had devoured those parts of her, scraped her clean, and she was hollow, so endlessly hollow. I felt an echo of that emptiness as Clem prepared to strike Phelan down, her magic gathering.

He stiffened and inhaled a sharp breath, his realization coming a moment too late.

I lunged forward and cast a shield. My magic came between them, absorbing the brunt of force that had been directed at Phelan. The shock of my interference rocked all three of us, and we stumbled back a few paces, our surroundings rumbling in response. A crack formed in the floor, and the blood began to drain through it, filling the ballroom with a perpetual trickling sound.

I regained my balance and stood a few paces away, my hand aching. I watched as Clem likewise straightened her willowy frame. Auburn hair tangled across her face like a net. I remembered that feeling; I could nearly sense it over my own face. Her eyes met mine over the fissure and blood and shadows and firelight, and she smiled, as if she had been waiting all along for me to appear.

"Anna!" the countess cried in relief. "Thank gods, dear one. Finish what my sons cannot. Break this dream, Anna, and I will extravagantly reward you."

I hardly paid her any attention. I was focused on Clem. I stepped over the crack in the floor, into her striking range. We circled each other, prey and predator, girl and phantom. I was both, and yet I felt like neither. My emotions were snarled, cold and hot feelings entwined together, radiating a pleasant numbness in my chest.

How was I to defeat her? I knew her arsenal of spells. As she knew mine.

Clem at last came to a halt.

I mirrored her motions.

Over the slender slope of her shoulder, I saw the dais behind her. The throne, gleaming like it was carved from bones, and Emrys standing beside it, watching me with wicked amusement. And then the countess walked into that view, waiting on the dais stairs. She was positioning herself, I realized. As soon as I broke this dream, she would claim the sovereignty of the mountains.

And more than anything . . . I didn't want to bend the knee to her. I didn't want to see her sit on that throne.

I held Clem's stare, and I knew she saw the cascade of my thoughts. My desire for her to take victory over the dream.

She nodded and lifted her hand toward Lady Raven. Down went the countess, with a shriek and a tumble. She lay prostrate on the stairs, frozen. Had my phantom just killed her?

There was no time for me to wonder. Clem pivoted and shot a spell at Lennox next, even though he was still writhing along the floor, wounded. He went limp as a rag doll, limbs splayed out.

Phelan, I thought, and panicked. I took a step toward him, the phantom's spell grazing my ear. The enchantment hit him square in the chest, and I watched, wide-eyed, as a trail of blood began to flow from his nose. He sank to his knees, his gaze fastened to me. I was the last thing he saw as he surrendered to the floor.

And then my father, who was swift, but not swift enough when the nightmare was his daughter. He could have struck Clem down; he could have broken the dream. But he hesitated, and she took advantage of that moment. Down he went, like a folding house of cards.

I stared, stricken, at his unconscious form. Blood also trickled from his nose.

I tried to convince myself this was just a dream; they weren't dead. But a wave of devastation broke over me, and pain sparked from my chest up to my neck. As if I had been branded. Hissing, I touched my throat. My fingertips traced sleek marks, embedded in my skin.

"The throne is yours for the taking," said Clem. "I will concede, but only to you."

I stared at her. Before I knew it, I struck her down with a spell, aiming for her heart. She melted into smoke, into oblivion, and I realized on shaking legs that I had just vanquished the nightmare.

My eyes drifted to the dais. To the throne, where Emrys continued to wait. He held out his hand, inviting me to take the chair.

I took a step closer to it. Suddenly, it was all I could see, all I desired. I walked through blood, stepped over the countess's body, and I was rising, rising to take it. All the things I could do, all the things I could change.

My ambition was broken by Emrys, whose gaze flickered beyond me, as if someone else had entered the hall. I paused on the steps; a warning crept over my skin. Someone was following me.

I spun to see who it was but was met by the blur of a shield, swinging to knock me off my feet. Pain bloomed across my skull, burst behind my eyes.

And down I went. Deep into the darkness.

It was peaceful; the darkness held me like a vise. But when the light started to creep in, I was met by a sea of strange sensations.

Cold fingers tracing my face. Cold fingers on my neck, covering my throat.

A ring of voices, calling a name that sparked nothing within me. *Anna? Anna!*

A pant of breath, breaking through the watery commotion, saying, "No, let me take her. She's mine."

Arms carrying me, up into the clouds. Down into the depths of the mountain. A soft fur and bed and the crackle of fire. The smell of pine and meadow grass.

"Clem."

It was Phelan, trying to rouse me.

My head felt split open. My chest wept with pain.

"Get the dagger out," I whispered to him, but I couldn't open my eyes or show him where I hurt.

"*Clem.*"

I drifted away from him and his hands, down into a place where not even dreams could reach.

39

When I woke, my memories were scrambled.

It was afternoon again, but the light was icy and tinged in blue, as if a storm brewed beyond the windows. I was lying on a bed of furs, Phelan close beside me. I watched his chest rise and fall as he dozed. Slowly, I put the pieces together, and I remembered what had led me here, shut away in his room with a splitting headache.

The moment I moved, he woke.

"Easy, Clem."

"I want to sit forward," I croaked, and he eased me up. The world spun, and I fought a wave of nausea, settling against the wooden headboard. "How long have I been asleep?"

"For several hours." Phelan moved off the bed to stir the fire in the hearth and pour me a cup of water. He brought it to me, and I took long, greedy drafts. "It's about noon now, although the snow is making it difficult to tell time."

I glanced out the window, struck by the haunting beauty of the snow as it fell. I watched its dance for a moment longer, until I raised my hand to feel the back of my head. There was a tender lump, hidden in my snarled hair.

"Who hurt you, Clem?" Phelan asked.

"It wasn't the nightmare," I replied. "Someone struck me."

I didn't tell him that I had been ascending to take the throne. Or that I had stepped over his mother's prone form to do it.

I remembered the blur of wood and steel, just before impact. I hadn't been struck by a spell, but by a shield. Something of the physical world. Had it been the duke? Or had it been someone like Mr. Wolfe?

My suspicions stirred. Whoever had rendered me unconscious didn't want the curse to end; if they had, they would have taken the throne, instead of leaving it empty until the sun rose and the chair vanished along with Emrys, waiting for evening to reappear.

Phelan was quiet. His silence drew my eyes to him, and he studied me with a frown.

"What's wrong?"

"You're changing, Clem."

"How do you mean?" My heart gave a nervous twitch, as if he sensed the shadows gathering within me. But he only sat on the edge of the bed and caressed my hair.

"There's more auburn in your hair now. And your neck . . ." His fingers traced my throat. "The gill scars have returned."

I swallowed and touched the sleek scars. "I saw my phantom strike you and my father down, and I thought you both were dead."

Phelan's hand drifted from me. "Not dead, but in a painful sleep. I don't think I care to encounter your dream form again anytime soon."

He was teasing me, but my face felt too stiff for a smile.

"Did you know that your mother wants to kill me, Phelan?"

"No, Clem. I swear that I didn't know she wanted to see you dead. And even if I had known, if she had told me the full extent of her plans, I would have *never* revealed you to her."

My thoughts hung on his words. *Revealed you to her.*

I looked at him, saw the crushed hope and anguish within his eyes. "But you told me to *hold my act*. You have held my secret as your own, playing this charade alongside me. So you must have come to realize that she planned me harm, or else it wouldn't have mattered if I was Anna."

He briefly covered his mouth with his hand as if deep in thought, but when he met my gaze once more, I saw that I had spoken truth.

"Clem . . ."

"Tell me the truth, Phelan," I said. "I'm sick of people lying to me. And if you can't be honest . . . you and I are done being partners."

He drew a sharp breath. "Then let there be no more lies between us, Clem. I knew she wanted to keep tabs on you and your father after you left Hereswith. She told me to find you. I didn't know why and I didn't question her. But I should have. I didn't know she wanted to harm you, not until she told me the entirety of her plans."

"When you came home and trashed the library."

"You'll never let me forget it, will you?" he countered with a slight smile. But the mirth faded as he continued, "I couldn't bear to see anything happen to you. Yes, I told you to hold the act, and I've been carrying it alongside you, because I don't care for my mother's plans."

His voice held a tremor, one that made me think his heart was beating in his throat. He slid off the bed and sank to his knees.

"You told me to get on my knees before you and apologize," he said. "This is me saying I'm sorry, for all that I have done to you, for all the heartache I have caused, for giving you no choice but to resort to the wildest of plans to ease the pain I wrought. I don't deserve your forgiveness, but this one thing I seek, so that I may remain near you."

I must have stared at him for a long, excruciating moment, because he whispered my name. I shifted across the mattress, sitting on the edge of the bed before him, my feet touching the floor. I still was afraid to speak—even his name might break me—and I took his face in my hands.

Phelan's arms came around me. "Tell me what you want me to do," he said. "Tell me to leave, and I will."

My fingers slid into his hair. "Stay," I whispered.

He kissed the shine of scars on my neck. His fingers traced the curve of my back as he kissed my collarbones, down to where my heart pounded a stilted dance of flesh trying to break away from stone, and stone determined to hold fast.

Whatever came tonight, I hoped it ushered the end. For I didn't know how much longer I could withstand this veneer.

"Why does your mother want to kill me?" I asked, to dampen the embers flaring between us.

Phelan leaned back so he could look up at me. His hands drifted to my hips, a warm, possessive touch. "You're a threat to her."

"In what way?"

"You're Ambrose Madigan's daughter. Emrys Madigan's niece. The blood of the mountains runs through you." He paused, but his dark eyes measured mine. "You're a strong contender for the sovereign claim of Seren."

I snorted. "And so are you and Lennox. And so is Olivette."

"My mother doesn't see Olivette as a threat."

"Are you certain, Phelan? Perhaps you should still warn Nura."

He pressed his lips together but nodded. "Yes, you're right. I should warn them both. But Mr. Wolfe is devoted to my mother. She gave him favor and protection in the era before the curse and I don't see him turning against her now. I have no doubt he will support my mother's claim to sovereignty."

"And do you?" I countered. "Do you support your mother's claim?"

"No."

This is the moment, I thought. The moment I told him what I hoped for. Who I wanted to see bring life back to these mountains.

There was a knock on the door.

Phelan stiffened. He eased my hair forward, so that it flowed over my shoulders, concealing the auburn strands as well as the scars in my neck. Reluctantly, he went to answer the door.

It was the countess. She stood on the threshold, holding a platter of roasted hen.

"What is it, Mother?" he asked, sounding just as surprised as I felt.

Lady Raven glanced at me, her eyes as cold as the snow drifting beyond the window. "I hope you have recovered from last night, Anna."

"You're interrupting her rest, Mother."

"She has been resting for hours, and in case you forgot, Phelan . . . *all* of us suffered a hard night," Lady Raven stated. "I would like to speak to Anna alone."

"I don't think—"

"It's all right, Phelan," I said.

He didn't want to leave me alone with his mother. I read the lines in his brow, the set of his jaw. I noticed how his hands clenched and released as he strode past the countess, out into the shadows of the corridor.

As I felt the draft of his leaving, I wondered if she had discovered my deceit. If she knew who I was beneath my guise.

Perhaps the countess had come to kill me.

Lady Raven kicked the door shut. She crossed the chamber to set the platter of hen down on the table.

"You shouldn't have troubled yourself, lady," I said.

"Oh, this is not for you," she replied. "It is for the troll."

I blinked. "The one called Mazarine?"

"Yes. Brin of Stonefall."

I hadn't seen Mazarine since the day we'd arrived. She had kept to herself in her chambers. I often forgot about her presence.

"The duke tried to poison me early this morning," the countess said, brusque.

"He did?"

"Yes. And so the time has come for me to finally rid myself of him."

"Are you certain it was the duke?"

"He is no duke," she all but snarled. "He is a master of coin, and his greed knows no bounds. It took me nearly eighty years to locate him after the curse. That was the extent of his desire to never be found."

"How were you able to find him, lady?"

"My sons," she replied, glancing at me. "The duke, who was close friends with my late husband, treated my boys as his own when they were born. When his wife died and he remained childless, he began to lavish great gifts upon us. Particularly Phelan, who needed intensive schooling to amount to anything."

I held my tongue, although I burned to give a retort. I thought of Phelan's self-deprecation on the first new moon we had fought together. How he believed himself unworthy of his title and magic, even though he had striven twice as hard as me to earn the illumination.

"Three years ago," she continued, oblivious to my ire, "the duke approached me about naming Phelan as his heir, the future Duke of Bardyllis. And I do not know why, but it roused my suspicions.

It took me another two years to fully understand that this was not Lord Deryn but my old companion from the mountain, and that he must also know where Brin of Stonefall was hiding herself, for as the spymistress of Seren she once wielded the ancient and hazardous magic of guises."

Hold your act. I heard Phelan's voice in my memory. *Hold your act. . . .*

But how close the countess was to uncovering me. I felt as if I walked on glass.

"So you desire to kill the duke for vengeance, because he evaded and deceived you for so long?" I asked.

"I desire to kill him because he is going to oppose the curse breaking," she said. "He does not want to see the Seren court reinstated. He does not want to see the new moon nightmares come to an end. It is too lucrative for him, this business of taxing dreams."

Her words sank into me slowly, like a long knife, and for a moment I wavered, overcome with doubt. The duke said he would support me as well as Phelan. And yet the countess believed he would oppose anyone claiming the sovereignty.

I felt her gaze, an icy assessment of my demeanor, and I rallied, focusing on her.

"So you want to bribe Mazarine with a chicken?"

The countess smiled, as if I were some adorable, dense creature. "No, child. The hen is poisoned. And once Mazarine falls, her magic crumbles. The master of coin will lose his guise as duke, and then he will have nothing. No title, no prowess, no fortune. He will have no choice but to support my plans to end this curse."

"Oh," I said. "A brilliant move, Countess."

"Indeed. Now, deliver the chicken to Mazarine. But do not rush away. Delay and talk to her, to ensure she begins to eat it. Trolls are vain creatures, and they like stories and shrewd company. You will do fine, Anna." Lady Raven was obviously scared of Mazarine. And she was sending me in her stead.

"I'm not in danger from this troll, am I, lady?"

The countess opened the door and looked at me. Another one of her pitying expressions. "No, my dear. So long as you give her the hen." She took a step over the threshold but then paused.

I braced myself, my hand eager to find my dagger, hidden in my boot.

"Oh, and Anna?" she added, just before she departed. "Last night, you hesitated, and the nightmare got the best of you. See that you don't let it happen again."

40

Ten minutes later, I knocked on Mazarine's door with a headache and a chicken. She had chosen a room in the northern wing of the fortress, where the colder, darker chambers sat with minimal sunshine and an interior view of the mountains.

"Who knocks?" she growled through the iron-latticed wood.

"It's Anna Neven," I replied, balancing the platter of hen.

I heard her footsteps as she approached the door. The multiple locks turning. And then I stood face-to-face with her, and a frightening smile lit her face. Her yellow teeth flashed like amber.

"Anna," she crooned. "It has been a while. Do come in."

I entered, struck at once by the abundance of candlelight and the heavy scent of moss and damp stone that filled her chamber. Her windows were open, and snow was swirling into the room. The temperature was frigid.

"Careful," she warned. "The floor is slick in some places. And mortal bones are quick to fracture."

I took heed of her warning and set the platter down on the table, which was scattered with chicken bones, all split and sucked dry. I felt her presence trailing me like a shadow.

"And what is this?" she asked.

"A gift from the countess," I replied.

"Ah, my old beloved enemy," said the troll, bending her head close to the hen. She sniffed it, her nose scrunching in distaste.

"It's poisoned," I said.

"Any fool could smell it and come to that conclusion," Mazarine said, straightening. "Why does she poison me?"

"She wants to use you to strike at the duke, who I suppose I should begin calling the master of coin."

"Ah, I see. Her ambition never ceases to amaze me." She studied me closer, one eye smaller than the other. "And you are involved with the heiress?"

"For now."

"You have surprised and delighted me, mortal girl."

"How so?"

"You have used your guise to the greatest advantage. You find yourself in a dangerous game to secure a new sovereign, and yet you move effortlessly. Tell me, does your stone heart still hold true, unmovable as this mountain?"

"I've guarded it well," I carefully replied, but I could still taste Phelan's lips on mine. I still saw him on his knees before me, captivated. I still heard the way he said my name.

"Time will tell, won't it?" Mazarine said, as if she sensed the cracks in me.

"May I ask you a question?"

"Perhaps."

I took that as a yes. I held her beady gaze and asked, "Can I trust the duke? The master of coin?"

"Hmm." She drummed her fingers on the table, her long nails clicking on the wood. "Can you trust him, you ask. He often says one thing and does another in secret. Who do you think spread rumors of how great the cruel duke was a century ago? And yet who bribed the guard at the duke's door the night of the assassination? The master of coin. But who promised the master of coin an endless cave of jewels and gold once she reigned? The heiress, who you call countess."

Her answer did nothing to bolster my reassurance. The duke might be playing me, or he could be genuine, eager to see the countess's ultimate plans dashed.

"Does that answer your query, mortal girl?"

"Yes."

"But there is another question in your eyes. Speak it, Clementine of Hereswith. I will answer with truth."

It was so cold in this room I could see my breath, and the snow was swirling, gathering in my hair. And yet I had never felt more alive than at that moment.

"Will you support Phelan if he takes the throne?"

She must have been expecting this question, because she answered it smoothly. "I support *you*."

"But I'm not a worthy contender."

"You are a daughter of the mountain, even beneath the veil of my magic." Mazarine began to walk a circle around me. "You have crept into my stone of a heart and softened me, to my immense dismay and utter astonishment. I would support your claim without fail, but if you forgo it yourself, I would support your choice of sovereign."

She rendered me speechless.

And it pleased her. She came to a halt before me, studying my face. "I always knew you would help guide us home."

"What do you mean?" I asked.

"I used to watch the world spin from my third-story windows in Hereswith," Mazarine began. "Time does not feel the same to me as it does to you; minutes are long and empty, and seasons feel endless. Yet I was patient. I was waiting. Waiting for someone to come along to set things in motion. The moment I saw that red hair of yours—you were eight, skipping along the street beside your father—I knew that you would be that change. Ambrose would never want it, of course. I could smell his fear every new moon; he wanted you to lead a normal, safe life despite the bruise our curse had left on your soul. But fathers often underestimate their daughters, don't they?"

Her words roused emotion in me. *How ironic*, I thought, *if I crack and crumble right here and now, at her feet.* The one who had disguised me.

She must have sensed it. She took hold of my chin, her fingers frigid against the flush of my cheeks. Her long nails bit into my skin, reminding me to be careful. To bury my feelings. "Take care tonight, Clementine. The end draws nigh and many of us are not as we seem."

"Do you know who struck me last night?"

"I was not watching the hall," she replied, releasing me. "But the smith is wholly devoted to the heiress, in case you did not know."

And she picked up the countess's platter of hen and tossed it out the open window.

I walked the fortress corridors after my meeting with Mazarine, finding my way into the Duke of Seren's abandoned chambers. The suite that Anna in the dream had guided me to.

It was a different experience to see this chamber in the daylight. The walls were wainscoted with painted oak panels. A massive tapestry dressed one wall, and the marble hearth held a heap of ashes. There were four large windows curtained with red damask and a set of balcony doors that remained wide open, ushering in wisps of snow. The bed was large and sunken in the middle, framed by a grand headboard carved with mountains and moons, and there was a reading chair in one corner, flanked by bookshelves.

I stopped before the bloodstain on the floor.

I imagined Emrys drawing his blade over the duke's throat, and the duke fighting, clawing for life. It had been a nightmare, a new moon. A bewitching, soul-changing hour.

A mountain wind sighed through the balcony doors. It touched a wardrobe in the corner, whose carven doors were slightly ajar. Something silver flashed within, and I stepped around the blood and snow to behold the heart of the wardrobe.

The knight's armor hung within.

I stared at it a moment, remembering it from Elle Fielding's dream, from the nights I had fought beside Phelan.

I reached out to trace its steel. A chill raced up my arm.

"Even now, you are not afraid."

The voice took me by surprise. I spun to see Emrys standing a few paces away from me, the stain of blood between us, holding gravity like a hole in the floor.

I took a frantic step away from the wardrobe, but I felt trapped. The balcony was at my back, but my uncle was impeding my path to the corridor.

"Forgive me," I said in a calm voice. "I shouldn't have wandered here."

"I seek no apologies," he replied. Even his voice was like my father's—deep and gentle. A rumble of thunder. "You are free to explore this place, niece."

I tensed.

Emrys seemed to know the cause of it, because he glanced over his shoulder to look at the open doorway and then said, "Rest assured. No one comes near this suite but me. And now you, I suppose. We can speak freely here."

I struggled to believe him. Someone could be lingering just outside the door, eavesdropping. Someone like the countess or Lennox . . .

But I drew in a deep breath and calmed the flutter of my pulse.

"Do you take delight in harming magicians on the new moon?"

He grimaced. "Ah, I was waiting for you to bring that up. My sincerest apologies, Clementine. I did not know it was you."

"It doesn't matter if you knew it was me or not."

"Oh, but it does," Emrys countered. "You are my brother's only child. I would long for death if I had inadvertently killed you."

I didn't know what to say in response. I glanced around the room, looking at anything but him. My terrible, murderous uncle.

"Imonie told me a story about you."

"Did she?" He sounded amused. "Which one, Clementine?"

"I prefer Clem."

"Very well. *Clem.*"

I met his gaze, for he had not taken his eyes from me, as if measuring the depth of my guise. "She told me how you were abandoned on her doorstep one summer night. How she disliked babies but she came to love you both. One of you was quiet and intellectual, the other wild and reckless."

"I take it you have discovered which one your father is?"

"Yes, I believe that I know," I said, but I didn't share my thoughts with him. "Have you spoken to your mother yet?"

"No. Why should I?" he countered. "Imonie fled with all the others and left me to my fate."

"A fate you carved for yourself. In this very room."

"That may be, but they say a mother's love is unconditional."

I fell silent, unwilling to argue with him. But my gaze wandered back to the suit of armor. The bloodstains marring the steel.

"You wounded Phelan twice on the new moon," I said. "Why him? Why not Lennox?"

"Wounded, yes, but I did not kill him," Emrys replied. "Nor would I have. I knew Phelan was important to his mother as well as the master of coin. To strike him would be to strike them both, which was quite effective in getting the court to return home, because here you all are."

I was quiet again, pensive.

"Clem," he said. "Clem, do you have no compassion for me? I have carried the curse that the entire court deserved to bear, living alone in this place with nightmares, unable to die, unable to leave. I carried it so the others could lead normal lives despite our collective treachery, and so they did for an entire century. Do you fault me for growing lonely here? For wanting to see the end?"

"I don't begrudge your loneliness, uncle," I said. "But nor do I have compassion for you."

I began to walk around the bloodstain, my posture stiff, as if I expected him to interfere with my departure. He didn't move, not until I was almost to the door, and he turned on his heel.

"Wait, Clem. There is one more thing I would ask you."

I paused.

"I understand that you are close to Lady Raven," Emrys began in a careful tone. "Does the heiress plan to harm your father?"

"If she did, I think he would have appeared in her dream last night," I said.

"As you appeared?"

I nodded. "She dislikes him, but she has set her attention on others in this fortress. Besides, I don't think you truly care about what happens to my father."

Emrys went rigid. "What makes you say that?"

"Have you even spoken to him since he returned?" I asked. "Do you still judge him, resent him for being the one who escaped your fate? So close, you and he once were. So close that Imonie couldn't even tell the two of you apart when you were boys. She said you would take each other's punishments. That is how deep Ambrose's love for you was. And I don't presume to know what it's like to share a face with another. But whatever it is you're holding against my father . . . you should see it settled, before night falls. Because I think he misses you, more than he will ever confess. That's why he became the warden of Hereswith—to be close to the mountain. To be close to *you*."

I had shocked my uncle into silence. But he laid his hand over his heart and said, "As you say, then." He granted me another bow, but I was gone before he could lift his head.

I returned to my bedroom and saw another note had been slipped beneath my door.

The paper unfolded like wings; I stared at the familiar slant of Imonie's handwriting until the words seemed to melt away.

Do not trust your eyes alone.

41

Night arrived with a whisper of snow. It seemed like the fortress had carried Mazarine's words from earlier that day, delivering them down the winding corridors and slipping them under doors like notes. *The end draws nigh.* Because all of us appeared in the hall that night, dressed in our finest and armed for the unknown.

Mr. Wolfe was present with Nura and Olivette, who was much recovered, although her arm was still bandaged. Mazarine sat at one of the tables loudly crunching her chicken bones, much to the countess's chagrin. The countess sat at a table on the opposite side of the hall, close to the dais, of course. Lennox was at her side, pale faced and sullen, the wound in his shoulder bound in swaths of linen. His arm was in a sling. A rapier sat on the table between them, in addition to a crossbow. Phelan was pacing, lost in his thoughts. The duke stood in one corner draped in shadows, as if he was keenly uncomfortable witnessing a nightmare manifest. I caught a glimmer behind him, and realized it was a weapon of some sort, which he must have pilfered from the fortress armory. And then my parents and Imonie. Mama and Imonie took a seat before one of the hearths, but my father remained standing, his gaze expectantly fixed on the dais. Waiting for the throne and his brother to appear.

It seemed to take forever, but I suppose when you are waiting for something to happen, the minutes feel as long and heavy as years.

I stood between shadows and firelight, looking beyond the windows, where the snow froze like lace.

A bittersweet thought crossed my mind.

This might be the last waking nightmare I faced.

As soon as I came to terms with that truth, time flowed swift and true once more, and the throne materialized, limned in fire-light. It quietly beckoned to us all to *come, come and claim me* until a door opened in the wall behind it, and Emrys stepped onto the dais, coming to a rest beside the chair.

This dream arrived gently. I smelled it first—sweet mountain wind, summer grass, cherry galettes still warm from the oven.

A mountain cottage unfurled around us, the walls made of stacked stone, lichens dangling from the thatched roof. The windows were open, inviting rivers of sunshine into the small, simple chamber. There was a kitchen nook with pots and herbs hanging from the rafters, and a worn table that held bowls of abandoned porridge. A few tattered pieces of furniture sat around a hearth.

Books were stacked on a mantel, as was a vase of wildflowers.

I heard the sounds of children playing. Fighting, more like it. One boy laughed, the other began to sob.

And there was Imonie. She appeared in the kitchen of the house, and she was younger, but that scowl still marked her face. She cursed and set down a steaming pan of galettes, following the sound of distress to the back door.

"Boys? *Boys*, inside, now!"

Two auburn-haired boys spilled into the house. They were identical save for the objects they held. One wielded a wooden sword. The other one, the boy who was loudly wailing, held up a book with ripped pages.

"He tore the pages out of it, Mam!"

Imonie's nostrils flared as she looked at the twin with the sword. Her wild one. Emrys.

"Is this true?" she asked him.

"Yes," Emrys replied, solemn.

"Apologize to your brother, then."

Emrys huffed, but he looked at Ambrose and said, "I'm sorry for tearing pages from your book."

The apology did nothing to ease the sting in Ambrose's heart. He retreated to the divan by the hearth and lay facedown on it, weeping into the cushion until he fell asleep.

"You must be gentler, son," Imonie said to Emrys. "What do I tell you every night before bed?"

"To think before I act," Emrys grumbled.

"Give me the sword, then. You will not get to play with it for a week, as punishment," Imonie said, and held out her hand.

Emrys surrendered his wooden sword to her with a sigh.

The scene melted away, instantly replaced with another. The twins were older. They were young men, now—the age my father and Emrys were frozen at—and I struggled to identify who was who as they walked a corridor of the fortress.

"The time is now," one of them whispered. The shadows danced across his face but his eyes were luminous, as if he burned from within.

"Are you certain?"

"Yes."

"When?"

"Raven deems the new moon will be appropriate."

"But what does Lora think? What of your wife?"

"She supports me. She supports this plan."

Silence fell between the brothers. With a pang, I realized that I couldn't identify whose dream this was. If it belonged to my father or to Emrys.

"I will not move forward with these plans, not without you, brother."

A long sigh. "Fine. I will join you, then. I seem destined to keep you out of trouble."

The dream shifted again, pulling us along its currents.

We were in the Duke of Seren's bedchamber. Isidore stood near the foot of his bed, reading a letter by firelight. The night was dark, bitterly cold. Emrys was present, dressed in the blue robes of an advisor. He withdrew a dagger silently, but its blade flashed a warning.

My uncle sliced Isidore's neck.

The duke gasped his name, a name that rose like a hiss of smoke, the sound of a curse sparking—*"Emrys"*—before he sank to his knees, his blood pooling on the floor. Hunched but still breathing, Isidore held out his hand and called to the moon, to nightmares. He cursed his court and died facedown in his blood.

Emrys ran the halls, his heart beating in his throat. A woman with long brown hair and a scar on her face was waiting for him in the courtyard. The stars bled in the sky as she embraced him, and her voice trembled when she said, "We have to go. We cannot stay here." She took the dagger he had slain the duke with and threw it over the balcony. It clattered among the rocky slopes.

The dream took us to the mountain passage, to the opening in the foothills. Two wide doors that I had passed through days ago.

The court was fleeing. I saw them all—the master of coin, the heiress. Mr. Wolfe. Mazarine. My father holding the hand of the woman named Lora. His wife, I realized, and my alarm began to swell.

The only member of the court who could not pass from the mountain was Emrys.

Emrys in his blue robes.

"Come, brother." Ambrose beckoned him, frowning. He stood in the grass and the sun, but his twin remained in the shadows of the passage.

"I cannot, Ambrose," Emrys said. "The mountain holds me captive."

Ambrose passed over the threshold and took his brother's hand, struggling to draw him out, into the light. A sound of pain rose from Emrys. Steam began to rise from his garments, as if he was catching fire.

"Go," he cried, shoving Ambrose into the grass. "Go and forge new lives. I will hold the curse."

The doors closed.

Both Imonie and Ambrose stood in the foothills for a long while, staring at the wooden doors that had sealed. The place where they had been separated from Emrys.

Lora eventually drew my father away, but she had grown old. Her hair was gray, her body withered. She was old but my father was not, and he wept over her grave when she died. It was Imonie who pulled him up and led him to Endellion.

"Death follows me, Mam," my father said to her. "Nothing good comes from my hands."

"Then you must determine to make something new with your hands, son," Imonie replied.

He heeded her, and magic bloomed in his palms.

Imonie turned away and my mother appeared, young and bright and alive, her beauty like a flame that my father couldn't look away from.

Sigourney tore the fabric from her skirt and wrapped something small within it. A baby, and she extended it to Ambrose.

"Your daughter," she said, and my father took me in his arms for the first time.

The world grew quiet as he gazed at me. Quiet until a tiny flash of gold caught the light. A golden scale just above my small, fresh heart.

If I had thought it was difficult to pierce Anna's and Clem's hearts to break a dream, then it was impossible to imagine driving a dagger into my infant form.

I stood and trembled at the edges of the dream—my father's dream.

I stared at him, how he held me, how he smiled at me.

The wonder faded when my real father stepped forward. He approached his phantom, and when he held out his hands, dream Ambrose surrendered me into his arms.

I also moved forward.

My father paid me no heed, gazing down at the baby in his arms. With polished confidence, he withdrew his dagger. Both light and darkness danced on the blade as he lifted it, and my breath hung in my throat when a scream split the air.

My mother rushed to him, horrified. I didn't know if it was actually my mother or her phantom. The realms bled together, and I was lost between what was real and what was imagined.

My father didn't spare my mother a glance. He drove his dagger into the baby's chest, swift and deep, and the baby let out a wail as the dream broke at last. The infant turned into smoke, slipping through my father's arms. And the strange world that had been layering around us melted away.

I closed my eyes until the colors had passed, until the only sound I could hear was my breath, whistling through my teeth.

The hall was silent, and I opened my eyes to behold my father.

He stared at me. He still held the dagger in his hand, and I wanted to ask if he had harbored any doubt before he had plunged that blade into my heart. If it had been difficult for him, even if he had kept his senses straight.

I was both relieved and angry. I was grateful the nightmare had broken, and yet I wanted to shout at him, *How could you?*

But his eyes were jaded and cold. A stranger's gaze. And the longer I studied him . . . I realized he was not my father. It was Emrys, wearing my father's clothes and aging spell, pretending to be him.

Do not trust your eyes alone, Imonie had warned me.

I swallowed the knot in my throat and looked at the dais, where my father stood beside the throne, stripped of his glamour and dressed as Emrys. My father in those blue robes. His cheeks shone with tears.

The truth was slow to overtake me. But I felt its sting, and I acknowledged that my father was not who I believed him to be.

He knew the taste of blood.

"Daughter."

I glanced back at Emrys, shocked he was speaking to me, continuing with this charade.

I heard something buzz by my ear, felt it whoosh and nearly graze my cheek. And I watched as an arrow sank into Emrys's chest.

It happened so quickly. I didn't believe my own eyes, not until Emrys's blood began to drip down his chest and he gasped. It was a sound to summon the spirit of death. A mortal blow. He slowly sank to his knees and I rushed to catch him, easing him to the floor.

"Where is my brother?" he rasped, clutching my hand. The aging glamour faded, leaving behind a young yet ancient face, marred in pain.

"I'm here," my father replied. He knelt on the other side of Emrys, drawing his brother into his arms. "I was supposed to shield you this time, Em. You fooled me."

You fooled me.

I dwelled on my conversation with Emrys from earlier that day. He had asked if my father was in danger. I had said no, but Emrys had seen through the countess. He must have convinced his brother to swap roles to keep him safe.

I looked up to see Lady Raven standing nearby with the crossbow in her hands. Her shock seemed to radiate from witnessing someone in the deathless court die. She trembled as Phelan yanked the weapon away from her.

"I could not let your life end like this," Emrys whispered to Papa. A pallor was creeping over his skin. I watched his blood continue to flow down his chest and drip onto the floor. "You have so much . . . to live for, Ambrose." He looked at me, and there was tenderness in his eyes.

I felt Imonie's presence draw near, and when she spoke, her voice was soft, agonized.

"Let me hold him."

I shifted away and let her take my place on the floor. My father eased Emrys into her arms and she held him close to her heart.

"Mam," Emrys whispered.

"Let me hold you one last time, my quiet boy," Imonie said with a smile, stroking the hair from his brow. "My scholar of dreams."

I remembered Imonie's story, her words like an echo returning to me after months. *Her quiet boy would deceive her, acting as his wild brother to take his punishments. And the wild boy would act as his quiet twin, to avoid her wrath when he strayed too far.*

I had assumed wrong.

I had thought my father was Imonie's quiet boy. But all this time . . . it had been Emrys. The boy who had loved books and school and peaceful spaces, who had wept when my father tore the pages in his book. Who had let my father wear his robes to deceive and kill the duke. Who had taken the fall for my father's crime.

Emrys closed his eyes.

Imonie continued to hold him. And he breathed his last in her arms.

42

A wail rose from my father. His brother's blood stained the floor and Papa buried his face in his palms and wept.

It was the sound of a heart breaking.

The waves of his grief cut through me. I stared at Papa, at his bloodied hands. He was Imonie's wild boy. The assassin. A reckless coward.

And I was his daughter.

The betrayer's blood ran through my veins like quicksilver.

I rose, my feet throbbing with pins and needles. I drew a deep breath to steady myself, my gaze roaming the hall. My mother rushed to Papa's side. Mr. Wolfe remained at a respectful distance, but his eyes were wide with shock. Nura and Olivette walked toward me, but I had no time to go to them, to try and sort the tangle of my emotions.

Someone was rushing to the dais, their boots clicking over the stone floor.

I knew it was the countess before I turned to look in that direction. She was ascending the stairs, furtively glancing over her shoulder to see if any of us were following her. Because of that action, she didn't see Mazarine emerge from the shadows behind the chair, a crossbow in her hands. The troll shot at the countess before I could yell an order for her to hold her fire. The arrow sank into Lady Raven's thigh, violently halting her progression, and she emitted a scream that made the hair lift on my arms.

The countess collapsed on the stairs.

Lennox stood and watched like he was hewn from stone, but Phelan rushed to assist her, gently easing the countess up and carrying her to the table.

"You'll be fine, Mother," he said as he briefly examined her wound.

The countess whimpered and then promptly fainted from the pain.

Mazarine continued to linger by the throne, guarding it with her crossbow. The hall fell painfully quiet, and then the troll looked at me. She arched her brow and said, "Clem?"

She'd blown my cover. The one who had cast her magic upon me now unapologetically exposed me. And yet . . . I found that I didn't care.

I was relieved.

"Clem?" Nura echoed.

I glanced at my friends. Olivette's brow wrinkled with confusion, but Nura was furious. The pieces had just come together for her, and I watched the betrayal brighten her eyes.

I walked to the dais stairs, expecting someone to protest my approach. For all they knew, I was about to claim the sovereignty for myself. But the silence held and simmered, and I paused on the steps and looked at Phelan.

"Phelan," I called to him. I watched his face slacken in surprise. "Phelan, will you join me on the dais?"

He slowly left his mother's side, as if he understood my intentions and was resisting. But he ascended as I knew he would, and he stood before me, casting a wary glance at Mazarine.

"What is this about, Clem?" he whispered, but his voice carried. Everyone could hear us.

"I want you to claim the sovereignty of Seren," I said. "Will you sit on the throne and reinstate a new court? Will you restore the mountain duchy and bring her people home?"

He stared at me for a long moment. And then he said, "Why not you?"

I swallowed scathing laughter, but I glanced at my father, who continued to sit on the floor. He had ceased weeping and now watched the events unfolding on the dais with rapt attention.

I returned my gaze to Phelan and whispered, "I'm unworthy."

Phelan shook his head. "I've never heard something more ridiculous, Clem. You're not your father, as I'm not my mother."

"I don't want it."

"Nor do I," he countered.

I sighed, weary of arguing with him. "Will you do it for me, Phelan? For Olivette and Nura? For the people whose nightmares you once fought, for those who are lost and displaced and yet dream of the mountains? Who dream of home?"

He closed his eyes, and I knew my words had stirred something in him. I waited, and when he looked at me again, my worry and my fear began to slip away.

"I will do this, Clem, but only if you are there beside me."

"Where else would I be?" I teased with a smile.

He reached out and traced my face, and I knew that he would do this for me. I knew that he was the one to bring life back to these mountains.

Mazarine stepped aside and Phelan turned to the throne. He began to close the distance between himself and the chair. I watched at first, eager to see this curse come to its end. But then I felt a prickling at the nape of my neck. A warning that someone was staring at me, which seemed absurd, as everyone in the hall was beholding this moment. But the past two nights, I had been attacked from behind. I had not guarded my back.

I spun to study the hall.

Everyone was just as they had been—Imonie held Emrys, my parents sat on the floor beside a puddle of blood, Nura and Olivette and Mr. Wolfe stood three tables away transfixed, the countess lay unconscious on a tabletop with Lennox at her side, and Mazarine remained close with her crossbow.

And then I realized I was missing someone.

The duke. The master of coin.

I had not seen him since the beginning of the night.

The fires in the hearth continued to cast light, but there were endless pools of shadows. And from one of those shadows the master of coin stepped forward, a crossbow braced against his chest, aimed at the throne.

His avarice was so keen that he had no qualms in killing his own "investment." *The countess is right*, I thought. The master of coin didn't want to see this curse broken. It would ruin the life he had built for himself in Endellion. All the money that dreams brought into his hands.

He let the arrow fly. It sang in the air.

I only had a breath to react. I was the only one who saw him, my eyes trained upon the arrow's path. All my spells disintegrated in my memory. I couldn't summon a single shield.

And so I didn't think. I merely reacted—I let my body respond—and I stepped between Phelan and the master of coin. I took the arrow in my chest, hoping it would find the stone of my heart.

The arrow met me with startling force, blowing me off my feet. I slid along the floor and then came to a stop, gasping. I gazed down at myself like this body belonged to someone else, with this shaft of wood that protruded from my chest and the blood that began to spill like wine. The pain surged when I tried to breathe, when I felt the sting of my wound.

And then the screams rose. My mother's. Olivette's. Imonie's. My father's.

Phelan gathered me in his arms and together we sat at the footstool of the throne. He was saying my name, over and over— *Clem, Clem, Clem*—like it was a prayer, like it was an answer. Like he didn't know what to do without me.

"Phelan," I managed to say, and I must have sounded like my old self, because it calmed him.

He quieted, caressing my face. Fear burned in his eyes like embers. I tried to breathe and felt the excruciating pinch in my lungs again. A pressure sat on my chest, and pain crackled between my ribs.

My parents hovered, as did Mazarine. They were frantically speaking; their words rushed over me like a river. I wanted to tell them to *be quiet*, and I closed my eyes. Clenched my teeth. Ordered myself to keep drawing breath even though it was agonizing. And then the silence came, and it was beautiful and cold and calm, like resting underwater. I knew why the words had faded, because a shiver raced across my skin, and I began to change.

I opened my eyes. My guise started to crack along my arms, up my neck, across the planes of my face like ice.

Phelan continued to hold me against his chest. His warmth seeped into me, and I could hear his heart pounding, humming-bird swift in his breast. I watched the wonder in his face. It eclipsed the terror, the agony.

And I breathed and I broke and I transformed in his arms.

Mazarine's ancient magic relinquished me. I watched Anna Neven crumble and fall away, and she lay in fragments around me, like pieces of stained glass.

My hair was long copper waves once more. My two inches of height and my full lips and the dimples in my cheeks and my brown eyes all came back to me, just as I remembered them. And yet I could not explain why I felt like a different girl.

Until I breathed again and felt my heart struggle to beat.

The arrow had not broken the stone within me. A wound had not ushered my breaking. It had been my decision to take an arrow for Phelan. For I couldn't imagine a world with him gone.

And the last stone of my heart turned into dust.

"Mazarine," my father said in a ragged voice. I felt his hand touch my hair. "Mazarine, can you do something?"

Mazarine gazed down at me. I saw that her guise had started to crack as well. Half of her face was human, and half of her face was troll. She was breaking, and I wondered why. Wondered until she laid her hand upon my chest, as if sensing the state of my heart. And I knew she had come to care for me.

"Her heart is weakening," she said. When she drew her hand back, her fingers were drenched in my blood. "And the curse still stands. Perhaps . . ."

She had no chance to finish her statement.

Phelan rose with me in his arms.

I wanted to ask him, *What are you doing?* But my voice . . . I couldn't find it. Yet he seemed to know my thoughts, because he said, "I don't want to do this without you."

I released a tremulous breath—*all right, as you wish*—and he walked us to the throne.

He claimed the sovereignty with me in his arms. We sat together, as one, and the curse came undone.

A wind tore through the hall. It was violent at first, the makings of a storm, and it extinguished the fires and made the shadows twine and dance. The windows shattered one by one, raining glass and lead. The snow swept in. I thought that we would all be torn apart, blown into pieces.

But sometimes things must break before they can be made whole again, so that they can be forged into something stronger.

The wind died, escaping out the open windows, and the snow gathered on the floor.

It was a quiet, peaceful night. A night for dreams. And magic teemed, thick and cold, in the air.

I looked at Phelan only to discover he was already gazing at me.

The pain in my chest was relentless. I couldn't draw breath, and I made a sad, gurgling sound. Blood filled my mouth, and I knew I had reached the end of myself. And yet I wasn't afraid.

I began to let go. It was a sweet surrender, to not have to hold on to things so fiercely as I had before. To open my hands and my heart and be who I wanted to be.

"Clem," Phelan whispered.

It was the last thing I heard.

Mazarine suddenly appeared before us. In one swift stroke, she yanked the arrow from my heart.

I closed my eyes and surrendered to the rush of darkness.

43

One does not expect to wake after their heart has stopped beating, after they have slipped into the cold, quiet dark. One also does not expect to return to the light only to be greeted by a troll.

Mazarine sat beside me, her human form gone, shed like scales. She was just as I remembered from that fateful September day months ago: a jagged face like rocks, teeth overlapping her lips, stained with old blood. Coarse hair that shone silver, threaded with leaves and sticks and thorny vines. Her twin horns gleamed like bones.

She noticed my stirring and smiled, which roused a tiny flame of fear in me.

"My mortal girl awakens," she said. "Sit forward and drink."

I didn't tell her I felt weak and shaky, and that my chest smoldered with pain. I didn't think it wise to oppose her, even if her love for me had made her disguise break, and she helped me sit forward in my bed.

I blinked against the streams of sunlight that flooded in through the balcony doors. I didn't recognize this room. It was far grander than the one I had originally chosen for myself, and I frowned, rubbing the ache in my temples.

"Mazarine . . . where am I?"

"The fortress in the clouds," she answered, lifting a wooden cup of cold water to my lips. "The Duchy of Seren. The realm of Azenor. Drink, Clementine."

I sighed, exasperated by her replies, but began to sip the water. It washed through me, trickling into the parched places of my soul, and I felt refreshed.

And then Mazarine added, "My duchess."

I promptly choked on the water.

"What did you call me?" I rasped, coughing. The pain flared in my chest, and I groaned, laying my hand over my heart. I could feel linen bandages wrapped snugly around me, beneath my chemise. But my wound was still bright and tender. I wondered how long it would take before I could breathe without feeling that pinch of pain.

"I called you duchess," the troll replied.

"Why? I'm not your duchess."

She cocked her gnarled brow at me. "You do not remember, Clementine?"

I traced through my memories. Bloodstains, darkness, wind, shattering glass. Breaking and breathing and arrows and dreams and the rhythm of Phelan's heart against my cheek.

"I remember, but Phelan is the one who claimed the throne," I said.

"You both did. You sat as one; you broke the curse as one." Mazarine paused, watching the emotions ripple across my face. "You are not pleased, child?"

"I . . . I didn't *want* this!"

"Nor did he. Which means the two of you are perfect for this task."

"So he is duke?"

"Aye."

"And I am duchess?"

"That's what I said, wasn't it?"

I swallowed a hysterical laugh. "But . . . how can you call us that? We aren't married."

Mazarine shrugged, utterly unperturbed. "You and Phelan are still bound by commitment and magic of your own making. You are partners."

I was quiet, overwhelmed.

"The two of you are like iron, sharpening the other," Mazarine said. "I sense that he could not do this without you, and you would not want to do it without him. Together you are stronger, a balance. You will both lead the duchy into a new era."

I groaned again and covered my face with my hands. But I couldn't deny that I felt a small thrill when I imagined this new path before me.

The door opened.

I glanced up to see it was Imonie, and my heart lifted at the sight of her.

The lines on her face eased when she beheld me awake and sitting in bed. But then she looked at Mazarine, and her scowl returned with vengeance.

"You've upset her," Imonie stated.

"I have kept this extraordinary yet fragile mortal alive," Mazarine replied smoothly. "I believe gratitude is in order?"

Imonie huffed, but she nodded. "You have my eternal gratitude, Brin of Stonefall."

Mazarine made a smug noise. But she set down my water cup and rose. "I will be just outside the door if you need me, Your Grace."

It took me a moment to realize she was addressing *me*, and I cleared my throat and nodded. "Thank you, Mazarine. *Brin*."

The troll left, shutting the door behind her.

Imonie quietly took her place, her eyes never leaving my face.

"How are you feeling, Clementine?" she asked.

"I've been better. How long have I been asleep?"

"For a week."

"A *week*?"

Imonie nodded. "Your parents and I have been worried sick, but that troll would only let us visit you once a day." She reached forward to take my hand, a rare display of affection from her.

I smiled and squeezed her fingers with what strength I could find, which was still faint.

"Can I get you anything, Clementine? Water, tea, food?"

My stomach was indeed empty, but I wasn't hungry for food. I leaned back into my array of pillows and said, "Will you tell me a story?"

A flicker of surprise passed over Imonie's face. But then she smiled and smoothed the wrinkles from my blankets.

And my grandmother told me the stories of the mountains.

My parents visited not long after Imonie departed. Papa brought in a tray of soup, soft bread, and tea, and my mother acted like she was going to feed it to me until I took the spoon.

They perched on either side of my bed, watching me eat.

"I'm going to be fine," I said, seeking to reassure them. But my hand trembled as I lifted the spoon to my lips. I knew I still had many weeks of recovery before me, and I wondered where Phelan was, but I was too proud to ask after him.

"Where is the countess?" I asked instead.

"She's recovering," Papa replied. "She plans to leave the mountains and return to Endellion once she is able to travel. Lennox will accompany her. She'll be under house arrest for a while, per Phelan's wishes."

"And what of the duke? The master of coin?"

My parents were silent, provoking me to look up from my soup.

"He fled the hall after he shot you," Mama said. "And after Mazarine removed the arrow and tended to you, she hunted him down. He was hiding in one of the lower levels of the fortress."

"Is he dead?" I asked.

My father nodded.

I didn't pity the master of coin, not after seeing the extent of his greed. But I would certainly need to speak to Mazarine about how I wanted to dole out punishment in the days to come.

"Mazarine has taken up her service to you with unfaltering allegiance," my mother stated, as if she had read the trail of my thoughts. "I believe she has appointed herself as your guard."

"And let her remain that way, Clem," my father pleaded. "She is stubborn and frightening, but she will protect you."

"Yes, I think I'll keep her." I set down my soup, feeling nauseated. After a week of being asleep, I had filled my stomach too swiftly. I reached for the teapot but my father beat me to it, pouring me a cup. He even knew how much cream and honey to stir into it. And then I realized there was tea, when there had not been before, and I whispered, "Where did the tea come from?"

"Phelan has opened the fortress," Papa replied. "He has been busy while you slept, traveling and gathering resources and people. This place has returned to life."

I fell quiet, listening. And while the walls around me were thick . . . I caught a faint trace of laughter. A rumble of furniture being shifted. The clang of something like pots. Doors opening and closing.

My unworthiness rose. My fears and worries nipped at my thoughts and I suddenly felt very small and very unprepared.

I looked at my parents and said, "Will you both help me? Will you both stay with me? I don't know what I'm doing."

Papa made a sound, and I think he was swallowing his tears. He leaned close to me and dropped a kiss on my brow, and I knew he would walk beside me, that he would be with me for the hard days as well as the good days.

My mother took my hand in hers, a hand full of magic and love and gentleness. "We will help you, Clementine. Whatever you need, we will be here for you."

She exchanged a glance with my father, one that made my breath catch.

I thought about the different paths we had each taken—vengeance and fear and anger and solitude and pain—and yet how all three of us had ended up here, in this strange moment of new beginnings.

I'd once believed that magic and secrets and beliefs had torn us apart. But in the end, I think it wove us back together with stronger threads.

The next day, Mazarine said it was time for me to get up and walk. I bathed and dressed with her assistance, and then I stood beside the hearth, holding on to the back of a chair. My head swam, and my legs felt like pudding, but I was not about to say such things to the troll.

"I think . . . I think I need a cane," I said.

"Will we do?"

I glanced up to see Nura and Olivette enter my chamber. I hadn't dared to hope that they had remained in the fortress after the curse's breaking. I hadn't dared to hope that they would want to see me, speak with me.

But here they were. Olivette was broadly grinning, her face flushed and ribbons braided into her blond hair. Nura was far more reserved, dressed in a sleek black dress, and I still sensed her pain over my deceit. But her eyes were gentle when they met mine. An invitation to make things right between us.

They each offered me an arm, and I walked between them, through the winding corridors of the fortress.

We passed people I had never seen before, people who were carrying crates and bags of produce and stacks of linens, working to transform this place into home. All of them paused to curtsy or bow to me, and I thought I might die from the embarrassment.

"Here," Nura suggested, guiding us to the courtyard doors. "Let's walk the gardens. You need fresh air."

We stepped outside. The snow was ankle deep on the ground, hiding the plants in white, but the sky was cloudless and ached a vibrant blue. We walked a stone path that had been cleared, through icy rosebushes and a trellis of vines. I soon grew sore for breath, and my friends guided me to a stone bench that overlooked the city of Ulla.

The three of us sat, their legs close to mine, and I swallowed the lump in my throat. I had hurt them, and I hated myself for it.

"How are you feeling, Ann—I mean, Clem," Olivette asked, flustered. "I should probably call you *Your Grace*, actually, shouldn't I?"

"Don't be silly," I said, and nudged her. "Call me Clem."

An awkward lull encompassed us.

"What comes next for the two of you?"

Nura glanced at Olivette. "Should we tell her, Oli?"

"Tell me what?" I demanded.

"We should," Olivette agreed with a wily grin. "Phelan asked us to be part of your new court."

The news was a pleasant surprise, one that buoyed my spirits, but Olivette gave me no time to respond.

"I'm not sure what we will be yet," she continued. "Perhaps your advisor?"

"Or your spymistress?" Nura added.

"Or even the mistress of coin?"

"Or your guard?"

"All of this to say . . . we want to join you in the restoration," Olivette concluded. "If you will have us."

I laughed, which drummed up the ache in my chest, and slipped my arms around them. "You can both be whatever you desire. I'm thrilled you're staying." I fell silent for a moment, and then added, "And I'm sorry, for deceiving you both for so long."

"We have questions," Nura said. "We want to know why and how you did what you did."

I let out a shaky breath. "Ah, where do I even begin?"

Olivette leaned closer to me. "Begin at the beginning."

My mind wandered back to that moment in Hereswith when I sat in Mazarine's library, drawing her twelfth portrait by candlelight.

And so that was where I began.

It took me most of the day to tell them the story. We shared a pot of tea and a tray of cold cuts and cheese and fruit in the afternoon before Mazarine called me back to rest in bed.

I heeded her, because only a fool wouldn't.

My slumber was deep, full of flashes of dreams that I struggled to remember when I woke. My room was dark, lit by the fire in my hearth and a few candles. I slipped from my bed and gingerly reached for a robe and my boots, walking to the door.

Mazarine was in the corridor, on guard. But she allowed me to walk, and she followed me to the courtyard doors. She stood watch as I walked the gardens alone, savoring the quiet splendor of night, how the snow crunched beneath my steps, how the world looked different beneath the moon and stars.

I found a bench and sat, shivering and cold and feeling more alive than I ever had before.

I don't know how long I was there before he came. But I soon heard his quiet tread on the snow, and I felt his presence draw near.

"Her Grace looks well rested," said Phelan.

I glanced over my shoulder to see him standing beneath the trellis of glittering vines. He wore simple clothes—just his boots and trousers and a white shirt—and his hair was loose, dark as raven wings. A woolen cloak was fastened at his neck.

"And His Grace looks the same," I said wryly, and he joined me on the bench.

"How are you, truly, Clem?" he asked, and then noticed what I was wearing—a thin robe. "And why aren't you wearing a cloak, for gods' sake!" He unbuckled his and draped it over my shoulders.

I sank into the cloak's warmth, hiding a smile. "I grow stronger every day. And you? I hear you've been busy."

"To the uttermost. But it's given me something to do while I waited for you to wake."

We fell quiet, content to simply sit beside each other.

Phelan whispered, "May I hold you?"

My heart stirred, beating a heady song within my blood. But I said, "Someone might see us." Which was ridiculous, as I could only dimly discern him in the dark.

Phelan laughed. "I really don't care."

Once, he had been afraid of what others thought of him. Once, I had been bent by revenge and coldness and believed myself stronger alone.

I shifted toward him and he drew me onto his lap. Our fingers entwined and I rested in his embrace. We sat like that for a moment, admiring the starlit sky, until I turned to face him.

"What do you dream of, Phelan?" I asked.

"What do I dream of?" he countered, amused. "By night or by day?"

Of course, I wanted to know the things he beheld at night, the dreams that rose from his darkest places. But more than that . . . I wanted to know what he wanted.

"By day," I said.

He glanced beyond me, where the mountains rested in the moonlight, glazed in ice. "I used to dream of being someone worthy, and so I became a magician. And then I dreamt of finding somewhere I belonged, where I could use my magic for the good of others. I never thought I would find it in Seren, but the past couple of days have proven to me that purpose can be found in unexpected places." He paused, his gaze tracing me. "What about you, Clem? What do you dream of by day?"

I closed my eyes, as if I could see my desire, resting just beyond my reach. "I dream of finding a new home. Of bringing something broken back together, and not just with magic but with stories and friendship and good food."

When I looked at Phelan again, I caught a glimmer in his eyes, as if he dreamt the same things as me. I leaned closer to him until our lips met, polite and cautious and then hungry and familiar, and my heart was suddenly racing. But for the first time in months, there was no pain.

"I have something for you," he said with a smile, drawing away from me.

Intrigued, I listened as he reached for something in his pocket, how it crinkled in his hands like parchment.

"What is it?" I asked warily.

He set something long and square in my palms, hidden beneath paper and twine. There was a hint of joy in his voice when he told me, "Open it later."

44

I opened it later that night, when I was alone in my bedchamber.
I pulled away the parchment and twine, and for a moment I
merely stared at what rested within. And then I touched it, hesi-
tantly, as if it might bring me pain to remember.

A sketchbook full of empty pages. Three sticks of sharpened
charcoal.

I slowly began to draw again.

It didn't take long until I craved to draw a portrait of myself. My
skill was raw, nothing as it had once been when I'd surrendered it
for a stone heart, but whenever I had a spare moment, I was in my
room, drawing. Eager to regain what I had lost.

Eventually, I had a mirror brought into my bedchamber.

I arranged myself before it, sketchbook open to a fresh page,
charcoal ready in hand, the window drapes parted to welcome
winter sunshine.

I studied my face in the mirror and began to render it on paper. But with each glance from the paper to the glass . . . I realized that I was drawing someone I didn't recognize. A girl with gleaming teeth and fallen stars in her long, red hair. A girl with cold, determined eyes.

My hand shook.

I stopped and set down the charcoal, staring at my reflection. Mazarine's words rose to memory. *Your true reflection will always shine brightly upon a mirror.*

Perhaps one day I would draw what was reflected. Perhaps one day, I'd be ready to acknowledge what truly dwelled on the other side of the glass. What I was becoming. But it was not that day, and I closed my sketchbook with a snap.

I rose and turned away from the mirror.

ACKNOWLEDGMENTS

It's December 31 and I'm finally sitting down to write the acknowl-edgments for this fourth (how is that even possible?!) book of mine. I wanted to save this moment for the last day of 2020, a year that all of us will vividly remember. A year that brought immense challenges and heartache and a new way of life. It would be remiss of me if I did not mention working on this book all through the chaos of 2020, and to illuminate the people who made this book its best version, even as they were called to stay home and sud-denly had to balance work and family and feelings of isolation and worry and fatigue and illness. I had moments when it felt difficult to open my manuscript and focus on what I had created, but I also think so many of us found peace and joy and wonder in books this year—writing them, revising them, and reading them—and my words now will never be enough to express my gratitude to the people who joined me on this journey and carried me through 2020.

To Suzie Townsend, agent extraordinaire. Thank you for making one of my greatest dreams a reality, for loving my stories and finding them the best homes, and for always being there for me. You are the best. To Dani Segelbaum, who helps me with vital behind-the-scenes things . . . I truly couldn't do this without your assistance and insight, and I'm so thankful for you. To Mia Roman, Veronica Grijalva, and Victoria Hendersen, who all have been instrumental in my foreign rights and sales—thank you for working so endlessly and finding a home for my stories overseas. To the New Leaf Dream Team—I'm so honored to be one of your authors. Thank you for investing in me and my books.

To Karen Chaplin, my editor. Thank you for continuing to fearlessly step into the convoluted and verbose worlds I create and helping me find the threads to bring together to make a stronger story. It's been an honor to work on four novels with you. To Rosemary Brosnan, I'm so delighted to be published by your inimitable team at Quill Tree Books. Thank you for loving my stories and giving them a place on the shelf. To my publicist, Lauren Levite, who brought so many wonderful opportunities my way despite the strangeness of 2020—thank you. To Bria Ragin, who has been with me and my stories since my debut year . . . thank you for all your notes and lovely emails. To my copy editor (I'm truly in awe of you!) who will forever be changing my greys into grays—thank you for polishing this manuscript. To my proofreaders, who help catch errors and ensure I'm making sense—thank you. To the production team, the marketing team, the sales team, the design team . . . y'all are simply amazing and I am eternally thankful for you and your expertise. To Molly Fehr and your absolutely gorgeous design ideas—I'm so happy that I got to have you for two book covers! To Annie Stegg Gerard, who illustrated the cover of my dreams—I'm in love with how beautiful it is. To Virginia Allyn, who illustrated the gorgeous map. I was thrilled to discover you were going to create another map for my book!

To my wonderful critique partner, Isabel Ibañez, who made this year so much better with your stories and phone talk walks and insights into my messy first drafts—thank you, sweet friend.

To Ciannon Smart, thank you for reading an early copy. You inspire me in countless ways and I'm excited to see your books take flight.

To my readers, in the United States and abroad, who are so lovely and have encouraged me on the days when I felt like giving up. Thank you. I would not be where I am today without you. If there is a dream in your heart, one you're secretly holding on to, I hope this is the year when you begin to see it come true.

To Mom and Dad, for always believing in me and my writing, even when I didn't. You taught me all the magic I ever needed to know, and this book is for you. To my siblings—Caleb, Gabriel, Ruth, Mary, and Luke. Our D&D campaign has been one of the highlights of this year for me, and I love each of you fiercely. To my family—my grandparents and aunts and uncles and cousins and in-laws—and my friends, thank you for always supporting this dream of mine.

To Sierra, who *loved* the quarantine because it meant we were home with you all the time. I have yet to write a story where a dog fails to appear, all because of you.

To Ben, my other half. At the beginning of this year, you told me, "2015 Becca would be very proud of 2020 Becca." And that image has stayed with me, all through the ups and downs. To see how much I've grown and changed in the last five years—to realize how much I've accomplished. I can't help but look forward to all the good things yet to come. Thank you for dreaming alongside me, always.

And to my Heavenly Father, for taking this small dream of mine and turning it into paper and ink. *Soli Deo Gloria*.

Don't miss
Sisters of Sword & Song,
another thrilling fantasy novel by Rebecca Ross.

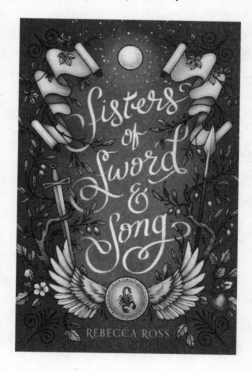

—➤· 1 ·◄—

Evadne

E vadne stood beneath the olive tree watching Maia climb with a knife clenched in her teeth. The sun was setting, but the breeze was warm, sighing from the west, where the Origenes Sea churned just beyond the grove. It would storm by evening; Evadne could sense it coming on the wind. And then tomorrow would arrive, the day her family had been anticipating for eight long years.

One more sleep until I see her, Evadne thought, hardly remembering why she was standing in the grove until she heard Maia slip and catch herself on a limb. The tree shuddered in protest although Maia was the smallest of their family, hardly reaching Evadne's shoulder in height. She had insisted she be the one to climb.

"Can anyone see us?" Maia asked once she had regained her balance, her words blurred by the blade still held by her teeth.

Evadne glanced around the grove. They were at the thick heart of it; the grass was spangled with light, and the branches rustled with the breeze. She could hear sounds of the villa—voices and laughter—echoing in the distance. Both of their fathers should be together, working at the oil press on the far side of the property.

"We are alone, Maia."

Maia cut the branch and let it drop to the ground, right at Evadne's feet. She cut another, her knife ticking against the bark.

"Do you think your father will know, Eva?"

"That we cut from the god tree?" Evadne gathered the green-and-silver leaves, staring up as Maia balanced on the tree's warped limbs. She imagined a god tumbling through such branches, breaking his wings, and said, "Well, if my father realizes it, I will simply tell him it was all for Halcyon, and what can he say to that?"

Maia swiftly traded one worry for another. "Do you think Halcyon will recognize me tomorrow?"

"You are her cousin. Of course she will recognize you." But despite her confidence, Evadne had gnawed on this same worry for days. She had not seen Halcyon in eight years.

Evadne remembered the morning Halcyon had departed, had traced it so many times in her memory that she often dreamt about it at night. Evadne, nine years old, propped on a crutch, her ankle bandaged as she stood in the courtyard. Halcyon, twelve years old, hair bound back in braids, her belongings packed in a satchel, waiting to ride with their father to the city of Abacus.

"Don't go, don't go." Evadne had wept, clinging to her sister.

But Halcyon had smiled and said, "I must, Eva. The gods will it."

"Do not tell her this," Maia said, shifting to another branch, "but I was once jealous of your sister."

"So was I," Evadne confessed and with a shock discovered that the flame was still there, burning within her. *So am I,* her mind amended. *I am jealous of Halcyon, although I do not want to be.*

Maia stopped cutting to look at her, and for a moment, Evadne feared she had spoken her secret aloud.

"Do not mistake me," Maia rushed to say. "I was relieved *someone* in our family finally inherited *something* good. Halcyon deserved to make a name for herself. But . . . I do wish you and I could have something, too."

"Yes," Evadne agreed.

She and Maia were like the other members in their family. Void of magic, all because of their ancestor, a disgraced god who had fallen into this very olive tree centuries ago to break his wings. Or so the legend stated. That was why Evadne's father disliked anyone touching it, or climbing it, or harvesting from it. The tree had been the end of Kirkos, god of the wind. But it had also been a beginning. The beginning of this grove, of their family.

"Why would a god be so *foolish*?" Evadne had often ranted to her mother when they worked at the loom. "He had everything. Why give it all up?"

Truly, her anger stemmed from the fact that she was magicless and common and bound to live the same dull life every day until she returned to the dust. All because of Kirkos's choice to fall.

And her mother would only smile, a gentle but shrewd smile. "One day you will understand, Eva."

Well, Evadne believed she already understood. The truth was Kirkos had flown over this piece of land, a grove that was called Isaura, and had seen a mortal woman harvesting olives. He had come to love her so ardently that he had surrendered his immortality and power to remain on Earth with her, living as a mortal man, to tend the grove at her side, to give her children, to be buried beside her when he died.

If any of his descendants aspired to ascend within their court, it would not be by inherited magic but by some other gift or strength.

Which Halcyon had done.

"Do you think we have gathered enough?"

Maia's inquiry brought Evadne back to the present. She glanced at her armload of olive clippings. "Yes, more than enough. We should get back. Our mothers will be wondering what has taken us so long."

"Perhaps they will think one of the gods flew over the grove and—literally—fell in love with us," Maia said brightly as she dropped from the tree. It was a frequent quip of their family, but Evadne still laughed.

"Lightning never strikes in the same place twice, Maia. Sorry to disappoint you."